MATHEMATICS IN ACTION

Taken from:

Mathematics in Action: Prealgebra Problem Solving, Second Edition
by The Consortium for Foundation Mathematics

*Mathematics in Action: An Introduction to
Algebraic, Graphical, and Numerical Problem Solving,* Third Edition
by The Consortium for Foundation Mathematics

PEARSON
Custom
Publishing

PEARSON
Addison
Wesley

Cover images courtesy of Photodisc/Getty

Taken from:

Mathematics in Action: Prealgebra Problem Solving, Second Edition
by The Consortium for Foundation Mathematics
Copyright © 2008 by Pearson Education, Inc.
Published by Addison Wesley
Boston, Massachusetts 02116

Mathematics in Action: An Introduction to Algebraic, Graphical, and Numerical Problem Solving, Third Edition
by The Consortium for Foundation Mathematics
Copyright © 2008 by Pearson Education, Inc.
Published by Addison Wesley

This special edition published in cooperation with Pearson Custom Publishing.

Printed in the United States of America

10 9 8 7 6 5 4 3 2 1

ISBN 0-536-08905-1

2007361211

KL

Please visit our web site at *www.pearsoncustom.com*

PEARSON CUSTOM PUBLISHING
501 Boylston Street, Suite 900, Boston, MA 02116
A Pearson Education Company

Contents

CHAPTER 2   PROBLEM SOLVING WITH RATIONAL NUMBERS: ADDITION AND SUBTRACTION OF INTEGERS, FRACTIONS, AND DECIMALS   **79**

CHAPTER 6   VARIABLE SENSE   393

APPENDIXES

To the Student

The book in your hands is most likely very different from any mathematics book you have seen before. In this book, you will take an active role in developing the important ideas of arithmetic and beginning algebra. You will be expected to add your own words to the text. This will be part of your daily work, both in and out of class and for homework. It is the belief of the authors that students learn mathematics best when they are actively involved in solving problems that are meaningful to them.

The text is primarily a collection of situations drawn from real life. Each situation leads to one or more problems. By answering a series of questions and solving each part of the problem, you will be led to use one or more ideas of introductory college mathematics. Sometimes, these will be basic skills that build on your knowledge of arithmetic. Other times, they will be new concepts that are more general and far reaching. The important point is that you won't be asked to master a skill until you see a real need for that skill as part of solving a realistic application.

Another important aspect of this text and the course you are taking is the benefit gained by collaborating with your classmates. Much of your work in class will result from being a member of a team. Working in small groups, you will help each other work through a problem situation. While you may feel uncomfortable working this way at first, there are several reasons we believe it is appropriate in this course. First, it is part of the learn-by-doing philosophy. You will be talking about mathematics, needing to express your thoughts in words—this is a key to learning. Secondly, you will be developing skills that will be very valuable when you leave the classroom. Currently, many jobs and careers require the ability to collaborate within a team environment. Your instructor will provide you with more specific information about this collaboration.

One more fundamental part of this course is that you will have access to appropriate technology at all times. Technology is a part of our modern world, and learning to use technology goes hand in hand with learning mathematics. Your work in this course will help prepare you for whatever you pursue in your working life.

This course will help you develop both the mathematical and general skills necessary in today's workplace, such as organization, problem solving, communication, and collaborative skills. By keeping up with your work and following the suggested organization of the text, you will gain a valuable resource that will serve you well in the future. With hard work and dedication you will be ready for the next step.

The Consortium for Foundation Mathematics

WHOLE NUMBERS

Do you remember when you first started learning about numbers? From those early days, you went on to learn more about numbers—what they are, how they are related to one another, and how you operate with them.

Whole numbers are the basis for your further study of arithmetic and introductory algebra used throughout this book. In Chapter 1, we will see whole numbers in real-life use, clarify what you already know about them, and learn more about them.

The U.S. Bureau of the Census tracks information yearly about educational levels and income levels of the population in the United States (http://www.census.gov). In 2004, the bureau reported that more than one in four adults holds a bachelor's degree. The bureau also presented data on average 2004 earnings and education level for all workers, aged 18 and older. Some of the data is given in the table below.

ACTIVITY 1.1

Education Pays

OBJECTIVES

1. Read and write whole numbers.

2. Compare whole numbers using inequality symbols.

3. Round whole numbers to specified place values.

4. Use rounding for estimation.

5. Classify whole numbers as even or odd, prime, or composite.

6. Solve problems involving whole numbers.

1. a. What is the average income of those workers who had some college? An associate's degree? A high school graduate? A bachelor's degree?

b. Which group of workers earned the most income in 2004? Which group earned the least income?

c. What does the table indicate about the value of an education in the United States?

 Learning to Earn

AVERAGE 2004 EARNINGS BY EDUCATIONAL LEVEL: WORKERS 18 YEARS OF AGE AND OLDER								
EDUCATIONAL LEVEL	All workers combined	Not high school graduates	High school graduates	Some college	Associate's degree	Bachelor's degree	Master's degree	Doctor- ate degree	Professional degree
AVERAGE INCOME LEVEL	$37,897	$19,041	$28,631	$30,173	$36,021	$51,568	$67,073	$93,033	$114,878

d. How does the census information relate to your decision to attend college?

Whole Numbers

The earnings listed in the preceding table are represented by **whole numbers.** The set of whole numbers consists of zero and all the counting numbers, 1, 2, 3, 4, and so on. Whole numbers are used to describe "how many" (for example, the dollar values in Problem 1). Each **whole number** is represented by a **numeral,** which is a sequence of symbols called *digits.* The relative placement of the **digits** (0, 1, 2, 3, 4, 5, 6, 7, 8, and 9) in our standard base-10 system determines the value of the number that the numeral represents.

EXAMPLE 1   *What does the numeral 3547 represent? What is the place value of 3 in the number 3547?*

SOLUTION

3547 is the numeral representing 3 thousands, 5 hundreds, 4 tens, and 7 ones. It is read and written in words as "three thousand five hundred forty-seven." In this number, the digit 3 has a **place value** of one thousand (1000). This means that the digit 3 represents 3000 of the units in the number 3547.

2. What are the place values of the other digits in the number 3547?

3. a. Write the number 30,928 in words.

b. What are the place values of the digits 8 and 9 in the number 30,928?

For ease in reading a number in the base-10 system, digits are grouped in threes with each grouping of three separated by a comma. The triples are named as shown in the following table. Beginning with the second triple from the right and moving to the left, the triples are named thousands, millions, billions, etc. For example, the number 548,902,473,150 is written in the following table.

GROUP	Billions			Millions			Thousands			Ones		
TRIPLES	Hundreds	Tens	Ones	Hundreds	Tens	Ones	Hundreds	Tens	Ones	Hundreds	Tens	Ones
EXAMPLE	5	4	8	9	0	2	4	7	3	1	5	0

The number in the preceding table is read "five hundred forty-eight billion, nine hundred two million, four hundred seventy-three thousand, one hundred fifty."

4. Write the earnings from Problem 1a in words.

5. The digit 0 occurs twice in the number in the preceding table. What is the place value of each occurrence?

Comparing Whole Numbers

The place value system of writing numbers makes it easy to compare numbers. For example, it is easy to see that an income of $30,173 is less than an income of $36,021 by comparing the values 0 and 6 in the thousands place. You can represent the relationship by writing 30,173 < 36,021. Alternatively, you can say that $36,021 is greater than $30,173 and write 36,021 > 30,173. Such statements involving the symbols < (less than) and > (greater than) are called **inequalities.**

6. In the 2004 census, Oregon's population was counted as 3,594,586 and Oklahoma's was 3,523,553. Which state had the greater population?

PROCEDURE

Comparing Two Whole Numbers

1. Use the symbol > to write that one number is *greater than* another. For example, 8 > 3 is read from left to right as "eight is greater than three."
2. Use the symbol < to write that one number is *less than* another. For example, 3 < 8 is read from left to right as "three is less than eight."
3. Use the symbol = to write that two numbers *are equal.* For example, 2 + 1 = 3 is read from left to right as "two plus one is equal to three."
4. Compare two numbers by reading each of them from left to right to find the first position where they differ. For example, 7,180,597 and 7,180,642 first differ in the hundreds place. Since 6 > 5, write 7,180,642 > 7,180,597. Alternatively, 7,180,597 < 7,180,642 is also correct because 5 < 6.

Rounding Whole Numbers

The U.S. Bureau of the Census provides United States population counts on the Internet on a regular basis. For example, the bureau estimated the population at 297,963,037 persons on January 23, 2006. Not every digit in this number is meaningful because the population is constantly changing. Therefore, a reasonable approximation is usually sufficient. For example, it would often be good enough to say the population is about 298,000,000, or two hundred ninety-eight million.

The process of determining an approximation to a number is known as **rounding.**

PROCEDURE

Rounding a Whole Number to a Specified Place Value

1. Underline the digit with the place value to which the number will be rounded, such as "to the nearest million" or "to the nearest thousand."
2. If the digit directly to its right is *less than 5*, keep the digit underlined in step 1 and replace all the digits to its right with zeros.
3. If the digit directly to its right is *5 or greater*, increase the digit underlined in step 1 by 1 unit and replace all the digits to its right with zeros.

EXAMPLE 2   *Round 37,146 to the nearest ten thousand.*

SOLUTION

The digit in the ten thousands place is 3. The digit to its right is 7. Therefore, increase 3 to 4 and insert zeros in place of all the digits to the right. The rounded value is 40,000.

---

7. On another date in 2004, the U.S. Bureau of the Census gave the U.S. population as 285,691,501 persons.

    a. Approximate this count by rounding to the nearest million.

    b. Approximate the count by rounding to the nearest ten thousand.

Classifying Whole Numbers: Even or Odd, Prime or Composite

At times, it can be useful to classify whole numbers that share certain common features. One way to classify whole numbers is as even or odd. **Even numbers** are those that are evenly divisible by 2. That is, an even number is any number that when divided by 2 has a remainder equal to 0. A whole number that is not even is **odd.** Odd numbers are those that when divided by 2 leave a remainder of 1.

8. When an odd number is divided by 2, what is its remainder? Give an example.

9. Is 0 an even number? Explain.

10. By examining the digits of a whole number, how can you determine if the number is even or odd?

Whole numbers can also be classified as prime or composite. Any whole number greater than 1 that is divisible *only* by itself and 1 is called **prime.** For example, 5 is divisible only by itself and 1, so 5 is prime. A whole number greater than 1 that is not prime is called **composite.** For example, 6 is divisible by itself and 1, but also by 2 and 3. Therefore, 6 is a composite number. Also, 1, 2, 3, and 6 are called the **factors** of 6.

11. Is 21 prime or composite? Explain.

12. Is 2 prime or composite? Explain.

13. a. List all the prime numbers between 1 and 30.

b. How many even numbers are included in your list?

c. How many even prime numbers do you think there are? Explain.

Problem Solving with Whole Numbers

The United States Bureau of Labor Statistics provides data for various occupations and the education levels that they usually require. The bureau lists 19 occupations that typically require an associate's degree. The occupations are listed in the table on page 6.

The table also provides **median** yearly salaries for 2001. A median value in a data set is a value that divides the set into an upper half and a lower half of values. One-half of all salaries for a given occupation are below the median salary and the other half are above the median salary. For instance, one-half of males working in health technology earned less than $33,950 and the other half earned more than $33,950 in 2001.

On the Job...

OCCUPATION	2001 MALE MEDIAN ANNUAL SALARY ($)	2001 FEMALE MEDIAN ANNUAL SALARY ($)
Managerial and professional specialty occupation	52,260	35,160
Management-related occupations	48,550	34,100
Technical, sales, and administrative support	31,950	20,040
Health technology and technicians	33,950	23,850
Technologies and technicians except health	45,110	29,740
Sales occupations	32,730	13,040
Administrative support, including clerical work	26,740	21,140
Protective service occupations	34,340	17,560
Professional specialty occupations	51,400	34,410
Farming, forestry, and fishing occupations	13,710	7,060
Precision, production, craft, and repair occupations	31,040	21,700
Operators, fabricators, laborers	23,590	16,330
Armed forces	31,920	33,890

14. a. The salaries in the preceding table are rounded to what place value?

b. Is the median income of males in precision and craft occupations more than that of males in the armed forces? Explain how you obtained your answer.

c. Which two female occupations are closest in median annual salaries?

d. Which occupation has the lowest median salary for women? For men? The highest median salary for women? For men?

e. If you rounded the median salary of male health technicians to the nearest thousand dollars, how would you report the salary? Would you be over-estimating or underestimating the salary?

f. If you rounded the median salary of female administrative support to the nearest thousand dollars, how would you report the salary? Would you be overestimating or underestimating the salary?

**SUMMARY
ACTIVITY 1.1**

1. A **whole number** is represented by a **numeral** consisting of a sequence of **digits.** The relative placement of the **digits** determines the value of the number that the numeral represents.

2. Each digit in a numeral has a **place value** determined by its relative placement in the numeral. Numbers are compared for size by comparing their corresponding place values. The symbols < (read "less than") and > (read "greater than") are used to compare the size of the numbers.

3. **Rounding** a given number to a specified place value is used to approximate its value. Rules for rounding are provided on page 4.

4. Whole numbers are classified as even or odd. **Even numbers** are those that are divisible by 2 leaving no remainder. Any number that is not even is an **odd number.**

5. Whole numbers are also classified as **prime** or **composite.** A number is **prime** if it is greater than 1 and divisible only by itself and 1. A whole number greater than 1 that is not prime is called **composite.** The **factors** of a number are all the numbers that divide evenly into the given number.

1. The sticker price of a new Lexus is thirty-four thousand two hundred eighty-five dollars. Write this number as a numeral.

2. The total population of the United States on December 21, 2005, was estimated at 297,922,224. Write this population count in words.

3. China has the largest population on Earth, with a population of approximately one billion, three hundred six million, three hundred thirteen thousand eight hundred twelve. Write this population estimate as a numeral.

4. The average earned income for a person with a master's degree is $67,073. Round this value to the nearest thousand. To the nearest hundred.

5. One estimate of the world population toward the end of 2005 was 6,486,411,859 people. Round this value to the nearest million. The nearest billion.

6. You use a check to purchase this semester's textbooks. The total is $243.78. How will you write the amount in words on your check?

7. Explain why 90,210 is less than 91,021.

8. Determine whether each of the following numbers is even or odd. In each case, give a reason for your answer.

   a. 22,225   **b.** 13,578   **c.** 1500

   a.

   b.

   c.

9. Determine whether each of the following numbers is prime or composite. In each case, give a reason for your answer.

   a. 35   **b.** 31   **c.** 51

10. Some of the occupations that earn the highest income in the twenty-first century require a bachelor's degree. They are listed in the following table with their median annual salaries for 2001.

OCCUPATION	MALE MEDIAN ANNUAL SALARY ($)	FEMALE MEDIAN ANNUAL SALARY ($)
Managerial and professional specialty occupation	52,255	35,160
Management-related occupations	48,553	34,104
Professional specialty occupations	51,399	34,411

a. Round each median salary for males to the nearest thousand.

b. Round each median salary for females to the nearest thousand.

c. Is the median salary for females in management-related occupations as much as that of females in professional specialty occupations? Justify your answer.

11. You are researching information on buying a new sports utility vehicle (SUV). A particular SUV that you are considering has a manufacturer's suggested retail price (MSRP) of $31,310. The invoice price to the dealer for the SUV is $28,707. Do parts a and b to estimate how much bargaining room you have between the MSRP and the dealer's invoice price.

a. Round the MSRP and the invoice price each to the nearest thousand.

b. Use the rounded values from part a to estimate the difference between the MSRP and invoice price.

ACTIVITY 1.2

Bald Eagles

OBJECTIVES

1. Add whole numbers by hand and mentally.

2. Subtract whole numbers by hand and mentally.

3. Estimate sums and differences using rounding.

4. Recognize the associative property and the commutative property for addition.

5. Translate a written statement into an arithmetic expression.

In the 1700s, there were an estimated 25,000 to 75,000 nesting bald eagle pairs in what are now the contiguous 48 states. By the 1960s, there were less than 450 nesting pairs due to the destruction of forests for towns and farms, shooting, and DDT and other pesticides. In 1972, the federal government banned the use of DDT. In 1973, the bald eagle was formally listed as an endangered species. By the 1980s, the bald eagle population was clearly increasing. The following map of the contiguous 48 states displays the number of nesting pairs of bald eagles for each state. There are two numbers for each state. The first is for 1982, and the second is for 2000.

 Safe Again?

Bald Eagle Pairs
In the lower 48 State
1982 vs 2000

Totals
1982: 1480 pairs
2000: 6471 pairs

Data: U.S. Fish and Wildlife Service
*Last complete census was conducted in 1999

Addition of Whole Numbers

EXAMPLE 1   *What was the total number of nesting bald eagle pairs in New York and Pennsylvania in 1982?*

SOLUTION

Calculate the total number of bald eagle nesting pairs in 1982 in New York and Pennsylvania by combining the two sets. Note that each eagle on the next page represents a bald eagle nesting pair.

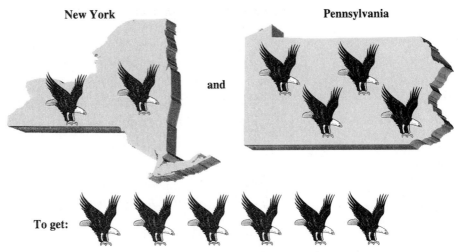

New York   and   Pennsylvania

To get:

Total of New York and Pennsylvania

In whole-number notation, $2 + 4 = 6$.

EXAMPLE 2 *Calculate the total number of bald eagle pairs in California and Colorado in 2000.*

SOLUTION

To calculate the total number of bald eagle pairs in California and Colorado in 2000, combine the 151 pairs in California and 42 pairs in Colorado using addition.

a. Set up the addition vertically so that the place values are aligned vertically.

b. Add all the digits in the ones place.

c. Add all the digits in the tens place.

Tens: Add the $5 + 4$
in tens place to get 9.

Hundreds: Bring down
the 1.

Ones: Add the $1 + 2$ in the
ones place to get 3.

$$
\begin{array}{r}
151 \\
+\ 42 \\
\hline
193
\end{array}
$$

The numbers that are being added, 151 and 42, are called **addends.** Their total, 193, is called the **sum.**

1. a. Calculate the total number of bald eagle pairs in New York and Pennsylvania in 2000.

b. Calculate the total number of bald eagle pairs in Idaho and Minnesota in 2000.

c. In part b, does it make a difference whether you set up the addition
113 + 681 or 681 + 113?

The order in which you add two numbers does not matter. This property of
addition is called the **commutative property.** For example,

$$17 + 32 = 32 + 17$$

EXAMPLE 3 *Calculate the total number of bald eagle pairs in South Carolina
and Texas in 2000 by setting up the addition vertically.*

SOLUTION

Set up the addition vertically. There are two methods for determining the sum.

Method 1:	*Method 2:*
Sums of Digits in Place Value	Regroup to Next Higher Place Value

Method 1:

Sums of Digits in Place Value

$$
\begin{array}{r}
153 \\
+ 78 \\
\hline
11 \\
120 \\
100 \\
\hline
231
\end{array}
$$

adding 3 ones + 8 ones
adding 5 tens + 7 tens

Method 2:

Regroup to Next Higher Place Value

Regroup 1 to hundreds place.
Regroup 1 to tens place.

$$
\begin{array}{r}
1\,1 \\
153 \\
+ 78 \\
\hline
231
\end{array}
$$

⎳ 3 + 8 = 11, write 1 in ones place.

2. a. Calculate the total number of bald eagle pairs in New York and Ohio in
2000 using method 1.

b. Calculate the total number of bald eagle pairs in New York and Ohio in
1998 using method 2.

c. Calculate the total number of bald eagle pairs in Texas, New Mexico, and
Arizona in 2000 using method 1.

d. Calculate the total number of bald eagle pairs in Texas, New Mexico, and Arizona in 2000 using method 2. Compare this result to the one obtained in part c.

3. a. Mentally calculate the total number of bald eagle pairs in California, New Mexico, and Arizona in 2000 by determining the sum of two numbers, then adding the sum to the third number.

b. Does it make a difference which two numbers you add together first?

When calculating the sum of three whole numbers, it makes no difference whether the first two numbers or the last two numbers are added together first. This property of addition is called the **associative property.** For example,

$$(143 + 4) + 36 = 143 + (4 + 36).$$

4. a. Mentally calculate the total number of bald eagle pairs in Washington, Oregon, and California in 1982.

b. Mentally calculate the total number of bald eagle pairs in Washington, Oregon, and California in 2000.

c. Explain the process you used to add these numbers.

5. a. Choose five states and calculate the total number of nesting bald eagle pairs in 1982.

b. Calculate the total number of nesting bald eagle pairs in 2000 for the five states you chose in part a.

Estimating Sums of Whole Numbers

Estimation is useful for adding several numbers quickly and for checking that a given sum is reasonable. One way to estimate is to round each number (addend) to the same place value.

EXAMPLE 4   *Estimate the total number of nesting pairs in Florida, South Carolina, and Virginia in 2000. Then calculate the exact sum.*

SOLUTION

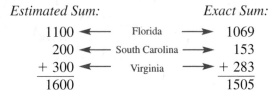

Estimated Sum:		*Exact Sum:*
1100 ⟵ Florida ⟶		1069
200 ⟵ South Carolina ⟶		153
+ 300 ⟵ Virginia ⟶		+ 283
1600		1505

In Example 4, the estimate is higher than the exact sum. An estimate may be higher, lower, or occasionally equal to the exact sum. Notice that the exact sum 1505 is reasonable for the given data because it is close in value to the estimated sum 1600.

6. a. Estimate the number of nesting pairs in Louisiana, Maine, and Arizona in 1982.

   b. Calculate the exact number of pairs in 1982.

   c. Estimate the number of nesting pairs in Louisiana, Maine, and Arizona in 2000.

   d. Calculate the exact number of pairs in 2000.

   e. Compare the exact results to your estimates. State whether the estimates are higher, lower, or the same as the exact results. Do your estimates indicate that your exact results are reasonable for the data given?

EXAMPLE 5   Subtraction of Whole Numbers

The number of bald eagle nesting pairs in 1982 for New York and the combined total for New York and Pennsylvania are given in the following graphic. Calculate the number of nesting pairs in Pennsylvania.

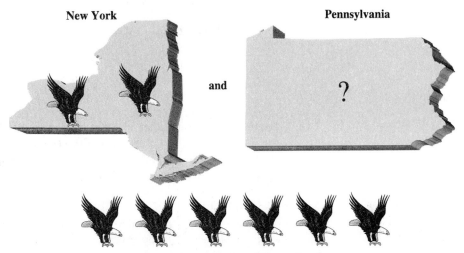

Total of New York and Pennsylvania

The picture suggests that the problem is to find the **missing addend.** In symbols, the calculation can be written in terms of addition as **2 + ? = 6.** By thinking of a number that added to 2 gives 6, you see that the answer is 4 pairs of bald eagles.

Alternatively, by thinking of taking away (**subtracting**) 2 from 6, the answer is the same, 4 pairs of bald eagles. In symbols, the calculation is written as **6 − 2 = ?**

> **Subtraction** is finding the difference between two numbers. The operation of subtraction involves taking away. In Example 5, take 2 bald eagle nesting pairs away from 6 bald eagle nesting pairs to get the difference, 4 nesting pairs.

7. a. How many more bald eagle nesting pairs were there in 2000 than in 1982 in Oregon?

b. Set up the calculation using addition.

c. Set up the calculation using subtraction.

EXAMPLE 6 *How many more nesting pairs were in Georgia than were in Alabama in 2000?*

SOLUTION

$$
\begin{array}{r}
4\ 15 \\
\cancel{5}5 \\
-\ 2\ 7 \\
\hline
2\ 8
\end{array}
$$

Convert 1 ten to 10 ones.
add ones to 5 to obtain 15 ones.
Subtract 7 from 15, and subtract 2 from 4.

Check using addition:

$$
\begin{array}{r}
28 \\
+\ 27 \\
\hline
55
\end{array}
$$

Formally, the number that is subtracted is called the **subtrahend.** The number subtracted from is called the **minuend.** The result is called the **difference.** To check subtraction, add the difference and the subtrahend. The result should be the minuend.

$$
\begin{array}{r}
55 \\
-\ 27 \\
\hline
28
\end{array}
$$
  minuend
  subtrahend
  difference

Check using addition:

$$
\begin{array}{r}
28 \\
+\ 27 \\
\hline
55
\end{array}
$$

Here, addition is used to check subtraction. Addition is called the **inverse** operation for subtraction.

8. **a.** Determine the difference between the number of nesting pairs in Louisiana in 2000 and 1982.

   b. What number is being subtracted? Why?

9. **a.** Calculate the increase in the population of nesting pairs in Michigan from 1982 to 2000.

   b. Determine the difference between the number of nesting pairs in Wisconsin and in Minnesota in 2000.

   c. Determine the difference between the number of nesting pairs in Wisconsin and Minnesota in 1982.

10. a. Estimate the difference between the number of nesting pairs in Florida and in Washington in 2000.

b. Determine the exact difference.

c. Was your estimate higher or lower than the exact difference?

11. a. To what place value should you round to estimate the difference between the number of nesting pairs in Louisiana and in California in 2000?

b. The highest place value is the hundreds. Would it make sense to round to the hundreds place? Why or why not?

Add or Subtract?

When you set up a problem, it is sometimes difficult to decide if you need to do addition or subtraction. It is helpful if you can recognize some key phrases so that you will write a correct arithmetic expression. An **arithmetic expression** consists of numbers, operation signs $(+, -, \cdot, \div)$, and sometimes parentheses.

The following tables contain some typical key phrases, examples, and corresponding arithmetic expressions for addition and subtraction.

ADDITION			SUBTRACTION		
KEY PHRASE	EXAMPLE	ARITHMETIC EXPRESSION	KEY PHRASE	EXAMPLE	ARITHMETIC EXPRESSION
sum of	sum of 3 and 5	$3 + 5$	difference of	difference of 12 and 7	$12 - 7$
increased by	7 increased by 4	$7 + 4$	decreased by	95 decreased by 10	$95 - 10$
plus	12 plus 10	$12 + 10$	minus	57 minus 26	$57 - 26$
more than	5 more than 6	$6 + 5$	less than	5 less than 23	$23 - 5$
total of	total of 13 and 8	$13 + 8$	subtracted from	12 subtracted from 37	$37 - 12$
added to	45 added to 50	$50 + 45$	subtract	8 subtract 5	$8 - 5$

12. Translate each of the following into an arithmetic expression.

a. 34 plus 42

b. difference of 33 and 22

c. 100 minus 25

d. total of 25 and 19

e. 17 more than 102

f. 14 subtracted from 28

g. 81 increased by 16

h. 50 less than 230

i. 250 decreased by 120

j. sum of 18 and 21

k. 101 added to 850

**SUMMARY
ACTIVITY 1.2**

1. Numbers that are added together are called **addends.** Their total is the **sum.**

2. To add numbers: Align them vertically according to place value. Add the digits in the ones place. If their sum is a two-digit number, write down the ones digit and carry the tens digit to the next column as a number to be added. Repeat with the next higher place value.

3. The order in which you add two numbers does not matter. This property of addition is called the **commutative property.**

4. When calculating the sum of three whole numbers, it makes no difference whether the first two numbers or the last two numbers are added together first. This property of addition is called the **associative property.**

5. Estimation is useful for adding or subtracting numbers quickly and to check the reasonableness of an exact calculation. One way to estimate is to round each number to its highest place value. In most cases, it may be better to round to a place value lower than the highest one.

6. Subtraction is used to find the difference between two numbers. The operation of subtraction involves *taking away.*

The number that is subtracted is called the **subtrahend.** The number being subtracted from is called the **minuend.** The result is called the **difference.** To check subtraction, add the difference and the subtrahend. The result should be the minuend.

To subtract: Align the subtrahend under the minuend according to place value. Subtract digits having the same place value. Regroup from a higher place value, if necessary.

**EXERCISES
ACTIVITY 1.2**

1. Determine the sum using method 1 (sum of the digits by place values) as shown in Example 3.

   a. 256
      + 35

   b. 617
      +149

   c. 51
      382
      + 77

2. Determine the sum using method 2 (regroup to next higher place value) as shown in Example 3.

   a. 159
      + 27

   b. 924
      +138

   c. 51
      382
      + 77

3. Determine the sum of 67 and 75.

   a. $67 + 75$

   b. $75 + 67$

   c. Are the sums in parts a and b the same?

   d. What property of addition is demonstrated?

4. Determine the sum. Do the addition in the parentheses first.

   a. $34 + (15 + 71)$

   b. $(34 + 15) + 71$

   c. Are the sums in parts a and b the same?

   d. What property of addition is demonstrated?

5. a. Estimate the sum: $171 + 90 + 226$

   b. Determine the actual sum.

   c. Was your estimate higher, lower, or the same as the actual sum?

Exercise numbers appearing in color are answered in the Selected Answers appendix.

6. a. Estimate the sum: 326 + 474

b. Determine the actual sum.

c. Was your estimate higher, lower, or the same as the actual sum?

7. Evaluate.

a. 123 − 91   **b.** 543 − 125   **c.** 78 − 49

d. 1002 − 250   **e.** 2001 − 1962   **f.** 696 − 384

8. a. Subtract the year in which you were born from this year.

b. Is the difference you obtain your age?

c. Have you had your birthday yet this year? Does this affect your answer in part b?

9. This week, you took home $96 from your part-time job. You owe your mother $39.

a. Estimate the amount of money that you will have after you pay your mother.

b. Determine the actual amount of money you will have after you pay your mother.

10. In 2000, there were 113 bald eagle nesting pairs in Idaho, 770 in Wisconsin, and 564 in Washington.

a. Estimate the total number of nesting pairs in all three states.

b. Determine the actual total.

c. Is your estimate higher or lower than the actual total?

11. In 2000, there were 371 nesting pairs in Oregon and 362 nesting pairs in Michigan.

a. Estimate the difference between the nesting pairs in Oregon and Michigan.

b. If you round both numbers to the hundreds place, what is your estimate?

c. If you round both numbers to the tens place, what is your estimate?

d. Which is the better "estimate"? Explain.

12. Translate each of the following into an arithmetic expression.

a. 13 plus 23

b. 108 minus 15

c. difference of 70 and 58

d. total of 45 and 79

e. 7 more than 12

f. 13 subtracted from 28

g. 85 increased by 8

h. 52 less than 300

i. 25 decreased by 12

⁂ ACTIVITY 1.3

Summer Camp

OBJECTIVES

1. Multiply whole numbers and check calculations using a calculator.

2. Multiply whole numbers using the distributive property.

3. Estimate the product of whole numbers by rounding.

4. Recognize the associative and commutative properties for multiplication.

You accept a job working in the kitchen at a small, private summer camp in New England. One hundred children attend the 8-week program under the supervision of 24 staff members. The job pays well, and it includes room and board with every other weekend off. One of your responsibilities is to pick up supplies twice a week at a local wholesale food club. Some of the items listed on this week's order form appear in the following receipt from the food club.

QUANTITY	ITEM	UNIT PRICE ($)
8	1 CASE (24 BOTTLES) 10-OZ BOTTLES OF JUICE	8.99
20	36 1.55-OZ MILK CHOCOLATE BARS	11.19
12	36 1-OZ SERVINGS OF CREAM CHEESE	6.39
18	32 1.25-OZ GRANOLA BARS	6.99
6	1 BOX OF 15 CARTONS OF 1 DOZ. LARGE EGGS	8.99
10	4-LB PACKAGE HOT DOGS (40 COUNT)	6.69
12	10-LB PACKAGE HAMBURGER (40 COUNT)	12.99
16	24-PACK HOT DOG ROLLS	2.39
18	24-PACK HAMBURGER ROLLS	2.39
30	2-LOAF PACK 20-OZ BREAD (20 SLICES)	2.39
12	42-COUNT VARIETY PACKAGE OF CHIPS	7.99
8	200-COUNT PACKAGE 9" PLATES	6.99
1	1500-COUNT PACKAGE DISPENSER NAPKINS	10.39
4	500-COUNT PACKAGE SPOONS	5.69
2	500-COUNT PACKAGE KNIVES	5.69
3	500-COUNT PACKAGE FORKS	5.69

1. The total number of bottles of juice purchased can be represented by the following sum.

$$24 + 24 + 24 + 24 + 24 + 24 + 24 + 24 = \underline{\hspace{1.5cm}}$$

   a. Calculate this sum directly.

   b. Calculate this sum using your calculator.

   c. Is there a more efficient (shorter) way to do this calculation?

Multiplication of whole numbers is repeated addition. The sum $24 + 24 + 24 + 24 + 24 + 24 + 24 + 24$ can be rewritten as the **product** $8 \cdot 24$ or 8×24. The operation sign "$\times$" is the multiplication symbol generally used in arithmetic courses, but the symbol "$\cdot$" is more common in algebra. The whole numbers 8 and 24 are called **factors** of the product 192. To do the multiplication by hand, set up the calculation vertically as follows.

$$
\begin{array}{r}
24 \\
\times\ 8 \\
\hline
32 \\
160 \\
\hline
192
\end{array}
$$

32   **Multiply 8 times 4.**

160   **Multiply 8 times 20.**

192   **Add 32 and 160.**

Multiplication works when set up vertically because 24 can be written as $20 + 4$ and the factor 8 multiplies both the 20 and the 4. Set up horizontally, the calculation is written as follows:

$$8 \cdot 24 = 8 \cdot (20 + 4) = 8 \cdot 20 + 8 \cdot 4 = 160 + 32 = 192$$

Rewriting $8 \cdot (20 + 4)$ as $8 \cdot 20 + 8 \cdot 4$ is an example of the **distributive property of multiplication over addition.**

2. a. Calculate the total number of cartons of eggs you are to purchase this week.

b. Calculate the number of 9-inch plates you will purchase.

The multiplication for the total number of hamburger rolls can be set up vertically or horizontally.

Vertically:

$$
\begin{array}{r}
24 \\
\times\ 18 \\
\hline
32 \\
160 \\
240 \\
\hline
432
\end{array}
$$

32   **Multiply 8 times 4.**

160   **Multiply 8 times 20.**

240   **Multiply 10 times 24.**

Horizontally:

$$18 \cdot 24 = \underbrace{18 \cdot (20 + 4) = 18 \cdot 20 + 18 \cdot 4}_{\text{Distributive property}} = 360 + 72 = 432$$

3. a. How many ounces of juice are there in one case of juice from the wholesale club?

b. Use your answer in part a to calculate the total number of ounces of juice needed this week.

c. How many bottles of juice are needed?

d. Use your answer in part c to calculate the total number of ounces of juice needed this week.

e. Compare your answers for parts b and d. Explain why you think these answers should be the same.

The property illustrated in Problems 3b and 3d is the **associative property of multiplication.** For example,

$$5 \cdot (4 \cdot 7) = (5 \cdot 4) \cdot 7$$

4. Describe the associative property of multiplication in your own words.

5. Calculate the total number of eggs on the list in two ways using the associative property.

6. The multiplication to determine the total number of hamburger rolls can be set up two ways.

$$\begin{array}{r} 24 \\ \times 18 \\ \hline \end{array} \quad \text{or} \quad \begin{array}{r} 18 \\ \times 24 \\ \hline \end{array}$$

a. Determine the product for each of the two multiplication problems.

b. Explain why the answers are the same.

The mathematical property illustrated in Problem 6a is the **commutative property of multiplication.** For example,

$$8 \cdot 4 = 4 \cdot 8$$

7. Describe the commutative property of multiplication in your own words.

8. a. Determine the total number of hamburgers and the total number of hamburger rolls you need to purchase.

   b. Do you need to change the number of packages of hamburger rolls? Explain why or why not.

9. One 1500-count package of dispenser napkins is purchased.

   a. Using multiplication, calculate the total number of napkins purchased.

   b. If you multiply any whole number by 1, what is the result?

   c. If you multiply any whole number by zero, what is the result?

Estimation

You may not have easy access to a calculator at summer camp. So you may need to multiply or check multiplication mentally or by hand. To calculate the total number of individual 1-ounce servings of cream cheese, you need to multiply 12 times 36. The product can be estimated by rounding.

- Round 12 down to 10.
- Round 36 up to 40.
- Multiply 10 times 40.
- The estimated product is _____

10. a. Multiply 12 and 36 to determine the actual number of servings of cream cheese.

   b. What is the difference between the actual number of servings and the estimated number of servings?

11. a. Estimate the total number of granola bars in the order.

   b. Determine the actual number of granola bars.

c. What is the difference between the actual number and the estimated number of granola bars?

PROCEDURE

Estimating Products

- Round each factor to a large enough place value so that you can do the multiplication mentally.
- There is no one correct answer when estimating, only a reasonable answer.

---

12. Estimate the total number of chocolate bars.

13. Estimate the total number of individual snack packs of chips.

SUMMARY
ACTIVITY 1.3

1. Multiplication properties of whole numbers

Any whole number times 1 remains the same.

Any whole number times 0 is 0.

2. Distributive property

A whole number placed in front of a set of parentheses containing a sum or difference of two numbers multiplies each of the inside numbers.

$$3 \cdot (7 + 2) = 3 \cdot 7 + 3 \cdot 2 \quad \text{or} \quad 5 \cdot (10 - 4) = 5 \cdot 10 - 5 \cdot 4$$

3. Associative property

When multiplying three whole numbers, it makes no difference which two numbers are multiplied first.

$$(2 \cdot 5) \cdot 7 = 2 \cdot (5 \cdot 7)$$

4. Commutative property

Changing the order of two whole numbers when multiplying them produces the same product.

$$3 \cdot 6 = 6 \cdot 3$$

5. Estimating products

Round each factor to a large enough place value so that you can do the multiplication mentally.

There is no one correct answer when estimating, only reasonable answers.

1. Multiply vertically. Verify your answer using a calculator.

a. 34
    × 4

b. 529
    × 8

c. 67
    × 5

d. 807
    × 9

e. 125
    × 8

f. 2001
    × 25

g. 75
    × 52

h. 1967
    × 105

2. a. Multiply 8 and 47 by rewriting 47 as 40 + 7 and use the distributive property to obtain the result.

   b. Multiply 8 and 47 vertically.

3. a. Multiply 12 and 36 by rewriting 36 as 30 + 6 and use the distributive property to obtain the result.

   b. Multiply 12 and 36 vertically.

4. Three 500-count packages of forks are purchased.

   a. Use addition to determine the total number of forks.

b. Use multiplication to determine the total number of forks.

5. Ten 40-count packages of hot dogs are purchased.

a. Determine the total number of hot dogs by calculating $10 \cdot 40$.

b. Calculate: $40 \cdot 10$.

c. What property of multiplication is demonstrated by the fact that the answers to parts a and b should be the same?

6. a. Evaluate: $72 \cdot 23$

b. Evaluate: $23 \cdot 72$

c. Are the answers to parts a and b the same?

d. What property do the results of this exercise demonstrate?

7. Evaluate by finding the product in parentheses first.

a. $7 \cdot (13 \cdot 20)$ **b.** $(7 \cdot 13) \cdot 20$

c. Are the answers to parts a and b the same?

d. What property do the results in parts a and b demonstrate?

8. You purchase twelve 42-count packages of variety chips for the summer camp.

a. Estimate the total number of individual packages of chips purchased.

b. Determine the actual number of individual packages you purchased.

c. Is the estimated total higher or lower than the actual total?

9. You purchase sixteen 24-pack hot dog rolls this week.

a. Estimate the total number of hot dog rolls.

b. Determine the actual number of hot dog rolls.

c. Is the estimated total higher or lower than the actual total?

✻**ACTIVITY 1.4**

College Supplies

OBJECTIVES

1. Divide whole numbers by "grouping."

2. Divide whole numbers "by hand" and by calculator.

3. Estimate the quotient of whole numbers by rounding.

4. Recognize the noncommutative property for division.

School Supplies

It is the beginning of a new semester and time to purchase supplies. You and five fellow students decide to shop at a discount office supply store. The six of you purchase the following items.

QUANTITY	ITEM	UNIT PRICE ($)
3	8-PACK NUMBER 2 PENCILS	2.89
3	5-PACK MECHANICAL PENCILS	3.95
3	4-PACK REFILLABLE MECHANICAL PENCILS	3.58
2	10-PACK ASSORTED GEL RETRACTABLE PENS	9.98
3	2-PACK BALLPOINT PENS	6.18
2	4-PK LIQUID PAPER	6.98
3	10-PACK ASSORTED HIGHLIGHTERS	9.98
3	5-PACK PERMANENT MARKERS	3.49
6	400-COUNT PACKAGE 8.5" X 11" COLLEGE-RULED PAPER	3.09
20	POCKET FOLDERS	0.18
12	THREE-SUBJECT SPIRAL NOTEBOOK	4.72
4	5-COUNT PACK REPORT COVERS	5.18
3	500-COUNT PACK 3" X 5" INDEX CARDS	2.78

There are three 8-count packages of number-two pencils or a total of 24 pencils, illustrated below.

These 24 pencils need to be divided among the six of you. To set this up as a division calculation, write either $24 \div 6$, $24/6$, or $6\overline{)24}$.

DEFINITION

The number *being divided* is called the **dividend.** The number that divides the dividend is called the **divisor.** Here, the number 6 is the divisor, and the number 24 is the dividend. The **quotient** is the result of the division. In this case, 4 is the quotient.

$$\begin{array}{r} 4 \leftarrow \text{quotient} \\ \text{divisor} \rightarrow 6\overline{)24} \leftarrow \text{dividend} \end{array}$$

If 24 pencils are distributed evenly among the six of you, you will each get 4 pencils.

You used division to distribute the 24 pencils equally among yourselves. The result was 4 pencils per student. In general, you use division to separate items into a specified number of equal groupings.

> The two ways the division process can be stated:
>
> $$dividend \div divisor = quotient, \text{ with a possible remainder,}$$
>
> or, in long division format,
>
> $$divisor{\overline{)dividend}}^{\text{quotient with a possible remainder}}.$$

Multiplication and division are **inverse operations.** This means that the division $24 \div 6 = 4$ can be written as the multiplication $4 \cdot 6 = 24$, and vice versa.

1. **a.** Your group buys three 5-packs of mechanical pencils. Distribute these 15 pencils evenly among the six of you. How many pencils will each of you receive? Are there any pencils left over?

   b. Identify the divisor and the dividend. What is the quotient? What is the remainder, if any?

2. **a.** How many gel pens are there in the two packages of 10-count assorted gel retractable pens?

   b. Distribute the gel pens evenly among the six of you. Set up as a division problem. What is the quotient? What is the remainder, if any?

> To check division, multiply the quotient and the divisor, then add the remainder. The result should be the dividend.
>
> $$(quotient \times divisor) + remainder = dividend$$

3. Check the division you did in Problem 2.

Division can be considered as repeated subtraction of the divisor from the dividend, with a remainder left over.

EXAMPLE 1   *You buy 20 pocket folders. Distribute them evenly among the six of you.*

SOLUTION

a. Use long division.

$$
\begin{array}{r}
3 \\
6\overline{)20} \\
18 \\
\hline
2
\end{array}
$$

b. Use repeated subtraction.

$$
\begin{array}{r}
20 \\
-\ 6 \\
\hline
14 \\
-\ 6 \\
\hline
8 \\
-6 \\
\hline
2
\end{array}
$$

6 can be subtracted from 20 three times.

3 is the quotient.

2 is the remainder.

In general, when you divide, you are repeatedly subtracting multiples of the divisor from the dividend until no whole multiples remain.

EXAMPLE 2   *Your group purchased three 500-count packs of 3" × 5" index cards. Distribute these 1500 index cards evenly among the six of you. How many index cards do you each get?*

SOLUTION

Use a long division problem process to determine that each of you receives 250 index cards with none left over.

$$
\begin{array}{r}
250 \\
6\overline{)1500} \\
-12 \\
\hline
30 \\
-30 \\
\hline
00
\end{array}
$$

6 does not divide into 1. 6 does divide into 15 two times.
Write down the product 2 · 6 = 12. Subtract 12 from 15.
Bring down 0, the next digit. 6 divides into 30 five times.
Write down the product 5 · 6 = 30. Subtract 30 from 30.
Bring down the last 0. 6 divides into 0 zero times.
The remainder is 0.

4. a. Your group purchased six 400-count packages of 8.5" × 11" college-ruled paper. If these packages are distributed equally among the six of you, how many packages will you each receive?

b. Suppose 52 packages are distributed equally among 52 students. How many packages will each student receive?

c. How many times can you subtract 52 from 52?

d. What result do you get when you divide any nonzero number by itself?

5. There was a stapler in the shopping cart, but you returned it to the shelf because all of you already had one.

   a. How many staplers will you receive from this shopping expedition?

   b. Use your calculator to divide zero by six. What is the result? Try dividing zero by another nonzero whole number. What is the result?

   c. Use your calculator to divide 6 by 0. What happens?

If you try to divide by zero, a basic or scientific calculator will display the letter E to signify an error. Graphing calculators usually display the word ERROR with a message. The reason is that if you change $6 \div 0 = ?$ to a multiplication calculation, it becomes $0 \cdot ? = 6$. No whole number works because zero times any whole number is zero, not 6. This means that $6 \div 0$ has no answer. Another way to say this is that $6 \div 0$ is **undefined.**

   d. Explain why 9 divided by 0 is undefined.

DEFINITION

Division Properties Involving 0 and 1	**Example:**
• Any whole number divided by itself is 1.	$34 \div 34 = 1$
• Any whole number divided by 1 is itself.	$6 \div 1 = 6$
• 0 divided by any nonzero whole number is 0.	$0 \div 10 = 0$
• Division by 0 is undefined.	$7 \div 0$ is undefined.

6. Three 10-count packs of assorted highlighters contain a total of 30 highlighters.

   a. By doing the division $30 \div 6$, determine the number of highlighters each student will receive.

   b. Do you get the same result by doing the division, $6 \div 30$?

   c. Does the commutative property hold for division? That is, does $6 \div 30 = 30 \div 6$?

Rent and Utilities

This year, you decide to rent an apartment near campus with three other students. The rent is $1150 per month, basic telephone service is $41 per month, and the average monthly utility bill is $173.

To estimate your share of the monthly telephone service charge, you would round $41 to the tens place and get $40. Dividing $40 by 4 (students), you estimate your share to be $10 per month.

> To estimate a quotient, first estimate the divisor and the dividend using numbers that allow for easier division mentally or by hand. For example, estimate $384 \div 6$ by rounding 384 to 400 and replacing 6 by 5. The estimate is $400 \div 5 = 80$, which is 16 more than the exact result, 64.

7. a. Estimate your share of the rent by rounding $1150 to the thousands place and then dividing by 4.

   b. Is your estimate lower or higher than the actual amount that you owe?

8. a. Estimate your share of the utility bill by rounding $173.

   b. Is your estimate lower or higher than the actual amount that you owe?

9. Estimate your share of the monthly telephone service charge by rounding.

10. a. Add the monthly charges for rent, telephone, and utilities. Calculate your actual share of this sum. Verify your calculation using your calculator.

b. Compare your actual share of the monthly expenses with the sum of the individual estimates for the monthly rent, telephone, and utility costs.

11. a. Estimate: $19,500 \div 78$

b. Determine the exact answer.

c. Is your estimate lower, higher, or the same?

12. a. Estimate: $5880 \div 120$

b. Determine the exact answer.

c. Is your estimate lower, higher, or the same?

13. a. Estimate: $30,380 \div 490$

b. Determine the exact answer.

c. Is your estimate lower, higher, or the same?

Division Properties of Whole Numbers

1. In general, use division to separate items into a specified number of equal groupings.

2. The numbers involved in the division process have specific names:
   dividend ÷ divisor = quotient with a possible remainder,
   or, in long division format,

$$\text{divisor)}\overline{\text{dividend}}^{\text{quotient with a possible remainder}}.$$

3. To check division, multiply the quotient by the divisor, then add the remainder. The result should be the dividend.

$$(\text{quotient} \times \text{divisor}) + \text{remainder} = \text{dividend}$$

4. Multiplication and division are **inverse operations.**

5. Division is *not* commutative. Example: $10 \div 5 \neq 5 \div 10$

Division Properties Involving 0 and 1

6. Any whole number divided by itself is 1.

7. Any whole number divided by 1 remains the same.

8. 0 divided by any nonzero whole number is 0.

9. Division by 0 is undefined.

Estimating a Quotient

10. To estimate a quotient, first estimate the divisor and the dividend by numbers that provide a division easily done mentally or by hand.

1. Calculate the following. As part of your answer, identify the quotient and remainder (if any).

   a. $56 \div 7$

   b. $112 \div 4$

   c. $95 \div 3$

   d. $222 \div 11$

   e. $506 \div 13$

   f. $587 \div 23$

   g. $0 \div 15$

   h. $15 \div 0$

2. Six students purchase seven 5-packs of report covers to distribute evenly among themselves.

   a. Determine the total number of report covers to be distributed.

   b. How many report covers will each student receive?

   c. Set the calculation up as a long division and divide.

   d. Identify the divisor and the dividend. What is the quotient? What is the remainder, if any?

   e. Are there any report covers left over?

   f. Do this problem again using "repeated subtraction."

Exercise numbers appearing in color are answered in the Selected Answers appendix.

3. Four students will share equally three 500-count packages of 3" × 5" index cards.

   a. Determine the total number of index cards to be distributed.

   b. How many index cards will each student receive?

   c. Set up the calculation as a long division and divide.

   d. Identify the divisor and the dividend. What is the quotient? What is the remainder, if any?

   e. Are there any index cards left over?

4. a. Divide: 24 ÷ 8.

   b. Do you get the same result by doing the division 8 ÷ 24?

   c. Does the commutative property hold for division? That is, does 24 ÷ 8 = 8 ÷ 24?

5. Your college campus has many more students who drive to campus than it has parking spaces. Even if you arrive early, it is difficult to find a parking space on any Monday, Wednesday, or Friday. The college is planning for future growth and in assessing the current parking problem estimates that 825 additional parking spaces will be needed. There are several parcels of land that will each accommodate a 180-car parking lot.

   a. Estimate the number of parking lots that are needed.

b. Determine the actual number of parking lots that are needed by first dividing 825 by 180.

c. Was your estimate too high or too low?

6. a. Estimate: 3850 ÷ 52

b. Find the exact answer.

c. Is your estimate lower, higher, or the same?

7. a. Estimate: 28,800 ÷ 314

b. Find the exact answer.

c. Is your estimate lower, higher, or the same?

Astronomical Distances

✳ **ACTIVITY 1.5**

Reach for the Stars

OBJECTIVES

1. Use exponential notation.

2. Factor whole numbers.

3. Determine the prime factorization of a whole number.

4. Recognize square numbers and roots of square numbers.

5. Recognize cubed numbers.

6. Apply the multiplication rule for numbers in exponential form with the same base.

On a clear night, thousands of stars are visible. Some stars appear larger and brighter than others. Their distances from Earth also vary greatly. For instance, the distance to the star Altair is about 100,000,000,000,000 miles. These distances are so large that they are unmanageable as written whole numbers. It is easier to write very large numbers using exponents. The distance from Earth to Altair is approximately one hundred trillion miles and can be written in exponential form as 10^{14} miles. The exponent, 14, means to use the base, 10, as a factor 14 times.

$$\overset{\text{exponent}}{10^{14}} = \underbrace{10 \cdot 10 \cdot 10 \cdot 10 \cdot 10 \cdot 10 \cdot 10 \cdot 10 \cdot 10 \cdot 10 \cdot 10 \cdot 10 \cdot 10 \cdot 10}_{\text{10 is used as a factor 14 times.}}$$
$$= 100{,}000{,}000{,}000{,}000$$

A whole-number **exponent** indicates the number of times the **base** is used as a factor. An exponent is also called a **power.** Note that 10 can be written as 10^1. When there is no exponent, it is understood to be 1. A number such as 10^{14} is in **exponential form** and is read as "ten to the fourteenth power."

1. The distance from Earth to the Great Whirlpool Galaxy is 10^{20} miles. Write this distance as a whole number.

2. **a.** Refer to the chart in Problem 3 and write the distance from Earth to Barnard's Galaxy as a whole number.

   b. Now write the distance to Barnard's Galaxy in base 10 using an exponent.

   c. Is it easier to write this distance as a whole number or as a number in base 10 using an exponent?

   d. Discuss the relationship between the number of zeros that make up this whole number and the exponent when you write this number as a power of 10.

3. Fill in the missing whole numbers and powers of 10.

Way Out There...

CELESTIAL BODY	DISTANCE FROM EARTH IN MILES	WRITTEN USING AN EXPONENT
Barnard's Galaxy, first known dwarf galaxy, discovered in 1882	10,000,000,000,000,000,000	10^{19}
Brightest quasar, 3C 273		10^{22}
Comet Hale-Bopp on April 6, 2091		10^{10}
Double star Shuart 1	1,000,000,000,000,000	10^{15}
First magnitude star, Altair	100,000,000,000,000	
First near-Earth asteroid, Eros, at its closest	10,000,000	
Great Whirlpool Galaxy	100,000,000,000,000,000,000	
Ionosphere		10^{2}
Mars on Nov. 2, 2001	100,000,000	
Million-star globular cluster Omega Centauri	100,000,000,000,000,000	
Nothing known about things at this distance		10^{12}
Russian *Molnyia* (Lightning) communications satellites at highest altitude		10^{4}
Saturn on Oct. 17, 2015	1,000,000,000	
Space shuttle when you lose sight of it	1,000	
Stratosphere	10	
Typical near-Earth asteroid when it flies by	1,000,000	

EXAMPLE 1 *A space shuttle is no longer visible to the naked eye when it is* $1000 = 10^3$ *miles away from an observer. Since 10 can be written as the product* $2 \cdot 5$, *you can rewrite* 10^3 *as* $(2 \cdot 5)^3$. *By the associative and commutative properties of multiplication* $(2 \cdot 5)^3$ *is equal to* $2^3 5^3$. *Therefore, 1000 can be written as*

$$1000 = 10^3 = (2 \cdot 5)^3 = (2 \cdot 5)(2 \cdot 5)(2 \cdot 5) = (2 \cdot 2 \cdot 2)(5 \cdot 5 \cdot 5) = 2^3 5^3$$

4. Use the associative and commutative properties of multiplication to show how or explain why $(3 \cdot 5)^2$ is equal to $3^2 \cdot 5^2$.

When a number is written as a product of its factors, it is called a **factorization** of the number. When all the factors are prime numbers, the product is called the **prime factorization** of the number. (Recall that a prime number is a whole number greater than 1 whose only whole-number factors are itself and 1.)

Fundamental property of whole numbers: For any whole number, there is only one prime factorization.

Notice that $2^3 5^3$ is a factorization of 1000 written in exponential form. It is also a prime factorization of 1000 because the factors, 2 and 5, which appear as base numbers, are both prime numbers.

5. a. $10 \cdot 10 \cdot 10 = 10^3$ is a factorization of 1000. Is 10^3 a prime factorization of 1000? Explain.

b. In Example 1, 10^3 was rewritten as $(2 \cdot 5)^3$. Is $(2 \cdot 5)^3$ a prime factorization of 1000?

c. If you ignore the order of the factors, how many prime factorizations of 1000 are there?

6. a. List the prime numbers that are less than 50.

b. What is the smallest prime number?

7. a. Determine the prime factorization of 90.

b. Describe a way to find the prime factorization of any whole number.

c. Use your method in part b to find the prime factorization of 100.

8. The distance to the double star Shuart 1 is 1,000,000,000,000,000, or 10^{15}, miles. Determine the prime factorization of this number. Write your result in both types of exponential form similar to those in Problem 5.

9. The National Collegiate Athletic Association (NCAA) Men's Basketball Tournament is a major TV event each year. Sixty-four colleges are invited to participate in the tournament based on their seasonal records and performance in their conference playoffs. The teams are then paired and half of the teams are eliminated after each round of play. After round one, there are 32 teams, then 16, 8, 4, 2, and, finally, 1.

a. Determine the prime factorization of the numbers 64, 32, 16, 8, 4, and 2 and write each number using an exponent. The first entry, 64, is done for you.

NUMBER OF TEAMS	PRIME FACTORIZATION	WRITTEN USING AN EXPONENT
64	$2 \cdot 2 \cdot 2 \cdot 2 \cdot 2 \cdot 2$	2^6
32		
16		
8		
4		
2		
Winner		

b. Describe the pattern for the exponents in the last column of this chart.

c. If you continue the pattern in the last column and write 1 in terms of base 2, what exponent would you attach to base 2?

Any nonzero whole number raised to the zero power is equal to 1.

EXAMPLE 2   The Square of a Number *In geometry, a square is a rectangle in which all the sides have equal length. The area of a square is a product of two factors, each equal to the length of a side. In exponential form, you say that the length is squared.*

A square with sides 1 unit in length has an area equal to 1 square unit.	$\square^1$ 1	$1^2 = 1$
A square with sides 2 units in length has an area equal to 4 square units.	2 2	$2^2 = 4$
A square with sides 3 units in length has an area equal to 9 square units.	3 3	$3^2 = 9$

10. a. Determine the area of a square whose sides are 5 units in length.

    b. Determine the area of a square whose sides are 11 units in length.

11. Explain how to determine the square of any number.

A whole number is **square** (sometimes called a *perfect square*) if it is the product of a whole number times itself. For example, 36 and 100 are both square numbers because $36 = 6^2$ and $100 = 10^2$.

12. a. Draw a square that has an area of 49 square units on the grid.

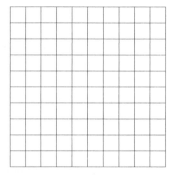

    b. What is the length of each side?

EXAMPLE 3   **The Cube of a Number** *In geometry, a cube is a box in which all the edges have equal length. The volume or space inside the cube is the product of three factors, each equal to the length of an edge. We say the volume is the length of the edge cubed. The following pictures illustrate this idea.*

A cube with edges 1 unit in length has a volume equal to 1 cubic unit.		$1^3 = 1$
A cube with edges 2 units in length has a volume equal to 8 cubic units.		$2^3 = 8$
A cube with edges 3 units in length has a volume equal to 27 cubic units.		$3^3 = 27$

13. a. Determine the volume of a cube whose edges are 4 units in length.

b. Determine the volume of a cube whose edges are 8 units in length.

14. Explain how to determine the cube of any number.

15. You are a cake designer and have a client who is organizing a Monte Carlo Night for a charity benefit. The client wants several pairs of cakes that look like a pair of dice (cubes) . You have 6-inch square pans. The square area of the bottom of the cake in each pan will be 36 square inches.

a. How high will a cake have to be to represent a die (cube)?

b. What will be the volume of the cube cake in cubic inches?

Perhaps you showed the calculation in Problem 15.b as $6^2 \cdot 6^1 = 6 \cdot 6 \cdot 6 = 216$ cubic inches. Note that $6^2 \cdot 6^1$ is equivalent to 6^3 in value and that the sum of the exponents is $2 + 1 = 3$.

When multiplying two numbers written in exponential form that have the same base, add the exponents. This sum becomes the new exponent attached to the original base. For example,

$$5^4 \cdot 5^3 = 5^7,$$

since the product is the result of multiplying seven factors of 5.

$$(5 \cdot 5 \cdot 5 \cdot 5)(5 \cdot 5 \cdot 5) = 5^7$$

16. The Great Whirlpool Galaxy is one million times farther away from Earth than the first-magnitude star Altair. Use exponents to express this relationship (refer to chart in Problem 3).

17. Rewrite the following numbers using a single exponent. Check with your calculator.

a. $10^5 \cdot 10^4$

b. $4^7 \cdot 4^5$

EXAMPLE 4   **Ceramic Tile** *Ceramic floor tiles can be square and measure 1 foot by 1 foot in size. If you want to tile a square space that is 5 feet by 5 feet as shown in the figure, you would need 25 ceramic tiles. The 5-foot sides are called the* **dimensions** *of the 25 square foot area.*

Numerically, you express the relationship between the dimensions and the area as $5 \cdot 5 = 5^2 = 25$. *The factor, 5, appears twice in this factorization of 25, and is called the* **square root** *of 25. Using symbols,* $\sqrt{25} = 5$, *which is read as "the square root of 25 is 5."*

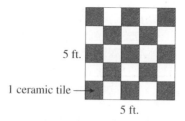

5 ft.

1 ceramic tile ⟶

5 ft.

18. a. Determine the dimensions of the square area that you could tile with 81 ceramic tiles.

b. Determine the dimensions of the square area that you could tile with 144 ceramic tiles.

19. a. Determine the square roots of 64 and 225.

    b. If your calculator has a square root key ⬭ , check your answers in part a.

20. a. Can you tile a square area with 100 1-foot-square tiles? Explain.

    b. Can you tile a square area with 24 of the 1-foot-square tiles? Explain.

**SUMMARY
ACTIVITY 1.5**

1. A whole-number **exponent** indicates the number of times to use the **base** as a factor. A number written as 10^{14} is in **exponential form.** The expression 10^{14} is called a power of 10.

2. Writing a number as a product of its factors is called **factorization.** When all the factors are prime numbers, the product is called the **prime factorization** of the number. A **prime number** is a whole number greater than 1 whose only whole number factors are itself and 1.

3. **Fundamental property of whole numbers:** For any whole number, there is only one prime factorization.

4. Any nonzero whole number raised to the **zero power** equals 1.

5. When multiplying numbers written in exponential form that have the same base, add the exponents. This sum becomes the new exponent attached to the original base. For example,

$$9^4 \cdot 9^3 = 9^7.$$

6. A **square** is a rectangle in which all the sides have equal length. The area of a square is a product of two factors, each equal to the length of a side, that is, the length squared.

7. A whole number is a perfect **square** if it can be rewritten as the product of two whole-number factors that are equal, that is, as the square of a whole number. For example, 36 is a perfect square because $6^2 = 36$.

8. The **square root** of a whole number is one of the two equal factors whose product is the whole number. For example, 6 is the square root of 36 because $6^2 = 36$. Using symbols, $\sqrt{36} = 6$.

1. The distance from Earth to Alnilam, the center star in Orion's Belt, is 10^{16} miles. Write 10^{16} as a whole number.

2. The distance from Earth to the Large Magellanic Cloud, a satellite galaxy of the Milky Way, is 10,000,000,000,000,000,000 miles. Write this distance in exponential form.

3. Determine two prime numbers between 50 and 60.

4. How many prime numbers are there between 60 and 70? List them.

5. List all possible factorizations of the following numbers.

   a. 6   **b.** 15

   c. 35   **d.** 22

   e. How many different factorizations do each of these numbers have?

6. **a.** List all possible factorizations of 30 and 105.

   b. How many different factorizations do each of these numbers have?

7. **a.** List all possible factorizations of 4, 9, and 25.

   b. What do the factorizations of these three numbers share in common?

8. Determine the prime factorizations of each number.

   a. 12   **b.** 75

   c. 42   **d.** 96

9. Computers come with 1024, 512, 256, 128 or 64 MB of RAM (random access memory). Write 1024, 512, 256, 128, and 64 as powers of 2.

10. Write each exponential form as a whole number.

   a. 3^0 **b.** 9^2 **c.** 5^4

   d. 2^5 **e.** 12^2

11. Write each expression using a single exponent. Check your answers with a calculator.

   a. $5^3 \cdot 5^8$ **b.** $9^2 \cdot 9^5$

   c. $7^4 \cdot 7^7$ **d.** $7^5 \cdot 7^0$

12. Determine the square root of each number.

   a. 64   **b.** 81   **c.** 121

   d. 169   **e.** 225   **f.** 400

13. Determine if the given area is the area of a square that has a whole-number length.

   a. 144 square feet   **b.** 160 square feet

   c. 664 square feet   **d.** 256 square feet

✳**ACTIVITY 1.6**

You and Your Calculator

OBJECTIVES

1. Use order of operations to evaluate arithmetic expressions.

2. Use order of operations to evaluate formulas involving whole numbers.

A calculator is a powerful tool for problem solving. Calculators come in many sizes and shapes and with varying capabilities. Some calculators perform only basic operations such as addition, subtraction, multiplication, division, and square roots. Others also handle operations with exponents, perform operations with fractions, and do trigonometry and statistics. There are also calculators that graph equations and generate tables of values; some even manipulate algebraic symbols.

Unlike people, however, calculators do not think for themselves and can only perform tasks in the way that you instruct them (or program them). Therefore, if you understand the properties of numbers, you will understand how a calculator operates with numbers. In particular, you will learn the order in which your calculator performs the operations you request.

If you do not have a calculator for this course, perform the calculations using paper and pencil. There are many skills in this activity that are important to your understanding of whole numbers.

1. a. Use your calculator to determine the sum $126 + 785$.

b. Now, input $785 + 126$ into your calculator and evaluate. How does this sum compare to the sum in Problem 1?

c. If you use numbers other than 126 and 785, does reversing the order of the numbers change the result? Explain by giving examples.

d. What property is demonstrated in this problem?

2. Is the commutative property true for the operation of subtraction? Multiplication? Division? Explain by giving examples for each operation.

Mental Arithmetic

It is sometimes necessary to do mental arithmetic (that is, *without* your calculator or paper and pencil). For example, to evaluate $3 \cdot 29$ without the aid of your calculator, think about the multiplication as follows: 29 can be written as $20 + 9$. Therefore, $3 \cdot 29$ can be written as $3 \cdot (20 + 9)$, which can be evaluated as $3 \cdot 20 + 3 \cdot 9$. The product $3 \cdot 29$ can now be thought of as $60 + 27$, or 87. To summarize,

$$3 \cdot 29 = 3 \cdot (20 + 9) = 3 \cdot 20 + 3 \cdot 9 = 60 + 27 = 87.$$

3. What property did the above calculation demonstrate?

4. Another way to express 29 is 25 + 4 or 30 − 1.

    a. Express 29 as 25 + 4 and use the distributive property to multiply 3 · 29.

    b. Express 29 as 30 − 1 and use the distributive property to multiply 3 · 29.

5. Evaluate mentally the following multiplication problems using the distributive property. Verify your answer using your calculator.

    a. 6 · 72

    b. 3 · 109

6. a. Evaluate 10 + 7 · 3 mentally and record the result. Verify your answer using your calculator.

    b. What operations are involved in the calculation in part a?

    c. In what order did you and your calculator perform the operations to get the answer?

    d. Evaluate (10 + 7) · 3 and record your result. Verify using your calculator.

    e. Why is the result in part d different from the result in part a?

Order of Operations

Operations on numbers are performed in a universally accepted order. Scientific and graphing calculators are programmed to perform operations in this order. Part of the order of operations priority convention is as follows.

1. Perform multiplication and division before addition and subtraction.
2. If both multiplication and division are present, perform the operations in order from left to right.
3. If both addition and subtraction are present, perform the operations in order, *from left to right*.

EXAMPLE 1   *Evaluate* $12 - 2 \cdot 4 + 5$ *without a calculator.*

SOLUTION

$12 - 2 \cdot 4 + 5$ Do multiplication before addition and subtraction.

$= 12 - 8 + 5$ Subtract 8 from 12 since you encounter it first as you read from left to right.

$= 4 + 5$ Add.

$= 9$

7. Perform the following calculations *without* a calculator. Then use your calculator to verify your result.

   a. $24 \div 4 + 8$ **b.** $24 \div 4 - 2 \cdot 3$

   c. $6 + 24 - 4 \cdot 3 - 2$ **d.** $6 + 2 \cdot 9 - 16 \div 4$

Notice the importance of the "from left to right" rule for both multiplication/division and addition/subtraction. For example, $12 \div 4 \cdot 3 = 3 \cdot 3 = 9$ by performing the operations left to right. If multiplication is performed before division, the result is 1 (try it and see). This shows the need for a decision on which of these calculations is correct. All the arithmetic experience that people had over hundreds of years led to the decision to do multiplication/division from left to right. That decision became part of the order of operations agreement.

Check that $12 \div 4 \cdot 3 = 9$ by entering $12 \div 4 \cdot 3$ all at once on your calculator.

8. Perform the following calculations without a calculator. State which operations you must perform first, and why. Then use your calculator to verify your result.

   a. $15 \div 5 \cdot 3$ **b.** $7 \cdot 8 \div 4$

   c. $15 - 6 \div 2 + 4$ **d.** $20 + 3 - 5 + 8$

Some expressions involve parentheses. For example, the expression $15 \div (1 + 2)$ means 15 divided by the sum of 1 and 2. The calculation is $15 \div (1 + 2) = 15 \div 3 = 5$. This observation leads to a fourth convention for order of operations priorities.

4. Parentheses are grouping symbols that are used to override the standard order of operations. Operations contained in parentheses are performed first.

9. a. Evaluate $24 \div (2 + 6)$ without your calculator.

b. Use your calculator to evaluate $24 \div (2 + 6)$. Did you obtain 3 as a result? If not, then perhaps you entered the expression $24 \div 2 + 6$ and your answer is 18.

c. Explain why the result of $24 \div 2 + 6$ is 18.

EXAMPLE 2   *Evaluate* $2 \cdot (3 + 4 \cdot 5)$ *without a calculator.*

SOLUTION

$2 \cdot (3 + 4 \cdot 5)$ Evaluate the arithmetic expression in parentheses first using order of operations.

$= 2 \cdot (3 + 20)$ First do the multiplication inside the parentheses, then the addition.

$= 2 \cdot 23$

$= 46$ Multiply the result by the 2 that was outside of the parentheses.

10. Evaluate the following mentally and verify on your calculator.

a. $6/(3 + 3)$ 　　　　　　　　　　　 **b.** $(2 + 8)/(4 - 2)$

c. $24 \div (4 + 8)$ 　　　　　　　　　　 **d.** $24 \div (4 - 2) \cdot 3$

e. $(6 + 24) \div (4 \cdot 3 - 2)$ 　　　　　 **f.** $(6 + 2) \cdot 9 - 16 \div 4$

g. $5 + 2 \cdot (4 \div 2 + 3)$ 　　　　　　 **h.** $10 - (12 - 3 \cdot 2) \div 3$

Exponentiation

Recall that $5 \cdot 5$ can be written as 5^2 (read "5 squared"). Besides multiplying 5 times 5, there are two additional ways to square a number on your calculator. Try Problem 11 if you have a calculator. Otherwise, go to Example 3.

11. a. One way to evaluate 5^2 is to use the ⬚ key. Input 5 and then press the ⬚ key. Do this now and record your answer.

b. Another way to evaluate 5^2 is to use the exponent key. Depending on your calculator, the exponent key may resemble $\boxed{x^y}$, $\boxed{y^x}$, or $\boxed{\wedge}$. To calculate 5^2, input 5, press the exponent key, then enter $\boxed{2}$ and press $\boxed{\text{ENTER}}$. Do this now and record your answer.

EXAMPLE 3   Order of Operations Involving Exponential Expressions

a. Evaluate 5^3.

SOLUTION

5^3 can be written as $5 \cdot 5 \cdot 5 = 125$. Verify your answer using a calculator.

b. Evaluate the expression $20 - 2 \cdot 3^2$.

SOLUTION

To evaluate the expression $20 - 2 \cdot 3^2$, follow the steps:

$20 - 2 \cdot 3^2$ Evaluate all exponents as you read the arithmetic expression from left to right.

$= 20 - 2 \cdot 9$ Do all multiplication and division as you read the expression from left to right.

$= 20 - 18$ Do all addition and subtraction as you read the expression from left to right.

$= 2$

An exponential expression such as 5^3 is called a **power** of 5, as you will recall from Activity 1.5. The **base** is 5 and the **exponent** is 3. When a power is contained in an expression, it is evaluated *before* any multiplication or division, but only after operations in parentheses.

12. If you have a calculator, enter the expression $20 - 2 \cdot 3^2$ into your calculator and verify the result in Example 3 above.

13. Evaluate the following numerical expressions by hand. Verify using a calculator.

    a. $6 + 3 \cdot 4^3$ **b.** $2 \cdot 3^4 - 5^3$

    c. $2^2 \cdot 3^2 \div 3 - 2$ **d.** $3^2 \cdot 2 + 3 \cdot 2^3$

14. Evaluate each of the following arithmetic expressions mentally or by hand. Perform the operations in the appropriate order and then use your calculator to check your results.

    a. $18 - 2 \cdot (8 - 2 \cdot 3) + 3^2$ **b.** $3^4 + 5 \cdot 4^2$

    c. $128/(16 - 2^3)$ **d.** $(17 - 3 \cdot 4)/5$

e. $5 \cdot 2^3 - 6 \cdot 2 + 5$

f. $5^2 \cdot 5^3$

g. $2^3 \cdot 3^2$

h. $4^2 + 4^3$

i. $500 \div 25 \cdot 2 - 3 \cdot 2$

j. $(3^2 - 6)^2$

SUMMARY
ACTIVITY 1.6

1. The **commutative property** states that the order in which you add or multiply two whole numbers gives the same result. The commutative property does *not* hold for subtraction or division.

2. $3(10 - 2) = 3 \cdot 10 - 3 \cdot 2$ is an example of the **distributive property.**

3. An exponential expression such as 5^3 is called a **power** of the base number 5. The **base** is 5 and the **exponent** is 3. The exponent indicates how many times the base is written as a factor. When a power is contained in an arithmetic expression, it is evaluated before any multiplication or division.

4. **Order of operations** for arithmetic expressions containing parentheses, addition, subtraction, multiplication, division, and exponentiation:

   a. Operations contained within parentheses are performed *first* before any operations outside the parentheses. All operations are performed in the following order.

   b. Evaluate all exponents as you read the expression from left to right.

   c. Do all multiplication and division as you read the expression from left to right.

   d. Do all addition and subtraction as you read the expression from left to right.

EXERCISES
ACTIVITY 1.6

1. Evaluate each expression. Check your answers with a calculator.

   a. $7(20 + 5)$

   b. $7 \cdot 20 + 5$

   c. $7 \cdot 20 + 7 \cdot 5$

   d. $20 + 7 \cdot 5$

   e. Which two of the preceding arithmetic expressions have the same answer?

   f. State the property that produces the same answer for that pair of expressions.

2. Evaluate each expression. Check your answers with a calculator.

   a. $20(100 - 2)$ **b.** $20 \cdot 100 - 2$

   c. $20 \cdot 100 - 20 \cdot 2$ **d.** $100 - 20 \cdot 2$

   e. Which two of the preceding arithmetic expressions have the same answer?

   f. State the property that produces the same answer for that pair of expressions.

3. Evaluate each expression using order of operations.

   a. $17 \cdot (52 - 2)$ **b.** $(90 - 7) \cdot 5$

4. Evaluate each expression using the distributive property.

   a. $17 \cdot (52 - 2)$ **b.** $(90 - 7) \cdot 5$

5. Perform the following calculations *without a calculator*. After solving, use your calculator to check your answer.

   a. $45 \div 3 + 12$ **b.** $54 \div 9 - 2 \cdot 3$

   c. $12 + 30 \div 2 \cdot 3 - 4$ **d.** $26 + 2 \cdot 7 - 12 \div 4$

6. a. Explain why the result of $72 \div 8 + 4$ is 13.

   b. Explain why the result of $72 \div (8 + 4)$ is 6.

7. Evaluate the following expressions. Check your answers with a calculator.

   a. $48/(4 + 4)$ **b.** $(8 + 12)/(6 - 2)$

c. $120 \div (6 + 4)$ **d.** $64 \div (6 - 2) \cdot 2$

e. $(16 + 84) \div (4 \cdot 3 - 2)$ **f.** $(6 + 2) \cdot 20 - 12 \div 3$

g. $39 + 3 \cdot (8 \div 2 + 3)$ **h.** $100 - (81 - 27 \cdot 3) \div 3$

8. Evaluate the following expressions. Check your answers with a calculator.

   a. $15 + 2 \cdot 5^3$ **b.** $5 \cdot 2^4 - 3^3$

   c. $5^2 \cdot 2^3 \div 10 - 6$ **d.** $5^2 \cdot 2 - 5 \cdot 2^3$

9. Evaluate each of the following arithmetic expressions by performing the operations in the appropriate order. Check your answers with a calculator.

   a. $37 - 2 \cdot (18 - 2 \cdot 5) + 1^2$ **b.** $3^5 + 2 \cdot 10^2$

   c. $243/(36 - 3^3)$ **d.** $(75 - 2 \cdot 15)/9$

   e. $7 \cdot 2^3 - 9 \cdot 2 + 5$ **f.** $2^5 \cdot 5^2$

   g. $2^3 \cdot 2^5$ **h.** $5^3 + 2^6$

   i. $1350 \div 75 \cdot 5 - 15 \cdot 2$ **j.** $(3^2 - 4)^2$

What Have I Learned?

Write your explanations in full sentences.

1. Would you prefer to win $1,050,000 or $1,005,000? Use the idea of place value to explain how you determined your answer.

2. Suppose you want to get a good deal on leasing a car for 3 years (36 months) and you do some checking. The following is some preliminary information that you found in car ads in your local newspaper. Note that these costs do not include other fees such as tax. Those fees are ignored in this problem.

CAR MODEL	DOWN PAYMENT*	MONTHLY FEE
Honda Pilot	$1,995	$277
Toyota Tundra	$2,999	$229
Mercury Mountaineer	$1,594	$299
Ford Explorer	$3,268	$249
Dodge Durango	$2,254	$259

*The down payment includes the first monthly fee.

   a. At first, you round off the down payments to the nearest thousand and the monthly fee to the nearest 100 so you can mentally estimate the total payments for each car. Does your estimate allow you to say which car is the most expensive to lease and which is the least expensive to lease? Explain.

CAR MODEL	DOWN PAYMENT*	DOWN PAYMENT ESTIMATE TO THE NEAREST THOUSAND	MONTHLY FEE	MONTHLY FEE ESTIMATE TO THE NEAREST HUNDRED	ESTIMATED TOTAL COST
Honda Pilot	$1,995		$277		
Toyota Tundra	$2,999		$229		
Mercury Mountaineer	$1,594		$299		
Ford Explorer	$3,268		$249		
Dodge Durango	$2,254		$259		

b. What would be better choices for rounding off the down payment costs and the monthly fee to estimate the leasing costs for each car? Use your choices to get new estimates.

CAR MODEL	DOWN PAYMENT*	DOWN PAYMENT ESTIMATE TO THE NEAREST HUNDRED	MONTHLY FEE	MONTHLY FEE ESTIMATE TO THE NEAREST TEN	ESTIMATED TOTAL COST
Honda Pilot	$1,995		$277		
Toyota Tundra	$2,999		$229		
Mercury Mountaineer	$1,594		$299		
Ford Explorer	$3,268		$249		
Dodge Durango	$2,254		$259		

c. Use your calculator to determine the actual total cost for each car from the actual down payment and the monthly fee. Do the actual costs show the same cars as most expensive and least expensive that you named in part b?

CAR MODEL	DOWN PAYMENT*	MONTHLY FEE	TOTAL COST
Honda Pilot	$1,995	$277	
Toyota Tundra	$2,999	$229	
Mercury Mountaineer	$1,594	$299	
Ford Explorer	$3,268	$249	
Dodge Durango	$2,254	$259	

d. From this exercise, what conclusions can you make about the usefulness of rounding off numbers in calculations that you need to make so you can compare costs.

3. a. Explain a procedure you could use to determine if 37 is a composite or prime number.

b. Check to see if your procedure works for a number greater than 100, say 101. Explain why it works or does not work.

c. What is the largest prime number that *you know*? Do you think it is the largest prime number there is? Give a reason for your answer.

d. How many prime numbers do you think there are in all? Give a reason for your answer. Compare your answer with those of your classmates.

4. a. For which two operations does the commutative property hold? Give an example in each case.

b. For which two operations does the commutative property fail to hold? Give an example in each case.

5. a. Is it true that $(69 + 21) + 17 = 69 + (21 + 17)$? Justify your answer by calculating each side of the statement. In each case, add the numbers in the parentheses first.

b. What arithmetic property did you demonstrate in part a?

c. Does the same property hold true for $(69 - 21) - 17 = 69 - (21 - 17)$? Justify your answer.

6. Try this experiment: Ask a friend or classmate to calculate 9×999 by the usual vertical method. Then ask the person to calculate $9(1000 - 1)$ by using the distributive property.

   a. What is the correct answer in each case?

   b. Which calculation do you each think is "easier"? Why?

   c. Show how you would calculate 9×9990 by using the distributive property.

7. Division of whole numbers can be considered as repeated subtraction.

   a. Use this idea to divide 12 by 4. Show your calculation and the result.

   b. Does this idea work when you try to divide 12 by 0? Explain.

How Can I Practice?

1. You bought a laptop computer and wrote a check for two thousand one hundred six dollars. The price tag read $2016.

   a. Write the amount of the check in numeral form.

   b. Did you pay the correct amount, too much, or too little? Explain.

2. Currently, the disease diabetes affects an estimated 21,000,000 Americans, and about 1,500,000 new cases are diagnosed each year. What are the place values to which each estimate apparently is rounded?

3. In 2001, the National Institutes of Health (NIH) spent about 690 million dollars for diabetes research. However, the cost of diabetes to the nation is more staggering. In 2002, it was estimated that 132 billion dollars was spent on health care and other costs related to diabetes. How many times more is spent in health care costs than in research? Write your answer to the nearest whole number.

4. In 2004, the median household income level in the United States was $44,389. Round this amount to the nearest hundred dollars.

5. On a web site, the distance from Earth to the Sun was given as 92,955,807 miles. Round this distance to

   a. the nearest thousand miles.

   b. the nearest million miles.

6. Calculate each of the following by hand. Check your answer with a calculator.

   a.   523
       + 108

   b.   1052
       + 957

   c.   3051
          1282
       + 327

7. Evaluate each of the following by hand. Check your answer with a calculator.

   a. $283 - 95$ **b.** $233 - 145$

   c. $67 - 39$ **d.** $1003 - 349$

8. Translate each of the following into an arithmetic expression and calculate by hand. Check your answer with a calculator.

   a. 67 plus 25   **b.** the difference between 24 and 18

   c. 98 minus 15   **d.** total of 104 and 729

   e. 25 more than 495   **f.** 33 subtracted from 67

   g. 145 increased by 28   **h.** 34 less than 156

   i. 95 decreased by 25

9. Multiply by hand. Check your answer with a calculator.

   a. $\begin{array}{r} 25 \\ \times\ 9 \\ \hline \end{array}$ **b.** $\begin{array}{r} 347 \\ \times\ 6 \\ \hline \end{array}$ **c.** $\begin{array}{r} 167 \\ \times\ 17 \\ \hline \end{array}$ **d.** $\begin{array}{r} 227 \\ \times\ 109 \\ \hline \end{array}$

10. a. Multiply 3 times 45 in a vertical format.

   b. Use the distributive property to calculate $3(40 + 5)$.

   c. Use the distributive property to calculate $3 \cdot 49$.

11. Calculate. As part of your answer, identify the quotient and remainder (if any).

   a. $126 \div 4$ **b.** $312 \div 4$

   c. $195 \div 13$ **d.** $224 \div 12$

12. a. Estimate $3212 \div 414$.

    b. Find the exact answer.

    c. Is your estimate lower, higher, or the same?

13. Determine and list all the prime numbers between 30 and 50.

14. Determine and list all factors of the following numbers.

    a. 12   **b.** 21

    c. 71   **d.** 18

15. Determine the prime factorizations of the following numbers.

    a. 24   **b.** 63

16. Determine the prime factorizations of the following numbers. Write your answers in exponent form.

    a. 27   **b.** 125

    c. What do the two prime factorizations have in common?

17. Write as whole numbers.

    a. 8^0 **b.** 12^2

    c. 3^4 **d.** 2^6

18. Write each numerical expression using a single exponent.

    a. $7^3 \cdot 7^9$ **b.** $11^5 \cdot 11^7$

    c. $13^2 \cdot 13^0$ **d.** $9 \cdot 9^2 \cdot 9^3$

19. Determine the square root without using a calculator. Approximate if necessary. Check your answer with a calculator.

    a. 4   **b.** 24   **c.** 225

    d. 36   **e.** 90

20. Evaluate each of the following arithmetic expressions by performing the operations in the appropriate order. Use your calculator to check your results.

    a. $7 - 3 \cdot (8 - 2 \cdot 3) + 2^2$ **b.** $3 \cdot 2^5 + 2 \cdot 5^2$

    c. $144/(24 - 2^3)$ **d.** $(36 - 2 \cdot 9)/6$

    e. $9 \cdot 5 - 5 \cdot 2^3 + 5$ **f.** $1^5 \cdot 5^1$

    g. $2^3 \cdot 2^0$ **h.** $7^2 + 7^2$

    i. $(3^2 - 4 \cdot 0)^2$

21. Determine the arithmetic property expressed by each numerical statement.

    a. $25(30) = 30(25)$

    b. $15(9) = 15(10 - 1) = 15 \cdot 10 - 15 \cdot 1$

    c. $(11 + 21) + 39 = 11 + (21 + 39)$

22. Determine if each of the following numerical statements is true or false. In each case, justify your answer.

a. $7(20 + 2) = 7(22)$

b. $4(11)(10) = 10(11)4$

c. $25 - 10 - 4 = 25 - (10 - 4)$

d. $1/0 = 1$

SUMMARY

The bracketed numbers following each concept indicate the activity in which the concept is discussed.

CONCEPT / SKILL	DESCRIPTION	EXAMPLE
Place value [1.1]		

MILLIONS			THOUSANDS			ONES		
Hundreds	Tens	Ones	Hundreds	Tens	Ones	Hundreds	Tens	Ones

CONCEPT / SKILL	DESCRIPTION	EXAMPLE
Read and write whole numbers [1.1]	Start at the left and read each digit and its place value.	2345 is read "two thousand three hundred forty-five."
Round whole numbers to specified place value [1.1]	If the digit immediately to the right of the specified place value is *5 or more*, add 1 to the digit in the specified place and change all the digits to its right to zero. If the digit immediately to the right of the specified place value is *less than 5*, do not change the digit in the specified place but change all the digits to its right to zero.	157 rounded to the tens place yields 160. 152 rounded to the tens place yields 150.
Prime numbers [1.1], [1.5]	A **prime number** is a whole number greater than 1 whose only whole-number factors are itself and 1.	2, 3, 7, 11, 13, 17, 19, 23,. . .
Addend, sum [1.2]	The numbers being added are called **addends.** Their total is called the **sum.**	$\underset{\text{addend}}{12} + \underset{\text{addend}}{11} = \underset{\text{sum}}{23}$
Addition property of zero [1.2]	The sum of any whole number and zero is the same whole number.	$5 + 0 = 5$
Commutative property of addition [1.2]	Changing the **order** of the addends yields the same sum.	$9 + 8 = 8 + 9 = 17$
Associative property of addition [1.2]	Given three addends, it makes no difference whether the first two numbers or the last two numbers are added first.	$5 + (6 + 7)$ $= (5 + 6) + 7 = 18$
Add whole numbers by hand and mentally [1.2]	***To add:*** Align numbers vertically according to place value. Add the digits in the ones place. If their sum is a two-digit number, write down the ones digit and regroup the tens digit to the next column as a number to be added. Repeat with next higher place value.	1 129 **Regroup 1 to tens place.** + 17 146 9 + 7 = 16; **write 6 in ones place.**

CONCEPT / SKILL	DESCRIPTION	EXAMPLE
Subtrahend, minuend, difference [1.2]	The number being subtracted is called the **subtrahend.** The number it is subtracted from is called the **minuend.** The result is called the **difference.**	$32 - 18 = 14$ minuend subtrahend difference
Subtract whole numbers by hand and mentally [1.2]	*To subtract:* Align the subtrahend under the minuend according to place value. Subtract digits having the same place value. Regroup from a higher place value, if necessary.	$\overset{5\,12}{\cancel{6}2}$ Regroup from tens. 2 changes to 12. -15 Subtract 5 from 12. $\overline{47}$
Estimate sums and differences using rounding [1.2]	One way to estimate is to round each number (addend) to its highest place value. In some cases, it may be better to round to a place value lower than the highest one.	*Exact Sum:* *Estimate:* $\begin{array}{r}780\\219\\+\ 164\\\hline 1163\end{array}$ $\begin{array}{r}800\\200\\+\ 200\\\hline 1200\end{array}$
Missing addend approach to subtraction [1.2]	Minuend − subtrahend = difference can be written as subtrahend + difference = minuend.	$10 - 6 = ?$ can be written $6 + ? = 10.$
Key phrases for addition [1.2]	• Sum of • Increased by • More than • Plus • Total of • Added to	15 *increased by* 10: $15 + 10$ 3 *more than* 7: $7 + 3$ Total of 10 and 25: $10 + 25$
Key phrases for subtraction [1.2]	• Difference between • Minus • Decreased by • Less than • Subtracted from	50 *decreased by* 16: $50 - 16$ 6 *less than* 92: $92 - 6$ 7 *subtracted from* 15: $15 - 7$
Factor, product [1.3]	**Factors** are numbers being multiplied. The result is called the **product.**	$12 \cdot 8 = 96$ factor factor product
Multiplication as repeated addition [1.3]	4 times 30 can be thought of as $30 + 30 + 30 + 30$.	$9 \cdot 5 = 9 + 9 + 9$ $ + 9 + 9 = 45$ $5 \cdot 9 = 5 + 5 + 5 + 5$ $ + 5 + 5 + 5 + 5 + 5 = 45$
Multiply whole numbers [1.3]	*To multiply:* Align numbers vertically by place value. Starting with the rightmost digit of the bottom factor, multiply each place value of the top factor. Repeat using the next rightmost digit of the bottom factor. Add the resulting products, to get the final product.	$\begin{array}{r}37\\\times\ 4\\\hline 28\\120\\\hline 148\end{array}$ product of 7 times 4 product of 30 times 4 sum of 28 and 120
Multiplication by 1 [1.3]	Any whole number multiplied by 1 remains the same.	$134 \cdot 1 = 134$
Multiplication by 0 [1.3]	Any whole number multiplied by 0 is 0.	$45 \cdot 0 = 0$

CONCEPT / SKILL	DESCRIPTION	EXAMPLE
Distributive property of multiplication over addition [1.3]	A whole number placed immediately to the left or right of a set of parentheses containing the sum or difference of two numbers multiplies each of the inside numbers.	$8 \cdot 24$ or $32 \cdot 5$ $= 8 \cdot (20 + 4)$ $= (30 + 2) \cdot 5$ $= 8 \cdot 20 + 8 \cdot 4$ $= 30 \cdot 5 + 2 \cdot 5$ $= 160 + 32$ $= 150 + 10$ $= 192$ $= 160$
Commutative property of multiplication [1.3]	Changing the **order** of the factors yields the same product.	$5 \cdot 12 = 12 \cdot 5 = 60$
Associative property of multiplication [1.3]	When multiplying three factors, it makes no difference whether the first two numbers or the last two numbers are multiplied first. The same product results.	$(5 \cdot 7) \cdot 12$ $= 5 \cdot (7 \cdot 12) = 420$
Estimate products [1.3]	Round each factor to a large enough place value so that you can do the multiplication mentally. There is no one correct answer when estimating.	$284 \longrightarrow 300$ $525 \longrightarrow \times 500$ estimate: 150,000
Divisor, dividend [1.4]	The number being divided is called the **dividend.** The number that divides is called the **divisor.**	$3\overline{)45}$ divisor dividend
Quotient [1.4]	A whole number representing the number of times the divisor can be subtracted from the dividend is called a **quotient.**	quotient 15 $3\overline{)45}$ divisor dividend
Remainder [1.4]	The **remainder** is the whole number left over after the divisor has been subtracted from the dividend as many times as possible.	quotient 15 remainder 2 $3\overline{)47}$ ← dividend divisor $\underline{45}$ 2
Divide whole numbers [1.4]	$\begin{array}{r} 17 \\ 6\overline{)104} \\ \underline{6} \\ 44 \\ \underline{42} \\ 2 \end{array}$ **6 does not divide into 1. 6 does divide into 10 one time. Write down the product 1 · 6 = 6. Subtract 6 from 10. Bring down the next digit, 4. 6 divides into 44 seven times. Write down the product 7 · 6 = 42. Subtract 42 from 44.** remainder	
Check division [1.4]	To check division, multiply the quotient times the divisor, then add the remainder. The result should be the dividend. (quotient × divisor) + remainder = dividend	$\begin{array}{r} 3 \\ 7\overline{)25} \\ \underline{21} \\ 4 \end{array}$ Check: $3 \cdot 7 + 4 = 25$

CONCEPT / SKILL	DESCRIPTION	EXAMPLE
Inverse operations [1.4]	Multiplication and division are inverse operations	$3 \cdot 4 = 12$ $12 \div 4 = 3$
Division properties involving 0 [1.4]	0 divided by any nonzero whole number is 0. Division by 0 is undefined.	$0 \div 42 = 0$ $42 \div 0 = undefined!$
Division properties involving 1 [1.4]	Any nonzero whole number divided by itself is equal to 1. Any whole number divided by 1 remains the same.	$71 \div 71 = 1$ $23 \div 1 = 23$
Division is not commutative [1.4]	The dividend and the divisor can *not* be interchanged without changing the quotient (unless the dividend and the divisor are the same whole number).	$9\overline{)81} \neq 81\overline{)9}$
Estimate a quotient [1.4]	To estimate a quotient, first estimate the divisor and the dividend by numbers that provide a division easily done mentally or by hand.	estimate $\overset{35}{18\overline{)680}} \longrightarrow 20\overline{)700}$
Exponent, base [1.5]	A whole-number **exponent** indicates the number of times to use the **base** as a factor.	$10^4 = 10 \cdot 10 \cdot 10 \cdot 10$ $= 10{,}000$
A whole number raised to the zero power [1.5]	Any nonzero whole number raised to the zero power equals 1.	$2^0 = 1, \ 50^0 = 1, \ 200^0 = 1$
Exponential form of a whole number [1.5]	A number written as 10^4 is in **exponential form.** 10 is the base and 4 is the exponent. The exponent indicates how many times the base appears as a factor.	10 is used as a factor 4 times. $10^4 = \overbrace{10 \cdot 10 \cdot 10 \cdot 10}$ $= 10{,}000$
Multiplication rule for numbers in exponential form [1.5]	When multiplying numbers written in exponential form with the *same base*, add the exponents. This sum becomes the new exponent attached to the original base.	$7^2 7^6 = 7^8$ $3^2 3^5 3^7 = 3^{14}$
Factor whole numbers [1.5]	Writing a number as a product of its factors is called **factorization.**	$12 = 1 \cdot 12 = 12 \cdot 1$ $12 = 2 \cdot 6 = 6 \cdot 2$ $12 = 4 \cdot 3 = 3 \cdot 4$
Prime factorization form of a whole number [1.5]	A number written as a product of its prime factors is called the **prime factorization** of the number.	$60 = 2 \cdot 2 \cdot 3 \cdot 5$

CONCEPT / SKILL	DESCRIPTION	EXAMPLE
Finding the prime factorization of a whole number [1.5]	Determine the prime factors of the number and write the number as a product of the prime factors.	$60 = 2 \cdot 2 \cdot 3 \cdot 5$
Recognizing square whole numbers [1.5]	A whole number is a **perfect square** if it can be rewritten as the square of a whole number.	$36 = 6^2$ and $100 = 10^2$
Recognizing roots of square numbers [1.5]	13 is the **square root** of 169 because 13 times 13 is 169.	$\sqrt{25} = 5$ because $5^2 = 25$
Order of operations [1.6]	**Order of operations** for arithmetic expressions containing parentheses, addition, subtraction, multiplication, division, and exponentiation: **a.** Operations contained within parentheses are performed *first*—before any operations *outside* the parentheses. All operations are performed in the following order. **b.** Evaluate all exponents as you read the expression *from left to right.* **c.** Do all multiplication and division as you read the expression *from left to right.* **d.** Do all addition and subtraction as you read the expression from *left to right.*	$2 \cdot (3 + 4^2 \cdot 5) - 9$ $= 2 \cdot (3 + 16 \cdot 5) - 9$ $= 2 \cdot (3 + 80) - 9$ $= 2 \cdot (83) - 9$ $= 166 - 9$ $= 157$

1. When you move into a new apartment, you and your roommates stock up on groceries. The bill comes to $143. How will you write this amount in words on your check?

2. The chance of winning in New York State Lotto is 1 out of 22,528,737. Write 22,528,737 in words.

3. Put the following whole numbers in order from smallest to largest: 108,901; 180,901; 108,091; 108,910; and 109,801.

4. What are the place values of the digits 0 and 9 in the number 40,693?

5. Determine whether each of the following numbers is even or odd. In each case, give a reason for your answer.

   a. 333   **b.** 1378   **c.** 121

6. Determine whether each of the following numbers is prime or composite. In each case, give a reason for your answer.

   a. 145   **b.** 61

   c. 2   **d.** 121

7. **a.** Round 1,252,757 to the thousands place.

   b. Round 899 to the tens place.

8. Perform the indicated operations. Check your answers with a calculator.

   a.   7982   **b.**   235   **c.**   231
        + 969   45   − 54
                                  59
                                 210
                                +347

   d.   5344   **e.** 654 − 179
          −4682

Answers to all Gateway exercises are included in the Selected Answers appendix.

73

9. Rewrite the statement $113 - 41 = 72$ as a statement in terms of addition.

10. a. What property of addition does the statement $(8 + 5) + 5 = 8 + (5 + 5)$ demonstrate?

   b. What property of addition does the statement $4 + (7 + 6) = 4 + (6 + 7)$ demonstrate?

   c. Why is the expression $11 + 89 + 0$ equal to the expression $11 + 89$?

11. Are the numerical expressions $5 - 2$ and $2 - 5$ equal? What does this mean in terms of a commutative property for subtraction?

12. a. Estimate the sum: $510 + 86 + 120 + 350$.

   b. Determine the actual sum.

   c. Was your estimate higher or lower than the actual sum? Explain.

13. Translate each verbal expression into an arithmetic expression.

   a. The sum of thirty and twenty-two

   b. The difference between sixty-seven and fifteen

   c. One hundred twenty-five decreased by forty-four

   d. 175 less than 250

   e. The product of twenty-five and thirty-six

   f. The quotient of fifty-five and eleven

   g. The square of thirteen

   h. Two to the fifth power

   i. The square root of forty-nine

   j. The product of twenty-seven and the sum of fifty and seventeen

14. a. Write $5 \cdot 61$ as an addition calculation and find the sum.

b. How does the sum you obtained in part a compare to $5 \cdot 61$ when calculated as a product?

c. Write 61 as $60 + 1$ and use the distributive property to evaluate the product of 5 and 61.

15. a. Determine the product of $4 \cdot 29$ by rewriting 29 as $30 - 1$ and then using the distributive property.

b. Is it faster to mentally multiply $4 \cdot 29$ or $4 \cdot 30 - 4 \cdot 1$?

c. Multiply $6 \cdot 98$ by using the distributive property.

16. a. What property of multiplication does the statement $8 \cdot (6 \cdot 12) = (8 \cdot 6) \cdot 12$ demonstrate?

b. What property of multiplication does the statement $4 \cdot (7 \cdot 6) = 4 \cdot (6 \cdot 7)$ demonstrate?

c. Why is the expression $1 \cdot (4 + 5)$ equivalent to the expression $(4 + 5)$?

17. a. Determine the quotient of $72 \div 12$ by repeatedly subtracting 12 from 72.

b. Determine the quotient and remainder of $86 \div 16$ by repeatedly subtracting 16 from 86.

18. Calculate $12 \div 6$ and then $6 \div 12$. Use the results to determine if the commutative property holds for division.

19. In each case, perform the indicated operation. Check your answer with a calculator.

    a. $\begin{array}{r} 2096 \\ \times\quad 87 \\ \hline \end{array}$ **b.** $15\overline{)231}$

    c. $(41 \cdot 3) \cdot 7$ **d.** $41 \cdot (3 \cdot 7)$

    e. $27 \div 27$ **f.** $0 \div 27$

    g. $27 \div 0$ **h.** $24\overline{)6572}$

20. a. Estimate $329 \cdot 75$.   **b.** Determine the exact answer.

    c. Is your estimate lower, higher, or the same?

21. a. Estimate $1850 \div 42$.   **b.** Determine the exact answer.

    c. Is your estimate lower, higher, or the same?

22. In converting 63 feet into yards, suppose you divided 63 by 3 and obtained 20 yards. Check to see if you calculated correctly.

23. Explain the difference between the expressions $1 \div 0$ and $0 \div 1$.

24. a. If you divide any whole number by 1, what is the result? Give an example.

    b. If you divide the number 5634 by itself, what is the result? Does this property apply to any whole number you choose? Explain.

25. List all whole-number factors of each of the following numbers.

   a. 350

   b. 81

   c. 36

26. Determine the prime factorization of each of the following numbers.

   a. 350   b. 81   c. 36

27. Write each number as a whole number in standard form.

   a. 6^0 b. 7^2

   c. 2^5 d. 25^0

28. a. Write 81 as a power of 9.   b. Write 81 as a power of 3.

   c. Write 625 as a power of 25.   d. Write 625 as a power of 5.

29. Write each number using a single exponent.

   a. $3^3 \cdot 3^7$ b. $5^{33} \cdot 5^{12}$ c. $21^0 \cdot 21^{19}$

30. Determine which of the following numbers are perfect-square numbers. In each case, explain your answer.

   a. 25   b. 125

   c. 121   d. 100

   e. 200

31. Determine the square root of each of the following numbers.

    a. 16   **b.** 36   **c.** 289

32. Which of the following numbers are perfect squares?

    a. 40   **b.** 400   **c.** 10

    d. 10,000   **e.** 1000

33. Evaluate each of the following arithmetic expressions by performing the operations in the appropriate order. Verify using your calculator.

    a. $48 - 3 \cdot (18 - 2 \cdot 7) + 3^2$ **b.** $2^4 + 4 \cdot 2^2$

    c. $243/(35 - 2^3)$ **d.** $(160 - 2 \cdot 25)/10$

    e. $7 \cdot 2^3 - 9 \cdot 2 + 5$ **f.** $2^3 \cdot 3^2$

    g. $6^2 + 2^6$ **h.** $(3^2 - 2^3)^2$

34. Do the expressions $6 + 10 \div 2$ and $(6 + 10) \div 2$ have the same result when calculated? Explain.

PROBLEM SOLVING WITH RATIONAL NUMBERS: ADDITION AND SUBTRACTION OF INTEGERS, FRACTIONS, AND DECIMALS

Chapter 1 deals with counting numbers that represent quantities greater than zero, and for this reason counting numbers are also called *positive numbers*. However, quantities like debits in business or electrical charges in physics and chemistry require numbers that represent negative quantities. Such numbers are called negative numbers. Positive and negative counting numbers and zero, taken together, form a number system called the *integers.*

In some situations, a quantity is divided into parts; or in other situations, two quantities are compared. These situations require numbers called fractions. Another name for a fraction is *rational number.* In this chapter, you will solve problems involving integers and fractions. In Chapter 4, you will learn why fractions are also called ratios or rational numbers.

| CLUSTER 1 | Adding and Subtracting Integers |

ACTIVITY 2.1

Make Me an Offer

OBJECTIVES

1. Use the basic steps for problem solving.

2. Translate verbal statements into algebraic equations.

3. Use the basic principles of algebra to solve real-world problems.

Many students believe "I can do math. I just can't do word problems." In reality, you learn mathematics so you can solve practical problems in everyday life and in science, business, technology, medicine, and most other fields.

On a personal level, you solve problems every day while balancing your checkbook, remembering an anniversary, or figuring out how to get more exercise. Most everyday problems don't require algebra, or even arithmetic, to be solved. But the basic steps and methods for solving any problem can be discussed and understood. In the process you will, with practice, become a better problem solver.

Solve the following problem any way you can, making notes of your thinking as you work. In the space provided, record your work on the left side. On the right side, jot down in a few sentences what you are thinking as you work on the problem.

"Night Train" Henson's Contract

1. "Night Train" Henson is negotiating a new contract with his team. He wants $800,000 for the year with an additional $6000 for every game he starts. His team offered $10,000 for every game he starts, but only $700,000 for a base salary. How many games would he have to start to make more with the team's offer?

SOLUTION TO THE PROBLEM	YOUR THINKING

2. Talk about and compare your methods for solving the problem above with classmates or your group. As a group, write down the steps you all went through from the very beginning to the end of your problem solving.

Experience has shown that there is a set of basic steps that serve as a guide to solving problems.

PROCEDURE

Basic Steps for Problem Solving Solving any problem generally requires the following four steps.

1. Understand the problem.
2. Develop a strategy for solving the problem.
3. Execute your strategy to solve the problem.
4. Check your solution for correctness.

In Problems 3–6 that follow, compare your group's strategies for solving "Night Train" Henson's problem with each of the four basic steps for problem solving.

Let's consider each of the steps 1 through 4.

Step 1. Understand the problem.   This step may seem obvious, but many times this is the most important step, and is the one that commonly leads to errors. Read the problem carefully, as many times as necessary. Draw some diagrams to help you visualize the situation. Get an explanation from available resources if you are unsure of any details.

3. List some strategies you could use to make sure you understand the "Night Train" Henson problem.

Step 2. Develop a strategy for solving the problem. Once you understand the problem, it may not be at all clear what strategy is required. Practice and experience is the best guide. Algebra is often useful for solving a math problem but is not always required.

4. How many different strategies were tried in your group for solving the "Night Train" problem? Describe one or two of them.

Step 3. Execute your strategy to solve the problem. Once you have decided on a strategy, carrying it out is sometimes the easiest step in the process. If you really understand the problem, and are clear on your strategy, the solution should happen almost automatically.

5. When you decided on a strategy, how confident did you feel about your solution? Give a reason for your level of confidence.

Step 4. Check your solution for correctness. This last step is *critically important*. Your solution must be reasonable, it must answer the question, and most importantly, it must be correct.

6. Are you absolutely confident your solution is correct? If so, how do you know?

Solution: "Night Train" Henson's Contract

As a beginning problem solver, you may find it useful to develop a consistent strategy. Examine the following way you can solve "Night Train's" problem by applying some algebra tools as you follow the four basic steps of problem solving.

Step 1. Understand the problem.   If you understand the problem, you will realize that "Night Train" needs to make $100,000 more with the team's offer (800,000 − 700,000) to make up for the difference in base salary. So he must start enough games to make up for this difference. Otherwise, he should not want the team's offer.

Step 2. Develop a strategy for solving the problem.   With the observation above, you could let the variable x represent the number of games "Night Train" has to start to make the same amount of money with either offer. Then we note that he would make $4000 more (10,000−6000) for each game with the team's offer. So, $4000 for each game started times the number of games started must equal $100,000.

Step 3. Execute your strategy for solving the problem.   You can translate the statement above into an equation, then apply the fundamental principle of equality to obtain the number of games started. Let x represent the number of games started.

$4000 times the number of games started equals $100,000.

$$4000x = 100,000$$
$$4000x \div 4000 = 100,000 \div 4000$$
$$x = 25$$

The solution to your equation says that "Night Train" must start in 25 games to make the same money with each deal.

Your answer would be: "Night Train" needs to play in more than 25 games to make more with the team's offer.

Step 4. Check your solution for correctness.   This answer seems reasonable, but to check it you should refer back to the original statement of the problem. If "Night Train" plays in exactly 25 games his salary for the two offers can be calculated.

"Night Train's" demand: $800,000 + $6000 · 25 = $950,000

Team's offer: $700,000 + $10,000 · 25 = $950,000

If he starts in 26 games, the team's offer is $960,000, but "Night Train's" demand would give him only $956,000. These calculations confirm the solution.

There are other ways to solve this problem. But the above solution gives you an example of how algebra can be used. Use algebra in a similar way to solve the following problems. Be sure to follow the four steps of problem solving.

Additional Problems to Solve

7. You need to open a checking account and decide to shop around for a bank. Acme Bank has an account with a $10 monthly charge, plus 25 cents per check. Farmer's Bank will charge you $12 per month, with a 20-cent charge per check. How many checks would you need to write each month to make Farmer's Bank the better deal?

   Step 1. Understand the problem.

Step 2. Develop a strategy for solving the problem.

Step 3. Execute your strategy to solve the problem.

Step 4. Check your solution for correctness.

8. The perimeter of a rectangular pasture is 2400 feet. If the width is 800 feet, how long is the pasture?

Step 1. Understand the problem.

Step 2. Develop a strategy for solving the problem.

Step 3. Execute your strategy to solve the problem.

Step 4. Check your solution for correctness.

Translating Statements into Algebraic Equations

The key to setting up and solving many word problems is recognizing the correct arithmetic operations. If there is a known formula, like the perimeter of a rectangle, then the arithmetic is already determined. Sometimes there is *only* the language to guide you.

In Problems 9–12, translate each statement into an equation. In each statement, let the unknown number be represented by the letter x.

9. The sum of 35 and a number is 140.

10. 144 is the product of 36 and a number.

11. What number times 7 equals 56?

12. The difference between the regular price and sale price of $245 is $35.

13. In Problems 9, 10, and 12 above, the verb "is" translates into what part of the equation?

14. Solve each of the equations you wrote in Problems 9–12.
    a.   **b.**

    c.   **d.**

The Four Steps of Problem Solving

Step 1. Understand the problem.

a. Read the problem completely and carefully.

b. Draw a sketch of the problem, if possible.

Step 2. Develop a strategy for solving the problem.

a. Identify and list everything you know about the problem, including relevant formulas. Add labels to the diagram if you have one.

b. Identify and list what you want to know.

Step 3. Execute your strategy to solve the problem.

a. Write an equation that includes the known quantities and the unknown quantity.

b. Solve the equation.

Step 4. Check your solution for correctness.

a. Is your answer reasonable?

b. Is your answer correct? (Does it answer the original question? Does it agree with all the given information?)

In Exercises 1–10, translate each statement into an equation, then solve the equation for the unknown number.

1. An unknown number plus 425 is equal to 981.

2. The product of some number and 40 is 2600.

3. A number minus 541 is 198.

4. The sum of an unknown number and 378 is 2841.

Exercise numbers appearing in color are answered in the Selected Answers appendix.

5. The quotient of some number and 9 is 63.

6. The prime factors of 237 are 79 and an unknown number.

7. 13 plus an unknown number is equal to 51.

8. The difference between a number and 41 is 105.

9. 642 is the product of 6 and an unknown number.

10. The sum of an unknown number and itself is 784.

In Exercises 11–17, solve the following problems by applying the four steps of problem solving. Use the strategy of solving an algebra equation for each problem.

11. In preparing for a family trip, your assignment is to make the travel arrangements. You can rent a car for $75 per day with unlimited mileage. If you have budgeted $600 for car rental, how many days can you drive?

12. You need to drive 440 miles to get to your best friend's wedding. How fast must you drive to get there in 8 hours?

13. Your goal is to save $1200 to pay for next year's books and fees. How much must you save each month if you have 5 months to accomplish your goal?

14. You have enough wallpaper to cover 240 square feet. If your walls are 8 feet high, how wide a wall can you paper?

15. In your part-time job selling kitchen knives, you have two different sets available. The better set sells for $35, the cheaper set for $20. Last week you sold more of the cheaper set, in fact twice as many as the better set. Your receipts for the week totaled $525. How many of the better sets did you sell?

16. A rectangle that has an area of 357 square inches is 17 inches wide. How long is the rectangle?

17. A rectangular field is 5 times longer than it is wide. If the perimeter is 540 feet, what are the dimensions (length and width) of the field?

w
$\ell = 5w$

The Hindus introduced negative numbers to represent debts, the first known use was by Brahmagupta in about 628 A.D. However, the history of mathematics shows that it took a long time for negative numbers to be accepted by everyone, including mathematicians, and that didn't happen until the 1600s.

1. Show with an example how you can represent a temperature less than 0 degrees Fahrenheit.

2. Can a number be used to represent a checking account balance less than $0? Explain.

3. Sometimes you might want to know how far above or below sea level an object is located (for example, an airplane or a school of fish).

   a. What number would you use to represent sea level? Explain.

   b. How would you represent the depth of an object that is below sea level? Describe an example.

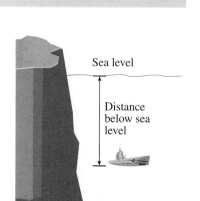

Sea level

Distance below sea level

A number less than zero is a negative number. Negative numbers are indicated by a dash, −, to the left of the number such as −20, −100, and −6.25. In a similar way, a positive number, for example positive three, can be written as +3. However, most of the time, a positive three is simply written as 3. This is true for positive numbers in general.

4. If you gain 10 pounds you can represent your change in weight by the number 10. What number represents a loss of 10 pounds?

Integers and the Number Line

The collection of all of the counting numbers, zero, and the negatives of the counting numbers is called the set of **integers**: {. . . −4, −3, −2, −1, 0, 1, 2, 3, 4, . . .}. The positive counting numbers are called *positive integers* and the negative counting numbers are called *negative integers*. Note that the terms *counting numbers* and *positive whole numbers* mean the same collection of numbers.

A good technique for visualizing integers is to use a number line. A number line is a line with evenly spaced tick marks. A tick mark is a small line segment perpendicular to the number line. Each tick mark on the following number line represents an integer. Notice that the negative integers are to the left of zero and the positive integers are to the right of zero. The numbers increase as you read from left to right.

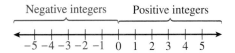

5. a. Give an example of a positive integer, a negative integer, and an integer that is neither negative nor positive, and place these integers on a number line.

   b. Describe a situation in which integers might be used. What would zero represent in the situation you describe?

6. You start the month with $225 in your checking account with no hope of increasing the balance during the month. You place the balance on the following number line.

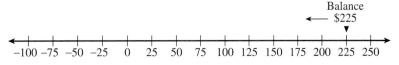

   a. During the first week, you write checks totaling $125. What is the new balance in your checking account after week 1? Place that balance on the number line above.

   b. During week 2, your checks added up to $85. Compute the amount left in your checking account after 2 weeks and place that amount on the number line.

   c. During week 3, you wrote a check for $15. What is the new balance in your checking account after 3 weeks? Place that amount on the number line.

    d. During the last week in the month your car is towed and you must write a check for $50 to get it back. What is the new balance in your checking account after 4 weeks? Place that amount on the number line.

Comparing Integers

Sometimes it is important to decide if one integer is greater than or less than another integer. The number line is one way to compare integers. Recall that on a number line as you move from *left to right* integers *increase* in value.

    7. a. Which is warmer: $-10°F$ or $-16°F$? Use a number line to help explain your answer.

    b. Which checking account balance would you prefer, $-$60$ or $-$100$? Explain.

    c. Which is closer to sea level, a depth of -20 feet or -80 feet? Explain.

    d. On a number line the larger number is to the _____ (right/left) of the smaller number.

Symbols for Comparing Integers

The symbol for "less than" is $<$. The statement $3 < 5$ is read as "3 is less than 5" or "3 is smaller than 5". The statement $-10 < -2$ is read as "-10 is less than -2", and the statement is true because -10 is to the left of -2 on the number line.

The symbol for "greater than" is $>$. The statement $6 > 4$ is read "6 is greater than 4" or "6 is larger than 4". The statement $-7 > -12$ is read "-7 is greater than -12", and the statement is true because -7 is to the right of -12 on the number line.

The symbols $<$ and $>$ are called **inequality symbols.**

    8. Identify which of the following statements are true and which are false.

    a. $-3 > -5$ **b.** $20 < -100$

    c. $0 > -40$ **d.** $-30 < -50$

Absolute Value on the Number Line

The absolute value of a number is a useful idea in working with positive and negative numbers. You may have noticed that on the number line an integer has two parts: its distance from zero and its direction (to the right or left of 0). For example, the 7 in −7 represents the number of units that −7 is from 0 and the dash ("−") represents the direction of −7 to the left of 0. Note that +7 or 7 is also 7 units from 0, but to the right.

9. a. What is the increase in temperature (in °F) if the temperature moves from 0°F to 8°F? How many degrees does the temperature decrease if the temperature moves from 0°F to −10°F?

    b. Which is further away from a $0 balance in a checking account, $150 or −$50? Explain.

    c. How far from sea level (0 feet altitude) is an altitude of 200 feet? How far from sea level (0 feet altitude) is an altitude of −20 feet?

> On the number line, the **absolute value** of a number is represented by the distance the number is from zero. Since distance is always considered positive or zero, the absolute value of a number is *always* positive or zero.

For example, the absolute value of −5 is 5 since −5 is 5 units from zero on the number line. The absolute value of 8 is 8 since 8 is 8 units from zero on the number line.

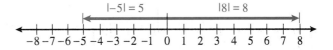

Note that this distance from zero is always positive or zero whether the number is to the left or the right of zero on the number line.

10. Determine the absolute value of each of the following integers.

    a. 47   **b.** −30

    c. −64   **d.** 56

> To represent the absolute value of a number in symbols, enclose the number in vertical lines. For example, $|7|$ represents the absolute value of 7, which is 7; $|-32|$ represents the absolute value of −32, which is 32.

11. Determine the following.

    a. $|-12|$ **b.** $|127|$ **c.** $|0|$

12. a. What number has the same absolute value as -26?

    b. What number has the same absolute value as 45?

    c. Is there a number whose absolute value is zero?

    d. Can the absolute value of a number be negative?

> Two numbers that are the same distance from 0 are called **opposites**. For example, in Problem 12a and b, -26 and 26 are opposites and 45 and -45 are opposites. 0 is its own opposite.

On the number line, opposites are two numbers that are the same distance from zero but are on opposite sides of zero. The numbers 12 and -12 are opposites because each number is 12 units from zero, but they are on opposite sides of zero.

13. a. What number is the opposite of 22?

    b. What number is the opposite of -15 ?

    c. What number is the opposite of $|-7|$?

SUMMARY
ACTIVITY 2.2

1. Negative numbers are numbers that are less than zero.

2. The set of **integers** includes all the whole numbers (the counting numbers and zero) and their opposites (the negatives of the counting numbers).

3. If $a < b$, then a is to the left of b on a number line. If $a > b$, then a is to the right of b on a number line.

4. On the number line, the **absolute value** of a number a, written $|a|$, is the distance of a from zero. The absolute value of a number is always positive or zero.

5. Two numbers that are the same distance from zero on the number line but are on opposite sides of zero are called **opposites**. 0 is its own opposite.

EXERCISES
ACTIVITY 2.2

1. The ground floor of an apartment building is numbered zero.

   a. Describe the floor numbered -2.

   b. If you are on the floor numbered -3, would you take the elevator up or down to get to the floor labeled -1?

2. Express the quantities in each of the following as an integer.

   a. The Dow-Jones stock index lost 120 points today.

   b. The scuba diver is 145 feet below the surface of the water.

   c. A deposit of $50 into your checking account.

   d. The Oakland Raiders lost 15 yards on a penalty.

   e. A withdrawal of $75 from your checking account.

3. Write $<$ or $>$ between each of the following to make the statement true.

   a. 7   5   b. -5 4   c. -10 -15

   d. 0 -2 e. -4 -3 f. -50 0

Exercise numbers appearing in color are answered in the Selected Answers appendix.

4. Determine the value of each of the following.

   a. $|4|$ **b.** $|-13|$ **c.** $|32|$

   d. $|-7|$ **e.** $|0|$

5. **a.** What number is the opposite of -6?

   b. What number is the opposite of 8?

6. **a.** Which is warmer: $-3°F$ or $0°F$?

   b. Which is farther below sea level: -20 feet or -100 feet?

7. Data on exports and imports by countries around the world are often shown by graphs for comparison purposes. The following graph is one example. The number line in the graph represents net exports in billions of dollars for six countries. Net exports are obtained by subtracting total imports from total exports; a negative net export means the country imported more goods than it exported.

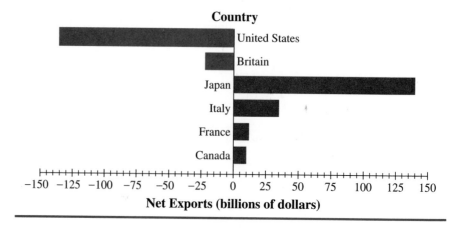

a. Estimate the net amount of exports for Japan. Is your answer a positive or negative integer? Explain what this number tells you about the imports and exports of Japan.

b. Estimate the net amount of exports for the United States. Is your answer a positive or negative integer? Explain what this number tells you about the imports and exports of the United States.

c. Determine the absolute value of the net amount of exports for Britain.

d. What is the opposite of the net amount of exports for Canada?

ACTIVITY 2.3

Maintaining Your Balance

OBJECTIVES

1. Add and subtract integers.

2. Identify properties of addition and subtraction of integers.

This activity guides you to learn the addition and subtraction of integers using concise and efficient rules. Through practice, you will make these rules your own.

Adding Integers

Suppose you use your checking account to manage all your expenses. You keep very accurate records. There are times when you must write a check for an amount that is greater than your balance. When you record this check, your new balance is represented by a negative number.

CHECK NUMBER	DATE	DESCRIPTION	SUBTRACTIONS (−)		ADDITIONS (+)		BALANCE 64	
	3/2/07	Paycheck			120			
381	3/4/07	Car repairs	167					
382	3/15/07	Clothes	47					

1. a. You deposit a paycheck for $120 from your part-time job. If the balance in your account before the deposit was $64, what is the new balance? Write the new balance in the check record above.

b. Determine the balance after making your car repair payment and record it in the check record above.

2. a. After writing a check in the amount of $47 for clothing, you realize that your account is overdrawn by $30. Explain why.

b. What integer would represent the balance at this point? Record that integer in the check record above.

c. Because you have a negative balance in your account, you decide to borrow $20 from a friend for expenses until you get an additional paycheck. What integer represents what you owe your friend?

d. What is the total of your checking account balance and the money you owe your friend?

In Problems 1 and 2, the integers being added had the same sign.

Problem 1: $64 + 120 = 184$

Problem 2: $-30 + (-20) = -50$

Note that when you add two negative numbers such as -30 and -20, the sign of the answer is negative. The 50 in the answer is obtained by neglecting the sign of -30 and -20 and simply adding 30 to 20. This is the same as adding the absolute values of -30 and -20.

This leads to the following rule.

> **Rule 1:** To add two numbers with the same sign, add the absolute values of the numbers. The sign of the sum is the same as the sign of the numbers being added.

3. Combine the following integers.

    a. $-18 + (-26)$ **b.** $17 + 108$ **c.** $-48 + (-9)$

4. a. You finally get paid. You cash the check for $120 and give $10 to your friend. Now, what do you owe your friend?

    b. You deposit the remaining $110 into your checking account. What is the new balance? Recall that you were overdrawn by $30.

In Problem 4a and 4b, the integers being added have different signs.

    Problem 4a: $-20 + 10 = -10$
    Problem 4b: $-30 + 110 = 80$

Note that when you add two numbers with different signs, such as -30 and 110, the sign of the result will be the same as the sign of the number with the greater absolute value. Since $|110| = 110$, $|-30| = 30$, and $110 > 30$, the sign of the result will be positive. To calculate the answer, ignore the signs of the numbers and subtract the smaller absolute value from the larger one. Therefore, $-30 + 110 = 110 - 30 = 80$.

5. Explain why the sum $-20 + 10$ is -10.

6. Add the following integers, using the observations just discussed.

    a. $40 + (-10)$ **b.** $-60 + 85$

    c. $-50 + 30$ **d.** $25 + (-35)$

The discussion above leads to the following rule.

> **Rule 2:** To add two integers with different signs, determine their absolute values and then subtract the smaller from the larger. The sign of the result is the sign of the number with the larger absolute value.

7. Add the following integers.

   a. $4 + 8$ **b.** $4 + (-8)$ **c.** $-3 + (-6)$

   d. $10 + (-8)$ **e.** $(-7) + (4)$ **f.** $-3 + (+8)$

Subtracting Integers

The current balance in your checking account is $195. You order merchandise for $125 and record this amount as a debit. That is, you enter the amount as $-$125. The check was returned because the merchandise was no longer available. Adding the $125 back to your checking account balance of $70 brings the balance back to $195.

$$70 + 125 = \$195$$

You also figured that if you had subtracted the debit from the $70, you would get the same result. That means you reasoned that

$$70 - (-125) = 70 + 125 = \$195.$$

Of course, you prefer the simpler method of balancing your checkbook by adding the opposite of the debit, that is, adding the credit to your account. But subtracting the debit shows *an important mathematical fact*. The fact is that *subtracting a negative number is always equivalent to adding its opposite*. In the expression $70 - (-125)$, the term $-(-125)$ is replaced by $+125$ and $70 - (-125)$ becomes $70 + 125$.

8. Evaluate the following.

   a. $7 - (-3)$ **b.** $-8 - (-12)$ **c.** $1 - (-7)$ **d.** $-5 - (-2)$

9. A friend had $150 in her checking account and wrote a check for $120. She calculated her checkbook balance as $150 - (+ \$120) = \$30$. You pointed out that she might as well have written $150 - \$120 = \$30$. Explain why.

10. Evaluate the following.

   a. $11 - (+7)$ **b.** $5 - (+8)$ **c.** $-7 - (+9)$ **d.** $-3 - (+2)$

The discussion and problems above lead to the following rule.

> **Rule 3:** To subtract an integer b from another integer a, change the subtraction to the addition of integer b's opposite. Then follow either rule 1 or rule 2 for adding integers.

> **PROCEDURE**
>
> The subtraction sign and the sign of the number being subtracted can be replaced by a single sign.
>
> $$a - (+b) = a - b$$
>
> $$a - (-b) = a + b$$
>
> For example, $-6 - (+2) = -6 - 2 = -8$ and $9 - (-4) = 9 + 4 = 13$.

11. Perform the following subtractions and state what rule(s) you used in each case.

    a. $-8 - 2$ **b.** $10 - (-3)$

    c. $-4 - (-6)$ **d.** $5 - 15$

    e. $-5 - (+8)$ **f.** $+2 - (+10)$

Adding or Subtracting More Than Two Integers

When adding or subtracting more than two numbers, add or subtract from left to right.

EXAMPLE 1   *To compute $4 + 6 - 3$, first add $4 + 6 = 10$. Then subtract 3 from 10 to obtain the answer of 7.*

EXAMPLE 2 $-3 - 7 + 5 = -10 + 5 = -5$

12. Perform the following calculations. Verify with your calculator.

    a. $-3 + 7 - 5$ **b.** $5 + 3 + 10$ **c.** $-2 - 4 + 5$

    d. $-4 - 2 - 4$ **e.** $3 - 7 - 6$ **f.** $-6 + 7 + 3 - 5$

Properties of Addition and Subtraction of Integers

13. a. Add: $9 + (-4)$

   b. Add: $-4 + 9$

   c. What property of addition is illustrated by comparing parts a and b?

14. a. Subtract: $5 - (-2)$

   b. Subtract: $-2 - (+5)$

   c. Is the operation of subtraction commutative? Explain.

15. a. Add the integers $5, -3, -9$ by first adding 5 and -3, and then adding -9.

   b. Add the integers given in part a: $5, -3, -9$, but this time first add -3 and -9, and then add 5 to the sum.

   c. Does it matter which two integers you add together first?

   d. What property is being demonstrated in part c?

SUMMARY
ACTIVITY 2.3

1. Rules for adding integers.

To add two numbers with the same sign, add the absolute values of the numbers. The sign of the sum is the same as the sign of the numbers being added.

For example:

$$7 + 9 = 16$$
$$-6 + (-5) = -11$$

To add two integers with different signs, determine their absolute values and then subtract the smaller from the larger. The sign of the sum is the sign of the number with the larger absolute value.

For example:

$$-5 + 9 = 4$$
$$10 + (-13) = -3$$

2. Rules for subtracting integers.

To subtract an integer b from an integer a, change the subtraction to the addition of the opposite of b, then follow the rules for adding integers.

For example:

$$5 - (-7) = 5 + 7 = 12$$
$$-5 - (+3) = -5 + (-3) = -8$$

3. Procedure for simplifying the subtraction of an integer from another integer.

The subtraction sign and the sign of the number that follows it can be replaced by a single sign.

$$a - (+b) = a - b$$
$$a - (-b) = a + b$$

For example,

$$-3 - (+6) = -3 - 6 = -9 \quad \text{and} \quad 7 - (-8) = 7 + 8 = 15$$

4. Commutative property of addition.

For all integers a and b, $a + b = b + a$.

For example:

$$6 + (-9) = (-9) + 6, \quad \text{since } -3 = -3$$

Note: The commutative property is not true in general for subtraction.

For example:

$$3 - 4 \neq 4 - 3, \quad \text{because } -1 \neq 1$$

5. Associative property of addition.

For all integers a, b, and c, $(a + b) + c = a + (b + c)$.

For example:

$$(4 + 5) + (-3) = 4 + (5 + (-3))$$
$$9 - 3 = 4 + 2$$
$$6 = 6$$

Note: The associative property is not true in general for subtraction.

For example:

$$(7 - 5) - 1 \neq 7 - (5 - 1)$$
$$2 - 1 \neq 7 - 4$$
$$1 \neq 3$$

Perform the indicated operation in Exercises 1–20.

1. $5 + (-7)$ **2.** $13 + (-17)$ **3.** $-32 + (+19)$

4. $-3 + (-2)$ **5.** $-21 - (-18)$ **6.** $-11 + 17$

7. $8 + (-8)$ **8.** $-54 - (+72)$ **9.** $3 + (-4) - 10$

10. $-5 - 6 + 3$ **11.** $-4 - 5 - 3$ **12.** $7 - (-3) - 7$

13. $4 + (-6) + 6$ **14.** $9 + 8 + (-3)$ **15.** $-4 - (-5) + (-6)$

16. The temperature increased by 8°F from -10°F. What is the new temperature?

17. The temperature was -7°F in the afternoon. That night, the temperature dropped by 5°F. What is the nighttime temperature?

18. The temperature increased 4°F from -1°F. What is the new temperature?

19. The temperature was 6°F in the morning. By noon, the temperature rose by 5°F. What was the noon temperature?

20. You began a diet on November 1 and lost 5 pounds. Then you gained 2 pounds over the Thanksgiving break. By how much did your weight change in November?

21. While descending into a valley in a hot air balloon, your elevation decreased by 500 feet from an elevation of −600 feet (600 feet below sea level). What is your new elevation?

22. a. You are a first-year lifeguard at Rockaway Beach and earn $403 per week. On August 28 you deposited a week's pay into your checking account. The balance of your account before the deposit was $39. What is the new balance?

b. Your $460 monthly rent is due on September 1. So on September 1 you write and record a $460 check. What is the new balance?

c. On September 4 you deposit your $403 paycheck. What is the new balance?

d. You write a $400 check on September 5 for your first installment on your college bill for the fall term. What is your new balance?

e. You write a check for groceries on September 10 in the amount of $78. What is your new balance?

f. You get your last lifeguard paycheck on September 11. What is your new balance?

23. The highest point in Asia is at the top of Mount Everest, which is 8850 meters above sea level. The lowest point in Asia is the Dead Sea at 408 meters below sea level.

   a. Write the elevation level of the Dead Sea as a signed number.

   b. What is the difference between the highest and the lowest points in Asia?

24. Profits and losses in millions of dollars per quarter over a 2-year period for a telecommunications company are shown in the bar graph. Determine the total profit or loss for the company over the 2-year period.

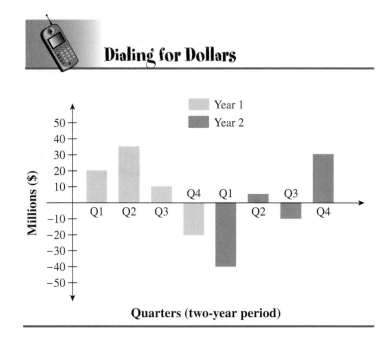

● **ACTIVITY 2.4**

What's the Bottom Line?

OBJECTIVES

1. Write formulas from verbal statements.

2. Evaluate expressions in formulas.

3. Solve equations of the form $x + b = c$ and $b - x = c$.

4. Solve formulas for a given variable.

You run a retail shop in a tourist town. To determine the selling price of an item, you add the profit you want to what the item cost you. For example, if you want a profit of $4 on a decorated coffee mug that cost you $3, you would sell the mug for $7.

1. a. Write a formula for the selling price of an item in terms of your cost for the item and the profit you want. In your formula, let C represent your cost; P, the profit on the item; and S, its selling price.

b. You make a profit of $8 on a wall plaque that costs you $12. Use your formula from part a to determine the selling price.

2. A particular style of picture frame has not sold well and you need space in the store to make room for new merchandise. The frames cost you $14 each and you decide to sell them for $2 less than your cost.

a. Write the value of your profit, P, as an integer.

b. Substitute the values for C and P in the equation $S = C + P$ and determine S, the selling price.

Problems 1 and 2 demonstrate the general method of determining an output from inputs. In the equation $S = C + P$, *the inputs are C and P* in the expression on the right side of the equation, and S is the output variable. Replacing C and P with their values in the expression and evaluating their sum determines the value of S.

3. A wristwatch costs you $35 and you sell it for $60. Substitute these values of C and S in the equation $C + P = S$ and solve the equation for P, the profit.

In Problem 3, the unknown value, P, is part of the expression on the left side of the equation. The output value of the equation, S, is known. Determining the unknown input value in the equation is called *solving the equation*.

4. You make a profit of $11 on a ring you sell for $25. Replace P and S with these values in the equation $C + P = S$ and solve for C, the cost.

5. You sell a large candle for $16 that cost you $19.

   a. Use the formula $C + P = S$ to determine your profit or loss.

   b. Comment on your profit for this sale.

To solve the equations in Problems 3–5, you subtracted a given number from each side of the equation to isolate the unknown variable. This is the same as adding the opposite of the given number to each side.

6. Substitute the given values into the equation $c = a + b$ and then determine the value of the remaining unknown variable.

   a. $a = 5, b = -17$ **b.** $a = 12, c = -30$

   c. $b = -4, c = -9$ **d.** $b = 7, a = -23$

   e. $c = 49, a = -81$ **f.** $a = -34, b = -55$

7. Substitute the given values into the equation $c = a - b$ and then determine the value of the remaining unknown variable.

    a. $a = 12, b = -19$ **b.** $b = 7, c = -42$

    c. $c = 36, b = 40$ **d.** $a = -17, b = 29$

Solving Formulas for a Given Variable

The process for solving formulas for a given variable is the same as the process for solving an equation. For example, to solve the formula $S = C + P$ for P, subtract C from both sides of the equation and simplify as demonstrated in Example 1.

EXAMPLE 1

$$S = C + P$$
$$S - C = C - C + P$$
$$S - C = 0 + P$$
$$S - C = P$$
$$P = S - C$$

8. The formula $r_1 + r_2 = r$ is used in electronics. Solve for r_1 .

9. The formula $p + q = 1$ is used in the study of probability. Solve for q.

10. The formula $P = R - C$ is used in business, where P represents profit; R, revenue or money earned; and C, cost of doing business. Solve for revenue, R.

To solve for cost, C, in the formula $P = R - C$ given in Problem 10, you add C to each side of the equation, simplify, and continue to solve, as demonstrated in Example 2.

EXAMPLE 2   *Solve $P = R - C$ for C.*

SOLUTION

$$P + C = R - C + C$$
$$P + C = R$$
$$-P + P + C = R - P$$
$$C = R - P$$

11. Solve for x in the equation $y = b - x$.

**SUMMARY
ACTIVITY 2.4**

1. To solve for x in formulas or equations of the forms $c = x + b$ or $c = b + x$, add the opposite of b to both sides of the equation to obtain $x = c - b$.

2. To solve the equation $b - x = c$ for x, add x to both sides of the equation to obtain $b = c + x$. Then subtract c from each side to obtain $b - c = x$.

**EXERCISES
ACTIVITY 2.4**

1. When you began your diet, you weighed 154 pounds. After 2 weeks, you weighed 149 pounds. You can express the relationship between your initial weight, final weight, and the change between them by the equation

$$154 + x = 149,$$

where x represents your change in weight in the 2 weeks.

a. Solve the equation for x.

b. Was your change in weight a loss or a gain? Explain.

2. a. Another way to write an equation expressing your change in weight during the first 2 weeks of your diet is to subtract the initial weight, 154, from your final weight, 149. Then the equation is $x = 149 - 154$, where x represents the change in weight. Determine the value of x.

b. Write a formula to calculate the amount a quantity changes when you know the final value and the initial value. Use the words *final value*, *initial value*, and *change in quantity* to represent the variables in the formula. (*Hint:* Use the equation from part a as a guide.)

3. Suppose you lost 7 pounds during August. At the end of that month, you weighed 139 pounds. Let I represent your initial weight at the beginning of August.

a. Write an equation representing this situation. (*Hint:* Use your formula from Problem 2b as a guide.)

b. Solve this equation for I to determine your weight at the beginning of the month.

4. a. The following table gives information about your diet for a 6-week period. For each week, write an equation to solve for the unknown amount using the variables indicated. Enter the equations into the table.

Losing Proposition

Week	1	2	3	4	5	6
Initial Weight, I	154			150	146	144
Ending Weight, E		149	150	146		
Weight Change, C	-3	-2	1		-2	-5
Equation						

b. Solve each equation in part a and complete the table. State whether you are evaluating an expression or solving the equation.

5. The sale price, S, of an item is the difference between the regular price, P, and the discount, D.

   a. Write a formula for S in terms of P and D.

   b. If a video game is discounted \$8 and sells for \$35, use the formula in part a to determine the regular price.

6. You write a check for \$37 to pay for a laboratory manual that you need for chemistry class.

   a. If the new balance in your checking account is \$314, write an equation to determine the original balance.

   b. Solve the equation to determine the original balance.

7. Solve each of the following formulas for the given variable.

   a. $K = C + 273$, for C

   b. $S = P - D$, for D

   c. $A = B - C$, for B

8. In each of the following, let x represent an integer. Then translate the given verbal expression into an equation and solve for x.

   a. The sum of an integer and 10 is -12.

   b. 9 less than an integer is 16.

   c. The result of subtracting 17 from an integer is -8.

   d. If an integer is subtracted from 10, the result is 6.

⊛ACTIVITY 2.5

Riding in the Wind

OBJECTIVES

1. Translate verbal rules into equations.

2. Determine an equation from a table of values.

3. Use a rectangular coordinate system to represent an equation graphically.

Windchill

Bicycling is enjoyable in New York State all year around, but it can get very cold in the winter. If there is a wind, it feels even colder than the actual temperature. This effect is called the windchill temperature, or windchill for short. The following table gives the actual temperature, T, and the windchill, W, for a 10 mph wind. Both are given in °F.

 Blowin' in the Wind

ACTUAL TEMPERATURE, T (°F)	−15	−10	−5	0	5	10
WINDCHILL, W, FOR A 10 mph WIND (°F)	−20	−15	−10	−5	0	5

1. a. Write a verbal rule that describes how to determine the windchill for a 10 mph wind, if you know the actual temperature.

b. Translate the verbal rule in part a into an equation where T represents the actual temperature and W represents windchill.

c. Use the equation in part b to determine the windchill, W, for a temperature of −3 °F.

d. Use the equation in part b to determine the actual temperature, T, for a windchill of −17°F.

Rectangular Coordinate System Revisited

To obtain a graphical view of the windchill data, you can plot the values in the table above on a rectangular coordinate grid. Notice that the table contains both positive and negative values for the actual temperature and the windchill.

Until now in this textbook, the horizontal (input) axis and the vertical (output) axis contained only nonnegative values. To plot the windchill data, you need to extend each axis in the negative direction.

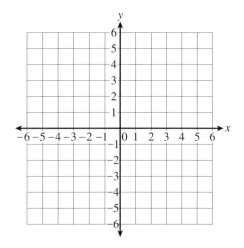

Now the grid has two complete number lines (axes) that intersect at a right (90°) angle at the **origin,** (0, 0). In this rectangular coordinate system, the two axes together divide the plane into four parts called **quadrants.** The quadrants are numbered as follows.

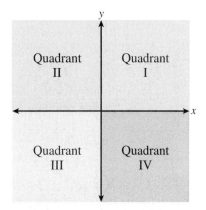

To locate the point with coordinates (−5, −10), start at the origin (0, 0) and move 5 units left on the horizontal axis. Then, move 10 units down, parallel to the vertical axis. The point (−5, −10) is located in quadrant III.

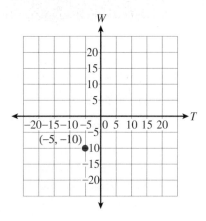

    2. a. Plot the remaining values from the windchill table on page 112 on the preceding grid.

b. The points you graphed were determined by the equation $W = T - 5$. The points and their pattern are a graphical representation of the equation. What pattern do the graphed points suggest? Connect the points on the graph in the pattern you see.

3. Scale and label the following grid and plot the following points.

a. $(2, -5)$ **b.** $(-1, 3)$

c. $(4, 2)$ **d.** $(0, -4)$

e. $(5, 0)$ **f.** $(-2, -6)$

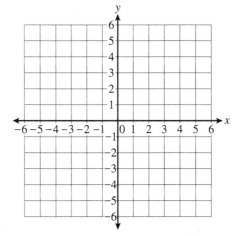

4. Without plotting the points, identify the quadrant in which each of the following points is located.

a. $(-12, 24)$ **b.** $(35, -26)$

c. $(56, 48)$ **d.** $(-28, -34)$

5. Identify the quadrant of each point whose coordinates have the given signs.

a. $(-, +)$ **b.** $(-, -)$

c. $(+, +)$ **d.** $(+, -)$

The Bicycle Shop

Your local sporting goods store sells a wide variety of bicycles priced from $80 to $500. The store sells bikes assembled or unassembled. The charge for assembly is $20 regardless of the price of the bike.

6. a. What is the price of a $100 bicycle with assembly?

b. What is the price of a $250 bicycle with assembly?

7. a. Write a verbal rule that describes how to determine the price of a bicycle with assembly.

b. Translate the verbal rule in part a into an equation where A represents the cost of the bicycle with assembly and U represents the price of the unassembled bicycle.

c. Use the equation in part b to determine the price, A, if the price of the bicycle is $160 without assembly.

d. Use the equation in part b to determine the price, U, of the unassembled bicycle if it cost $310 assembled.

8. Complete the following table.

PRICE WITHOUT ASSEMBLY, U	COST WITH ASSEMBLY, A
80	
	140
240	
	320
360	
460	480

9. a. Plot the values from the table in Problem 8 on an appropriately labeled and scaled coordinate system. Let P represent the input values on the horizontal axis. Let C represent the output values on the vertical axis.

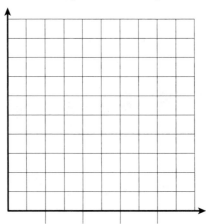

b. Connect the points on the graph to obtain a graphical representation of the equation in Problem 7b.

SUMMARY
ACTIVITY 2.5

Points on a rectangular coordinate system.

1. A point on a rectangular coordinate grid is written as an ordered pair in the form (x, y), where x is the input (horizontal axis) and y is the output (vertical axis).

2. Ordered pairs are plotted as points on a rectangular grid that is divided into four quadrants by a horizontal (input) axis and a vertical (output) axis.

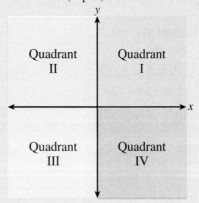

3. The sign of the coordinates of a point determine the quadrant in which the point lies.

x-COORDINATE	y-COORDINATE	QUADRANT
+	+	I
−	+	II
−	−	III
+	−	IV

**EXERCISES
ACTIVITY 2.5**

1. You make and sell birdhouses to earn some extra money. The following table lists the cost of materials and the total cost, both in dollars, for making the birdhouses.

Out on a Limb

Number of Birdhouses	1	2	3	4
Material Cost ($)	6	12	18	24
Total Cost ($)	8	14	20	26

a. Write a verbal rule that describes how to determine the total cost if you know the cost of the materials.

b. Translate the verbal rule in part a into an equation where T represents the total cost and M represents the cost of the materials.

c. Use the equation in part b to determine the total cost if materials cost $36.

d. Plot the values from the table above on an appropriately labeled and scaled rectangular coordinate system.

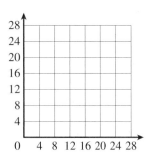

e. Connect the points on the graph to obtain a graphical representation of the equation in part d.

2. The sum of two integers is 3.

a. Translate this verbal rule into an equation where x represents one integer and y the other.

b. Use the equation in part a to complete the following table.

x	y
4	
	−3
−3	
	4
0	
	1

c. Plot the values from the table in part b on an appropriately labeled and scaled coordinate system.

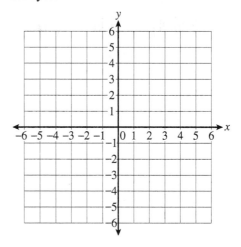

d. Connect the points on the graph to obtain a graphical representation of the equation in part a.

3. The difference of two integers is 5.

a. Translate this verbal rule into an equation where x represents the larger integer and y the smaller.

b. Use the equation in part a to complete the following table.

x	y
5	
	−6
−3	
	1
0	
	−1

c. Plot the values from the table in part b on an appropriately labeled and scaled coordinate system.

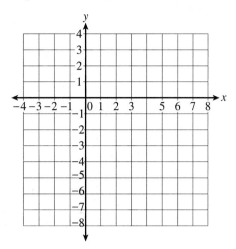

d. Connect the points on the graph to obtain graphical representation of the equation in part a.

CLUSTER 1 What Have I Learned?

1. Which number is always greater, a positive number or a negative number? Give a reason for your answer.

2. A number and its opposite are equal. What is the number?

3. Two numbers, x and y, are negative. If $|x| > |y|$, which number is smaller? Give an example to illustrate.

4. In each of the following, fill in the blank with a word that makes the statement true.

   a. When you add two positive numbers, the sign of the answer is always _____.

   b. When you add two negative numbers, the sign of the answer is always _____.

   c. The absolute value of zero is _____.

   d. When you subtract a negative number from a positive number, the answer is always _____.

   e. When you subtract a positive number from a negative number, the answer is always _____.

5. Describe in your own words how to add a positive number and a negative number. Use an example to help.

6. Describe in your own words how to add two negative numbers. Use an example to help.

7. Describe in your own words how to subtract two positive numbers. Use an example to help.

8. Describe in your own words how to subtract a positive number from a negative number. Use an example to help.

9. Describe in your own words how to subtract a negative number from a positive number. Use an example to help.

10. Describe in your own words how to subtract two negative numbers. Use an example to help.

11. Demonstrate how you would draw a rectangular coordinate grid to plot the following points: $(8, 90), (6, -50), (-4, 60), (0, 0), (-5, -50), (-7, 0)$.

12. You process concert ticket orders for a civic center in your hometown. There is a $3 processing fee for each order. Write a formula to represent the calculations you would do to determine the total cost of an order. State what the variables are in this situation and choose letters to represent them.

CLUSTER 1   # How Can I Practice?

1. Determine the opposite of each of the following.

   a. 3   **b.** -5 **c.** 0

2. Evaluate.

   a. $|-13|$ **b.** $|15|$ **c.** $-|-39|$ **d.** $-|39|$

3. Calculate.

   a. $15 + 36$ **b.** $-21 + 9$

   c. $18 + (-35)$ **d.** $-5 + (-21)$

   e. $-73 + 38 + (-49)$ **f.** $-21 + 45 + (-83) + (-5)$

   g. $-18 + 12 + 69 + 32 + (-56)$

   h. $14 + (-12) + (-25) + 7 + (-74)$

   i. $23 + (-45) + (-51) + 82$

   j. $-64 + (-49) + 28 + (-14) + 101$

4. Calculate.

   a. $16 - 62$ **b.** $36 - 82$

   c. $-14 - (-28)$ **d.** $-18 - (-6)$

   e. $24 - (-48)$ **f.** $45 - 54$

   g. $-39 - (-48) - 62$

   h. $63 - (-72) - 101 - (-53) - 205$

   i. $-81 - (-98) - 73 - (-49)$

Exercise numbers appearing in color are answered in the Selected Answers appendix.

5. Evaluate by performing the given operations.

   a. $-84 + 46 - (-98) - 108 - (-65)$

   b. $27 - 58 + (-72) - 85 - (-7)$

   c. $19 - 31 + (-42) + (-5)$

   d. $-51 + 27 - (-21) + 42$

   e. $-47 + 19 - (-12) + 71$

   f. $53 - 39 + (-88) - (-60)$

   g. $-89 - 11 + 45 - 61$

6. Evaluate the expression $x + y$, for each set of given values.

   a. $x = -18$ and $y = 7$

   b. $x = 13$ and $y = 8$

   c. $x = -21$ and $y = -12$

   d. $x = -17$ and $y = 5$

7. Evaluate the expression $x - y$, for each set of given values.

   a. $x = 14$ and $y = 6$

   b. $x = -16$ and $y = 9$

   c. $x = 23$ and $y = -62$

   d. $x = -27$ and $y = -32$

8. Solve the following equations and check your answer in the original equation.

a. $x + 21 = -63$

b. $x + 18 = 49$

c. $32 + x = 59$

d. $41 + x = -72$

e. $x - 17 = 19$

f. $x - 35 = 42$

g. $-22 + x = 16$

h. $-28 + x = 11$

9. Let x represent an integer. Translate the following verbal expression into an equation and solve for x.

a. The sum of an integer and 5 is 12.

b. 7 less than an integer is 13.

c. The difference of an integer and 8 is 6.

d. The result of subtracting 3 from an integer is 12.

10. The temperature in the morning was −9°F. The weather report indicated that by noon the temperature would be 4°F warmer. Determine the noontime temperature.

11. The temperature in the morning was −13°F. It was expected that the temperature would fall 5°F by midnight. What would be the midnight temperature?

12. The average temperature in July in town is 88°F. The average temperature in January in the same town is −5°F. What is the change in average temperature from July to January?

13. The temperature on Monday was −8°F. By Tuesday the temperature was −13°F. What was the change in temperature?

14. The temperature at the beginning of the week was −6°F, and at the end of the week it was 7°F. What was the change in the temperature?

15. **a.** Your favorite stock opened the day at $29 per share and ended the day at $23 per share. Let x represent the amount of your gain or loss per share. An equation that represents the situation is $29 + x = 23$. Solve for x.

   b. The following table represents the beginning and ending values of your stock for 1 week. Complete the table indicating the amount of your gain or loss per share, each day.

Opening Value	23	21	21	18	20
Closing Value	21	21	18	20	23
Gain or Loss, x					

c. What is the total change in your stock's value for this week?

16. The following graph represents net exports in billions of dollars for six countries represented on the number line. (Net exports are obtained by subtracting total imports from total exports.)

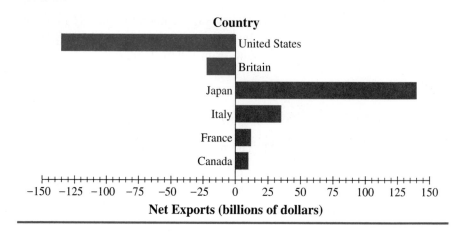

 The World of Exports

a. What is the difference between the net exports of Japan and Italy?

b. What is the difference between the net exports of Britain and France?

c. What is the total sum of net exports for the six countries listed?

17. A contestant on the TV quiz show *Jeopardy!* had $1000 at the start of the second round of questions (double jeopardy). She rang in on the first two questions, incorrectly answering a $1200 question but giving a correct answer to an $800 question. What was her score after answering the two questions?

18. The difference of two integers is -3.

    a. Translate this verbal rule into an equation, where x represents the smaller integer and y the larger.

    b. Use the equation you wrote in part a to complete the following table.

x	y
0	
	0
5	
	−2
−2	
	6

    c. Plot the values from the table in part b on an appropriately labeled and scaled coordinate system.

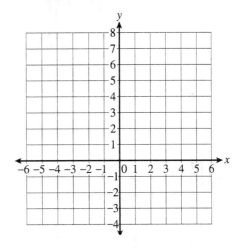

    d. Connect the points on the graph to obtain the graphical representation of the equation in part a.

Adding and Subtracting Fractions

✳ACTIVITY 2.6

Are You Hungry?

OBJECTIVES

1. Identify the numerator and the denominator of a fraction.

2. Determine the greatest common factor (GCF).

3. Determine equivalent fractions.

4. Reduce fractions to equivalent fractions in lowest terms.

5. Convert mixed numbers to improper fractions and improper fractions to mixed numbers.

6. Determine the least common denominator (LCD) of two or more fractions.

7. Compare fractions.

You decide to have some friends over to watch videos. After the first movie, you call the local sub shop to order three giant submarine sandwiches. When the subs are delivered, you pay the bill and everyone agrees to reimburse you, depending on how much they eat.

Because some friends are hungrier than others, you cut one sub into three equal (large) pieces, a second sub into six equal (medium) parts, and the third sub into twelve equal (small) parts.

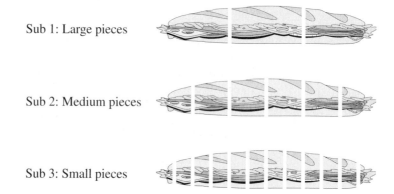

Sub 1: Large pieces

Sub 2: Medium pieces

Sub 3: Small pieces

What Is a Fraction?

1. a. Because the first sub is divided into three large equal pieces, each piece represents a fractional part of the whole sub. Write a fraction that represents what part of the whole sub each large piece represents.

b. What fraction of the sub does each medium piece represent? Explain.

c. What fraction of the sub does each small piece represent? Explain.

DEFINITIONS

The bottom number of a fraction is called the **denominator.** The denominator indicates the total number of equal parts into which a whole unit is divided.

The top portion of a fraction is called the **numerator.** The numerator indicates the number of equal parts that the fraction represents out of the total number of parts.

2. a. If you eat five small pieces, what fractional part of the whole sub did you eat? Explain.

b. What is the denominator of this fraction? How many equal segments does the fraction indicate the sub is divided into?

c. What is the numerator of this fraction? What does this number represent?

Note that the fraction line, which separates the numerator and denominator, represents "out of" or "divided by."

A fraction that has an integer numerator and a nonzero integer denominator is a **rational number.**

DEFINITION

A **rational number** is a number that can be written in the form $\frac{a}{b}$, where a and b are integers and b is not zero. Every integer is also a rational number, since an integer can be written as $\frac{a}{1}$.

Note that the denominator of a fraction cannot be zero. It would indicate that the whole is divided into zero equal parts, which makes no sense.

3. a. Suppose a friend is very hungry and he eats all three large pieces of the sub. What fraction represents the amount he ate?

b. What is the value of the fraction in part a? Explain.

c. If $\frac{6}{6}$ represents how much of the medium sub that was eaten, what is the value of the fraction?

d. In general, what is the value of a fraction whose numerator and denominator are equal but non-zero?

4. a. If you did not eat any of the large pieces of the first sub, what fraction represents the amount of the first sub that you ate?

b. What is the value of the fraction in part a?

c. If $\dfrac{0}{12}$ represents the amount that you ate of the third sub, what does the numerator indicate?

d. What is the value of the fraction $\dfrac{0}{12}$?

e. In general, what is the value of a fraction whose numerator is zero?

Equivalent Fractions

5. As you are cutting the subs, you notice that two medium pieces placed end-to-end measure the same as one large piece. Therefore, $\dfrac{2}{6}$ of the sub represents the same portion as $\dfrac{1}{3}$.

a. How many small pieces represent the same portion as one large piece?

b. What fraction of the sub does the number of small pieces in part a represent?

In Problem 5, three different fractions were used to represent the same portion of a whole sub. These fractions, $\dfrac{1}{3}, \dfrac{2}{6}$, and $\dfrac{4}{12}$, are called **equivalent fractions.** They represent the same quantity.

> To obtain a fraction equivalent to a given fraction, multiply or divide the numerator and the denominator of the given fraction by the same non-zero number.

6. a. Divide the numerator and the denominator of $\frac{2}{6}$ by 2 to obtain an equivalent fraction.

b. Multiply the numerator and denominator of $\frac{1}{3}$ by 4 to obtain an equivalent fraction.

7. Write the given fraction as an equivalent fraction with the given denominator.

a. $\dfrac{3}{10} = \dfrac{?}{20}$ **b.** $\dfrac{4}{5} = \dfrac{?}{30}$

c. $\dfrac{7}{11} = \dfrac{?}{33}$ **d.** $\dfrac{8}{9} = \dfrac{?}{72}$

Reducing a Fraction to Lowest Terms

8. a. What whole number is a factor of both the numerator and denominator of $\dfrac{1}{3}$?

b. What is the largest whole number that is a factor of both the numerator and denominator of $\dfrac{8}{12}$?

c. What is the largest whole number that is a factor of both the numerator and denominator of $\dfrac{6}{8}$?

If the largest factor of both the numerator and denominator of a fraction is 1, the fraction is said to be in **lowest terms.** For example, $\frac{1}{3}$, $\frac{3}{4}$, and $\frac{4}{5}$ are written in lowest terms.

The **greatest common factor** (GCF) of two numbers is the largest factor common to both numbers. For example, the GCF of 8 and 12 is 4.

PROCEDURE

Reducing a Fraction to Lowest Terms Fractions that are not in lowest terms can be reduced to an equivalent fraction that is in lowest terms by dividing the numerator and denominator by their greatest common factor (GCF). For example, to reduce the fraction $\frac{8}{12}$ to an equivalent fraction in lowest terms, divide the numerator and denominator by 4.

$$\frac{8}{12} = \frac{8 \div 4}{12 \div 4} = \frac{2}{3}$$

---

9. Reduce the following fractions to equivalent fractions in lowest terms.

   a. $\frac{6}{8}$ b. $\frac{6}{15}$

   c. $\frac{3}{8}$ d. $\frac{15}{25}$

Mixed Numbers and Improper Fractions

10. a. All of the first (large pieces) and second (medium pieces) subs are eaten and only one small piece of the third sub (small pieces) is left. Represent the amount eaten as the sum of a whole number and a fraction.

    b. Suppose all three subs were cut into twelve equal parts. How many twelfths were eaten if only one piece was left, as in part a? Write your answer in words and as a single fraction.

    c. Is the sum in part a equivalent to the fraction in part b? Explain.

The sum $2 + \frac{11}{12}$ is more conveniently written as $2\frac{11}{12}$ and is called a **mixed number**.

The fraction $\frac{35}{12}$ is called an **improper fraction** because the numerator is greater than or equal to the denominator. An improper fraction and a mixed number that represent the same quantity are called **equivalent**.

DEFINITIONS

An **improper fraction** is a fraction where the absolute value of the numerator is greater than or equal to the absolute value of the denominator. A **mixed number** is a sum of an integer and a fraction.

It is often helpful to convert mixed numbers into improper fractions and vice versa.

EXAMPLE 1 *Convert $2\frac{11}{12}$ to an improper fraction.*

SOLUTION

$$2\frac{11}{12} = 2 + \frac{11}{12} = \frac{2 \cdot 12}{1 \cdot 12} + \frac{11}{12} = \frac{24}{12} + \frac{11}{12} = \frac{35}{12}$$

Note in Example 1 that the integer 2 was rewritten as an equivalent fraction with denominator 12 so it could be added to the fractional part $\frac{11}{12}$. This observation leads to a shortcut method to convert a mixed number to an improper fraction:

$$2\frac{11}{12} = \frac{2 \cdot 12 + 11}{12} = \frac{35}{12}$$

PROCEDURE

Converting a Mixed Number to an Improper Fraction To convert a mixed number to an improper fraction, multiply the whole-number part by the denominator and add the numerator. The result is the numerator of the improper fraction. The denominator stays unchanged.

EXAMPLE 2 *Convert $\frac{35}{12}$ to a mixed number, in lowest terms.*

SOLUTION

$$\begin{array}{r} 2 \\ 12\overline{)35} \\ -24 \\ \hline 11 \end{array}$$

$$\frac{35}{12} = 2 + \frac{11}{12} = 2\frac{11}{12}$$

PROCEDURE

Converting an Improper Fraction to a Mixed Number To convert an improper fraction to a mixed number, divide the numerator by the denominator. The quotient is the whole-number part of the mixed number, the remainder is the numerator of the fractional part, and the divisor is the denominator of the fractional part.

11. Write the following mixed numbers as improper fractions in lowest terms.

   a. $1\dfrac{5}{8}$ **b.** $4\dfrac{9}{12}$

   c. $5\dfrac{6}{10}$

12. Write the given improper fractions as mixed numbers in lowest terms.

   a. $\dfrac{5}{2}$ **b.** $\dfrac{24}{10}$ **c.** $\dfrac{21}{7}$ **d.** $\dfrac{3}{3}$

Comparing Fractions: Determining Which Fraction Is Larger

13. Suppose one group of friends ate four medium pieces and another group ate ten small pieces.

   a. What fractional part of the sub did the first group eat?

   b. What fractional part of the sub did the second group eat?

   c. Use the graphics display of the subs at the beginning of this activity to help determine which group ate more.

It is much easier to compare fractions that have the same denominator.

14. Write $\dfrac{4}{6}$ as an equivalent fraction with a denominator of 12.

It is easy to see that $\dfrac{10}{12}$ is larger than $\dfrac{8}{12}$ since they have the same denominator and $10 > 8$.

15. Which is the larger fraction, $\dfrac{5}{8}$ or $\dfrac{3}{4}$?

Problems 13, 14 and 15 show that two or more fractions are easily compared if they are expressed as equivalent fractions having the same (common) denominator. Then the fraction with the largest numerator is the largest fraction.

> **DEFINITIONS**
>
> A **common denominator** of two or more fractions is a number that is a multiple of each denominator. For example, $\dfrac{3}{4}$ and $\dfrac{5}{6}$ have common denominators of 12, 24, 36, ...
>
> The **least common denominator (LCD)** of two fractions is the smallest common denominator. For example, the LCD of $\dfrac{3}{4}$ and $\dfrac{5}{6}$ is 12.

In general, to determine the LCD, identify the largest denominator of the fractions involved. Look at multiples of the largest denominator. The smallest multiple that is divisible by the smaller denominator(s) is the LCD.

EXAMPLE 3   *Determine the least common denominator of* $\dfrac{1}{6}$ *and* $\dfrac{3}{8}$.

SOLUTION

In the case of $\dfrac{1}{6}$ and $\dfrac{3}{8}$, the larger denominator is 8.

The smallest multiple of the denominator 8 that is evenly divisible by the denominator 6 is the LCD, determined as follows:

$8 \cdot 1 = 8$ **8 is not a multiple of 6.**
$8 \cdot 2 = 16$ **16 is not a multiple of 6.**
$8 \cdot 3 = 24$ **24 is a multiple of 6, therefore 24 is the LCD.**

16. a. Write $\dfrac{1}{6}$ and $\dfrac{3}{8}$ as equivalent fractions each with a denominator of 24.

b. Use the result from part a to compare $\dfrac{1}{6}$ and $\dfrac{3}{8}$.

17. Compare the following fractions and determine which is larger.

   a. $\frac{3}{5}$ and $\frac{1}{2}$ **b.** $\frac{3}{8}$ and $\frac{1}{3}$ **c.** $\frac{1}{4}$ and $\frac{3}{16}$

SUMMARY
ACTIVITY 2.6

1. The **greatest common factor (GCF)** of two or more numbers is the largest number that is a factor of each of the given numbers.

2. To write an **equivalent fraction,** multiply or divide both the numerator and denominator of a given fraction by the same number.

3. To reduce a fraction to an equivalent fraction in lowest terms, divide the numerator and the denominator by their GCD.

4. To convert a mixed number to an improper fraction, multiply the whole-number part by the denominator and add the numerator. The result is the numerator of the improper fraction; the denominator stays unchanged.

5. To convert an improper fraction to a mixed number, divide the numerator by the denominator. The quotient is the whole-number part of the mixed number and the remainder becomes the numerator of the fractional part; the denominator stays unchanged.

6. To find the **least common denominator (LCD)** of two or more fractions, identify the largest denominator and look at multiples of it. The smallest multiple that is divisible by the other denominator(s) is the LCD.

7. To compare two or more fractions, express them as equivalent fractions with a common positive denominator. The fraction with the largest numerator is the largest fraction.

EXERCISES
ACTIVITY 2.6

Determine the missing number.

1. $\frac{2}{3} = \frac{?}{12}$ 2. $\frac{3}{4} = \frac{?}{20}$

Reduce the given fraction to an equivalent fraction in lowest terms.

3. $\frac{9}{15}$ 4. $\frac{8}{28}$

Exercise numbers appearing in color are answered in the Selected Answers appendix.

Use the inequality symbols < or > to compare the following fractions.

5. $\dfrac{5}{12}$ and $\dfrac{1}{3}$

6. $\dfrac{3}{7}$ and $\dfrac{2}{5}$

Reduce the following improper fractions to lowest terms and convert to mixed numbers.

7. $\dfrac{5}{3}$

8. $\dfrac{21}{14}$

Convert the following mixed numbers to improper fractions in lowest terms.

9. $3\dfrac{3}{8}$

10. $5\dfrac{6}{8}$

11. You and your sister ordered two individual pizzas. You ate $\dfrac{3}{4}$ of your pizza and your sister ate $\dfrac{5}{8}$ of her pizza. Who ate more pizza?

Your pizza   Your sister's pizza

12. You and your friend are painting a house. While you painted $\dfrac{2}{12}$ of the house, your friend painted $\dfrac{3}{18}$ of the house. Who painted more?

13. In a basketball game, you made 4 baskets out of 12 attempts. Your teammate made 3 baskets out of 8 attempts.

  a. What fraction of your attempted shots did you make?

  b. What fraction of your teammate's attempted shots did she make?

  c. Who was the more accurate shooter?

14. An Ivy League college accepts 5 students for every 100 that apply. What fraction of applicants is accepted? Write your result in lowest terms.

15. You have two pieces of lumber. One piece measures 6 feet long and the second piece measures $\frac{25}{4}$ feet long.

a. Write $\frac{25}{4}$ as a mixed number.

b. Write 6 as an improper fraction with a denominator of 4.

c. Which piece is longer? Explain.

16. Measuring with rulers provides an opportunity to test your understanding of fractions. Use the following graphic of a ruler to answer the following questions about measuring the line segment drawn above the ruler.

a. Look at the ruler and determine the number of $\frac{1}{4}$-inch segments in one inch.

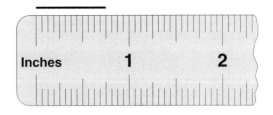

b. How many $\frac{1}{4}$-inch segments did the given line measure?

c. How long is the given line segment (in inches)?

d. Measure the given line segment in $\frac{1}{8}$ -inch units.

e. Finally, measure the given line segment in $\frac{1}{16}$ -inch units.

f. Explain why the three fractional answers in parts c, d, and e are equivalent.

g. Another line segment measures $\frac{2}{3}$ inch. Is it longer or shorter than the given line segment? Explain.

ACTIVITY 2.7

Food for Thought

OBJECTIVE

1. Add and subtract fractions and mixed numbers with the same denominators.

Many recipes include ingredients that are measured in terms of fractions and mixed numbers. For example, a cake recipe may call for $2\frac{1}{2}$ cups of flour, $\frac{1}{2}$ teaspoon of baking powder, etc. Sometimes you may want to change a recipe and will have to do some basic calculations with the fractions and mixed numbers.

Adding and Subtracting Fractions with Same Denominators

EXAMPLE 1   *You are preparing a meal to celebrate your mother's birthday. You use her favorite recipes to make a zucchini bread for dinner and a chocolate birthday cake. The recipes call for $\frac{1}{4}$ teaspoon of baking powder for the bread and $\frac{3}{4}$ teaspoon of baking powder for the cake. How much baking powder do you need?*

SOLUTION

Add the amounts of baking powder to obtain the total amount you will need.

$$\frac{1}{4} + \frac{3}{4} = \frac{4}{4} = 1.$$

You will need 1 teaspoon of baking powder.

Example 1 illustrates a procedure to add or subtract fractions with the same denominator. Note that fractions with the same denominators are sometimes referred to as **like fractions**.

> To add two like fractions, add the numerators and keep the common denominator:
>
> $$\frac{a}{c} + \frac{b}{c} = \frac{a+b}{c}$$
>
> To subtract one like fraction from another, subtract one numerator from the other and keep the common denominator:
>
> $$\frac{a}{c} - \frac{b}{c} = \frac{a-b}{c}$$

1. For each of the following, perform the indicated operation. Convert improper fractions to mixed numbers. Write the result in lowest terms.

   a. $\dfrac{1}{3} + \dfrac{1}{3}$ b. $\dfrac{3}{5} + \dfrac{4}{5}$ c. $\dfrac{3}{10} + \dfrac{9}{10}$ d. $\dfrac{3}{8} + \dfrac{5}{8}$

e. $\dfrac{6}{7} - \dfrac{4}{7}$ **f.** $\dfrac{7}{8} - \dfrac{3}{8}$ **g.** $\dfrac{1}{4} - \dfrac{3}{4}$ **h.** $\dfrac{3}{18} - \dfrac{5}{18}$

Note that the results of the subtraction in parts g and h are negative. A fraction that represents a negative number is written with the negative sign in front of the fraction or in the numerator. That is, $-\dfrac{a}{b}$ and $\dfrac{-a}{b}$ are two ways of writing the same fraction.

For example, $\dfrac{-2}{3}$ and $-\dfrac{2}{3}$ are two ways to write the same number.

Adding Mixed Numbers with Like Fraction Parts

EXAMPLE 2   *A Scandinavian rye bread recipe calls for* $3\dfrac{1}{4}$ *cups of white flour and* $2\dfrac{1}{4}$ *cups of rye flour. What is the total amount of flour in the bread?*

SOLUTION

$$3\dfrac{1}{4} = 3 + \dfrac{1}{4} \qquad \text{Definition of mixed number}$$

$$+\, 2\dfrac{1}{4} = 2 + \dfrac{1}{4}$$

$$= 5 + \dfrac{2}{4} \qquad \text{Sum of integer part and fraction part}$$

$$= 5\dfrac{1}{2} \qquad \text{Answer in reduced form}$$

The total amount of flour in the bread is $5\dfrac{1}{2}$ cups.

PROCEDURE

Adding Mixed Numbers To add mixed numbers with the same denominators, add the integer parts and the fraction parts separately. If the sum of the fraction part is an improper fraction, convert it to a mixed number and add the integer parts. Reduce the fraction part to lowest terms if necessary.

2. For each of the following, perform the indicated operation. Write the fractional part of the mixed number in lowest terms.

a. $10\dfrac{3}{7} + 15\dfrac{2}{7}$ **b.** $1\dfrac{1}{6} + 9\dfrac{5}{6}$

c. $12\frac{1}{8} + 48\frac{5}{8}$

d. $1\frac{13}{16} + 4\frac{5}{16}$

Subtracting Mixed Numbers with Like Fraction Parts

EXAMPLE 3   *Your bread machine holds a maximum of $5\frac{1}{4}$ cups of flour. You want to use a favorite recipe that calls for $6\frac{3}{4}$ cups of flour. By how much must your recipe be reduced so you will be able to use the bread machine?*

SOLUTION

Subtract $5\frac{1}{4}$ from $6\frac{3}{4}$ to determine if there is more flour than can be held by your machine.

$$6\frac{3}{4} = \;\; + 6 + \frac{3}{4} \qquad \text{Positive mixed number definition}$$

$$\underline{-5\frac{1}{4} = -5 - \frac{1}{4}} \qquad \text{Subtraction of a mixed number}$$

$$= 1 + \frac{2}{4} \qquad \text{Result of subtraction}$$

$$= 1 + \frac{1}{2}$$

$$= 1\frac{1}{2} \qquad \text{Answer in final form}$$

There are $1\frac{1}{2}$ cups more than the machine can hold, so it can't be used unless the recipe is reduced by $1\frac{1}{2}$ cups.

> To subtract mixed numbers, both the integer parts and the fraction parts must be subtracted.

3. Perform each subtraction. Write the fractional part of the mixed number in lowest terms.

a. $13\frac{5}{7} - 9\frac{4}{7}$

b. $9\frac{5}{6} - 8\frac{1}{6}$

c. $45\frac{9}{13} - 17\frac{5}{13}$

d. $14\frac{11}{16} - 4\frac{5}{16}$

4. You need $5\frac{1}{3}$ tablespoons of butter to bake a small apple tart and have one stick of butter, which is 8 tablespoons. How much butter will you have left after you make the tart?

5. The purpose of baseboard molding in a room is to finish the area where the wall meets the floor. A carpenter got a good deal on the molding he wanted because he was willing to buy the last $112\frac{3}{10}$ feet of it that the store had. If he used $96\frac{9}{10}$ feet to finish two rooms, how much did he have left over?

6. Adding and subtracting like fractions and mixed numbers are used in a variety of situations. For example, consider the ingredient amounts in the following beef stew recipe.

Basic Beef Stew

$2\frac{1}{8}$ cups of chunked, cooked beef	$1\frac{5}{8}$ cups chopped onions
$3\frac{3}{8}$ cups of broth	2 cups chunked carrots
$\frac{1}{8}$ cup of garlic salt	$1\frac{7}{8}$ cups chopped potatoes

a. You need to mix all of these ingredients together in a large mixing bowl. To determine what size mixing bowl to use, add all ingredient amounts listed in the recipe. What is the total number of cups of ingredients in the stew?

b. Your mixing bowls come in 10-cup, 15-cup, and 20-cup sizes. Which mixing bowl should you use? Explain.

c. How much space do you have for mixing the ingredients in the bowl you have chosen?

d. A friend who does not like potatoes is coming to dinner. So you decide to take the potatoes out of the recipe. Use subtraction to determine the new total number of cups of ingredients in the potato-free version of the stew.

7. A negative mixed number such as $-4\frac{3}{7}$ is defined as $-4 - \frac{3}{7}$. Use this information to perform the indicated operations for each of the following.

a. $-4\frac{3}{7} + 2\frac{2}{7}$

b. $-2\frac{3}{8} - \left(-5\frac{2}{8}\right)$

c. $-4\frac{2}{9} - 7\frac{8}{9}$

SUMMARY
ACTIVITY 2.7

Add or Subtract Fractions or Mixed Numbers with the Same Denominator

1. To add or subtract fractions with the same denominator, add or subtract the numerators and write the sum or difference over the given denominator.

2. To add or subtract mixed numbers that have the same denominator, add or subtract the integer parts and the fraction parts separately. Then combine the parts into the form $a\frac{b}{c}$.

3. A fraction or the fractional part of a mixed number in an answer should always be written in lowest terms.

EXERCISES
ACTIVITY 2.7

Perform the indicated operation. Write all results in lowest terms.

1. $\dfrac{3}{8} + \dfrac{3}{8}$

2. $\dfrac{4}{5} - \dfrac{1}{5}$

3. $\dfrac{5}{12} + \dfrac{1}{12}$

4. $\dfrac{5}{8} - \dfrac{3}{8}$

5. $\dfrac{2}{3} + \dfrac{2}{3}$

6. $\dfrac{9}{4} - \dfrac{6}{4}$

7. $\dfrac{1}{4} + \dfrac{5}{4}$

8. $\dfrac{20}{12} - \dfrac{4}{12}$

9. $2\dfrac{2}{5} + 5\dfrac{1}{5}$

10. $4\dfrac{5}{7} - 3\dfrac{2}{7}$

11. $3\dfrac{1}{4} + 2\dfrac{1}{4}$

12. $8\dfrac{2}{5} - 5\dfrac{4}{5}$

13. $-7\dfrac{4}{9} + 5\dfrac{2}{9}$

14. $6\dfrac{11}{17} - 8\dfrac{15}{17}$

15. $8\dfrac{7}{11} + \left(-13\dfrac{5}{11}\right)$

16. $-14\dfrac{7}{8} - \left(-3\dfrac{3}{8}\right)$

17. $-12\dfrac{5}{13} - 8\dfrac{9}{13}$

18. A pizza is cut into 8 equal slices. You eat 2 slices and your friend eats 3 slices.

  a. What fraction of the pizza did you and your friend eat?

  b. What fraction of the pizza is left?

19. You take home $400 a month from your part-time job as a cashier. Each month you budget $120 for car expenses, $160 for food, and the rest for entertainment.

a. What fraction of your take-home pay is budgeted for car expenses?

b. What fraction of your take-home pay is budgeted for food?

c. What fraction of your take-home pay is budgeted for entertainment?

20. Your bedroom measures $12\frac{1}{8}$ feet by $10\frac{3}{8}$ feet. You want to put a wallpaper border around the perimeter of the room. How much wallpaper border do you need? Remember, the perimeter of a rectangle is the sum of the lengths of the four sides of the rectangle.

The highlight of your summer was a cross-country trip to see your college friends. You drove a total of 2400 miles to get there and made stops along the way to do some sightseeing.

1. The first day, you drove 600 miles and stopped to see statues of famous historical figures in a Wax Museum. What fraction of the 2400 miles did you complete on the first day? Write the fraction in lowest terms.

2. The second day, you drove only 400 miles so you could visit an art gallery that featured the works of M. C. Escher. What fraction of the 2400 miles did you complete on the second day? Write the fraction in lowest terms.

3. a. You completed $\frac{1}{4}$ of the total 2400-mile mileage on the first day and $\frac{1}{6}$ of the total mileage on the second day. Write a numerical expression that can be used to determine what fraction of the 2400-mile trip you completed on the first two days.

   b. How is this addition problem different from those of the previous activity?

Recall (Activity 2.7) that to add or subtract two or more fractions, they all must have the same denominator. Also recall (Activity 2.6) that a common denominator for a set of fractions can be determined by finding a number that is a multiple of each of the denominators in the fractions to be added or to be subtracted.

4. In Problem 3 you can choose any number that is divisible by both 4 and 6 as the common denominator. List at least four numbers divisible by both 4 and 6.

Is 12 one of the numbers that you listed in Problem 4? Notice that 12 is divisible by both 4 and 6 and that it is the smallest such number. Therefore, 12 is the **least common denominator (LCD)** of $\frac{1}{4}$ and $\frac{1}{6}$.

5. a. Write $\frac{1}{4}$ as an equivalent fraction with a denominator of 12.

b. Write $\frac{1}{6}$ as an equivalent fraction with a denominator of 12.

c. Add the two like fractions.

6. On the third day, you drove 800 miles and stopped to see a flower garden where the leaf and petal arrangements form mathematical patterns. What fraction of the 2400 miles did you complete on the third day? Write the fraction in lowest terms.

7. You completed $\frac{5}{12}$ of the trip on the first two days and $\frac{1}{3}$ of the trip on the third day. What fraction of the trip did you complete on the first three days?

8. During the fourth day, you drove another 200 miles and stayed at the Motel 8, where the windows were all regular octagons. What fraction of the 2400 miles did you complete on the fourth day? Write the fraction in lowest terms.

9. You completed $\frac{3}{4}$ of the trip on the first three days and $\frac{1}{12}$ of the trip on the fourth day. What fraction of the trip did you finish in the first four days?

10. What fraction of the trip do you have to complete to get to your friends on the fifth day?

Solving Equations

Problem 10 can also be solved using algebra. If x represents the fractional part of the trip to be completed on the fifth day, then

$$x + \frac{5}{6} = 1.$$

Recall that this equation may be solved for x by *subtracting* $\frac{5}{6}$ from both sides of the equation.

$$x + \frac{5}{6} - \frac{5}{6} = 1 - \frac{5}{6}$$

$$x = \frac{6}{6} - \frac{5}{6} = \frac{1}{6}$$

So, you have $\frac{1}{6}$ of the trip to complete on the fifth day.

11. Once you arrive, you and your friends compare college experiences, grades and the different methods professors use to determine grades. For example, the final grade in one of your courses is determined by quizzes, exams, a project, and class participation. Quizzes count for $\frac{1}{4}$ of the final grade, exams $\frac{1}{3}$, and the project $\frac{1}{4}$ of the final grade.

    a. If x represents the fractional part of the final grade for class participation, write an equation relating x, $\frac{1}{4}$, $\frac{1}{3}$, $\frac{1}{4}$, and 1.

    b. Solve the equation for x.

12. You decide to make lunch and discover that you all like salad. Your favorite recipe for a simple salad dressing is made of oil and vinegar. You need a total of $2\frac{1}{2}$ cups of salad dressing, of which $1\frac{7}{8}$ cups is oil.

    a. If x represents the amount of vinegar to be used in the salad dressing, write an equation relating the amounts of oil and vinegar for the $2\frac{1}{2}$ cups of salad dressing.

    b. Solve the equation for x.

13. You are still hungry after eating the salad and order a submarine sandwich. The total weight of a sub is the sum of the weights of its ingredients. A formula for total weight is give by $W = M + C + R + V$, where M is the weight of the meat, C is the weight of the cheese, R is the weight of the roll, and V is the weight of all the other ingredients, such as lettuce, tomato, and so on. Use this formula to calculate the weight of a regular submarine sandwich that includes $\frac{1}{4}$ pound of meat, $\frac{1}{8}$ pound of cheese, a $\frac{1}{2}$ pound roll and other ingredients weighing $\frac{1}{4}$ pound.

**SUMMARY
ACTIVITY 2.8**

1. To determine the **least common denominator (LCD)** of fractions,

   a. Identify the largest denominator of the fractions involved.

   b. Look at multiples of the largest denominator. The smallest multiple that is divisible by the smaller denominator(s) is the LCD.

2. To add or subtract fractions with different denominators,

   a. Find the LCD and convert each fraction to an equivalent fraction, that has the LCD you found.

   b. Add or subtract the numerators of the equivalent fractions to obtain the new numerator, leaving the LCD in the denominator.

   c. If necessary, reduce the resulting fraction to lowest terms.

   d. If the result is an improper fraction, convert it to a mixed number where appropriate.

**EXERCISES
ACTIVITY 2.8**

In Exercises 1–17, perform the indicated operation.

1. $\dfrac{1}{6} + \dfrac{1}{2}$

2. $\dfrac{3}{8} - \dfrac{1}{4}$

3. $-\dfrac{2}{5} + \dfrac{9}{10}$

4. $3\frac{1}{3} + 1\frac{1}{6}$

5. $5\frac{7}{12} + 8\frac{13}{16}$

6. $12\frac{3}{4} + 6\frac{2}{5}$

7. $5\frac{2}{12} + 3\frac{7}{18}$

8. $12\frac{1}{4} - 7\frac{1}{8}$

9. $14\frac{3}{4} - 6\frac{5}{12}$

10. $11 - 6\frac{3}{7}$

11. $12\frac{1}{4} - 5$

12. $8\frac{5}{6} - 3\frac{11}{12}$

13. $4\frac{3}{11} - 2\frac{9}{22}$

14. $-7\frac{5}{8} + 2\frac{1}{6} = -7 + 2 - \frac{5}{8} + \frac{1}{6}$

15. $-9\frac{3}{5} + \left(-3\frac{4}{15}\right)$

16. $2\frac{2}{7} - \left(-3\frac{3}{8}\right)$

17. $-5\frac{2}{5} + \left(-6\frac{4}{9}\right)$

18. You are considering learning to play the piano and check with a friend about practice time. For 3 consecutive days before a recital, she practiced $1\frac{1}{4}$ hours, $2\frac{1}{2}$ hours, and $3\frac{2}{3}$ hours. What was her total practice time for 3 days?

19. A favorite muffin recipe calls for $2\frac{2}{3}$ cups of flour, 1 cup of sugar, $\frac{1}{2}$ cup of crushed cashews, and $\frac{5}{8}$ cup of milk, plus assorted spices. How many cups of batter does the recipe make?

20. A student spends $\frac{1}{3}$ of a typical day sleeping, $\frac{1}{6}$ of the day in classes, and $\frac{1}{8}$ of the day watching TV.

    a. If x represents the fraction of the rest of the day available for study, write an equation describing the situation.

b. Solve the equation for x.

21. The final grade in one of your friend's courses is determined by a term paper, exams, quizzes, and class participation. The term paper is worth $\frac{1}{5}$, the exams $\frac{1}{3}$, and the quizzes $\frac{1}{4}$ of the final grade.

   a. If x represents the fractional part of the final grade for class participation, write an equation describing the situation.

   b. Solve the equation for x.

22. A cake recipe calls for $3\frac{1}{2}$ cups of flour, $1\frac{1}{4}$ cups of brown sugar, and $\frac{5}{8}$ cup of white sugar. What is the total amount of dry ingredients?

23. To create a table for a report on your word processor, you need two columns, each $1\frac{1}{2}$ inches wide, and five columns, each $\frac{3}{4}$ inch wide. Will your table fit on a piece of paper $8\frac{1}{2}$ inches wide?

24. Your living room wall is 14 feet long. You want to buy a couch and center it on the wall. You have two end tables, each $2\frac{1}{4}$ feet long, that will be on each side of the couch. You plan to leave $1\frac{1}{2}$ feet next to each end table for floor plants. Determine how long a couch you can buy.

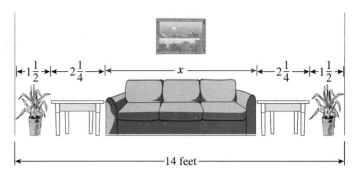

a. If x represents the length of the couch, write an equation describing the situation.

b. Solve the equation for x.

In Exercises 25–30, solve each equation for the unknown quantity. Check your answers.

25. $\dfrac{3}{10} = c - \dfrac{1}{5}$

26. $x - 3\frac{1}{2} = 6\frac{3}{4}$

27. $x + 4 = 2\frac{1}{2}$

28. $\dfrac{1}{2} + b = \dfrac{2}{3}$

29. $2\frac{1}{3} + x = 5\frac{5}{6}$

30. $x + 5\frac{1}{4} = -7\frac{1}{3}$

CLUSTER 2   # What Have I Learned?

1. a. How do you convert a mixed number to an improper fraction?

b. Give an example.

2. a. How do you convert an improper fraction to a mixed number?

b. Give an example.

3. Determine whether the following statements are true or false. Give a reason for each answer.

a. For a fraction to be called improper, the absolute value of the numerator has to be greater than the absolute value of the denominator.

b. The LCD of two denominators must be greater than or equal to either of those denominators.

c. $-6\frac{1}{4} = -6 + \frac{1}{4}$

d. $7\frac{2}{9} = \frac{65}{9}$

e. $\frac{2}{7} + \frac{4}{7} = \frac{6}{14}$

4. a. Outline the general steps in adding mixed numbers. Be sure to allow for differences when the denominators are the same or different.

b. Give an example of two or more mixed numbers with same denominators. Then determine their sum.

c. Give an example of two or more mixed numbers with different denominators. Then determine their sum.

5. a. Outline the general steps in subtracting mixed numbers. Be sure to indicate how you make a decision to regroup from the integer part.

b. Give an example of subtracting two mixed numbers with the same denominator. Then determine their difference.

c. Give an example of subtraction in which two mixed numbers have different denominators and you do *not* need to regroup. Then determine the difference.

d. Give an example of subtraction in which two mixed numbers have different denominators and you *do* need to regroup. Then determine the difference.

CLUSTER 2   # How Can I Practice?

1. Determine the missing numerators.

a. $\dfrac{3}{11} = \dfrac{?}{33}$

b. $\dfrac{5}{7} = \dfrac{?}{42}$

c. $\dfrac{8}{9} = \dfrac{?}{81}$

d. $\dfrac{7}{12} = \dfrac{?}{36}$

e. $\dfrac{13}{18} = \dfrac{?}{72}$

2. Convert the following mixed numbers into improper fractions in lowest terms.

a. $3\frac{7}{9}$

b. $5\frac{5}{8}$

c. $4\frac{3}{12}$

d. $10\frac{8}{13}$

e. $1\frac{27}{31}$

3. Convert the following improper fractions to mixed numbers in lowest terms.

a. $\dfrac{71}{32}$

b. $\dfrac{28}{13}$

c. $\dfrac{89}{12}$

d. $\dfrac{45}{5}$

e. $\dfrac{92}{14}$

Exercise numbers appearing in color are answered in the Selected Answers appendix.

4. Reduce the following fractions to lowest terms.

a. $\dfrac{12}{18}$

b. $\dfrac{8}{72}$

c. $\dfrac{36}{39}$

d. $\dfrac{42}{48}$

e. $\dfrac{54}{82}$

5. Rearrange the following fractions in order from smallest to largest.

$$\dfrac{3}{2}, \dfrac{1}{6}, \dfrac{3}{4}, \dfrac{5}{8}, \dfrac{11}{12}, \dfrac{3}{24}$$

6. When fog hit the New York City area, visibility was reduced to $\dfrac{1}{16}$ mile at JFK Airport, $\dfrac{1}{8}$ mile at LaGuardia Airport, and $\dfrac{1}{2}$ mile at Newark Airport.

a. Which airport had the best visibility?

b. Which airport had the worst visibility?

7. Add the following and write the result in lowest terms.

a. $\dfrac{4}{9} + \dfrac{7}{9}$

b. $\dfrac{13}{17} + \dfrac{5}{17}$

c. $1\dfrac{5}{12} + 3\dfrac{3}{4}$

d. $8\dfrac{6}{7} + 4\dfrac{5}{9}$

e. $5\dfrac{5}{12} + 3\dfrac{11}{18}$

f. $13 + 4\dfrac{9}{13}$

g. $-8\frac{4}{6} + \left(-25\frac{7}{24}\right)$

h. $-6\frac{17}{24} + \left(-12\frac{31}{48}\right)$

i. $-7\frac{6}{21} + \left(-8\frac{15}{39}\right)$

j. $-9\frac{3}{14} + \left(-11\frac{6}{35}\right)$

8. In each case, do the subtraction and write the result in lowest terms.

a. $\frac{9}{13} - \frac{2}{13}$

b. $13\frac{28}{54} - 2\frac{11}{54}$

c. $8\frac{15}{48} - 7\frac{5}{24}$

d. $11\frac{4}{9} - 7\frac{5}{24}$

e. $22\frac{8}{11} - 17\frac{15}{44}$

f. $46\frac{13}{28} - 34\frac{10}{56}$

g. $74\frac{3}{8} - 61$

h. $28\frac{7}{12} - 15$

i. $48 - 21\frac{5}{9}$

j. $72 - 13\frac{7}{12}$

k. $13\frac{2}{15} - 8\frac{4}{5}$

l. $14\frac{1}{36} - 7\frac{1}{6}$

m. $29\frac{7}{12} - 21\frac{15}{18}$

n. $23\frac{13}{42} - 18\frac{5}{7}$

o. $17\frac{9}{14} - 9\frac{8}{21}$

p. $16\frac{5}{8} - (-3\frac{7}{12})$

q. $-6\frac{4}{5} - (-7\frac{11}{15})$

r. $-13\frac{5}{6} - 8\frac{6}{7}$

9. While testing a new drug, doctors found that $\frac{1}{2}$ of the patients given the drug improved, $\frac{2}{5}$ showed no change in their condition, and the remaining patients got worse. What fraction of the patients taking the new drug got worse?

10. You purchased a roll of wallpaper that is $30\frac{1}{2}$ yards long. Your contractor used $26\frac{7}{8}$ yards to wallpaper one room. Is there enough wallpaper left on the roll for a job that requires 4 yards of wallpaper?

11. Solve each of the following equations for x.

a. $14\frac{3}{7} + x = 21$

b. $-17\frac{3}{5} + x = -12\frac{4}{5}$

c. $x - 13\frac{5}{6} = 17\frac{4}{7}$

d. $x + 8\frac{4}{9} = 19\frac{2}{3}$

e. $-18\frac{2}{11} + x = -23\frac{1}{3}$

| CLUSTER 3 | Adding and Subtracting Decimals |

ACTIVITY 2.9

What Are You Made of?

OBJECTIVES

1. Identify place values of numbers written in decimal form.

2. Convert a decimal to a fraction or a mixed number.

3. Compare decimals.

4. Read and write decimals.

5. Round decimals.

Have you ever wondered about the chemical elements that are contained in your body? According to the *Universal Almanac*, a 150-pound person is made up of the following elements.

It's Elementary

ELEMENT	WEIGHT IN POUNDS	ELEMENT	WEIGHT IN POUNDS
Oxygen	97.5	Cobalt	0.00024
Carbon	27.0	Copper	0.00023
Hydrogen	15.0	Manganese	0.00020
Nitrogen	4.5	Iodine	0.00006
Calcium	3.0	Zinc	Trace
Phosphorus	1.8	Boron	Trace
Potassium	0.3	Aluminum	Trace
Sulfur	0.3	Vanadium	Trace
Chlorine	0.3	Molybdenum	Trace
Sodium	0.165	Silicon	Trace
Magnesium	0.06	Fluorine	Trace
Iron	0.006	Chromium	Trace
		Selenium	Trace

Source: Universal Almanac

Note that the weights are expressed as **decimal numbers**. A number written as a decimal has an integer part to the left of the decimal point, and a fractional part that is to the right of the decimal point. Decimal numbers extend the place value system for whole numbers to include fractional parts. Also, decimal numbers, like fractions, may be used to express portions of a whole, that is, numbers less than 1.

Comparing Decimals

As you recall from Chapter 1, the place values for the integer part, to the left of the decimal point, are powers of 10: 1, 10, 100, 1000, etc. The place values for the fractional part of a decimal number, to the *right* of the decimal point, are powers of 10 in the denominator: $\frac{1}{10}, \frac{1}{100}, \frac{1}{1000}$, etc.

1. Does a 150-lb person have more sodium or potassium in their body? Explain why.

EXAMPLE 1   *The place values of the decimal number 79.653 are as follows.*

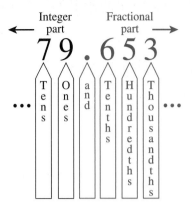

Therefore, $79.653 = 70 + 9 + \dfrac{6}{10} + \dfrac{5}{100} + \dfrac{3}{1000}$.

The fractional part of the number 79.653 is $\dfrac{6}{10} + \dfrac{5}{100} + \dfrac{3}{1000}$. Notice that the least common denominator of these three fractions is 1000. So,

$$\dfrac{6}{10} + \dfrac{5}{100} + \dfrac{3}{1000} = \dfrac{600}{1000} + \dfrac{50}{1000} + \dfrac{3}{1000} = \dfrac{653}{1000}.$$

Therefore, 79.653 can be written as $79\dfrac{653}{1000}$, which is read as "79 and 653 thousandths." Note that when reading decimal numbers, the word "and" separates the integer part from the fractional part, replacing the decimal point.

When a decimal number is written as a fraction or mixed number, the denominator corresponds to the place value of the rightmost digit in the decimal number. This leads to the following procedure to convert a decimal number to an equivalent fraction or mixed number.

PROCEDURE

Converting a Decimal Number to a Fraction or Mixed Number

1. Write the nonzero integer part of the number and drop the decimal point.
2. Write the fractional part of the number as the numerator of a fraction. The denominator is determined by the place value of the rightmost digit.
3. Reduce the fraction if necessary.

---

2. **a.** Write the weight of sodium given in the table as a fraction with denominator 1000.

b. Write the weight of potassium given in the table as a fraction with denominator 1000.

c. Compare the weights of potassium and sodium in the fraction form that you determined in parts a and b. Which one is larger?

There is a faster and easier method for comparing decimal numbers. Suppose you want to compare 2.657 and 2.68. The first step is to line up the decimal points as follows.

$$2.657$$
$$2.68\mathbf{0}$$

└─ Zero since no digit is present.

Now, moving left to right, compare digits that have the same place value. The digit in the ones and tenths places is the same in both numbers. In the hundredths place, 8 is greater than 5, and it follows that $2.68 > 2.657$.

> **PROCEDURE**
>
> **Comparing Decimal Numbers**
>
> **1.** First compare the integer parts (to the left of the decimal point). The number with the larger integer part is the larger number.
>
> **2.** If the integer parts are the same, compare the fractional parts (to the right of the decimal point).
>
>   **a.** Write the decimal parts as fractions with the same denominator and compare the fractions.
>
>   or
>
>   **b.** Line up the decimal points and compare the digits that have the same place value, moving from left to right. The first number with the larger digit is the larger number.

---

3. a. Use the method just described to determine if an average person has more sodium or potassium in his body.

b. Does the average person have more cobalt or iron in their body?

Reading and Writing Decimals

It is important to know how to name, read, and write decimal numbers as fractions. For example, 0.165 is named as "one hundred sixty-five thousandths." More generally, an extension of the place value system to the right of the decimal point is found in the following chart.

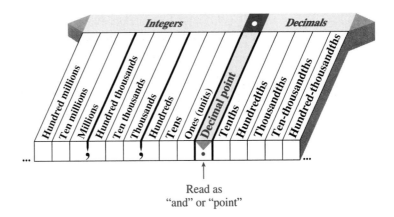

Read as
"and" or "point"

To read a decimal number, read the digits to the right of the decimal point as though they were *not* preceded by a decimal point, and then attach the place value of its rightmost digit. Use the word "and" to separate the integer part from the decimal or fractional part.

EXAMPLE 2   *The decimal number 251.737 is read two hundred fifty-one and seven hundred thirty-seven thousandths.*

4. a. Write in words the weight of potassium in a 150-pound body.

   b. Write in words the weight of the amount of copper in a 150-pound body.

   c. Which element would have a weight of "six hundred-thousandths" of a pound?

5. a. Write the number 9,467.00624 in words.

   b. Write the number 35,454,666.007 in words.

   c. Write the following number using decimal notation:
      four million sixty-four and seventy-two ten-thousandths.

   d. Write the following number using decimal notation:
      seven and forty-three thousand fifty-two millionths.

Rounding Decimal Numbers

In Chapter 1 you estimated whole numbers by a technique called rounding-off, or rounding for short. Decimal numbers can also be rounded to a specific place value.

EXAMPLE 3   *Round the weight of sodium in a 150-pound body by rounding to the tenths place.*

SOLUTION

Observe that 0.165 has a 1 in the tenths place and that 0.165 > 0.1. So the task is to determine whether 0.165 is closer to 0.1 or 0.2.

0.15 is exactly halfway between 0.1 and 0.2.

0.165 > 0.15, so 0.165 must be closer to 0.2.

There is approximately 0.2 pound of sodium in a 150-pound body.

PROCEDURE:

Rounding a Decimal Fraction to a Specified Place Value

1. If the specified place value is 10 or more, drop the fractional part and round the resulting whole number.
2. Otherwise, locate the digit with the specified place value.
3. If the digit directly to the right is less than 5, keep the digit in step 2 and delete all the digits to the right.
4. If the digit directly to the right is greater than or equal to 5, increase the digit in step 2 by 1 and delete all the digits to the right.

EXAMPLE 4   *Round 279.583 to the ones place.*

SOLUTION

The digit 9 in the ones place will either stay the same or increase by 1. Basically, you want to know whether the number is closer to 279 or 280. Since the tenths digit is 5, the number rounds to 280 (following step 4 in the procedure).

6. Copper's weight of 0.00023 lb, rounded to the nearest ten-thousandths place, is 0.0002 lb. Explain how this answer is obtained.

7. **a.** What is the weight of sodium, rounded to the nearest hundredth?

   b. What is cobalt's weight, rounded to the nearest ten-thousandth?

SUMMARY
ACTIVITY 2.9

- **Converting a Decimal to a Fraction or a Mixed Number**

  1. Write the nonzero integer part of the number and drop the decimal point.

  2. Write the fractional part of the number as the numerator of a new fraction, whose denominator is the same as the denominator of the place value of the rightmost digit.

  3. Reduce the fraction if necessary.

- **Comparing Decimal Numbers**

  Align the decimal points vertically and compare the digits that have the same place value, moving from left to right. The first number with the larger digit in the same value place is the larger number.

- **Reading and Writing Decimal Numbers**

  To name a decimal number, read the digits to the right of the decimal point as though they were not preceded by a decimal point, and then attach the place value of its rightmost digit. Use the word *and* to separate the whole-number part from the decimal or fractional part.

- **Rounding a Decimal Number to a Specified Place Value**

  1. If the specified place value is 10 or more, drop the fractional part and round the resulting whole number.

  2. Otherwise, locate the digit with the specified place value.

  3. If the digit directly to the right is less than 5, keep the digit in step 2 and delete all the digits to the right.

  4. If the digit directly to the right is greater than or equal to 5, increase the digit in step 2 by 1 and delete all the digits to the right.

EXERCISES
ACTIVITY 2.9

1. Using the table on page 160, list the chemical substances chlorine, calcium, iron, magnesium, iodine, cobalt, and manganese in the order in which their amounts are in your body from largest to smallest.

2. **a.** The euro, the basic unit of money in the European Union, was recently worth $1.28817 American dollars. Round to estimate the worth of 1 euro in cents.

   b. To what place did you round in part a?

Exercise numbers appearing in color are answered in the Selected Answers appendix.

3. a. The Canadian dollar was recently worth $0.889597. Round this value to the nearest cent.

   b. Round the value of the Canadian dollar to the nearest dime.

4. a. The Mexican peso was recently worth $0.0917. Round this value to the nearest cent.

   b. Round the value of the peso to the nearest dime.

5. a. Write 0.052 in words.

   b. Write 0.00256 in words.

   c. Write 3402.05891 in words.

   d. Write 64 ten thousandths as a decimal.

   e. Write one hundred twenty-five thousandths as a decimal.

   f. Write two thousand forty-one and six hundred seventy-three ten-thousandths as a decimal.

6. The *New York Times Almanac* reported that U.S. alcohol consumption from 1940–1990 (in gallons of ethanol, per person) was as follows.

YEAR	GALLONS PER PERSON			
	BEER	WINE	SPIRITS	ALL BEVERAGES
1940	0.73	0.16	0.67	1.56
1950	1.04	0.23	0.77	2.04
1960	0.99	0.22	0.86	2.07
1970	1.14	0.27	1.11	2.52
1980	1.38	0.34	1.04	2.76
1990	1.34	0.33	0.78	2.46

a. In which year was beer consumption the highest?

b. Round the amount of all beverage consumption in 1990 to the nearest tenth and write your answer as a mixed number.

c. In which year was the least amount of spirits consumed?

d. Write in words the amount of spirits consumption in 1970.

e. Round the amount of wine consumption to the nearest tenth in the years 1970, 1980, and 1990. Can you use the rounded values to determine when the most wine was consumed? Explain.

7. Circle either true or false for each of the following statements and explain your choice.

a. True or False: 456.77892 < 456.778902

b. True or False: 0.000501 > 0.000510

c. True or False: 7832.00375 rounded to the nearest thousandth is 7832.0038

d. True or False: Seventy-three and four hundred thousandths is written 73.0004.

ACTIVITY 2.10

Think Metric

OBJECTIVES

1. Know the metric prefixes and their decimal values.

2. Convert measurements between metric quantities.

The shop where you have a new job has just received a big contract from overseas. A significant part of your job will involve converting measurements in the English system to the metric system, used by most of the world. To find out more about changing measurements to the metric system, visit *www.metrication.com.*

The Old English system of measurement (for example, feet for length, pounds for weight) used throughout most of the United States was not designed for its computational efficiency. It evolved over time before the decimal system was adopted by Western European cultures. The metric system of measurement, which you may already know something about, was devised to take advantage of our decimal numeration system.

EXAMPLE 1   *A foot is divided into 12 equal parts, 12 inches. But as a fraction of a foot, $\frac{1}{12}$ is not easily expressed as a decimal number. The best you can do is approximate. One inch equals $\frac{1}{12}$ of a foot, or approximately $1 \div 12 \approx 0.08333$ feet. In the metric system, each unit of measurement is divided into 10 equal parts. So 1 meter (a little longer than 3 feet) is divided into 10 decimeters, each decimeter equaling $\frac{1}{10} = 0.1$ meter. In this case, the fraction can be expressed exactly as a simple decimal.*

1. How many decimeters are in 1 meter?

2. If the specifications for a certain part is 8 decimeters long, what is the length in meters?

In general, the metric system of measurement relies upon each unit being divided into 10 equal subunits, which in turn are divided into 10 equal subunits, and so on. The prefix added to the base unit signifies how far the unit has been divided. Starting with the meter, as the basic unit for measuring distance, the following smaller units are defined by Latin prefixes.

UNIT OF LENGTH	FRACTIONAL PART OF A METER
meter	1 meter
decimeter	0.1 meter
centimeter	0.01 meter
millimeter	0.001 meter

3. Complete each statement to show how many of each unit are in 1 meter.

_____ decimeters equal 1 meter.

_____ centimeters equal 1 meter.

_____ millimeters equal 1 meter.

So, in Latin, the prefixes mean exactly what you found in Problem 3: deci- is 10, centi- is 100, and milli- is 1000.

EXAMPLE 2   *Any measurement in one metric unit can be easily converted to another metric unit by simply relocating the decimal point.*
235 centimeters = 2.35 meters since 200 centimeters is the same as 2 meters and 35 centimeters is $\frac{35}{100}$ of 1 meter.

4. Express a distance of 480 centimeters in meters.

Abbreviations are commonly used for all metric units:

Going the Distance

METRIC UNIT OF DISTANCE	ABBREVIATION
meter	m
decimeter	dm
centimeter	cm
millimeter	mm

5. How would you express 2.5 m in centimeters?

6. Since there are 1000 mm in 1 m, how many meters are there in 4500 mm?

7. How many millimeters are there in 1 cm?

8. Which distance is greater, 345 cm or 3400 mm?

In the metric system, each place value is equivalent to the unit of measurement. Each digit can be interpreted as a number of units.

EXAMPLE 3   *The distance 6.358 meters can be expanded to 6 meters + 3 decimeters + 5 centimeters + 8 millimeters.*

9. Expand 7.25 meters, as in Example 3.

Larger metric units are defined using Greek prefixes.

UNIT OF LENGTH	ABBREVIATION	DISTANCE IN METERS
meter	m	1 meter
decameter	dam	10 meters
hectometer	hm	100 meters
kilometer	km	1000 meters

In practice, the decameter and hectometer units are rarely used.

10. How many meters are in a 10-kilometer race?

11. Convert 3450 meters into kilometers.

The metric system is also used to measure the mass of an object and volume. Grams are the basic unit for measuring the mass of an object (basically, how heavy it is). Liters are the basic unit for measuring volume (usually of a liquid). The same prefixes are used to indicate larger and smaller units of measurement.

12. Complete the following tables.

UNIT OF MASS	ABBREVIATION	MASS IN GRAMS
milligram	mg	
centigram	cg	
decigram	dg	
gram	g	1 g
decagram	dag	
hectogram	hg	
kilogram	kg	

UNIT OF VOLUME	ABBREVIATION	VOLUME IN LITERS
milliliter	mℓ	
centiliter	cℓ	
deciliter	dℓ	
liter	ℓ	
decaliter	daℓ	
hectoliter	hℓ	
kiloliter	kℓ	

SUMMARY
ACTIVITY 2.10

1. The basic metric units for measuring distance, mass, and volume are meter, gram, and liter respectively.

2. Larger and smaller units in the metric system are based on the decimal system. The prefix before the basic unit determines the size of the unit, as shown in the table.

UNIT PREFIX (BEFORE METER, GRAM, OR LITER)	ABBREVIATION	SIZE IN BASIC UNITS (METERS, GRAMS, OR LITERS)
milli-	mm, mg, mℓ	0.001
centi-	cm, cg, cℓ	0.01
deci-	dm, dg, dℓ	0.1
deca-	dam, dag, daℓ	10
hecto-	hm, hg, hℓ	100
kilo-	km, kg, kℓ	1000

EXERCISES
ACTIVITY 2.10

1. Convert 3.6 m into cm.

2. Convert 287 cm into m.

3. Convert 1.9 m into mm.

4. Convert 4705 mm into m.

5. Convert 4675 m into km.

6. Convert 3.25 km into m.

7. Convert 42.55 g into cg.

8. Convert 236 g into kg.

9. Convert 83.2 ℓ into mℓ.

10. Convert 742 mℓ into ℓ.

11. Which is greater, 23.67 cm or 237 mm?

12. Which is smaller, 124 mg or 0.15 g?

13. Which is greater, 14.5 mℓ or 0.015 ℓ?

Exercise numbers appearing in color are answered in the Selected Answers appendix.

ACTIVITY 2.11

Dive into Decimals

OBJECTIVES

1. Add and subtract decimals.

2. Compare and interpret decimal numbers.

In Olympic diving, a panel of judges awards a score for each dive. There is a preliminary round and a final round of dives. The preliminary round total and the scores of the five dives in the final round are given below for the top six divers in the women's 10-meter platform event at the 2004 Athens Olympics. The total score determines who wins the gold, silver, and bronze medals for first, second, and third place.

Going for Gold

DIVER	SCORE FOR PRELIMINARY ROUND	SCORES FOR FINAL ROUND					TOTAL SCORE
		DIVE 1	DIVE 2	DIVE 3	DIVE 4	DIVE 5	
Chantelle Newbery (Australia)	198.3	77.4	82.62	72.96	70.29	88.74	
Lishi Lao (China)	203.04	74.7	72.0	80.64	65.34	80.58	
Loudy Tourky (Australia)	192.87	80.1	85.44	55.68	78.21	69.36	
Emilie Heymans (Canada)	187.05	84.48	77.22	61.44	86.7	58.14	
Laura Wilkinson (USA)	194.02	64.32	75.84	79.2	61.38	74.46	
Ting Li (China)	198.33	69.3	83.52	52.2	51.33	91.8	

1. Based *only* on the preliminary round, which divers would have won the gold, silver, and bronze medals?

Adding Decimals

When adding whole numbers, add the digits in each place value position and regroup where needed. Add decimal numbers in a similar way.

2. a. Determine the total of the five dives in the final round for Chantelle Newbery.

b. Describe in words how to line up the digits when adding decimal numbers.

c. How do you locate the decimal point in your answer?

d. Add the preliminary round score for Chantelle Newbery to the total for the five dives in part a. This sum represents the total score for Chantelle in the competition.

3. Determine the total score for each of the six divers listed in the table and record your answer in the appropriate place in the table.

4. a. Which diver won the gold medal?

b. Which diver won the silver medal?

c. Which diver won the bronze medal?

5. Explain why Ting Li did not win the silver medal as predicted in Problem 1.

— PROCEDURE —

Adding Decimal Numbers

1. Line up the place values vertically with decimal points as a guide.
2. Add as usual.
3. Insert the decimal point in the answer directly in line with the decimal points of the numbers being added.

Subtracting Decimals

6. By how many points did the gold medalist win?

The answer to Problem 6 involves the subtraction of decimals. The procedure for subtracting decimal numbers is very similar to the procedure for adding decimal numbers.

7. Use the procedure for adding decimal numbers as a model to write a three-step procedure for subtracting decimal numbers.

8. For each diver, determine the difference between her highest and lowest scores in the final round for each diver.

    a. Chantelle Newbery   **b.** Lishi Lao   **c.** Loudy Tourky

    d. Emilie Heymans   **e.** Laura Wilkinson   **f.** Ting Li

9. Based on the results in Problem 8, which diver was most consistent? Explain.

10. Based *only* on the final round, which diver should have won the gold, silver, and bronze medals?

SUMMARY
ACTIVITY 2.11

Adding or Subtracting Decimals

1. Line up the place values vertically with decimal points as a guide.

2. Add or subtract as usual.

3. Insert the decimal point in the answer directly in line with the decimal points of the numbers being added.

EXERCISES
ACTIVITY 2.11

1. Perform the indicated operation. Verify your calculations with a calculator.

    a. $0.023 + 0.45$ **b.** $5.25 + 0.069 + 12$ **c.** $3.408 + 1.733$

    d. $5.008 - 0.079$ **e.** $0.0044 - 0.056$ **f.** $2.034 - 5.246$

2. You had $149.73 in your bank account on Monday. You wrote a check for $83.69 on Tuesday and two checks for $12.96 and $26.48 on Wednesday. You deposited your paycheck for $212.05 on Thursday and withdrew $50.00 in cash on Friday. What is the balance in your account?

3. You have $20 for groceries. Your shopping list has the following items: bagels ($2.99), cream cheese ($2.99), hummus ($2.69), olives ($4.49), cookies ($3.29), turkey ($2.09), and mustard ($2.49). Is $20 enough for everything on the list? If not, which item should you eliminate so that you will be within your budget?

4. Preparing a meal, you use several cookbooks, some with metric units and others with English units. To make sure you do not make a mistake in measuring, you check a book of math tables for the following conversions.

Measure for Measure

ENGLISH SYSTEM	METRIC SYSTEM
1 fluid ounce	0.02957 liters
1 cup	0.236588 liters
1 pint	0.473176 liters
1 quart	0.946352 liters
1 gallon	3.78541 liters

a. One recipe calls for mixing 1 pint of broth, 1 cup of cream, and 1 ounce of vinegar. What is the total amount of liquid, measured in liters?

b. Another recipe requires 1 gallon of water, 1 quart of milk, 1 one pint of cream. You have a 6-liter pan to cook the liquid ingredients. How much space (in liters) is left in the pan after you have added the three ingredients?

c. You also notice in the book of tables that there are 2 cups in a pint. Is this fact consistent with the information in the table above?

d. Based on the table, how many pints are there in 1 quart? Explain.

5. The results for the top eight countries in the women's gymnastics competition at the 2004 Athens Olympics are summarized in the following table. Each team's final score is the total of the scores for each of the four events: the vault, uneven bars, balance beam, and the floor exercise.

A Balancing Act

COUNTRY	VAULT	UNEVEN BARS	BEAM	FLOOR	TOTAL
Australia	27.449	27.1	26.974	27.324	
China	28.149	27.549	27.244	27.086	
France	28.162	27.011	27.537	27.449	
Romania	28.437	28.136	28.961	28.749	
Russia	28.325	28.137	28.511	28.262	
Spain	27.599	28.412	27.724	27.837	
Ukraine	28.099	28.199	28.024	27.987	
USA	28.387	28.524	28.499	28.174	

a. In each event, determine the order of the top three finishers.

b. Determine the totals for each country. What countries won the gold, silver, and bronze medals?

c. Consider the four event scores for each country. Which team had the largest difference between their lowest- and highest-scoring events? Which team had the smallest difference?

✳ **ACTIVITY 2.12**

Boiling, Freezing, and Financial Aid

OBJECTIVES

1. Add and subtract positive and negative decimal numbers.

2. Interpret and compare decimal numbers.

3. Solve equations of the type $x + b = c$ and $x - b = c$ involving decimal numbers.

Just as water can freeze to become a solid, or boil to become a gas, the elements of the earth can exist in solid, liquid, or gaseous form. For example, the metal mercury is a liquid at room temperature. Mercury boils at 673.9°F and freezes at −38.0°F.

1. What is the difference between the freezing point and the boiling point of mercury?

2. You have some mercury stored at a temperature of 75°F.

   a. By how many degrees Fahrenheit must the mercury be heated for it to boil?

   b. By how many degrees Fahrenheit must the mercury be cooled to freeze it?

3. The use of the element krypton in energy-efficient windows helps meet new energy conservation guidelines. Krypton has a boiling point of −242.1°F. This means that krypton boils and becomes a gas at temperatures above −242.1°F. Is krypton a solid, liquid, or gas at room temperature?

4. You have some krypton stored at −250°F in a special container in your laboratory.

   a. If you heat the krypton by 7.5°F, does it boil? If not, how much more must it be heated to become a gas?

   b. Krypton freezes and becomes a solid below −249.9°F. What is the difference between krypton's boiling and freezing points?

5. The melting points of various elements are given in parts a–d. In each part, circle the element with the higher melting point, then determine the difference between the two melting points.

   a. radon: −96°F, xenon: −169.4°F

   b. fluorine: −363.3°F, nitrogen: −345.8°F

    c. bromine: $-7.2°C$, cesium: $28.4\ °C$

    d. argon: $-308.6°F$, hydrogen: $434.6°F$

6. Complete the table to indicate whether each element is solid (below its freezing point), liquid (between its freezing and boiling points), or gas (above its boiling point) at 82°F.

How Low Can It Go?

ELEMENT	FREEZING POINT	BOILING POINT	STATE AT 82°F
Neon	−416.7°F	−411°F	
Lithium	356.9°F	2248°F	
Francium	80.6°F	1256°F	
Bromine	19.0°F	137.8°F	

Solving Equations Involving Decimal Numbers

In preparing the chemicals for a lab experiment in chemistry class, precise measurements are required. In Problems 7, 8 and 9, represent the unknown quantity with the variable x, and write an equation that accurately describes the situation. Solve the equation to get your answer.

7. You need to have precisely 1.250 grams of sulfur for your experiment. Your lab partner has measured 0.975 gram.

    a. How much more sulfur is needed?

    b. Convert your answer to milligrams.

8. You also need 2.120 grams of copper. This time your lab partner measures 2.314 grams of copper.

    a. How much of this copper needs to be removed for your experiment?

    b. Convert your answer to milligrams.

9. The acidic solution needed for your experiment must measure precisely 0.685 liter.

   a. How much water must be added to 0.325 liter of sulfuric acid and 0.13 liter of hydrochloric acid to result in the desired volume?

   b. Convert your answer to milliliters.

10. Solve each of the following equations for the unknown variable.

   a. $x + 51.78 = 548.2$

   b. $y - 14.5 = 31.75$

   c. $1.637 - z = 9.002$

   d. $0.1013 + t = 0$

SUMMARY **ACTIVITY 2.12**	• Adding or subtracting decimals

• Adding or subtracting decimals

   1. Line up the numbers vertically on their decimal points.

   2. Add or subtract as usual.

   3. Insert the decimal point in the answer directly in line with the decimal points of the numbers being added.

• To solve equations of the form $x + b = c$, add the opposite of b to both sides of the equation to obtain $x = c - b$.

• To solve equations of the form $x - b = c$, add b to both sides of the equation to obtain $x = b + c$.

1. Use the table on page 178 to answer the following questions.

   a. Determine the difference between the boiling point and freezing point of neon.

   b. Determine the difference between the freezing points of lithium and neon.

   c. Determine the difference between the boiling points of lithium and neon.

2. Perform the indicated operations. Verify by using your calculator.

   a. $30.6 + 1.19$ **b.** $5.205 + 5.971$ **c.** $1.78 - 1.865$

   d. $0.298 + 0.113$ **e.** $2.242 - 1.015$ **f.** $-18.27 + 13.45$

   g. $-20.11 - 0.294$ **h.** $-10.078 - 46.2$ **i.** $15.59 - 0.374$

   j. $-876.1 - 73.63$ **k.** $0.0023 - 0.00658$ **l.** $-0.372 + 0.1701$

3. You have a $95.13 balance in your checking account. You will deposit your paycheck for $125.14 as soon as you get it 3 days from now. You need to write some checks now to pay some bills. You write checks for $25.48, $69.11, and $33.15. Unfortunately, the checks are cashed before you deposit your paycheck. The bank pays the $33.15 check but charges a $15.00 fee. What is your account balance after you deposit your paycheck?

4. One milligram is one thousandth of a gram.

   a. Express 1 milligram as a part of a gram by writing one thousandth as a decimal.

   b. Your father takes 40 milligrams (mg) per day of Zocor, a cholesterol-reducing medication. Express 40 milligrams as a decimal part of a gram.

   c. Today, your father has taken 0.010 gram of Zocor. Let x represent the number of grams of Zocor he still needs today. Write an equation and solve for x.

5. A full bottle of Joy detergent contains 1.75 pints. Your son empties a partially used bottle of Joy into a half-pint container. The amount fits perfectly! Choose a variable to represent the amount of detergent already used, in pints. Write an equation for this situation, and solve for your variable, expressing the answer as a decimal.

6. A tube of Colgate Whitening Toothpaste and Mouthwash contains 4.6 ounces. Last month, your family used up a 7.5-ounce tube of toothpaste. Let t be the number of additional ounces you would need for your family this month. Write an equation and solve for t.

7. A dental floss package you have contains 91.4 meters of cinnamon-flavored dental floss. You also have a small package of dental floss that you notice contains only 11 meters of floss. Let x be the difference in length for the two kinds. Write an equation and solve for x.

8. Arm & Hammer baking soda deodorant weighs 56.7 grams. Sure Clear Dry deodorant weighs 45.0 grams. Let x be the difference in weight. Write an equation and solve for x.

9. Solve each equation for the given variable.

   a. $1.04 + 0.293 + x = 5.3$

b. $0.01003 - x = 0.0091$

c. $y - 7.623 = 84.212$

d. $1.626 + b = 14.503$

e. $x + 8.28 = 3.4$

f. $0.0114 + z = 0.005 + 0.0101$

10. You need precisely 1.25 grams of mercury for a lab experiment. If you have 0.76 gram of mercury in your test tube, how much more mercury do you need? Write an equation to solve for this unknown amount.

11. The human body requires many minerals and vitamins. The minimum daily requirement of magnesium has been set at 400 milligrams. If your intake today has been 0.15 gram, how many milligrams of magnesium do you still need to meet the minimum daily requirement? Write an equation to solve for this unknown amount.

What Have I Learned?

1. How do you determine which of two decimal numbers is the larger?

2. Why can zeros written to the right of the decimal point and after the right-most nonzero digit be omitted without changing its value?

3. **a.** Round 0.31 to the nearest tenth.

   b. Determine the difference between 0.31 and 0.3

   c. Determine the difference between 0.4 and 0.31

   d. Which of the two differences you calculated is smaller, the one in part b or in part c?

   e. In the light of your answer to part d, give a justification for the rounding off procedure.

4. Which step in the process of adding or subtracting decimals must be done first and very carefully?

5. Are the rules for addition or subtraction of decimals different from those of whole numbers?

CLUSTER 3   How Can I Practice?

1. Write the value of the given decimal number.

   a. 3495.065

   b. 71,008.0049

   c. 13,053.3891

   d. 6487.08649

2. Write the following in decimal notation.

   a. Eighty-two thousand, seventy-six and four hundred eight ten-thousandths.

   b. Six hundred eleven thousand, seven hundred twelve and sixty-eight hundred-thousandths.

   c. Three million, five thousand, ninety-two and forty-one thousandths.

   d. Forty-nine thousand, eight hundred nine and six thousand four hundred thirteen hundred-thousandths.

   e. Nine billion, five and twenty-eight hundredths.

   f. Ninety-three million, five hundred sixty-four thousand, seven hundred and forty-nine hundredths.

3. Rearrange the following decimals from smallest to the largest.

   a. 0.9   0.909   0.099   0.0099   0.9900

   b. 0.384   0.0987   0.392   0.561   0.0983

   c. 1.49   1.23   1.795   0.842   0.01423

   d. 0.0838   0.8383   0.3883   0.00888   0.3838

4. a. Round 639.438 to the nearest hundredth.

   b. Round 31.2695 to the nearest thousandth.

   c. Round 182.09998 to the nearest ten-thousandth.

   d. Round 59.999 to the nearest tenth.

5. Add the following decimals. Verify by using your calculator.

   a. $3.28 + 17.063 + 0.084$

   b. $628.13 + 271.78 + 68.456$

   c. $9628.13 + 271.78 + 6814.56 + 13.91$

   d. $171.004 + 18.028 + 51.68 + 4.5$

   e. $-69.73 + (-198.32)$

   f. $-131.02 + (-7.689)$

   g. $18.62 - 29.999$

   h. $-13.58 + 6.729$

   i. $258.1204 + 49.0683 + 71.099$

   j. $8171.004 + 4318.028 + 51.683 + 4.495$

6. Subtract the following decimals. Verify by using your calculator.

   a. $100 - 71.998$ **b.** $212.085 - 63.0498$

   c. $329.79 - 84.6591$ **d.** $8000.49 - 6583.725$

   e. $678.146 - 39.08$ **f.** $-72.43 - 8.058$

   g. $49.62 - (-6.088)$ **h.** $-18.173 - 12.59$

7. Evaluate.

   a. $x + y$, where $x = -7.29$ and $y = 4.8$

   b. $h + k$, where $h = -6.13$ and $k = -5.017$

   c. $x - y$, where $x = -13.478$ and $y = 7.399$

   d. $p - r$, where $p = -4.802$ and $r = -19.99$

8. Solve each of the equations for x.

   a. $x + 23.49 = -71.11$

   b. $x - 13.14 = 69.17$

   c. $-28.99 + x = -55.03$

   d. $35.17 + x = 12.19$

9. Your hourly salary was increased from $6.75 to $7.04. How much was your raise?

10. Convert 3872 mg to grams.   11. Convert 7.34 km to meters.

12. Convert 392 mℓ to liters.   13. Convert 0.64 kg to grams.

14. Convert 4.5 km to mm.   15. Convert 0.014 liter to mℓ.

16. The boundaries around a parcel of land measure 378 m, 725 m, 489 m, and 821 m. What is the perimeter, measured in kilometers?

17. You have 670 grams of carbon, but need precisely 2.25 kg for your experiment. How much more carbon do you need?

18. You start with 1.275 liters of solution in a beaker. Into four separate test tubes you pour 45 milliliters, 75 milliliters, 90 milliliters, and 110 milliliters of the solution. How much solution is left in your original beaker?

19. To prepare for you new job, you spent $25.37 for a shirt, $39.41 for pants, and $52.04 for shoes. How much did you spend?

20. The gross monthly income for your new job is $2105.96. You have the following monthly deductions: $311.93 for federal income tax, $64.72 for state income tax, and $161.11 for Social Security. What is your take-home pay?

The bracketed numbers following each concept indicate the activity in which the concept is discussed.

CONCEPT / SKILL	DESCRIPTION	EXAMPLE
The four steps of problem solving [2.1]	**Step 1.** Understand the problem.	Read the problem completely and carefully, draw a diagram, ask questions.
	Step 2. Develop a strategy for solving the problem.	Identify and list every quantity, known and unknown. Write an equation that relates the known quantities and the unknown quantity.
	Step 3. Execute your strategy to solve the problem.	Solve the equation.
	Step 4. Check your solution for correctness.	Is your answer reasonable? Is your answer correct?
Comparing integers [2.2]	The numbers increase from left to right on a number line. The further to the left a number is, the smaller it is.	$-18 < -3$ $-32 < 1$
Absolute Value [2.2]	The distance of a number from zero on the number line represents its absolute value. The absolute value of a number is always nonnegative.	$\lvert 0 \rvert = 0$ $\lvert -17 \rvert = 17$ $\lvert 13 \rvert = 13$
Adding/Subtracting Integers [2.3]	1. Rules for adding integers:	
	a. When adding two numbers with the same sign, add the absolute values of the numbers. The sign of the sum is the same as the sign of the numbers being added.	$4 + (+ 7) = 4 + 7 = 11$ $-3 + (-5) = -8$
	b. When adding two numbers with different signs, find their absolute values and then subtract the smaller from the larger. The sign of the sum is the sign of the number with the larger absolute value.	$-5 + (+7) = 2$ $+10 + (-13) = -3$

	2. Rules for subtracting integers: To subtract two integers, change the operation of subtraction to addition and change the number being subtracted to its opposite; then follow the rules for adding integers.	$-13 - (-5) =$
		    $-13 + 5 = -8$
		 $-11 - (+7) =$
		    $-11 + (-7) = -18$

CONCEPT / SKILL	DESCRIPTION	EXAMPLE
Evaluating expressions [2.4]	To evaluate an expression, substitute the given number for the letter. Perform the arithmetic, using the order of operations.	Evaluate $a - b$, where $a = 15$, $b = -7$. $15 - (-7) = 15 + 7 = 22$
Solving equations of the form $x + b = c$ and $x - b = c$ [2.4], [2.5], [2.8], [2.12]	• For $x + b = c$, add the opposite of b to both sides of the equation to obtain $x = c - b$. • For $x - b = c$, add b to both sides of the equation to obtain $x = c + b$.	$\begin{aligned} x + 3 &= 19 \\ -3 \quad &-3 \\ \hline x &= 16 \end{aligned}$ $\begin{aligned} x - 4 &= -2 \\ x - 4 + 4 &= -2 + 4 = 2 \\ x &= 2 \end{aligned}$

Points plotted on a rectangular coordinate system [2.5]

An ordered pair is always given in the form of (x, y), where x is the input and y is the output. The x-axis (horizontal) and the y-axis (vertical) determine a coordinate plane, divided into four quadrants numbered counterclockwise from the upper right.

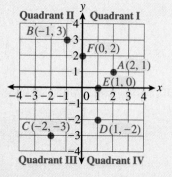

QUADRANT	X COORDINATE	Y COORDINATE
I	+	+
II	−	+
III	−	−
IV	+	−

A: $(2, 1)$
B: $(-1, 3)$
C: $(-2, -3)$
D: $(1, -2)$
E: $(1, 0)$
F: $(0, 2)$

Greatest common factor (GCF) [2.6]	The greatest common factor of two numbers is the largest factor of both numbers.	GCF of 18 and 12 is 6.
Equivalent fractions [2.6]	To write an equivalent fraction, multiply or divide both the numerator and the denominator of a given fraction by the same number.	$\dfrac{4}{5} = \dfrac{?}{25}$ $\dfrac{4}{5} \cdot 1 = \dfrac{4}{5} \cdot \dfrac{5}{5}$ $= \dfrac{20}{25}$
Reducing fractions [2.6]	To reduce a fraction to lowest terms, divide the numerator and denominator by their greatest common factor (GCF).	$\dfrac{6}{12} = \dfrac{6}{12} \div 1$ $= \dfrac{6}{12} \div \dfrac{6}{6}$ $= \dfrac{6 \div 6}{12 \div 6} = \dfrac{1}{2}$

CONCEPT / SKILL	DESCRIPTION	EXAMPLE
Converting mixed numbers into improper fractions [2.6]	To convert a mixed number into an improper fraction, multiply the whole-number part by the denominator and add the numerator. The result is the numerator of the improper fraction. The denominator remains unchanged.	$6\dfrac{2}{3} = \dfrac{6 \cdot 3 + 2}{3}$ $= \dfrac{20}{3}$
Converting improper fractions to a mixed number [2.6]	To convert an improper fraction to a mixed number, divide the numerator by the denominator. The quotient is the integer part of the mixed number. The remainder becomes the numerator and the denominator is unchanged.	$\dfrac{27}{4}; \quad \begin{array}{r} 6 \\ 4\overline{)27} \\ -24 \\ \hline 3 \end{array}$ $\dfrac{27}{4} = 6\dfrac{3}{4}$
Least common denominator (LCD) [2.6], [2.8]	To determine the LCD, identify the largest denominator of the fractions involved. Look at multiples of the larger denominator. The smallest multiple that is divisible by all the denominators involved is the LCD.	Find the LCD of $\dfrac{1}{12}, \dfrac{5}{18}$. The largest denominator is 18. Multiples of 18 are 18, 36, 54, ... So the LCD is 36.
Comparing fractions [2.6]	Write the fractions as equivalent fractions with a common denominator. The larger fraction is the one with the larger numerator.	Compare $\dfrac{6}{7}, \dfrac{8}{9}$. $\dfrac{6}{7} = \dfrac{54}{63}; \quad \dfrac{8}{9} = \dfrac{56}{63}$ $56 > 54$ $\dfrac{8}{9} > \dfrac{6}{7}$
Adding and subtracting fractional numbers with the same denominator [2.7]	• If you have two fractions with common denominators, you add and subtract them by adding or subtracting the numerators, leaving the denominator the same. • If you have an improper fraction as a result, convert it to a mixed number. • If the fraction in your answer is not in lowest terms, reduce it. • If you have a mixed number, you add or subtract the whole part separately.	$2\dfrac{13}{15} + 1\dfrac{7}{15}$ $= 3\dfrac{13+7}{15}$ $= 3\dfrac{20}{15}$ $\begin{array}{r} 1 \\ 15\overline{)20} \\ -15 \\ \hline 5 \end{array}$ $3 + 1\dfrac{5}{15} = 4\dfrac{5}{15} = 4\dfrac{1}{3}$
Adding and subtracting fractions with different denominators [2.8]	First find the LCD, then convert each fraction to an equivalent fraction, using the LCD you found. Add or subtract the numerators, leaving the LCD in the denominator. If you get an improper fraction, convert to a mixed number. If the fraction is not in lowest terms, reduce it.	Add: $\dfrac{3}{4} + \dfrac{5}{7}$ $\dfrac{3}{4} = \dfrac{21}{28}$ $+\dfrac{5}{7} = \dfrac{20}{28}$ $\overline{\qquad\quad \dfrac{41}{28}} = 1\dfrac{13}{28}$

CONCEPT / SKILL	DESCRIPTION	EXAMPLE
Converting a decimal to a fraction or a mixed number [2.9]	1. Write the nonzero integer part of the number and drop the decimal point. 2. Write the fractional part of the number as the numerator of a new fraction, whose denominator is the same as the place value of the rightmost digit. If possible, reduce the fraction.	3.0025 $= 3\frac{25}{10,000}$ $= 3\frac{1}{400}$
Comparing decimals [2.9], [2.11], [2.12]	To compare two or more decimals, line up the decimal points and compare the digits that have the same place value, moving from left to right. The first number with the largest digit in the same "value place" is the largest number.	Compare 0.035 and 0.038 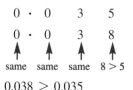 $0.038 > 0.035$
Reading and writing decimals [2.9]	To name a decimal number, read the digits to the right of the decimal point as an integer, and then attach the place value of its rightmost digit. Use "and" to separate the integer part from the decimal or fractional part.	• Write 3.42987 in words. three and forty-two thousand nine hundred eighty-seven hundred thousandths • Write "seven and sixty-nine thousandths" in standard form. 7.069
Rounding decimals [2.9]	1. Locate the digit with the specified place value. 2. If the digit directly to its right is less than 5, keep the digit that is in the specified place and delete all the digits to the right. 3. If the digit directly to its right is 5 or greater, increase this digit by 1 and delete all the digits to the right. 4. If the specified place value is located in the integer part, proceed as instructed in step 2 or step 3. Then insert trailing zeros to the right and up to the decimal point as place holders. Drop the decimal point.	Round 0.985 to the nearest hundredth. *Answer:* 0.99 Round 0.653 to the nearest hundredth. *Answer:* 0.65 Round 424.6 to the nearest ten. *Answer:* 420

CONCEPT / SKILL	DESCRIPTION	EXAMPLE

The metric system [2.10]

Basic metric units for measuring:

    distance : meter (m)

    mass : gram (g)

    volume : liter (ℓ)

Larger and smaller units in the metric system are based on the decimal system. The prefix before the basic unit determines the size of the unit, as shown in the table.

UNIT PREFIX	ABBR.	SIZE IN BASIC UNITS
milli-	m-	0.001
centi-	c-	0.01
deci-	d-	0.1
deca-	da-	10
hecto-	h-	100
kilo-	k-	1000

Example:

1000 mm = 1 m

100 cm = 1 m

10 dm = 1 m

0.001 m = 1 mm

0.01 m = 1 cm

0.1 m = 1 dm

1000 g = 1 kg

0.001 kg = 1 g

100 mℓ = 0.1 ℓ

243 mℓ = 0.243 ℓ

6.8 ℓ = 6800 mℓ

735 cm = 0.735 m

3.92 km = 3920 m

Adding and subtracting decimals [2.11], [2.12]

1. Rewrite the numbers vertically, lining up the decimal points.
2. Add or subtract as usual.
3. Insert the decimal point in the answer directly in line with the decimal points of the numbers being added.

Add: 3.689 + 41 + 12.07

```
   3.689
  41.000    Assume zeros for any
 +12.070    numbers not shown.
  ------
  56.759    Decimal point carries
            down.
```

1. Solve the following problem by applying the four steps of problem solving. Use the strategy of solving an algebra equation.

   Your average reading speed is 160 words per minute. There are approximately 800 words on each page of the textbook you need to read. Approximately how long will it take you to read 50 pages of your textbook?

2. Determine the absolute value for each of the following.

   a. $|15|$ **b.** $|23|$ **c.** $|0|$ **d.** $|-42|$ **e.** $|67|$

3. Perform the indicated operations.

   a. $4 - (+13)$ **b.** $11 - (+17)$ **c.** $5 - (-11)$

   d. $-2 + (-12)$ **e.** $27 + (-15)$ **f.** $15 + (-23)$

   g. $-18 + (-35)$ **h.** $-27 + (+21)$

4. Evaluate.

   a. $x - y$, where $x = 3$ and $y = -3$

   b. $-x + y$, where $x = 5$ and $y = -2$

   c. $-x - y$, where $x = -3$ and $y = -7$

   d. $x + y$, where $x = -2$ and $y = -5$

5. Solve for x.

   a. $x - 15 = -17$ **b.** $x + 7 = -12$ **c.** $x + 18 = 3$

   d. $-11 + x = 32$ **e.** $-23 + x = -61$

Answers to all Gateway exercises are included in the Selected Answers appendix.

195

6. Translate the following into equations where *x* represents the number. Then solve for *x*.

   a. A number increased by eighteen is negative seven.

   b. The sum of a number and eleven is twenty-nine.

   c. Fifteen increased by a number is negative twenty-eight.

   d. The difference of a number and twenty is thirty-nine.

   e. A number subtracted from eight is twelve.

   f. Seventeen subtracted from a number is forty-two.

   g. Thirteen less than a number is negative thirty-four.

7. Convert each to a mixed number.

   a. $\dfrac{63}{5}$

   b. $\dfrac{63}{7}$

   c. $\dfrac{77}{15}$

   d. $\dfrac{77}{13}$

8. Convert each to an improper fraction.

   a. $4\dfrac{3}{5}$

   b. $2\dfrac{5}{7}$

   c. $5\dfrac{2}{11}$

   d. $10\dfrac{3}{8}$

9. Compare the following fractions.

   a. $\dfrac{3}{7}\ \square\ \dfrac{2}{5}$

   b. $\dfrac{4}{11}\ \square\ \dfrac{1}{3}$

c. $\dfrac{4}{7} \ \square \ \dfrac{5}{8}$

d. $\dfrac{6}{11} \ \square \ \dfrac{1}{12}$

e. $\dfrac{7}{10} \ \square \ \dfrac{5}{8}$

f. $\dfrac{8}{11} \ \square \ \dfrac{3}{4}$

10. Perform the indicated operations. Leave your answer in lowest terms.

a. $\dfrac{6}{7} + \dfrac{5}{7}$

b. $-\dfrac{13}{15} + \dfrac{7}{15}$

c. $\dfrac{9}{11} - \dfrac{2}{11}$

d. $\dfrac{5}{8} + \dfrac{6}{7}$

e. $\dfrac{11}{13} + \dfrac{25}{39}$

f. $-\dfrac{5}{12} + \left(-\dfrac{17}{18}\right)$

g. $-\dfrac{4}{5} - \left(-\dfrac{13}{15}\right)$

h. $\dfrac{6}{11} - \left(+\dfrac{20}{33}\right)$

11. Perform the indicated operations. Leave your answer in lowest terms.

a. $14\dfrac{5}{7} + 10\dfrac{2}{7}$

b. $12\dfrac{1}{9} + 7\dfrac{5}{9}$

c. $9\dfrac{3}{20} + 4\dfrac{13}{20}$

d. $13\dfrac{5}{6} + 10\dfrac{7}{8}$

e. $11\dfrac{1}{9} + 8\dfrac{5}{6}$

f. $12\dfrac{3}{20} + 4\dfrac{3}{5}$

g. $3\dfrac{5}{8} + 7\dfrac{3}{4}$

h. $7\dfrac{5}{8} - 2\dfrac{1}{8}$

i. $23\dfrac{11}{13} - 12\dfrac{9}{13}$

j. $4\dfrac{15}{16} - 3\dfrac{3}{16}$

k. $10\dfrac{5}{9} - 4\dfrac{7}{12}$

l. $4\dfrac{1}{3} - 2\dfrac{1}{6}$

m. $10\dfrac{4}{5} - 4\dfrac{9}{10}$

n. $12\dfrac{3}{4} - 5\dfrac{5}{7}$

o. $8 - 3\dfrac{2}{3}$

p. $5\dfrac{3}{7} - 2$

q. $-3\dfrac{3}{10} + 7\dfrac{4}{5}$

r. $-5\dfrac{5}{9} + \left(-8\dfrac{5}{6}\right)$

s. $6\dfrac{3}{8} - \left(+8\dfrac{1}{6}\right)$ **t.** $10\dfrac{5}{9} - \left(-4\dfrac{3}{5}\right)$ **u.** $-11\dfrac{5}{9} + \left(-1\dfrac{7}{12}\right)$

v. $-15\dfrac{4}{9} - \left(-3\dfrac{1}{6}\right)$ **w.** $-7 - \dfrac{4}{5}$

12. Solve for x.

a. $x - 2\dfrac{5}{8} = 7\dfrac{1}{6}$ **b.** $x + 13\dfrac{7}{9} = 6\dfrac{3}{7}$ **c.** $-18\dfrac{3}{4} + x = -21\dfrac{1}{3}$

d. $16\dfrac{3}{11} + x = -17\dfrac{5}{22}$ **e.** $x + 17\dfrac{9}{14} = -6\dfrac{3}{7}$ **f.** $x - 3\dfrac{7}{12} = 5\dfrac{5}{18}$

13. Write the following numbers in words.

a. 849,083,659.0725

b. 32,004,389,412.23418

c. 235,000,864.587234

d. 784,632,541.00819

14. Write the following numbers in decimal notation.

a. Sixty-five million, seventy-three thousand, four hundred twelve and six hundred eighty-two ten-thousandths.

b. Eighty-nine billion, five hundred forty-nine thousand, six hundred thirteen and forty-eight thousandths.

c. Seven million, six hundred twelve thousand, eleven and five thousand, six hundred one hundred-thousandths.

15. Convert the following decimals to fractions and reduce to lowest terms.

    a. 0.0085   **b.** 3.834

    c. 4.25   **d.** 15.0125

    e. 7.12

16. Round 692,895.098442 to the nearest specified place values.

    a. hundredth   **b.** thousandth

    c. tenth   **d.** whole number

    e. hundreds   **f.** ten thousands

17. Rearrange the following groups of decimal numbers in order from smallest to largest:

    a. 4.078   4.78   4.0078   4.0708   4.00078   4.07008

    b. 3.00805   3.085   3.0085   3.00085   3.0805   3.85

    c. 8.046   8.0046   8.46   8.0406   8.00046   8.00406

18. Perform the indicated operations.

    a. $-16.78 + 4.29 + (-5.13)$

    b. $-15.79 + (-18.63) + (+63.49)$

    c. $-23.19 - (+8.93)$

    d. $-42.78 - (-19.41)$

    e. $-23.58 - (+17.39)$

19. Evaluate.

    a. $L + W$, where $L = 12.68$ and $W = 7.05$

    b. $P - D$, where $P = 98.99$ and $D = 14.85$

c. $K + L$, where $K = -17.32$ and $L = -4.099$

d. $S - T$, where $S = 3.98$ and $T = 0.125$

20. Solve for x.

    a. $x + 23.14 = 48.69$ **b.** $17.32 + x = -28.73$

    c. $x - 16.39 = 32.11$ **d.** $x - 22.03 = -41$

    e. $-18.79 + x = -11.32$

21. a. The temperature in the morning was $-9°$F and by noon the temperature increased by $3°$F. Determine the temperature at noon.

    b. The temperature at noon was $3°$F and by 7 P.M. the temperature dropped $5°$F. Determine the 7 P.M. temperature.

    c. The temperature in the morning was $-8°$F and by noon it was $-3°$F. Determine the change in the temperature.

    d. The temperature in the morning was $-9°$F and the evening temperature was $-14°$F. What was the change in the temperature?

22. You want to install a wallpaper border in your bedroom. The bedroom is rectangular, with length $12\frac{5}{12}$ and width $8\frac{1}{4}$ feet. How much wallpaper border would you use? (Remember that to find the perimeter of a rectangle you add up the four sides.)

23. On Sunday morning you went for your usual run. On the route you stopped and bought a newspaper and bagels. The newsstand is $\frac{1}{3}$ mile from your house. The distance from the newsstand to your favorite bagel shop is approximately $1\frac{3}{5}$ miles. How many miles did you run each way?

24. Your living room wall is 14 feet wide. You have a couch that is $6\frac{1}{3}$ feet long that is placed against the wall. You also have two end tables $2\frac{1}{8}$ feet wide on each side of the couch. You saw a bookcase that is $2\frac{5}{6}$ feet wide that you would like to buy, but you are not sure if it would fit in the remaining wall space. Would it?

25. Your new TV cost $179.99. There was a sales tax of $14.85. What was the final price of the TV?

26. You buy $18.35 worth of groceries and pay for them with a $20 bill. How much change would you receive?

27. A dress that usually sells for $67.95 is marked down by $10.19. What is the sale price of the dress?

28. A cook making $1504.75 a month has deductions of $157.32 for federal income tax, $115.11 for Social Security, and $45.12 for state income tax. What is the cook's take-home pay?

29. You had $62.05 in your bank account on Monday morning. On Tuesday, you wrote two checks for $25.12 and $13.59. On Wednesday, your friend who owes you $40 returned the money, and you deposited it in your bank account. On Thursday, knowing that you would deposit your paycheck on Friday, you wrote two checks for $117.50 and $85.38. On Friday, you deposited your paycheck for $359.13. When all your checks clear, how much money will you have in your bank account?

30. Plot the following points on the coordinate system:

    a. $(4, 3)$ **b.** $(-3, 4)$ **c.** $(0, -3)$

    d. $(-2, -3)$ **e.** $(-2, 0)$ **f.** $(6, -1)$

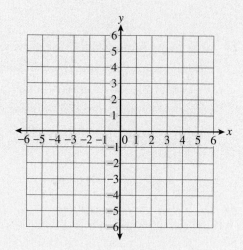

31. Convert 795 mg into grams.

32. Convert 2.75 km into meters.

33. Convert 25 ml into liters.

34. Convert 1.05 kg into grams.

35. Convert 2.35 km into mm.

36. Convert 0.085 liters into ml.

37. The boundaries around a parcel of land measure 455 m, 806 m, 423 m, and 795 m. What is the perimeter, measured in kilometers?

38. You have 285 grams of sulfur, but need precisely 1.25 kg for your experiment. How much more sulfur do you need?

39. You start with 1.92 liters of solution in a beaker. Into three separate test tubes you pour 95 mℓ, 150 mℓ, and 180 mℓ of the solution. How much solution is left in your original beaker? Let x represent the number of milliliters left in the original beaker.

CHAPTER 3

MULTIPLICATION AND DIVISION OF RATIONAL NUMBERS

Have you ever wondered how your college grade point average is computed? The skills involved are the same as those necessary to answer financial questions, to tile a bathroom, or to calculate a baseball player's batting average.

In Chapter 3, you will learn the skills needed for solving problems involving multiplying and dividing integers, fractions, and decimals.

CLUSTER 1	**Multiplying and Dividing Integers**

✳ ACTIVITY 3.1

Are You Physically Fit?

OBJECTIVES

1. Multiply and divide integers.

2. Perform calculations involving a sequence of operations.

3. Apply exponents to integers.

4. Identify properties of calculations involving multiplication and division with zero.

As a member of a health-and-fitness club, you have a special diet and exercise program developed by the club's registered dietitian and your personal trainer. Your weight gain (positive value) or weight loss (negative value) over the first 6 weeks of the program is recorded in the following table.

Weight and See

NUMBER OF WEEKS	1	2	3	4	5	6
CHANGE IN WEIGHT (LB.)	−3	−3	4	−3	−3	4

1. a. Counting only those weeks in which you gained weight, what was your weight gain during the 6-week period? Write your answer as an integer (signed number) and in words.

   b. Counting only those weeks in which you lost weight, what was your weight loss during the 6-week period? Write your answer as an integer (signed number) and in words.

c. Explain how you calculated the answers to parts a and b.

d. At the end of the first six weeks, what is the total change in your weight?

There are two ways to determine the answers to parts a and b of Problem 1. One way to determine the increase in weight in part a is by repeated addition:

$$4 + 4 = 8 \text{ lb.}$$

A second way uses the fact that multiplication is repeated addition. So, the increase in weight is also determined by the product:

$$4(2) = 8 \text{ lb.}$$

Similarly in part b, the weight loss is determined by repeated addition:

$$-3 + (-3) + (-3) + (-3) = -12.$$

Again similar to part a, multiplication can be used to determine the weight loss:

$$(-3)(4) = -12.$$

In general, **the product of a negative number and a positive number is negative.** This is true when a negative number is multiplied by a positive number, as Problem 1 showed. It is also true when a positive number is multiplied by a negative number. For example, the product, $3(-2)$ may be interpreted as adding two instances of 3 **but in the negative direction,** resulting in a negative product. That means $3(-2) = -6$.

2. Multiply each of the following; then check by using your calculator.

   a. $5(-2)$ b. $(-2)(5)$ c. $7(-8)$

   d. $-8(7)$ e. $6(-4)$ f. $-4(6)$

3. Compare parts a and b in Problem 2 as follows:

a. Compare the order of the factors. Are they the same or different?

b. Now compare the products. Do they have the same sign?

c. What conclusion can you make about multiplying a negative and positive number?

Problem 3 illustrates the fact that multiplication of integers is commutative. For example,

$$3(-2) = (-2)(3) = -6.$$

4. Compare parts c and d in Problem 2 and write what you observe. Do the same for parts e and f.

So far in this activity, you have seen that the product of two positive integers is positive and that the product of a positive integer and a negative integer is negative. One more case has to be considered to answer the question: What is the sign of the product of two negative integers? The following problem suggests a pattern that leads to the answer.

5. a. Fill in the blanks in the following table to complete the pattern begun in the first three lines:

$4(-2)$	-8
$3(-2)$	-6
$2(-2)$	-4
$1(-2)$	
$0(-2)$	
$-1(-2)$	
$-2(-2)$	
$-3(-2)$	
$-4(-2)$	
$-5(-2)$	

   b. What does the pattern you completed suggest about the sign of the product of two negative integers? Illustrate with a specific example.

6. In each of the following, multiply the two integers. Then check your answer using your calculator.

   a. $(-2)(-4)$ b. $-6(-7)$ c. $(-1)(4)$

   d. $5(-8)$ e. $(-3)(-9)$ f. $(-12)(3)$

Product of Two Integers

Rule 1:   The product of two integers with the same sign is positive.

$$(+)(+) = (+) \rightarrow (4)(5) = 20$$
$$(-)(-) = (+) \rightarrow (-4)(-5) = 20$$

Rule 2:   The product of two integers with opposite signs is negative.

$$(-)(+) = (-) \rightarrow (-4)(5) = -20$$
$$(+)(-) = (-) \rightarrow (4)(-5) = -20$$

Division of Integers

Your friend gained 15 pounds over a 5-week period. If his weight gain was the same each week, then the calculation $15 \div 5 = 3$ or $\dfrac{15}{5} = 3$ shows that he gained 3 pounds each week. You can check that a gain of 3 pounds per week is correct by multiplying 5 by 3 to obtain 15. In other words, the quotient $\dfrac{15}{5}$ is 3 because $5 \cdot 3 = 15$ by a multiplication check.

Another friend lost 15 pounds over the same 5-week period, losing the same amount each week. The calculation $-15 \div 5 = -3$ (or $\dfrac{-15}{5} = -3$) shows that she lost 3 pounds each week. The quotient $\dfrac{-15}{5}$ is -3. The product $5(-3) = -15$ shows the quotient $\dfrac{-15}{3}$ has to be -3.

7. Evaluate each of the following. Use the multiplication check to verify your answers.

   a. $27 \div 9$ **b.** $-32 \div 8$ **c.** $18 \div (-2)$

   d. $\dfrac{-10}{5}$ **e.** $\dfrac{21}{-7}$ **f.** $\dfrac{38}{2}$

8. **a.** Use the multiplication check for division to obtain the only reasonable answer for $(-22) \div (-11)$.

   b. What rule does part a suggest for dividing a negative integer by a negative integer?

c. Evaluate each of the following and verify your answer by the multiplication check.

    i. $(-42) \div (-7)$ **ii.** $\dfrac{-9}{-3}$ **iii.** $(-7) \div (-1)$

9. a. The sign of the quotient of two integers with the same sign is

    _____.

  b. The sign of the quotient of two integers with opposite signs is

    _____.

Quotient of Two Integers

Rule 1: The quotient of two integers with the same sign is positive.

$$\frac{(+)}{(+)} = (+) \longrightarrow \frac{12}{4} = 3$$

$$\frac{(-)}{(-)} = (+) \longrightarrow \frac{-12}{-4} = 3$$

Rule 2: The quotient of two integers with opposite signs is negative.

$$\frac{(-)}{(+)} = (-) \longrightarrow \frac{-12}{4} = -3$$

$$\frac{(+)}{(-)} = (-) \longrightarrow \frac{12}{-4} = -3$$

Calculations Involving a Combination of Operations

10. A friend joins you on your health-and-fitness program. The following table lists his weight loss and gain during a 5-week period.

WEEK	1	2	3	4	5
WEIGHT CHANGE (LB.)	−4	−3	2	−3	−2

Your friend computes his average weight change by adding the weekly changes in weight and then dividing the result by the number of weeks. You volunteer to check his results.

a. What is his change in weight for the 5 weeks?

b. What is your friend's average weight change for the 5-week period?

c. Did your friend have an average gain or an average loss of weight during the 5-week period? Explain.

11. The following table gives weight gains and losses for 16 persons during a given week.

NUMBER OF PERSONS	WEIGHT CHANGE
2	−5
3	−4
4	−3
2	−2
1	0
3	1
1	3

a. What is the weight change of the group during the given week?

b. What is the average weight change for the group of 16 persons?

c. Does this average change represent a weight gain or loss?

12. a. What is the sign of the product $(-3)(-5)(-7)(-2)$? Explain.

b. What is the sign of the product of $(-1)(-1)(-1)(-1)(-1)(-1)(-1)$? Explain.

c. If you multiplied 16 factors of -1, what would be the sign of the product?

d. What can you conclude about the sign of a product with an odd number of factors with negative signs?

e. What can you conclude about the sign of a product with an even number of factors with negative signs?

13. Perform the indicated operations. Check the results using your calculator.

    a. $-5 \cdot (-4)$ **b.** $-50 \div (-10)$

    c. $2 \cdot 6$ **d.** $6 \div 3$

    e. $-3(-6)(-2)$ **f.** $5(-3)(-4)$

    g. $-15 \div -3$ **h.** $2(-3)(5)(-1)$

    i. $(-2)(6)$ **j.** $60 \div (-5)$

    k. $(-1)(-1)(-1)(-1)(-1)(-1)$ **l.** $(-2)(-3)(-4)(5)(-6)$

Exponents and Negative Integers

The product $(-3)(-3)$ can be written as $(-3)^2$. The integer -3 is the factor that appears two times in the product and is called the **base.** The integer 2 represents the number of factors of -3 in the product and is called the **exponent.**

14. a. Evaluate $(-3)(-3)$.

    b. Evaluate $(-3)^2$ using the exponent key on your calculator. Be sure to key in the parentheses when you do the calculation.

    c. Suppose, when using your calculator, you omit the parentheses in $(-3)^2$ and instead you calculate the expression -3^2. Does -3^2 have the same value as $(-3)^2$?

You should think of -3^2 as the opposite of 3^2. Therefore,

$$-3^2 = -(3^2) = -(3)(3) = -9.$$

15. Evaluate the following expressions by hand. Use your calculator to check the results.

    a. -5^2 **b.** $(-5)^2$ **c.** $(-3)^3$

    d. -1^4 **e.** $2 - 4^2$ **f.** $(2 - 4)^2$

    g. $-5^2 - (-5)^2$ **h.** $(-1)^8$ **i.** $-5^2 + (-5)^2$

Multiplication and Division Involving 0

16. a. Recall that multiplication is repeated addition. For example, $4 \cdot 3 = 4 + 4 + 4$. Use this fact to write $0 \cdot 6$ as an addition problem.

    b. Compute the answer in part a.

    c. What is 0 times any integer? Explain.

17. a. Recall the multiplication check for division. For example, $8 \div 2 = 4$ because $2 \cdot 4 = 8$. Use the multiplication check to compute the answer to the division problem $0 \div 7$.

    b. What is 0 divided by any nonzero integer? Explain.

    c. Use the multiplication check to explain why $7 \div 0$ has no answer.

    d. Can any integer be divided by 0? Explain.

18. Evaluate each of the following, if possible. If not possible, explain why not.

    a. $0 \cdot (-8)$ **b.** $12 \cdot 0$ **c.** $0 \div 4$

    d. $-6 \div 0$ **e.** $0 \div (-6)$ **f.** $0 \div 0$

> When multiplying any integer by 0, the answer is 0. When dividing 0 by any nonzero integer, the answer is 0. No integer can be divided by 0.

SUMMARY
ACTIVITY 3.1

1. Product of Two Integers

   Rule 1: The product of two integers with the same sign is positive.

   $$(+)(+) = (+) \rightarrow (4)(5) = 20$$
   $$(-)(-) = (+) \rightarrow (-4)(-5) = 20$$

   Rule 2: The product of two integers with opposite signs is negative.

   $$(-)(+) = (-) \rightarrow (-4)(5) = -20$$
   $$(+)(-) = (-) \rightarrow (4)(-5) = -20$$

2. Quotient of Two Integers

   Rule 1: The quotient of two integers with the same sign is positive.

   $$\frac{(+)}{(+)} = (+) \rightarrow \frac{12}{4} = 3$$

   $$\frac{(-)}{(-)} = (+) \rightarrow \frac{-12}{-4} = 3$$

   Rule 2: The quotient of two integers with opposite signs is negative.

   $$\frac{(-)}{(+)} = (-) \rightarrow \frac{-12}{4} = -3$$

   $$\frac{(+)}{(-)} = (-) \rightarrow \frac{12}{-4} = -3$$

3. **a.** The base for $(-2)^4$ is -2; $(-2)^4 = (-2)(-2)(-2)(-2) = 16$.
   b. The base for -2^4 is 2; $-2^4 = -(2)(2)(2)(2) = -16$ because the expression -2^4 represents the opposite of 2^4.

4. **a.** The product of an integer and 0 is always 0.
   b. 0 divided by any nonzero integer is 0.
   c. No integer may be divided by 0.

EXERCISES
ACTIVITY 3.1

1. Determine the product or quotient. Check your results using your calculator.

   a. $-6 \cdot 7$

   b. $(3)(-8)$

   c. $8(-200)$

   d. $(-1)(7)$

   e. $8 \cdot 0$

   f. $(-3)(-268)$

   g. $-6(-40)$

   h. $-30 \div 6$

   i. $(-45) \div (-9)$

j. $-3 \div 0$ **k.** $-25 \div (-1)$ **l.** $0 \div (-6)$

m. $\dfrac{-64}{16}$ **n.** $\dfrac{-56}{-8}$ **o.** $\dfrac{0}{-167}$

2. Perform the following calculations. Check the results using your calculator.

   a. $(-2)(-4)(1)(-5)$ **b.** $(3)(-4)(2)(-4)(2)$ **c.** $(-1)(-1)(-1)(-1)$

   d. $(-1)(-5)(-11)$ **e.** -6^2 **f.** $(-6)^2$

   g. $(-4)^3$ **h.** -4^3

3. The daily low temperature in Lake Placid, New York, dropped 5 degrees Celsius per day for 6 consecutive days. Use a negative integer to represent the drop in temperature each day and calculate the total drop over the 6-day period.

4. You recently bought a piece of property in a rural area and need a well for your water supply. The well-drilling company you hire says they can drill down about 25 feet per day. It takes the company approximately 5 days to reach water. Represent the company's daily drilling rate by a negative integer and calculate the approximate depth of the water supply. Report your result as a negative integer.

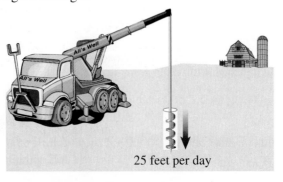

25 feet per day

5. You plan to dive to a shipwreck located 168 feet below sea level. You can dive at the rate of approximately 2 feet per second. Use negative integers to represent the distance below sea level in the following calculations.

   a. Calculate the depth you dove in 1 minute.

   b. Calculate where you are in relationship to the shipwreck after 1 minute.

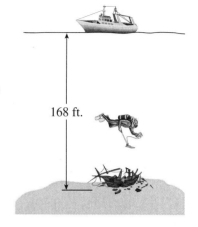

168 ft.

6. You are one of three equal partners in a company. Your company experienced a loss of $150,000 in 2002. What was your share of the loss? Write the answer in words and as a signed number.

7. The running back of your favorite football team lost 6 yards per carry for a total of a 30-yard loss. Use negative integers to represent a loss in yardage and calculate the number of plays that were involved in this yardage loss.

8. To discourage random guessing on a multiple-choice exam, the instructor assigns 5 points for a correct response, −2 points for an incorrect answer, and 0 points for leaving the question blank. What is the score for a student who had 22 correct answers, 7 incorrect answers, and left 6 questions blank?

9. You are interning at the weather station. This week the low temperatures were 4°C, −8°C, 4°C, −1°C, −2°C, −2°C, −2°C. Determine the average low temperature for the week.

10. It has not rained in northern New York State for a month. You are worried about the depth of the water in your boathouse. You need 3 feet of water so that your boat motor does not hit bottom and get stuck in the mud. Each week you measure the water depth. The initial measurement was 42 inches. The following table tells the story of the change in depth each week.

WEEK	1	2	3	4
CHANGE IN WATER LEVEL (INCHES)	−2	−2	−2	−3

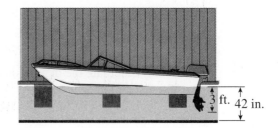

a. What was the depth of the water in your boathouse after week 1?

b. Determine the total change in the water level for the first 3 weeks.

c. Include the fourth week in part b. Determine the total change in the water level.

d. Determine the depth of the water in your boathouse after the fourth week.

e. Was your motor in the mud? Explain.

11. Each individual account in your small business has a current dollar balance, which can be either positive (a credit) or negative (a debit). Your records show the following balances.

−$230	−$230	$350	−$230	−$230	$350

What is the total balance for these accounts?

12. You wrote four checks, each in the amount of $23, for your daughters to play summer league soccer. You had $82 in your checking account and thought you had just enough to cover the checks.

a. Write an arithmetic expression and simplify to determine if you will have enough money.

b. What possible mathematical error made you believe you could write the four checks?

✳ACTIVITY 3.2

Integers and Tiger Woods

OBJECTIVES

1. Use order of operations with expressions involving integers.

2. Apply the distributive property.

3. Evaluate algebraic expressions and formulas using integers.

4. Solve equations of the form $ax = b$, where $a \neq 0$, involving integers.

The popularity of golf has increased greatly in recent years, due in large part to the achievements of Tiger Woods. In the 1997 Masters Tournament, played every year in Augusta, Georgia, Woods won by an amazing 12 strokes, the widest margin of victory the tournament has ever seen. At 21 years of age, he became the youngest golfer to win the Masters Tournament, and the first of African or Asian descent. By 2005 he added three more Masters victories to his record.

In the game of golf, the object is to hit a ball with a club into a hole in the ground with as few strokes (or swings of the club) as possible. The golfer with the lowest total number of strokes is the winner. A standard game consists of 18 different holes laid out in a parklike setting. Each hole, depending upon its length and difficulty, is assigned a number of strokes that represents the average number of strokes a very good player should expect to need to get the ball into the hole. This number is called *par* (hence the cliché you may have heard, "that's par for the course").

Most golfers refer to how their score relates to par; they give a score as the number of strokes above or below par. In this way, par acts like zero. Scoring at par can be represented by zero, scoring below par by a negative integer, and scoring above par by a positive integer. Golfers also use special terminology for the number of strokes above or below par, as summarized in the following table.

Getting the Swing of It ...

TERM	MEANING	DIFFERS FROM PAR
Double eagle	3 strokes less than par	−3
Eagle	2 strokes less than par	−2
Birdie	1 stroke less than par	−1
Par	Expected number of strokes	0
Bogey	1 stroke more than par	1
Double bogey	2 strokes more than par	2

In the Masters, the expected number of strokes to complete the 18 holes is 72. In the last round of the 2000 Masters Tournament, Tiger Woods had a score of 68. This meant that he completed the course in 4 fewer strokes than was expected. That is, he was 4 under par.

Rather than keeping a tally of the actual number of strokes, you can record the number of birdies, pars, bogeys, etc. For example, if you parred every hole, your score would be 72. You would not add or subtract anything to par.

1. Use the preceding table to answer the following questions.

    a. If you birdied each of the 18 holes at the Masters, what is your score?

    b. If you bogeyed every hole, what is your score?

c. If you birdied every hole on the first 9 holes, and bogeyed every hole on the last 9 holes, what is your score?

2. The Corning Country Club is the site of the LPGA Corning Classic Golf Tournament for Lady Professionals. The course consists of 18 holes and par is 70. One golfer summarized her scores for the first round by the following table.

Join the Club

SCORE ON A HOLE	NUMBER OF TIMES SCORE OCCURRED
Eagle: -2	1
Birdie: -1	5
Par: 0	9
Bogey: $+1$	2
Double bogey: $+2$	1

a. Describe the process you would use to determine the total number of strokes it took her to complete her first round (all 18 holes).

b. Calculate her score for the first round.

The golfer's first-round score can be determined by the arithmetic expression

$$70 + (-2) \cdot 1 + (-1) \cdot 5 + 0 \cdot 9 + 1 \cdot 2 + 2 \cdot 1.$$

The order of operations discussed in Chapter 1 is valid for all numbers, positive and negative. Therefore, in the given expression, multiplication is performed first (left to right) *before* addition or subtraction.

EXAMPLE 1   *Evaluate the expression* $7 + (-3) \cdot 5$ *using order of operations.*

$$7 + (-3) \cdot 5$$
$$= 7 + (-15) \qquad \text{Multiplication before addition}$$
$$= -8 \qquad \text{Addition of integers with opposite signs}$$

3. Evaluate the following expressions using the order of operations. Then check the answer with your calculator.

a. $6 + 4 \cdot (-2)$ **b.** $-6 + 2 - 3$ **c.** $(6 - 10) \div 2$

d. $-3 + (2 - 5)$

e. $(2 - 7) \cdot 5$

f. $-3 \cdot (-3 + 4)$

g. $-2 \cdot 3^2 - 15$

h. $(2 + 3)^2 - 10$

i. $-7 + 8 \div (5 - 7)$

4. a. Evaluate the expression $-2(-3 + 7)$ by first performing the operation within the parentheses.

b. Evaluate the expression $-2(-3 + 7)$ by using the distributive property. Recall that $a(b + c) = ab + ac$

c. Compare the results from parts a and b.

Evaluating Algebraic Expressions

The International Golf Championship on the Men's PGA tour, played annually at Castle Pines Golf Club, Castle Rock, Colorado, uses a rather unique scoring system. Rather than counting strokes, players are awarded points on each hole depending on how well they played the hole. The points are summarized in the following table.

Stroke of Luck

SCORE	POINTS
Double eagle	8
Eagle	5
Birdie	2
Par	0
Bogey	−1
Double bogey or worse	−3

A player's score could be determined by the following expression:

$$8 \cdot a + 5 \cdot b + 2 \cdot c + 0 \cdot d + (-1) \cdot e + (-3) \cdot f,$$

where a = number of double eagles; b = number of eagles; c = number of birdies; d = number of pars; e = number of bogeys; and f = number of double bogeys or worse.

5. Determine the score of golfer Corey Pavin if his round included no double eagles, 1 eagle, 5 birdies, 9 pars, 2 bogeys, and 1 double bogey.

The process in Problem 5 is an example of evaluating an expression involving integers. Recall from Chapter 2 that you can evaluate an algebraic expression when you know the value of each variable. To evaluate, replace each variable with its given value, then calculate using the order of operations.

EXAMPLE 2   *Evaluate the expression $3cd - 4d^2$ for $c = -2$ and $d = -5$.*

$$
\begin{aligned}
3cd - 4d^2 &= 3(-2)(-5) - 4(-5)^2 &&\text{Substituting values for } c \text{ and } d \\
&= 30 - 4(25) &&\text{Simplifying using the order of operations} \\
&= 30 - 100 &&\text{Simplifying using the order of operations} \\
&= -70
\end{aligned}
$$

6. Evaluate each of the following expressions for the given values.

a. $6a + 3b - a^2$ for $a = -5$ and $b = 4$

b. $-4xy + 3x - 6y$ for $x = -4$, $y = -5$

c. $\dfrac{7c - 2d^2}{-3w}$ for $c = -10$, $d = -4$ and $w = 2$

Solving Equations of the Form *ax = b* that Involve Integers

7. a. You join the fitness center and lose weight at the rate of 2 pounds per week for 10 weeks. Represent the rate of weight loss as a negative number and use it to determine your total weight loss.

b. Write a verbal rule that expresses your total weight loss in terms of the rate of weight loss per week and the number of weeks.

c. Let *t* represent the total weight loss, *r* the rate of weight loss per week, and *w* the number of weeks. Translate the verbal statement from part b into an equation.

d. One of the members of the Fitness Center lost a total of 42 pounds, represented by -42, at the rate of 3 pounds per week, represented by -3. Use the formula in part c to write an equation to determine the number of weeks it took the member to lose the weight.

e. Solve the equation in part d.

8. Solve the following equations for the given variables.

    a. $-4x = 36$ **b.** $6s = -48$ **c.** $-32 = -4y$

SUMMARY
ACTIVITY 3.2

1. The order of operations first introduced in Chapter 1 for whole numbers also applies to integers.

    a. Perform all operations *inside* parentheses.

    b. Apply *all exponents* as you read the expression from left to right.

    c. Perform all *multiplications and divisions* from left to right.

    d. Perform all *additions and subtractions* from left to right.

2. To evaluate formulas or expressions involving integers, substitute for the variables and evaluate using the order of operations.

3. To solve the equation $ax = c$ for x, where $a \neq 0$, divide each side of the equation by a to obtain $x = \dfrac{c}{a}$.

EXERCISES
ACTIVITY 3.2

1. In 2001, Tiger Woods again won the Masters Tournament. His performance in the last round (all 18 holes) is given in the following table.

 Mastering the Game

SCORE ON A HOLE	NUMBER OF TIMES SCORE OCCURRED
Birdie: -1	6
Par: 0	10
Bogey: $+1$	2

If par for the 18 holes is 72, determine Tiger's score in the last round of the tournament.

2. You own 24 shares of stock in a high-tech company and have been following this stock over the past 4 weeks.

WEEK	GAIN OR LOSS PER SHARE ($)
1	2
2	−3
3	4
4	−5

a. What is the net gain or loss in total value of the stock over the 4-week period?

b. If your stock was worth $18 per share at the beginning of the first week, how much was your stock worth at the end of the fourth week?

c. Let the variable x represent the cost per share of your stock at the beginning of the first week. Write an expression to determine the cost per share at the end of the fourth week.

d. Use the expression in part c to determine the value of your stock at the end of the fourth week if it was worth $27 per share at the beginning of the first week.

3. Evaluate the following. Check your results by using your calculator.

a. $3 + 2 \cdot 4$

b. $3 - 2(-4)$

c. $-2 + (2 \cdot 4 - 3 \cdot 5)$

d. $4 \cdot 3^2 - 50$

e. -6^2

f. $(-6)^2$

g. $(-2)^2 + 10 \div (-5)$

h. $12 - 3^2$

i. $-12 \div 3 - 4^2$

j. $(2 \cdot 3 - 4 \cdot 5) \div (-2)$

k. $(-13 - 5) \div 3 \cdot 2 \cdot 1$

l. $-5 + 9 \div (8 - 11)$

m. $14 - (-4)^2$

n. $3 - 2^3$

o. $3^2(-5)^2 \div (-1)$

4. Use the distributive property to evaluate the following.

a. $5(-3 + 4)$ **b.** $-2(5 - 7)$ **c.** $4(-6 - 2)$

5. Evaluate the following expressions using the given values.

a. $ab^2 + 4c$ for $a = 3, b = -5, c = -3$

b. $(5x + 3y)(2x - y)$ for $x = -4, y = 6$

c. $-5c(14cd - 3d^2)$ for $c = 3, d = -2$

d. $\dfrac{3ax - 4c}{4ac}$ for $a = -2, c = 4, x = -8$

6. You are on a diet to lose 15 pounds in 8 weeks. The first week you lost 3 pounds, and then you lost 2 pounds per week for each of the next 3 weeks. The fifth week showed a gain of 2 pounds, but the sixth and seventh each had a loss of 2 pounds. You are beginning your eighth week. How many pounds do you need to lose in the eighth week in order to meet your goal?

7. Translate each of the following into an equation and solve. Let x represent the number.

a. The product of a number and -6 is 54.

b. -30 times a number is -150.

c. -88 is the product of a number and 8.

d. Twice a number is -28.

8. Solve each equation.

a. $3x = 27$ 　　　　　 **b.** $9s = -81$ 　　　　　 **c.** $-24 = -3y$

d. $-5x = 45$ 　　　　　 **e.** $-6x = -18$

For Exercises 9–11, write an equation to represent the situation and solve.

9. On average, you can lose 5 pounds per month while dieting. Your goal is to lose 65 pounds. Represent each weight loss by a negative number. How many months will it take you to do this?

10. As winter approached in Alaska, the temperature dropped each day for 19 consecutive days. The total decrease in temperature was 57°F, represented by -57. What was the average drop in temperature per day?

11. Over a 10-day period the low temperature for International Falls, Minnesota, was recorded as -18°F on 3 days, -15° on 2 days, -10° on 2 days, and -8°, -5°, and -3° on the remaining 3 days. What was the average low temperature over the 10-day period?

What Have I Learned?

1. When you multiply a positive integer, n, by a negative integer, is the result greater or less than n? Give a reason for your answer.

2. **a.** When you multiply a negative integer, n, by a second negative integer, is the result greater or less than n? Explain your answer.

   b. Does your answer to part a depend on the absolute value of the second negative integer? Why or why not?

3. **a.** Complete the following table to list the rules for the multiplication and division of two integers.

MULTIPLICATION	DIVISION
$(+) \cdot (+) =$	$(+) \div (+) =$
$(+) \cdot (-) =$	$(+) \div (-) =$
$(-) \cdot (+) =$	$(-) \div (+) =$
$(-) \cdot (-) =$	$(-) \div (-) =$

   b. Use the table you completed above to show how the rules for division are related to the rules for multiplication of two integers.

4. How will you remember the rules for multiplying and dividing two integers?

5. When you multiply several signed numbers, some positive and some negative, how do you determine the sign of the product?

6. When a negative number is raised to a power, is the result negative? Illustrate your answer with examples.

7. Explain why -7^2 is not the same as $(-7)^2$.

How Can I Practice?

1. Calculate the following products and quotients. Use your calculator to check the results.

   a. $-2 \cdot 8$ **b.** $(5)(-6)$ **c.** $-8(-20)$

   d. $-9 \cdot 0$ **e.** $-36 \div 9$ **f.** $(-54) \div (-6)$

   g. $-8 \div 0$ **h.** $\dfrac{72}{-12}$ **i.** $\dfrac{-24}{-3}$

   j. $(-2)(-1)(3)(-2)(-1)$ **k.** $(5)(-1)(2)(-3)(-1)$

2. Evaluate each expression. Check the results using your calculator.

   a. $-6 + 4(-3)$ **b.** $10 - 5(-2)$

   c. $(6 - 26 + 5 - 10) \div -5^2$ **d.** $40 + 8 \div (-4) \cdot 2$

   e. $-14 + 8 \div (10 - 12)$ **f.** $-27 \div 3 - 6^2$

   g. $18 - 6 + 3 \cdot 2$ **h.** $-7^2 - 7^2$ **i.** $(-7)^2 - 7 \cdot 2 + 5$

3. Evaluate each expression using the given values of the variables.

   a. $4x - 3(x - 2)$, where $x = -5$

   b. $x^2 - xy$, where $x = -6$ and $y = 4$

   c. $2(x + 3) - 5y$, where $x = -2$ and $y = -4$

4. In hockey, a defenseman's plus/minus record (+/− total) determines his success. If he is on the ice for a goal by the opposing team, he has a −1. If he is on the ice for a goal by his team, he gets a +1. A defenseman for a professional hockey team has the following on-ice record for five games.

Shot...Score!

GAME	YOUR TEAM'S GOALS	OPPOSITION GOALS	+/− TOTAL
1	4	1	$1(4) + (-1)(1) = +3$
2	3	5	
3	0	3	
4	3	0	
5	1	6	

For example, an expression that represents his +/− total for game 1 is

$$1(4) + (-1)(1).$$

Evaluating this expression, he was a +3 for game 1.

a. Write an expression for each game and use it to determine the +/− total for that game.

b. Write an expression and use it to determine the defenseman's +/− total for the five games.

5. At the end of a hockey season a defenseman summarized his +/− total in the following chart. For example: In the first column, in three games his +/− total was +6. His total +/− for the 3 games was +18.

NO. OF GAMES	3	4	12	8	6	11	3	15	9	6	3
+/− TOTAL	+6	+4	+3	+2	+1	0	−1	−2	−3	−4	−5

Write an expression that will determine the +/− total for the season. What is his +/− total for the season?

6. The following table contains the daily midnight temperatures in Buffalo for a week in January.

A Balmy −12°

DAY	Sun.	Mon.	Tues.	Wed.	Thurs.	Fri.	Sat.
TEMP. (°F)	−3°	6°	−3°	−12°	6°	−3°	−12°

a. Write an expression to determine the average daily temperature for the week.

b. What is the average daily temperature for the week?

7. Translate each of the following into an equation and solve. Let x represent the number.

a. Three times a number is −15.

b. −54 is the product of −3 and what number?

c. The product of a number and −4 is 48.

d. 90 is the product of −3, −6, and a number.

| CLUSTER 2 | Multiplying and Dividing Fractions |

✦ACTIVITY 3.3

**Get Your
Homestead Land**

OBJECTIVES

1. Multiply and divide
fractions.

2. Recognize the sign of a
fraction.

3. Determine the reciprocal
of a fraction.

4. Solve equations of the
form $ax = b$, $a \neq 0$, that
involve fractions.

In 1862, Congress passed the Homestead Act. It provided for the transfer of
160 acres of unoccupied public land to each homesteader after paying a nominal
fee and living on the land for 5 years. As part of an assignment, you are asked to
determine the size of 160 acres, in square miles. Your research reveals that there
are 640 acres in 1 square mile, so you draw the following diagram, dividing the
square mile into four equal portions (quarters).

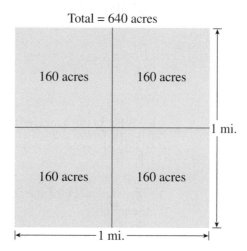

1. Use the diagram to determine the fractional part of the original square mile
that the 160 acres represents.

You decide to investigate further. Suppose each 160-acre homestead is further
divided into four equal squares. Each *new square* represents 40 acres, as
illustrated in the diagram.

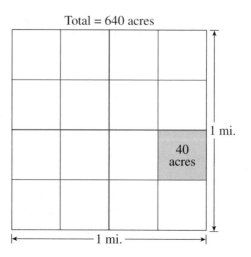

2. Use the diagram to determine the fractional part of the original square mile that 40 acres represents.

3. **a.** Use the diagram on the previous page to write the dimensions of a 40-acre square in terms of miles.

   b. What is the area of a 40-acre square in square miles?

4. Since the area of a square is determined by multiplying the lengths of two sides, you can combine the results of Problem 3a and b as follows:

$$\left(\frac{1}{4}\text{ mile}\right) \cdot \left(\frac{1}{4}\text{ mile}\right) = \frac{1}{16}\text{ sq. mi.}$$

   a. Suppose someone is able to acquire three adjacent lots of 40 acres along one side of the square mile. What fractional part of the square mile did he acquire?

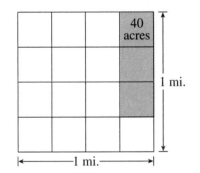

   b. What are the overall dimensions of this combined lot, in miles?

Because he acquired 3 of the 16 lots, the area in Problem 4a is $\frac{3}{16}$ square mile. The dimensions of his lot are $\frac{1}{4}$ mile by $\frac{3}{4}$ mile. So the area of his lot is

$$\frac{1}{4} \cdot \frac{3}{4} = \frac{3}{16}\text{ sq. mi.}$$

5. In Problems 3 and 4, you determined that $\frac{1}{4} \cdot \frac{1}{4} = \frac{1}{16}$ and $\frac{1}{4} \cdot \frac{3}{4} = \frac{3}{16}$.

   Describe in your own words a rule for multiplying fractions.

PROCEDURE

Multiplying Fractions To multiply fractions, multiply the numerators to obtain the new numerator and multiply the denominators to obtain the new denominator. Stated symbolically:

$$\frac{a}{b} \cdot \frac{c}{d} = \frac{ac}{bd}$$

EXAMPLE 1   *Multiply* $\frac{1}{2} \cdot \frac{3}{5}$.

SOLUTION

$$\frac{1}{2} \cdot \frac{3}{5} = \frac{1 \cdot 3}{2 \cdot 5} = \frac{3}{10}$$

EXAMPLE 2   *Multiply* $-\frac{2}{3} \cdot \frac{5}{7}$.

The rules for multiplying negative integers also apply to fractions.

SOLUTION

$$-\frac{2}{3} \cdot \frac{5}{7} = -\frac{2 \cdot 5}{3 \cdot 7} = -\frac{10}{21}$$

EXAMPLE 3   *Multiply* $28 \cdot \frac{3}{4}$.

Think of the whole number 28 as the fraction $\frac{28}{1}$, then multiply:
$\frac{28}{1} \cdot \frac{3}{4} = \frac{84}{4} = 21$.

EXAMPLE 4   *Multiply* $\frac{3}{8} \cdot \frac{1}{6}$.

SOLUTION

Multiply the fractions, $\frac{3}{8} \cdot \frac{1}{6} = \frac{3 \cdot 1}{8 \cdot 6} = \frac{3}{48}$.

Then reduce to lowest terms, $\frac{3}{48} = \frac{3 \cdot 1}{3 \cdot 16} = \frac{3}{3} \cdot \frac{1}{16} = 1 \cdot \frac{1}{16} = \frac{1}{16}$.

In Example 4, the common factor 3 in the numerator and denominator can be divided out, because, in effect, it amounts to multiplication by 1. It is actually preferable to remove (divide out) the common factor of 3 from both numerator and denominator before the final multiplication.

$$\frac{3}{8} \cdot \frac{1}{6} = \frac{\overset{1}{\cancel{3}} \cdot 1}{8 \cdot \underset{1}{\cancel{3}} \cdot 2} = \frac{1}{8 \cdot 2} = \frac{1}{16}$$

This will guarantee that your final answer will be written in lowest terms.

EXAMPLE 5   *Multiply* $-\frac{12}{25} \cdot -\frac{10}{9}$.

SOLUTION

$$-\frac{12}{25} \cdot -\frac{10}{9} = \frac{\overset{1}{\cancel{3}} \cdot 4 \cdot 2 \cdot \overset{1}{\cancel{5}}}{\underset{1}{\cancel{5}} \cdot 5 \cdot \underset{1}{\cancel{3}} \cdot 3} = \frac{4 \cdot 2}{5 \cdot 3} = \frac{8}{15}$$

Note that the common factors of 3 and 5 were divided out. This procedure is sometimes called *canceling common factors.*

If you don't divide out the common factors first, you will produce larger numbers that will need reducing. In this case, $-\dfrac{12}{25} \cdot -\dfrac{10}{9} = \dfrac{120}{225}$, where it is not as easy to determine the GCF and reduce to lowest terms.

Sign of a Fraction

Every fraction is a quotient that represents the division of two integers. For example, a 3-inch string divided into four equal lengths will result in strings of length $\frac{3}{4}$ inch $\left(3 \div 4 = \dfrac{3}{4}\right)$. As with integers, fractions may be positive or negative. For example, consider $-\dfrac{3}{4}$. Usually the negative sign precedes the fraction, indicating that the value of the fraction is less than zero. Since the quotient of two integers having opposite signs represents a negative fraction, dividing -3 by 4 will result in a negative fraction, as will 3 divided by -4.

$$\frac{-3}{4} = -\frac{3}{4} \quad \text{and} \quad \frac{3}{-4} = -\frac{3}{4}$$

These are 3 different ways to express exactly the same fraction.

6. Evaluate each of the following. Check your answers by using the fraction feature on your calculator.

a. $-\dfrac{2}{7} \cdot -\dfrac{4}{7}$ b. $\dfrac{4}{5} \cdot -\dfrac{8}{9}$ c. $-\dfrac{5}{4} \cdot \dfrac{-8}{9}$

Dividing Fractions

To understand division by a fraction, consider dividing a pie into three equal pieces. Each piece is equal to $1 \div 3 = \dfrac{1}{3}$ of the pie. But $\dfrac{1}{3}$ is also the same as $1 \cdot \dfrac{1}{3}$. This means that $1 \div 3 = 1 \cdot \dfrac{1}{3}$; that is, dividing 1 by 3 is equivalent to multiplying 1 by $\dfrac{1}{3}$. The number $\dfrac{1}{3}$ is called the **reciprocal** of 3. Note that the product $3 \cdot \dfrac{1}{3} = 1$. This example leads to the general definition for reciprocals.

> **DEFINITION**
>
> Two numbers are **reciprocals** of each other if their product is 1. Reciprocal pairs are either both positive or both negative. To obtain the reciprocal of the fraction $\dfrac{a}{b}$, interchange the numerator and the denominator to obtain the fraction $\dfrac{b}{a}$.

EXAMPLE 6   *Determine the reciprocal of the given number. Multiply the number and its reciprocal in the third column.*

SOLUTION

NUMBER	RECIPROCAL	PRODUCT
$\dfrac{2}{3}$	$\dfrac{3}{2}$	$\dfrac{2}{3} \cdot \dfrac{3}{2} = \dfrac{6}{6} = 1$
$-\dfrac{1}{4}$	$-\dfrac{4}{1} = -4$	$-\dfrac{1}{4} \cdot -\dfrac{4}{1} = \dfrac{4}{4} = 1$
-12	$-\dfrac{1}{12}$	$-\dfrac{12}{1} \cdot -\dfrac{1}{12} = \dfrac{12}{12} = 1$

7. a. Determine the reciprocal of each number. Show your calculation of the product of the number and its reciprocal in the third column.

NUMBER	RECIPROCAL	PRODUCT
6		
$-\dfrac{3}{5}$		
$\dfrac{1}{7}$		

b. Does 0 have a reciprocal? Explain.

8. Suppose you own a 4-acre plot of land and wish to subdivide it into plots that are each $\frac{2}{5}$ of an acre. How many such smaller plots would you have? Use repeated subtraction.

Your answer to Problem 8 was determined by repeatedly subtracting $\frac{2}{5}$ from the original 4 acres. $\left(4 - \frac{2}{5} = 3\frac{3}{5}, 3\frac{3}{5} - \frac{2}{5} = 3\frac{1}{5}, \text{etc.}\right)$ You could subtract $\frac{2}{5}$ ten times, since $\frac{2}{5} \cdot 10 = \frac{20}{5} = 4$ acres. Hence you could make ten $\frac{2}{5}$-acre plots.

A much more efficient way to determine the number of such plots is to divide 4 by $\frac{2}{5}$. (How many times does $\frac{2}{5}$ go into 4?) From Problem 8, you know $4 \div \frac{2}{5} = 10$. By changing this division to $4 \cdot \frac{5}{2}$ you will get the same result since $4 \cdot \frac{5}{2} = \frac{20}{2} = 10$. Note that $\frac{5}{2}$ is the *reciprocal* of $\frac{2}{5}$. This shows the way to a procedure for dividing any fractions.

$$4 \div \frac{2}{5} = \frac{\overset{2}{\cancel{4}}}{1} \cdot \frac{5}{\underset{1}{\cancel{2}}} = \frac{10}{1} = 10$$

PROCEDURE:

Dividing Fractions To divide fractions, multiply the dividend fraction by the reciprocal of the divisor fraction. The method for dividing fractions can be stated algebraically.

$$\underbrace{\frac{a}{b}}_{\text{dividend}} \div \underbrace{\frac{c}{d}}_{\text{divisor}} = \frac{a}{b} \cdot \underbrace{\frac{d}{c}}_{\text{reciprocal}} = \frac{ad}{bc}$$

EXAMPLE 7 *Divide* $\dfrac{3}{8} \div \dfrac{15}{16}$.

SOLUTION

$$\frac{3}{8} \div \frac{15}{16} = \frac{\overset{1}{3}}{\underset{1}{8}} \cdot \frac{\overset{2}{16}}{\underset{5}{15}} = \frac{\overset{1}{3} \cdot \overset{1}{2} \cdot 2 \cdot \overset{1}{4}}{\underset{1}{2} \cdot \underset{1}{4} \cdot 3 \cdot \underset{1}{5}} = \frac{2}{5}$$

9. Evaluate the following. Check your answers by using the fraction feature on your calculator.

   a. $\dfrac{7}{9} \div \dfrac{14}{15}$

   b. $\dfrac{6}{13} \div -24$

   c. $-\dfrac{18}{23} \div \dfrac{30}{-23}$

   d. $\dfrac{\dfrac{8}{15}}{\dfrac{-36}{45}}$

Solving Equations of the Form $ax = b, a \neq 0$, that Involve Fractions

10. Suppose you acquire a rectangular plot that contains 160 acres.

   a. What fractional part of a square mile (640 acres) does 160 acres represent?

   b. You measure one side of the 160-acre plot and obtain 880 feet. What fractional portion of a mile is 880 feet? (There are 5280 feet in one mile.)

The following diagram summarizes what you determined in Problem 10.

$$\text{area} = 160 \text{ acres} = \tfrac{1}{4} \text{ sq. mi.} \quad 880 \text{ ft.} = \tfrac{1}{6} \text{ mi.}$$

x mi.

11. Let *x* represent the length of the unknown side of the rectangular plot. Using the formula for the area of a rectangle, write an equation relating $\frac{1}{4}$ square mile, $\frac{1}{6}$ mile, and *x* miles.

You can solve the equation in Problem 11 for *x*, because it is of the form $ax = b$. What is new here is that *a* and *b* are fractions.

EXAMPLE 8   *Solve $\dfrac{1}{6}x = \dfrac{1}{4}$ to determine the unknown side of the rectangular plot in Problem 11.*

SOLUTION

Dividing both sides of the equation by $\dfrac{1}{6}$, is the same as multiplying both sides by 6.

$$\frac{6}{1} \cdot \frac{1}{6}x = \frac{1}{4} \cdot \frac{6}{1}$$

$$x = \frac{3}{2} \text{ or } 1\frac{1}{2}$$

The unknown side of the rectangular plot in Problem 11 is $1\frac{1}{2}$ miles.

12. Solve the following equations for the given variable.

   a. $\dfrac{2}{3}x = \dfrac{4}{9}$

   b. $\dfrac{4}{15}y = -\dfrac{2}{3}$

   c. $-\dfrac{3}{8}w = \dfrac{1}{2}$

   d. $\dfrac{x}{5} = \dfrac{3}{25}$ $\left(Hint: \dfrac{x}{5} = \dfrac{1}{5}x\right)$

SUMMARY
ACTIVITY 3.3

1. To **multiply fractions,**
   a. Divide out common factors between the numerator and denominator.
   b. Multiply the remaining numerators to obtain the new numerator and multiply the remaining denominators to obtain the new denominator.

$$\frac{a}{b} \cdot \frac{c}{d} = \frac{ac}{bd}$$

2. Two numbers are reciprocals of each other if their product is 1. Reciprocal pairs are either both positive or both negative. To obtain the reciprocal of the fraction $\frac{a}{b}$, switch the numerator and the denominator to obtain the fraction $\frac{b}{a}$. Zero does not have a reciprocal.

3. To **divide fractions,** multiply the dividend by the reciprocal of the divisor.

$$\frac{a}{b} \div \frac{c}{d} = \frac{a}{b} \cdot \frac{d}{c} = \frac{ad}{bc}$$

4. There are three different ways to place the sign for a negative fraction. For example: $-\frac{2}{5} = \frac{-2}{5} = \frac{2}{-5}$ are all the same number. $-\frac{2}{5}$ is the preferred notation.

5. To solve an equation of the form $\frac{a}{b}x = \frac{c}{d}$ for x, multiply each side by the reciprocal of $\frac{a}{b}$ to obtain

$$x = \frac{c}{d} \div \frac{a}{b} = \frac{c}{d} \cdot \frac{b}{a} = \frac{cb}{da}.$$

EXERCISES
ACTIVITY 3.3

1. Determine the reciprocal of each of the given numbers.

NUMBER	RECIPROCAL
$\frac{4}{5}$	
$-\frac{8}{3}$	
-7	

2. Multiply each of the following and express each answer in simplest form.

   a. $\frac{2}{7} \cdot \frac{3}{5}$ b. $\frac{5}{8} \cdot \frac{3}{7}$ c. $\frac{-5}{12} \cdot \frac{3}{-25}$ d. $\frac{-33}{12} \cdot \frac{15}{11}$

   e. $\frac{16}{27} \cdot \frac{-18}{24}$ f. $\frac{12}{7} \cdot \frac{3}{5}$ g. $\frac{17}{26} \cdot \frac{12}{18}$ h. $\frac{-4}{15} \cdot \frac{40}{-14}$

3. Divide each of the following and express each answer in simplest form.

a. $\dfrac{1}{5} \div \dfrac{1}{10}$

b. $\dfrac{-5}{9} \div \dfrac{25}{-21}$

c. $-8 \div \dfrac{8}{10}$

d. $-\dfrac{12}{26} \div \dfrac{8}{15}$

e. $\dfrac{\frac{-3}{10}}{\frac{-5}{9}}$

f. $\dfrac{\frac{23}{19}}{-46}$

4. a. As part of a science project, you do a study on the number of beans that actually sprout. You determine that approximately 9 out of 10 seeds germinate. Write this relationship as a fraction.

b. Your uncle has ordered 2500 bean seeds for his commercial garden. Assuming that 9 out of every 10 seeds sprout, how many bean plants can he expect to sprout?

5. a. You have purchased some land to start a game farm. Two-thirds of the rectangular piece of property will be used for the animals and three-fourths of that piece will be left as wilderness. Using the diagram of the farm shown here, mark off the part of the land that will be for the animals.

b. Shade the area that will be left as wilderness.

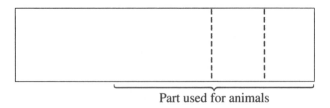

Part used for animals

c. What fractional part of the whole piece of land will be left as wilderness?

6. You are doing a survey for your statistics class and discover that $\frac{3}{4}$ of the students at the college take a math class; $\frac{1}{6}$ of these students take statistics. What fraction of the students at the college take statistics?

7. In your budget you have $\frac{1}{10}$ of your annual salary saved for your college tuition. If your annual salary is $24,350, how much will you have for your tuition?

8. You and five of your friends go back to your place for lunch between classes. Your roommate has eaten approximately $\frac{1}{4}$ of an apple pie you made. Your friends all want pie. What fractional part of the remaining pie can each of them have, if you decide not to have any?

9. How many $\frac{5}{8}$-inch-long pieces of wire can be made from a wire that is 20 inches long?

10. Translate each of the following into an equation and solve.

   a. The product of a number and 3 is $\frac{6}{5}$.

   b. $\frac{2}{3}$ times a number is -4.

   c. A number divided by 7 is 9.

   d. The quotient of a number and 2 is $\frac{3}{8}$.

   e. -15 is the product of a number and $\frac{-2}{3}$.

11. Solve the following equations for the given variable.

a. $\dfrac{3}{8}x = \dfrac{15}{16}$

b. $-\dfrac{x}{10} = \dfrac{4}{15}$

c. $\dfrac{2}{9}w = -\dfrac{4}{15}$

d. $\dfrac{-5}{24}y = \dfrac{15}{32}$

e. $-\dfrac{4}{25}t = -\dfrac{12}{15}$

f. $\dfrac{13}{27}x = \dfrac{20}{45}$

ACTIVITY 3.4

Tiling the Bathroom

OBJECTIVES

1. Multiply and divide mixed numbers.

2. Evaluate expressions with mixed numbers.

3. Calculate the square root of a mixed number.

You have decided it is time for a new floor in the bathroom. You tear up the old tile and repair the subfloor. You then measure the floor and determine the dimensions are 8 feet 8 inches by 12 feet 9 inches.

1. Use mixed numbers to express the dimensions of the bathroom in feet.

2. Round each dimension of the bathroom to the nearest foot, and then estimate the area of the bathroom.

3. Now use the dimensions in Problem 1 to determine the actual area two ways.

   a. First, change the mixed numbers to improper fractions and multiply.

   b. Second, consider the following diagram.

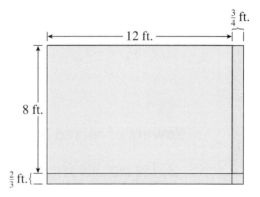

Calculate the area of each of the four regions and determine their sum.

4. Your answers to Problem 3a and b should agree. Based upon your estimate in Problem 2, are these answers reasonable? Explain.

PROCEDURE

Multiplying or Dividing Mixed Numbers

1. Change the mixed numbers to improper fractions.
2. Multiply or divide as you would proper fractions.
3. If the product is an improper fraction, convert it to a mixed number in reduced form.

In general, when a problem is given in mixed number form, the end result is usually expressed in mixed number form, too.

5. Multiply each of the following.

    a. $4\frac{2}{5} \cdot 3$

    b. $3\frac{1}{3} \cdot 1\frac{1}{5}$

    c. $-5\frac{5}{8} \cdot 5\frac{1}{3}$

6. Divide each of the following.

    a. $5\frac{1}{4} \div 3$

    b. $-5\frac{5}{6} \div -1\frac{3}{4}$

    c. $8\frac{2}{5} \div -2\frac{2}{9}$

Powers of Mixed Numbers

7. The new tile you have chosen has a symmetrical design. Each tile is a 6-inch-by-6-inch square containing a pink "plus" sign of width $1\frac{3}{4}$ inches, as illustrated here.

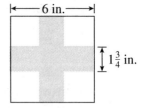

When the tiles are laid, a large white square is formed where the four tiles meet.

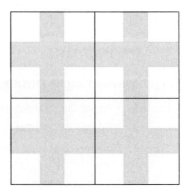

Studying the pattern formed by the four tiles makes you wonder whether there is more white than pink on a single tile.

a. What are the dimensions of each small white square on a single tile?

b. What is the total area of white on each tile? Express your answer as a mixed number.

c. What fraction of a single tile is white? Is there more pink or white on a single tile?

You can also determine the white area of an individual tile by thinking of the four small white squares as a single larger square, as seen in the four-tile drawing. From Problem 7a, each single white square on a single tile measures $2\frac{1}{8}$ inches on a side. Then the larger white square measures $s = 2 \cdot \left(2\frac{1}{8}\right)$ inches on a side. Using the formula $A = s^2$, the area of the larger white square is

$$A = \left(2 \cdot 2\frac{1}{8}\right)^2.$$

Recalling the order of operations, you need to first multiply within the parentheses before applying the exponent. When multiplying a mixed number by a whole number, one approach is to convert $2\frac{1}{8}$ to an improper fraction, $\frac{17}{8}$, and multiply by $\frac{2}{1}$.

$$\frac{17}{8} \cdot \frac{2}{1} = \frac{17 \cdot 2}{4 \cdot 2 \cdot 1} = \frac{17}{4}$$

Then, square to obtain

$$\left(\frac{17}{4}\right)^2 = \frac{17 \cdot 17}{4 \cdot 4} = \frac{289}{16} = 18\frac{1}{16}.$$

Caution: When multiplying with mixed numbers, be very careful not to confuse the addition implied by a mixed number with multiplication. A dot, or other multiplication symbol, *must* be present to show multiplication of numbers.

$$\left(6 \cdot \frac{1}{2} = 3, \text{ but } 6\frac{1}{2} = 6 + \frac{1}{2}\right)$$

EXAMPLE 1 *Evaluate* $\left(1\frac{2}{3}\right)^3$.

SOLUTION

$$\left(1\frac{2}{3}\right)^3 = \left(\frac{5}{3}\right)^3 \qquad \text{Convert the mixed number to an improper fraction.}$$

$$= \frac{5}{3} \cdot \frac{5}{3} \cdot \frac{5}{3} = \frac{125}{27} \qquad \text{Apply the exponent and multiply.}$$

$$= 4\frac{17}{27} \qquad \text{Convert back to a mixed number.}$$

8. Evaluate $\left(3 \cdot 2\frac{1}{3}\right)^3$.

Evaluating Expressions that Involve Fractions

To finish the bathroom floor, you decide to install baseboard molding around the base of each wall. You need the molding all the way around the room except for a 39-inch gap at the doorway. Recall the dimensions of the room are $8\frac{2}{3}$ feet by $12\frac{3}{4}$ feet. Converting 39 inches to $\frac{39}{12} = 3\frac{1}{4}$ feet, you determine that the number of feet of molding, M, that you need is given by the formula

$$M = 2l + 2w - 3\frac{1}{4},$$

where *l* is the length and *w* is the width of the room.

   9. Explain why this formula makes sense.

   10. Determine the amount of molding you need by evaluating the formula's expression for the given room dimensions.

In working with formulas, you frequently evaluate expressions. Here are more examples.

EXAMPLE 2   *Evaluate $3xy - y$, where $x = -\frac{3}{4}$ and $y = -2\frac{1}{2}$.*

SOLUTION

$$3\left(-\frac{3}{4}\right)\left(-2\frac{1}{2}\right) - \left(-2\frac{1}{2}\right) \qquad \text{Substituting the given values}$$

$$= 3\left(-\frac{3}{4}\right)\left(-\frac{5}{2}\right) - \left(-\frac{5}{2}\right) \qquad \text{Converting to improper fractions}$$

$$= \frac{45}{8} + \frac{5}{2} \qquad \text{Perform the calculations.}$$

$$= \frac{65}{8}$$

$$= 8\frac{1}{8} \qquad \text{Convert back to mixed number form.}$$

11. Evaluate $a - b(6 - c)$, where $a = -\dfrac{1}{4}, b = \dfrac{2}{3}, c = 1\dfrac{1}{2}$.

12. The heights of three brothers were measured as 6 feet 2 inches, 5 feet 10 inches, and 5 feet 9 inches. Use the formula

$$A = (a + b + c)/3$$

to determine the average height of the brothers.

In future algebra classes you will often need to evaluate expressions containing exponents.

EXAMPLE 3 *Evaluate $xy - y^2$, where $x = \dfrac{5}{6}$ and $y = -\dfrac{2}{3}$.*

SOLUTION

Substituting the given values $\left(\dfrac{5}{6}\right)\left(-\dfrac{2}{3}\right) - \left(-\dfrac{2}{3}\right)^2$,

$$= -\dfrac{5 \cdot 2}{6 \cdot 3} - \dfrac{2 \cdot 2}{3 \cdot 3}$$

$$= -\dfrac{5}{9} - \dfrac{4}{9}$$

$$= -\dfrac{9}{9}$$

$$= -1$$

13. Evaluate $a^2 - b(c - 2)^2$, where $a = \dfrac{1}{6}, \ b = \dfrac{5}{4}, c = \dfrac{8}{3}$.

14. A ball is thrown straight up in the air. Let h be the height, in feet, of the ball above the ground when it is thrown. Let v be the initial velocity, in feet per second, (that is, the velocity of the ball when it is thrown). Let t be the elapsed time, in seconds, since the ball was thrown. Then the height of the ball above the ground in feet, s, can be determined using the formula

$$s = h + vt - 16t^2.$$

Determine the height of a ball above the ground after $2\dfrac{1}{2}$ seconds, when it starts from a height of $5\dfrac{1}{2}$ feet and its initial velocity is 44 feet per second.

Hangtime and Square Roots

The term *hangtime* was made popular by sports reporters following Michael Jordan during the 1990s. Hangtime is the time of a basketball player's jump, measured from the instant he or she leaves the floor until he or she returns to the floor. Hangtime, *t*, depends on the height of the jump, *s*. These quantities are related by the equation

$$t = \frac{1}{2}\sqrt{s},$$

where *s* is the input variable measured in feet and *t* is the output variable measured in seconds.

To determine the hangtime of any jump, you need to take square roots. You can calculate the square root of a fraction by taking the square root of the numerator and denominator separately. Symbolically, this property of square roots is written as

$$\sqrt{\frac{a}{b}} = \frac{\sqrt{a}}{\sqrt{b}}, b \neq 0.$$

Hangtime:

$$t = \frac{1}{2}\sqrt{s}$$

EXAMPLE 4   *Determine* $\sqrt{2\frac{14}{25}}$.

SOLUTION

$\sqrt{2\frac{14}{25}} = \sqrt{\frac{64}{25}}$ Change mixed number to a fraction.

$= \frac{\sqrt{64}}{\sqrt{25}}$ By the property

$= \frac{8}{5}$ Find the square roots.

$= 1\frac{3}{5}$ Convert back to a mixed number.

15. a. Using the hangtime formula, determine the hangtime of a $\frac{9}{16}$-foot jump.

   b. Determine the hangtime of a $2\frac{1}{4}$-foot jump.

PROCEDURE

Determining the Square Root of a Fraction or a Mixed Number

1. If finding the square root of a mixed number, first change it to an improper fraction.
2. Determine the square root of the numerator.
3. Determine the square root of the denominator.
4. The square root of the fraction is the quotient $\dfrac{\text{square root of the numerator}}{\text{square root of the denominator}}$.
5. Write the result as a mixed number if necessary.

16. Calculate the following square roots.

   a. $\sqrt{\dfrac{9}{100}}$ b. $\sqrt{\dfrac{64}{49}}$ c. $\sqrt{\dfrac{81}{16}}$

SUMMARY
ACTIVITY 3.4

1. To multiply or divide mixed numbers:
   a. Change the mixed numbers to improper fractions.
   b. Multiply or divide as you would proper fractions.
   c. If the product is an improper fraction, convert it to a mixed number, then reduce if possible.

2. The rules for order of operation when evaluating expressions involving fractions and/or mixed numbers are the same as for integers and whole numbers.

3. To determine the square root of a fraction or a mixed number:
   a. Convert a mixed number to an improper fraction.
   b. Determine the square root of the numerator.
   c. Determine the square root of the denominator.
   d. Divide the square root of the numerator by the square root of the denominator.
   e. Write the result as a mixed number if necessary. Symbolically,

$$\sqrt{\frac{a}{b}} = \frac{\sqrt{a}}{\sqrt{b}}, b \neq 0.$$

1. Multiply and write your answer as a mixed number, if necessary.

    a. $3\dfrac{2}{3} \cdot 1\dfrac{4}{5}$

    b. $-2\dfrac{2}{15} \cdot 4\dfrac{1}{2}$

    c. $2\dfrac{4}{11} \cdot 4\dfrac{2}{5}$

    d. $\left(-5\dfrac{3}{8}\right) \cdot (-24)$

2. Divide and write your answer as a mixed number, if necessary.

    a. $3\dfrac{2}{7} \div 1\dfrac{9}{14}$

    b. $-1\dfrac{7}{8} \div \dfrac{3}{4}$

    c. $4\dfrac{2}{9} \div 8\dfrac{1}{3}$

    d. $\dfrac{-12\dfrac{2}{3}}{-3\dfrac{1}{6}}$

3. Simplify.

    a. $\left(\dfrac{2}{9}\right)^2$

    b. $\left(-\dfrac{3}{5}\right)^3$

    c. $\left(-\dfrac{4}{7}\right)^2$

    d. $\left(\dfrac{2}{3}\right)^5$

    e. $\sqrt{\dfrac{36}{81}}$

    f. $\sqrt{\dfrac{64}{100}}$

    g. $\sqrt{\dfrac{144}{49}}$

    h. $\sqrt{\dfrac{375}{15}}$

4. Evaluate each expression.

    a. $2x - 4(x - 3)$, where $x = 1\dfrac{1}{2}$

Exercise numbers appearing in color are answered in the Selected Answers appendix.

b. $a(a - 2) + 3a(a + 4)$, where $a = \dfrac{2}{3}$

c. $2x + 6(x + 2)$, where $x = 2\dfrac{1}{4}$

d. $6xy - y^2$, where $x = 1\dfrac{5}{16}$ and $y = \dfrac{1}{8}$

e. $4x^3 + x^2$, where $x = \dfrac{1}{2}$

5. The measurement of one side of a square rug is $5\dfrac{3}{4}$ feet. Determine the area of the rug in square feet $\left(\text{use } A = s^2\right)$.

6. As an apprentice at your uncle's cabinet shop, you are cutting out pieces of wood for a dresser. You need pieces that are $5\dfrac{1}{4}$ inches long. Each saw cut wastes $\dfrac{1}{8}$ inch of wood. The board you have is 8 feet long. How many pieces can you make from this board?

7. Solve the following equations.

a. $2\dfrac{3}{4}x = 22$

b. $6\dfrac{1}{8}w = -24\dfrac{1}{2}$

c. $-1\dfrac{4}{5}t = -9\dfrac{9}{10}$

d. $5\dfrac{1}{3}x = \dfrac{-5}{6}$

8. The maximum distance, d, in kilometers that a person can see from a height h meters above the ground is given by the formula

$$d = \frac{7}{2}\sqrt{h}.$$

   a. Use the formula to determine the maximum distance a person can see from a height of 64 meters.

   b. Use the formula to determine the maximum distance a person can see from a height of $20\frac{1}{4}$ meters.

9. An object dropped from a height falls a distance of d feet in t seconds. The formula that describes this relationship is $d = 16t^2$. A math book is dropped from the top of a building that is 400 feet high.

   a. How far has the book fallen in $\frac{1}{2}$ second?

   b. After $3\frac{1}{2}$ seconds, how far above the ground is the book?

   c. Another book was dropped from the top of a building across the street. It took $6\frac{1}{2}$ seconds to hit the ground. How tall is that building?

CLUSTER 2   What Have I Learned?

1. What would be the advantage of dividing both the numerator and denominator of a fraction by a common factor before multiplying fractions?

2. Will a fraction that has a negative numerator and a negative denominator be positive or negative?

3. What is the sign of the product when you multiply a positive fraction by a negative fraction?

4. What is the sign of the quotient when you divide a negative fraction by a negative fraction?

5. Explain, by using an example, how to divide a positive fraction by a negative fraction.

6. Explain, by using an example, how to multiply a negative fraction by a negative fraction.

7. Why do you have to know the meaning of the word *reciprocal* in this cluster?

8. When multiplying or dividing mixed numbers, what must be done first?

9. Explain how you would solve the following equation:

   one-fifth times a number equals negative four.

10. Explain the difference between squaring $\frac{1}{4}$ and taking the square root of $\frac{1}{4}$.

CLUSTER 2   # How Can I Practice?

1. Multiply and write each answer in simplest form. Use a calculator to check answers.

   a. $\dfrac{1}{9} \cdot \dfrac{2}{9}$ b. $\dfrac{10}{11} \cdot \dfrac{3}{13}$ c. $\dfrac{14}{9} \cdot \dfrac{-3}{28}$ d. $\dfrac{30}{35} \cdot \dfrac{10}{25}$

   e. $\dfrac{-9}{10} \cdot \dfrac{-4}{3}$ f. $-20 \cdot \dfrac{2}{35}$ g. $\dfrac{10}{9} \cdot \dfrac{87}{100}$ h. $\dfrac{3}{16} \cdot \dfrac{14}{-3}$

2. Divide and write each answer in simplest form. Use a calculator to check answers.

   a. $\dfrac{-3}{7} \div \dfrac{9}{7}$ b. $\dfrac{8}{11} \div \dfrac{12}{33}$ c. $-\dfrac{4}{9} \div -20$

   d. $\dfrac{24}{45} \div \dfrac{15}{18}$ e. $\dfrac{\dfrac{6}{7}}{-\dfrac{9}{14}}$ f. $\dfrac{-\dfrac{35}{10}}{-3}$

3. Multiply or divide and write each answer as a mixed number in simplest form. Use a calculator to check answers.

   a. $\dfrac{-1}{2} \cdot 5\dfrac{5}{6}$ b. $-2\dfrac{5}{6} \div \dfrac{3}{7}$ c. $-37\dfrac{1}{2} \cdot -1\dfrac{3}{5}$

   d. $7\dfrac{1}{5} \div 2\dfrac{2}{5}$ e. $2\dfrac{1}{3} \cdot 1\dfrac{1}{2}$ f. $-8\dfrac{1}{4} \div -1\dfrac{1}{2}$

4. Simplify.

   a. $-\left(\dfrac{4}{9}\right)^2$ b. $\sqrt{\dfrac{81}{121}}$ c. $\left(-\dfrac{3}{5}\right)^3$ d. $\sqrt{\dfrac{64}{49}}$

Exercise numbers appearing in color are answered in the Selected Answers appendix.

5. Evaluate each expression.

   a. $3x - 5(x - 6)$, where $x = -1\dfrac{2}{3}$

   b. $x^2 - xy$, where $x = \dfrac{1}{4}$ and $y = -1\dfrac{1}{3}$

6. Solve to determine the value of the unknown in each of the following.

   a. $-6x = 25$ b. $-42 = 5x$ c. $-63x = 0$

   d. $\dfrac{-1}{6}x = -12$ e. $\dfrac{2}{5} = -8x$ f. $\dfrac{-3}{4}x = \dfrac{-9}{16}$

7. According to an ad on television, a man lost 30 pounds over $6\dfrac{1}{4}$ months. How much weight did he lose per month?

8. On your last math test, you answered $\dfrac{7}{8}$ of the questions. Of the questions that you answered, you got $\dfrac{4}{5}$ of them correct. What fraction of the questions on the test did you get right?

9. A large-quantity recipe for pea soup calls for $64\dfrac{1}{2}$ ounces of split peas. You decide to make $\dfrac{1}{3}$ of the recipe. How many ounces of split peas will you need?

10. A large corporation recently reported that 16,936 employees were paid at an hourly rate. Approximately 1 out of every 5 of these workers earned $10 or more per hour. How many workers earned $10 or more per hour?

11. Your town has purchased a rectangular piece of land to develop a park. Three-fourths of the property will be used for the public. The rest of the land will be for park administration. The land will be divided so that $\frac{5}{6}$ of the public land will be used for picnicking and the remainder will be a swimming area.

▨▨▨ Picnics   *▨▨▨* Public area

a. Divide the rectangle into fourths and separate the public part from the park administration.

b. Shade the area that will be used for picnics.

c. Determine from the picture what fractional part of the whole piece of property will be used for picnics?

d. Write an expression and evaluate to show that part c is correct.

e. What fractional part of the property will be used by the park administration?

f. What fractional part of the property will be used for swimming?

g. Show that the fractional parts add up to the whole.

12. You drop your sunglasses out of a boat. Your depth finder on the boat measures 27 feet of water. You jump overboard with your goggles to see if you can rescue the glasses before they land on the bottom. You return for a gulp of air with your sunglasses in hand. You think they were about $\frac{2}{3}$ of the way down.

a. Estimate at what depth from the surface you found your glasses.

b. Write an expression that will show the distance from the surface of the water.

c. Evaluate the expression.

$$\frac{2}{\cancel{3}_1} \cdot \frac{\overset{9}{\cancel{27}}}{1} = 18.$$

13. a. Your swimming pool is 15 feet by 30 feet and will be filled to a height of $5\frac{1}{2}$ feet. Use $V = lwh$ (volume equals length times width times height) to determine the volume of the water in the pool.

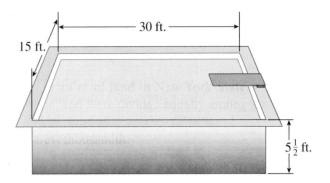

b. If 1 cubic foot of water weighs $62\frac{2}{5}$ pounds, determine the weight of the water.

14. You decide to drop a coin into the gorge at Niagara Falls. The distance the coin will fall, in feet s, and in time t, in seconds, is given by the formula $s = 16t^2$.

a. After $\frac{1}{2}$ second how far has the coin fallen?

b. How far is the coin from the top of the gorge after $2\frac{1}{2}$ seconds?

15. As a magician, you ask a friend to do this problem with you.

a. Ask your friend to select a number.

Then he should add three to the number.

Now have your friend multiply the result by $\frac{1}{3}$.

Next have him subtract 4.

Then, multiply by 6.

Finally, multiply by $\frac{1}{2}$, and ask your friend to tell you the answer.

Add 9 to the number your friend gives you. It will be the original number your friend selected.

b. Repeat part a with several numbers.

c. To determine the relationship between the original number selected and the final answer, let *x* represent the original number and write an expression to determine the final answer.

d. Simplify the expression.

| CLUSTER 3 | Multiplying and Dividing Decimals |

✳ ACTIVITY 3.5

Quality Points and GPA: Tracking Academic Standing

OBJECTIVES

1. Multiply and divide decimals.

2. Estimate products and quotients involving decimals.

Your college tracks your academic standing by an average called a *grade point average* (GPA). Each semester the college determines two grade point averages for you. One average is for the semester and the other includes all your courses up to the end of your current semester. The second grade point average is called a *cumulative GPA*. At graduation, your cumulative GPA represents your final academic standing.

At most colleges the GPA ranges from 0 to 4.0. A minimum GPA of 2.0 is required for graduation. You can track your own academic standing by calculating your GPA yourself. You may find this useful if you apply for internships or jobs at your college and elsewhere where a minimum GPA is required.

Quality Points and Multiplication

To calculate a GPA, you must first determine the number of points (known as quality points) that you earn for each course you take. The following problems will show you why.

1. Suppose that your schedule this term includes a four-credit literature class and a two-credit photography class. Is it fair to say that the literature course should be worth more towards your academic standing than the photography course? Explain.

The GPA gives more weight to courses with a higher number of credits than to ones with lower credit values. For example, a B in literature and an A in photography means that you have four credits each worth a B but only two credits that are each worth an A. To determine how much more the literature course is worth in the calculation of your GPA, you must first change the letter grades into quality point numerical equivalents. You then multiply the number of credits by the numerical equivalents of the letter grade to obtain the quality points for the course.

The following table lists the numerical equivalents of a typical set of letter grades.

Numerical Equivalents for Letter Grades

LETTER GRADES	A	A−	B+	B	B−	C+	C	C−	D+	D	D−	F
QUALITY POINTS (NUMERICAL EQUIVALENTS)	4.00	3.67	3.33	3.00	2.67	2.33	2.00	1.67	1.33	1.00	0.67	0.00

2. **a.** The table shows that each B credit is worth 3 quality points. How many quality points is your B worth in the four-credit literature course?

b. How many quality points did you earn in your two-credit photography course if your grade was an A?

3. a. Your grade was a B+ in a three-credit psychology course. How many quality points did you earn?

b. Complete the following table for each pair of grades and credits. For example, in the row labeled 4 credits and the column labeled A, the number of quality points is 4 × 4.00 or 16.00. Similarly, the number of quality points for a grade of C− in a two-credit course is 3.34.

		QUALITY POINTS FOR GRADE AND CREDIT PAIRS										
LETTER GRADES	A	A−	B+	B	B−	C+	C	C−	D+	D	D−	F
NUMERICAL EQUIVALENTS	4.00	3.67	3.33	3.00	2.67	2.33	2.00	1.67	1.33	1.00	0.67	0.00
COURSE CREDITS												
4 CREDITS	16.00											0.00
3 CREDITS			9.99									
2 CREDITS								3.34				
1 CREDIT										1.00		

4. A community college currently offers an internship course on geriatric health issues. The course, which includes one lecture hour and four fieldwork hours, is worth 1.5 credits.

a. Calculate the number of quality points for a grade of C in this course.

b. Estimate the number of quality points for a grade of C−.

c. Now, determine the exact number of quality points for a grade of C− by first multiplying 15 times 167, basically ignoring the decimal point, for the moment. Then, use your estimate in part b to determine where the decimal point should be placed.

Notice in Problem 4c that there are three digits to the right of the decimal point in your answer. This is the sum total of digits to the right of the decimal point in both factors. Example 1 illustrates how this pattern occurs.

EXAMPLE 1 *Why does 0.3 · 0.5 = 0.15?*

SOLUTION

Since $0.3 = \dfrac{3}{10}$ and $0.5 = \dfrac{5}{10}$, you have

$$0.3 \cdot 0.5 = \frac{3}{10} \cdot \frac{5}{10} \qquad \text{decimals to fractions}$$

$$= \frac{15}{100} \qquad \text{multiplying fractions}$$

$$= 0.15 \qquad \text{fractions to decimals}$$

Example 1 shows that the number of decimal places to the right of the decimal point in the product 0.15 has to be 2, one from each of the factors.

PROCEDURE

Multiplying Two Decimals

1. Multiply two numbers as if they were whole numbers, ignoring decimal points for the moment.
2. Add the number of digits to the right of the decimal point in each factor, to obtain the number of digits that must be to the right of the decimal point in the product.
3. Place the decimal point in the product by counting digits from the right.

EXAMPLE 2 *Multiply 8.731 by 0.25.*

SOLUTION

$$
\begin{array}{r}
8.731 \\
\times \ 0.25 \\
\hline
43655 \\
17462 \\
\hline
2.18275
\end{array}
$$

    8.731   3 decimal places
  × 0.25   2 decimal places

2.18275   5 decimal places

In Example 2, since 0.25 is $\frac{1}{4}$, and $\frac{1}{4}$ of 8.731 is approximately 2, you see that the general rule for multiplying two decimals placed the decimal point in the correct position.

5. Calculate the following products. Check the results using your calculator.

    a. $0.008 \cdot 57.2$

    b. $0.0201 \cdot -27.8$

    c. $-0.45 \cdot -3.12$

GPA and Division

Once you calculate the quality points you earned in a semester, you are ready to determine your GPA for that semester.

6. Suppose that in addition to the credit courses in literature, photography, and psychology that you took this term, you also enrolled in a one-credit weight training class. Using the following table to record your results, calculate the quality points for each course. Then determine the total number of credits and the total number of quality points. The calculation for literature has been done for you.

	CREDITS	GRADE	NUMERICAL EQUIVALENT	QUALITY POINTS
LITERATURE	4	B	3.00	12.00
PHOTOGRAPHY	2	A		
PSYCHOLOGY	3	B+		
WEIGHT TRAINING	1	B−		
TOTALS		n/a		

You earned 32.66 quality points for 10 credits this semester. To calculate the average number of quality points per credit, divide 32.66 by 10 to obtain 3.266. Note that dividing by 10 moves the decimal point in 32.66 one place to the left.

GPAs are usually rounded to the nearest hundredth, so your GPA is 3.27.

PROCEDURE

Determining a GPA

1. Calculate the quality points for each course.
2. Determine the sum of the quality points.
3. Determine the total number of credits.
4. Divide the total quality points by the total number of credits.

---

7. Your cousin enrolled in five courses this term and earned the grades listed in the following table. Determine her GPA to the nearest hundredth.

	CREDITS	GRADE	NUMERICAL EQUIVALENT	QUALITY POINTS
POETRY	3	C+		
CHEMISTRY	4	B		
HISTORY	3	A−		
MATH	3	B+		
KARATE	1	B−		
TOTALS		n/a	n/a	
			GPA	

In Problem 7, note that $42.66 \div 14$ is approximately $45 \div 15 = 3$. Therefore, the decimal point in 3.05 is correctly placed.

EXAMPLE 3 *In Problem 4, you read that a community college offers a 1.5 credit course to investigate issues in geriatric health. A co-worker told you he earned 4.5 quality points in that course. What grade did he earn?*

SOLUTION

To determine your co-worker's grade, divide the 4.5 quality points by 1.5 credits, written as $4.5 \div 1.5$. The division can be written as a fraction, $\frac{4.5}{1.5}$, where the numerator is *divided* by the denominator.

$$4.5 \div 1.5 = \frac{4.5}{1.5} \qquad \text{division as a fraction}$$

$$= \frac{4.5}{1.5} \cdot \frac{10}{10} \qquad \text{multiplying by } \tfrac{10}{10} = 1 \text{ to obtain equivalent fraction}$$

$$= \frac{45}{15} \qquad \text{multiplying fractions to obtain whole-number denominator}$$

$$= 3 \qquad \text{dividing numerator by denominator}$$

He earned a grade of B.

Example 3 leads to a general method for dividing decimals.

$$1.\overset{\displaystyle 3.}{\underset{\curvearrowright}{\big)}}\,{}_{\curvearrowright}$$

PROCEDURE

Dividing Decimals

1. Write the division in long division format.
2. Move the decimal point the same number of places to the right in both divisor and dividend so that the divisor becomes a whole number.
3. Place the decimal point in the quotient directly above the decimal point in the dividend and divide as usual.

EXAMPLE 4 **a.** *Divide* $\underbrace{92.4}_{\text{dividend}}$ *by* $\underbrace{0.25}_{\text{divisor}}$. **b.** *Divide* $\underbrace{0.00052}_{\text{dividend}} \div \underbrace{0.004}_{\text{divisor}}$.

SOLUTION

a. $0.25\overline{)92.40}$ becomes $25\overline{)9240}$. **b.** $0.004\overline{)0.00052}$ becomes $4\overline{)0.52}$.

$$
\begin{array}{r}
369.6 \\
25\overline{)9240.0} \\
-75 \\
\hline
174 \\
-150 \\
\hline
240 \\
-225 \\
\hline
150 \\
-150 \\
\hline
0
\end{array}
\qquad
\begin{array}{r}
0.13 \\
4\overline{)0.52} \\
-4 \\
\hline
12 \\
-12 \\
\hline
0
\end{array}
$$

8. Determine the following quotients. Check the results using your calculator.

    a. $11.525 \div 2.5$

    b. $-45.525 \div 0.0004$

    c. Calculate $-3.912 \div (-0.13)$ and round the result to the nearest ten thousandths.

9. You need to calculate your GPA to determine if you qualify for a summer internship that requires a cumulative GPA of at least 3.3. You had 14 credits and 44.5 quality points in the fall term. In the spring you earned 16 credits and 55.2 quality points. Did you qualify for the internship?

Estimating Products and Quotients

EXAMPLE 5   *You need to drive to campus, but your gas tank is just about empty. The tank holds about **18.5** gallons of gas. Today, gas is selling for **$2.489** per gallon in your town. Estimate how much it will cost to fill the tank.*

SOLUTION

Note that 18.5 gallons is about 20 gallons and $2.489 is about $2.50. Therefore, $20 \cdot 2.5 = \$50$. You will need approximately $50 to fill the tank.

PROCEDURE

Estimating Products of Decimals

1. Round each factor to one or two nonzero digits (the number you can handle easily in your head).
2. Multiply the results of step 1. This is your estimate.

10. Estimate the following products.

    a. $57.3 \cdot 615.3$

    b. $-0.031 \cdot 322.76$

    c. $7893.65 \cdot 0.0016$

d. If you multiply a positive number by a decimal between 0 and 1, is the product greater or smaller than the original number?

11. Your uncle teaches at a college in San Francisco where gas costs $3.259 a gallon. His car holds 17.1 gallons of gasoline.

  a. Estimate how much he would spend to fill an empty tank.

  b. Calculate the amount he would actually spend to fill an empty tank.

EXAMPLE 6   *In 2002, a Japanese research laboratory built the world's fastest supercomputer to study weather and other environmental conditions around Earth. The speed of the NEC Earth Simulator was reported at 35.6 teraflops, or trillions of mathematical operations per second. The next fastest supercomputer was listed as the IBM ASCII White-Pacific with a speed of 7.226 teraflops. Estimate how many times faster the Earth Simulator is than the White-Pacific.*

SOLUTION

35.6 is approximately 35 and 7.226 is about 7. Therefore,

$$\frac{35.6}{7.226} \approx \frac{35}{7} = 5.$$

The Earth Simulator is about 5 times faster than the White-Pacific.

PROCEDURE

Estimating Quotients of Decimals

1. Think of the division as a fraction with the dividend as the numerator and the divisor as the denominator.
2. Round the numerator and denominator to one or two nonzero digits (a number you can handle easily in your head).
3. Divide the results of step 2. This is your estimate.

12. Estimate the following quotients.

  a. $857.3 \div 61.53$

  b. $-0.0315 \div 32.2$

c. $8934.65 \div 0.0018$

d. If you divide a positive number by a decimal fraction between 0 and 1, is the quotient greater than or smaller than the original number?

SUMMARY
ACTIVITY 3.5

1. Multiplying two decimals:

   a. Multiply two numbers as if they were whole numbers, ignoring decimal points for the moment.

   b. Add the number of digits to the right of the decimal point in each factor, to obtain the number of digits that must be to the right of the decimal point in the product.

   c. Place the decimal point in the product by counting digits from the right.

2. Dividing decimals:

   a. Write the division in long division format.

   b. Move the decimal point the same number of places to the right in both divisor and dividend so that the divisor becomes a whole number.

   c. Place the decimal point in the quotient directly above the decimal point in the dividend and divide as usual.

3. Estimating products of decimals:

   a. Round each factor to one or two nonzero digits (the number you can handle easily in your head).

   b. Multiply the results of step a. This is your estimate.

4. Estimating quotients of decimals:

   a. Think of the division as a fraction, with the dividend as the numerator and the divisor as the denominator.

   b. Round the numerator and denominator to one or two nonzero digits (the number you can handle easily in your head).

   c. Divide the results of step b. This is your estimate.

EXERCISES
ACTIVITY 3.5

1. You drive your own car while delivering pizzas for a local pizzeria. Your boss said she would reimburse you $0.32 per mile for the wear and tear on your car. The first week of work you put 178 miles on your car.

   a. Estimate how much you will receive for using your own car.

   b. Explain how you determined your estimate.

   c. How much did you receive for using your own car?

2. Perform the following calculations. Use your calculator to check your answer.

   a. $-12.53 \cdot -8.2$ **b.** $115.3 \cdot -0.003$ **c.** $14.62 \cdot -0.75$

   d. Divide 12.05 by 2.5.   **e.** Divide 18.99729 by 78.

   f. Divide 14.05 by 0.0002.   **g.** $150 \div 0.03$

   h. $0.00442 \div 0.017$ **i.** $69.115 \div 0.0023$

3. You and some college friends go out to lunch to celebrate the end of midterm exams. There are six of you, and you decide to split the $47.98 bill evenly.

   a. Estimate how much each person owed for lunch.

   b. Explain how you determined your estimate.

   c. How much did each person actually pay? Round your answer to the nearest cent.

4. You have just purchased a new home. The town's assessed value of your home (which is usually much *lower* than the purchase price) is $68,700. For every $1000 of assessed value, you will pay $7.48 in taxes. How much do you pay in taxes?

5. Alex Rodriguez of the New York Yankees led the American League in home runs with 48 in the 2005 season. He also made 194 hits in 605 times at bat. What was his batting average? (Batting average = number of hits ÷ number of at bats.) Use decimal notation and round to the nearest thousandth.

6. The top-grossing North American concert tour between 1985 and 1999 was the Rolling Stones tour in 1994. The tour included 60 shows and sold $121.2 million worth of tickets.

   a. Estimate the average amount of ticket sales per show.

   b. What was the actual average amount of ticket sales per show?

c. The Stones 2005 tour broke their previous record, selling $162 million worth of tickets in 42 performances. What was the average amount of ticket sales per show in 2005, rounded to the nearest $1000?

7. In 1992, the NEC SX-3/44 supercomputer had a speed of 0.020 teraflops (trillions of mathematical operations per second).

a. How many times faster is the NEC Earth Simulator supercomputer whose speed is 35.6 teraflops?

b. In 1993, the speed of the Fujitsu NWT supercomputer was 0.124 teraflops. How many times faster was it than the NEC SX–3/44?

c. In 2005, a new supercomputer, designed specifically to simulate proteins for biology and drug research, the IBM Blue Gene/L (Watson), posted a speed of 91.3 teraflops. How many times faster was it than the NEC SX-3/44?

8. Your friend tracked his GPAs for his first three semesters as shown in the following table.

a. Calculate your friend's GPA for each of the semesters listed in the table. Record the results in the table.

	CREDITS	QUALITY POINTS	GPA
SEMESTER 1	14	36.54	
SEMESTER 2	15	49.05	
SEMESTER 3	16	45.92	

b. Determine his cumulative GPA for the first two semesters.

c. Determine his cumulative GPA for all three semesters.

ACTIVITY 3.6

Tracking Temperature

OBJECTIVES

1. Use the order of operations to evaluate expressions that include decimals.

2. Use the distributive property in calculations involving decimals.

3. Evaluate formulas that include decimals.

4. Solve equations of the form $ax = b$ that include decimals.

Temperature measures warmth or coolness of everything around us—in lake water, in the human body, in the air we breathe. The thermometer is Alaska's favorite scientific instrument. During the winter, says Ned Rozell at the Geophysical Institute of the University of Alaska at Fairbanks, "we check our beloved thermometers thousands of times a day."

Thermometers have scales whose units are called *degrees*. The two commonly used scales are Fahrenheit and Celsius. The Celsius scale is the choice in science. Most English-speaking countries began changing to Celsius in the late 1960s, but the United States is still the outstanding exception to this changeover.

Each scale was determined by considering two reference temperatures, the freezing point and the boiling point of water. On the Fahrenheit scale, the freezing point of water is taken as 32°F and the boiling point is 212°F. On the Celsius scale, the freezing point is taken as 0°C and the boiling point is 100°C. This leads to a formula that converts Celsius degrees to Fahrenheit degrees,

$$y = 1.8x + 32,$$

where y represents degrees Fahrenheit and x represents degrees Celsius.

1. Each year, the now-famous Iditarod Trail Sled Dog Race in Alaska starts on the first Saturday in March. Temperatures on the trail can range from about 5°C down to about −50°C.

   a. Use the formula $y = 1.8x + 32$ to convert 5°C to degrees Fahrenheit.

   b. Convert −50°C to degrees Fahrenheit.

   c. In a sentence, describe the temperature range in degrees Fahrenheit.

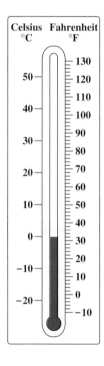

2. The Tour de France bicycle race is held in July in France. The race ends in Paris where July's temperature ranges from 57°F to 77°F. Use the formula $x = (y - 32) \div 1.8$ to convert these temperatures to degrees Celsius.

The previous problems show that expressions that involve decimals are evaluated by the usual order of operations procedures.

3. Evaluate the following expressions using order of operations. Use your calculator to check your answer.

   a. $100 + 100(0.075)(2.5)$

   b. $2(8.4 + 11.7)$

   c. $0.5(9.16 + 6.38) \cdot 4.21$

Solving Equations of the Form $ax = b$ that Involve Decimals

4. The Tour de France is held in 21 stages of varying distances. One stage runs from Orleans to Evry, a distance of 149.5 km. The best time for completing this stage was 3.2075 hours.

   a. Use the formula $d = rt$ to determine the average speed of the cyclists with the best time for this stage. Recall that d represents distance, t, time, and r, average speed.

   b. The distance in miles for this stage is 93.5 miles. Determine the average speed in terms of miles per hour (mph) for this stage.

The formula $d = rt$ is an example of an equation that is of the form $b = ax$. Problem 4 illustrates the fact that equations of the form $b = ax$ (or $ax = b$) that involve decimals are solved in the same way as those with whole numbers, integers, or fractions.

5. a. In the 2006 Iditarod Trail Sled Dog Race, the winner, Jeff King of Denali, Alaska, and his dog team ran the last leg of the race from Safety to Nome in 3.31 hours. The distance between these two towns is about 22.0 miles. What was the average speed of King's team?

   b. Jeff King finished the entire 2006 race in 9 days, 11 hours, 11 minutes, and 36 seconds. In terms of hours, this is 227.193 hours. The race followed the northern route of about 1112 miles. What was his team's average speed over the entire race?

Distributive Property

EXAMPLE 1 *The vegetable garden along the side of your house measures 20.2 feet long by 12.6 feet wide. You want to enclose it with a picket fence. How many feet of fencing will you need?*

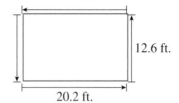

The diagram indicates that you can add the length to the width and then double it to determine the amount of fencing. Numerically, you write

$$2(20.2 + 12.6) = 2 \cdot 32.8 = 65.6 \text{ ft.}$$

Note that another way to solve the problem is to add *twice* the length to *twice* the width. Numerically,

$$2 \cdot 20.2 + 2 \cdot 12.6 = 40.4 + 25.2 = 65.6 \text{ ft.}$$

In either case, the amount of fencing is 65.6 feet. This means that the expression $2(20.2 + 12.6)$ is equal to the expression $2 \cdot 20.2 + 2 \cdot 12.6$. This example illustrates that the distributive property you learned for whole numbers, integers, and fractions also holds for decimal numbers.

The amount of fencing can be determined by using a formula for the perimeter of a rectangle. If P represents the perimeter, l, the length, and w, the width, then

$$P = 2(l + w) \quad \text{or} \quad P = 2l + 2w.$$

6. Your neighbor also has a rectangular garden, but its length is 10.5 feet by 13.8 feet wide. Use a perimeter formula to determine the distance around your neighbor's garden.

7. Next year you plan to make your garden longer and keep the width the same to gain more area for growing vegetables. You have not decided how much you want to increase the length. Call the extra length x. As you look at the diagram, note that a formula for the area of the new garden can be determined in two ways.

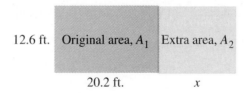

Method 1

a. Determine an expression for the new length in terms of x

b. Multiply the expression in part a by 12.6 to obtain the new area, A. Recall that area equals the product of the length and width, or $A = lw$.

Method 2

c. Determine an expression for the extra area, A_2.

d. Add the extra area, A_2, to the original area, A_1, to obtain the new area A.

8. Explain how you may obtain the expression in Problem 7d directly from the expression in Problem 8b by the distributive property.

9. Use the distributive property to simplify the following.

    a. $0.2(4x - 0.15) =$

    b. $3.4(2.05x - 0.1)$

10. Simplify each of the following expressions. Check the results using your calculator.

    a. $0.2 - 0.42(5.4 - 6)^2$

    b. $0.24 \div 0.06 \cdot 0.2$

    c. $4.96 - 6 + 5.3 \cdot 0.2 - (0.007)^2$

11. Evaluate the following.

    a. $2x - 4(y - 3)$, where $x = 0.5$ and $y = 1.2$

    b. $b^2 - 4ac$, where $a = 6$, $b = 1.2$, and $c = -0.03$

    c. $\dfrac{2.6x - 0.13y}{x - y}$, where $x = 0.3$ and $y = 6.8$

12. Evaluate the following using the order of operations. Check the results using your calculator.

   a. $(-0.5)^2 + 3$

   b. $(2.6 - 1.08)^2$

   c. $(-2.1)^2 - (0.07)^2$

**SUMMARY
ACTIVITY 3.6**

1. The rules that apply to whole numbers, integers, and fractions, *also apply to decimals.* They are:

- the order of operations procedure,
- the distributive property, and
- the evaluation of formulas

**EXERCISES
ACTIVITY 3.6**

In Exercises 1–4, calculate using the order of operations. Check the results using your calculator.

1. $48.5 - 10.34 + 4.66$

2. $0.56 \div 0.08 \cdot 0.7$

3. $10.31 + 8.05 \cdot 0.4 - (0.08)^2$

4. $-2.6 \cdot .01 + (-.01) \cdot (-8.3)$

In Exercises 5–7, evaluate the expression for the given values.

5. $\frac{1}{2}h(a + b)$, where $h = 0.3$, $a = 1.24$, and $b = 2.006$

6. $3.14\, r^2$, where $r = 0.25$ inches

7. $A \div B - C \cdot D$, where $A = 10.8$, $B = 0.12$, $C = 2.4$, and $D = 6$

Exercise numbers appearing in color are answered in the Selected Answers appendix.

8. You earn $7.25 per hour and are paid once a month. You record the number of hours worked each week in your table.

WEEK	1	2	3	4
HOURS WORKED	35	20.5	12	17.75

a. Write a numerical expression using parentheses to show how you will determine your gross salary for the month.

b. Simplify the expression in part a.

c. You think you are going to get a raise but don't know how much it might be. Write an expression to show your new hourly rate. Represent the amount of the raise by x.

d. Calculate the total number of hours worked for the month. Use it with your result in part c to write an expression to represent your new gross salary after the raise.

e. Use the distributive property to simplify the expression in part d.

f. Your boss tells you that your raise will be $0.50 an hour. How much did you make this month?

9. You have been following your stock investment over the past 4 months. Your friend tells you that his stock's value has doubled in the past 4 months. You know that your stock did better than that. Without telling your friend how much your original investment was, you would like to do a little boasting. The following table shows your stock's activity each month for 4 months.

Up with the Dow-Jones

MONTH	1	2	3	4
STOCK VALUE	decreased $75	doubled	increased $150	tripled

a. Represent your original investment by x dollars and write an algebraic expression to represent the value of your stock after the first month.

b. Use the result from part a to determine an expression for the value at the end of the second month. Simplify the expression if possible. Continue this procedure until you determine the value of your stock at the end of the fourth month.

c. Explain to your friend what has happened to the value of your stock over 4 months.

d. Instead of simplifying after each step, write a single algebraic expression that represents the changes over the 4-month period.

e. Simplify the expression in part d. How does the simplified algebraic expression compare with the result in part b?

f. Your stock's value was $4678.75 four months ago. What is your stock's value today?

10. Translate each of the following verbal statements into equations and solve. Let x represent the unknown number.

a. The quotient of a number and 5.3 is -6.7.

b. A number times 3.6 is 23.4.

c. 42.75 is the product of a number and -7.5.

d. A number divided by 2.3 is 13.2.

e. -9.4 times a number is 47.

11. Solve each of the following equations. Round the result to the nearest hundredth if necessary.

  a. $3x = 15.3$

  b. $-2.3x = 10.35$

  c. $-5.2a = -44.2$

  d. $15.2 = 15.2y$

  e. $98.8 = -4y$

  f. $4.2x = -\sqrt{64}$

12. You and your best friend are avid cyclists. You are planning a bike trip from Corning, New York, to West Point. On the Internet, you find that the distance from Corning to West Point is approximately 236.4 miles. On a recent similar trip, you both averaged about 35.4 miles per hour. You are interested in estimating the riding time for this trip to the nearest tenth of an hour.

  a. Reread the problem and list all the numerical information you have been given.

  b. What are you trying to determine? Give it a letter name.

  c. What is the relationship between the length of your intended trip, the rate at which you travel, and what you want to determine?

  d. Write an equation for the relationship in part c.

  e. Solve the equation in part d.

  f. Is your solution reasonable? Explain.

What Have I Learned?

1. When multiplying two decimals, how do you decide where to place the decimal point in the product? Illustrate with an example.

2. **a.** When faced with a division problem such as $2.35\overline{)1950.5}$, what would you do first?

   b. Explain how you would estimate this quotient.

3. How do the rules for order of operations and the distributive property apply to decimals?

4. Explain the steps you would take to determine the value for I from the formula $I = P + Prt$ if $P = 1500$, $r = 0.095$, and $t = 2.8$.

5. **a.** Each day, you estimate the average speed at which you are traveling on a car trip from Massachusetts to North Carolina. You keep track of the hours and mileage. Explain how you would use the formula $d = rt$ to determine your average speed.

b. Explain how the two formulas, $d = rt$ and $I = Pr$ are mathematically similar.

6. a. Give at least one reason why estimating a product or quotient would be beneficial.

b. Give a reason(s) for the steps you would take to estimate $15,776 \div 425$.

7. If you divide a negative number by a number between 0 and 1, is the quotient greater than or less than the original number? Give an example to illustrate your answer.

In Exercises 1–4, estimate the products and quotients.

1. $36.42 \cdot (-4.2)$

2. $-226.90 \cdot (-0.005)$

3. $14.62 \div (-0.75)$

4. Divide 43,096.48 by 78.4.

In Exercises 5–8, calculate the products and quotients. Check your result with a calculator.

5. $36.42 \cdot (-4.2)$

6. $-226.90 \cdot (-0.005)$

7. $14.625 \div (-0.75)$

8. $43,096.48 \div 78.4$

9. $0.63 \div 0.09 \cdot 0.5$

10. $30.38 + 4.05 \cdot 0.6 - (0.03)^2$

11. $-6.2 \cdot .03 + (-.01) \cdot (-6.3)$

12. Evaluate the expression $\frac{1}{2}h(a + b)$, where $h = 0.7$, $a = 3.45$, and $b = 5.00$.

13. Evaluate the expression πr^2, where $r = 0.84$ inches. Use 3.14 for π and round to the hundredths place.

14. Evaluate the expression $A \div B - C \cdot D$, where $A = 9.9$, $B = 0.33$, $C = 2.7$, and $D = 4$.

Translate each of the following verbal statements into equations and solve. Let x represent the unknown number.

15. The quotient of a number and -7.4 is 13.5.

16. A number times -9.76 is 678.32.

17. A number divided by -9.5 is 78.3.

Solve each of the following equations. Round to the nearest hundredths if necessary.

18. $7x = 5.81$

19. $-2.3x = 58.65$

20. $-5.2a = -57.72$

21. You buy a DVD player at a discount and pay $136.15. This discounted price represents seven-tenths of the original price. Answer the following questions to determine the original price.

   a. List all of the information you have been given.

   b. What quantity are you trying to determine?

   c. Write a verbal statement to express the relationship between the price you paid, the discount rate, and what quantity you want to determine.

   d. Select a letter to represent the original price. Then write an equation based on the verbal statement in part c.

   e. Solve the equation in part d to obtain the original price.

   f. Is your solution reasonable? Explain.

22. George Herman "Babe" Ruth was baseball's first great batter and is one of the most famous players of all time.

   a. In 1921, Babe Ruth played for the New York Yankees, hitting 59 home runs and making 204 hits out of 540 at bats. What was his batting average? Recall that batting averages are recorded to the nearest thousandth.

b. In 2001, Barry Bonds of the San Francisco Giants broke the single-season record for most home runs (73). During that season, he made 156 hits out of 476 at bats. What was his batting average?

c. Which of the two batting averages is the highest?

23. A student majoring in science earned the credits and quality points listed in the following table. Complete the table by determining the student's GPA for each semester and his cumulative GPA at the end of the fourth semester.

Majoring in Science

	CREDITS	QUALITY POINTS	GPA
SEMESTER 1	14	35.42	
SEMESTER 2	15	44.85	
SEMESTER 3	16	55.20	
SEMESTER 4	16	51.68	
CUMULATIVE GPA			

24. A sophomore at your college took the courses and earned the grades that are listed in the following table. Complete the table and determine the GPA to the nearest hundredth.

	CREDITS	GRADE	NUMERICAL EQUIVALENT	QUALITY POINTS
ENGLISH	3	C-	1.67	
PHYSICS	4	B	3.00	
HISTORY	3	C+	2.33	
MATH	4	A-	3.67	
MODERN DANCE	2	B+	3.33	
TOTALS		n/a	n/a	
GPA	n/a	n/a	n/a	

25. Every May since 1977, Bike New York offers cyclists a 42-mile tour of the five boroughs (counties) that make up New York City. In 2005, a week before the tour, the temperature was predicted to range from a low of 54°F to a high of 71°F. Determine these temperatures in degrees Celsius for your friend coming from Canada to do the tour. Recall the formula $x = (y - 32)1.8$ where x is the temperature in Celsius and y is the temperature in Farenheit.

26. In your chemistry class, you need to weigh a sample of pure carbon. You will weigh the amount that you have 3 times and take the average (called the *mean*) of the three weighings. The average weight is the one you will report as the actual weight of the carbon. The three weights you obtain are 12.17 grams, 12.14 grams, and 12.20 grams.

    a. Explain how you will calculate the average.

    b. Determine the average weight of the carbon to the nearest hundredth of a gram.

The bracketed numbers following each concept indicate the activity in which the concept is discussed.

CONCEPT / SKILL	DESCRIPTION	EXAMPLE
Multiply/divide integers with the same sign [3.1]	To multiply or divide two integers with the same sign: 1. Multiply or divide their absolute values. 2. The product or quotient will always be positive.	$(-6) \cdot (-7) = 42$ $4 \cdot 3 = 12$ $8 \div 2 = 4$ $(-20) \div (-4) = 5$
Multiply/divide integers with opposite signs [3.1]	To multiply or divide two integers with opposite signs: 1. Multiply or divide their absolute values. 2. The product or quotient will always be negative.	$(-42) \div 14 = -3$ $11 \cdot (-4) = -44$
Product of an even number of negative factors [3.1]	The product will be positive if you are multiplying an even number of negative integers.	$(-3) \cdot (-4) \cdot (-2) \cdot (-1)$ $= 24$
Product of an odd number of negative factors [3.1]	The product will be negative if you are multiplying an odd number of negative integers.	$(-3) \cdot (-4) \cdot (-2) = -24$
The distributive properties [3.2], [3.4], [3.6]	The distributive properties, $$a(b + c) = ab + ac$$ $$a(b - c) = ab - ac,$$ hold for rational numbers.	$\dfrac{3}{4}\left(\dfrac{1}{2} + \dfrac{1}{2}\right) = \dfrac{3}{4} \cdot \dfrac{1}{2} + \dfrac{3}{4} \cdot \dfrac{1}{2}$ $= \dfrac{3}{8} + \dfrac{3}{8} = \dfrac{6}{8} = \dfrac{3}{4}$ $\dfrac{1}{2}\left(\dfrac{3}{5} - \dfrac{2}{5}\right) = \dfrac{1}{2} \cdot \dfrac{3}{5} - \dfrac{1}{2} \cdot \dfrac{2}{5}$ $= \dfrac{3}{10} - \dfrac{2}{10} = \dfrac{1}{10}$
Order of operations [3.2], [3.4], [3.6]	The order of operation rules for rational numbers are the same as those applied to whole numbers.	$30.38 + 4.5 \cdot 0.6 - (0.3)^2$ $= 30.38 + 4.5 \cdot 0.6 - 0.09$ $= 30.38 + 2.7 - 0.09$ $= 33.08 - 0.09$ $= 32.99$
Negation of a squared number [3.2]	Negation, or determining the opposite, always follows exponentiation in the order of operations.	$-5^2 = -(5^2)$ $= -1 \cdot 25$ $= -25$
Evaluate expressions or formulas that involve integers, fractions, and decimals [3.2], [3.4], [3.6]	To evaluate formulas or expressions involving rational numbers, substitute for the variables and evaluate using the order of operations.	Evaluate $6xy - y^2$, where $x = \frac{1}{3}$ and $y = 3$. $6xy - y^2 = 6\left(\frac{1}{3}\right)(3) - 3^2$ $= 6 - 9 = -3$

CONCEPT / SKILL	DESCRIPTION	EXAMPLE
Solve $ax = b$ for x that involve integers, fractions, and decimals [3.2], [3.4], [3.6]	To solve the equation $$ax = b, a \neq 0,$$ you need to divide each side of the equation by a to obtain the value for x.	Solve $-3x = -216$. $$\frac{-3x}{-3} = \frac{-216}{-3}$$ $$x = 72$$
General problem-solving strategy [3.2], [3.4], [3.6]	To solve verbal problems: 1. Understand the problem. 2. Compile the information. 3. Solve the problem. 4. Check the equation for reasonableness.	
Multiply fractions [3.3]	To multiply fractions, multiply the numerators and the denominators. $$\frac{a}{b} \cdot \frac{c}{d} = \frac{ac}{bd}$$	$$\frac{3}{5} \cdot \frac{2}{7} = \frac{3 \cdot 2}{5 \cdot 7} = \frac{6}{35}$$
The negative sign for a negative fraction [3.3]	There are three different ways to place the sign for a negative fraction.	$-\dfrac{2}{5} = \dfrac{-2}{5} = \dfrac{2}{-5}$ are all the same number.
Reciprocals [3.3]	The reciprocal of a nonzero number, written in fraction form, is the fraction obtained by interchanging the numerator and denominator of the original fraction. The product of a number and its reciprocal is always 1.	The reciprocal of $\dfrac{5}{7}$ is $\dfrac{7}{5}$, because $\dfrac{5}{7} \cdot \dfrac{7}{5} = 1$.
Divide fractions [3.3]	To divide fractions: 1. Multiply the dividend by the reciprocal of the divisor. 2. Reduce to lowest terms. $$\frac{a}{b} \div \frac{c}{d} = \frac{a}{b} \cdot \frac{d}{c}$$	$$\frac{3}{8} \div \frac{5}{7} = \frac{3}{8} \cdot \frac{7}{5} = \frac{21}{40}$$ $$\frac{4}{5} \div \frac{2}{3} = \frac{4}{5} \cdot \frac{3}{2} = \frac{12}{10}$$ $$= \frac{6}{5} \text{ or } 1\frac{1}{5}$$
Multiplications and divisions involving 0 [3.1]	1. Any number times 0 is 0. 2. 0 divided by any nonzero integer is 0. 3. No integer may be divided by 0.	$3 \cdot 0 = 0$ $0 \div 6 = 0$ $6 \div 0$ is not possible.
Multiply mixed numbers [3.4]	To multiply mixed numbers: 1. Change the mixed numbers to improper fractions. 2. Multiply as you would proper fractions. 3. If the product is an improper fraction, convert it to a mixed number.	$$3\frac{1}{2} \cdot 4\frac{3}{8} = \frac{7}{2} \cdot \frac{35}{8}$$ $$= \frac{245}{16} = 15\frac{5}{16}$$

CONCEPT / SKILL	DESCRIPTION	EXAMPLE
Divide mixed numbers [3.4]	To divide mixed numbers: 1. Change the mixed numbers to improper fractions. 2. Divide as you would proper fractions. 3. If the quotient is an improper fraction, convert it to a mixed number.	$4\dfrac{5}{8} \div 2\dfrac{1}{3} = \dfrac{37}{8} \div \dfrac{7}{3}$ $= \dfrac{37}{8} \cdot \dfrac{3}{7} = \dfrac{111}{56}$ $= 1\dfrac{55}{56}$
Squaring fractions [3.4]	To determine the square of a fraction: 1. Determine the square of the numerator. 2. Determine the square of the denominator. 3. The square of the fraction is the quotient of the two squares. 4. Write the result as a mixed number if necessary.	$\left(\dfrac{3}{4}\right)^2 = \dfrac{3^2}{4^2} = \dfrac{9}{16}$
Square roots of fractions [3.4]	To determine the square root of a fraction: 1. Determine the square root of the numerator. 2. Determine the square root of the denominator. 3. The square root of the fraction is the quotient of the two square roots. 4. Write the result as a mixed number if necessary.	$\sqrt{\dfrac{25}{144}} = \dfrac{\sqrt{25}}{\sqrt{144}} = \dfrac{5}{12}$
Multiply decimals [3.5]	To multiply decimals: 1. Multiply two numbers as if they were whole numbers, ignoring decimal points for the moment. 2. Add the number of digits to the right of the decimal point in each factor, to obtain the number of digits that must be to the right of the decimal point in the product. 3. Place the decimal point in the product by counting digits from the right.	$\begin{array}{r} 23.4 \\ \times\, 2.45 \\ \hline 1170 \\ 936 \\ 468 \\ \hline 57.330 \end{array}$

CONCEPT / SKILL	DESCRIPTION	EXAMPLE
Divide decimal fractions [3.5]	To divide decimals: 1. Write the division in long division format. 2. Move the decimal point the same number of places to the right in both divisor and dividend so that the divisor becomes a whole number. 3. Place the decimal point in the quotient directly above the decimal point in the dividend and divide as usual.	$$\begin{array}{r} 56.7 \\ 2.3\overline{)130.41} \\ 115 \\ \hline 154 \\ 138 \\ \hline 161 \\ 161 \\ \hline 0 \end{array}$$
Estimate products [3.5]	To estimate products: 1. Round each factor to one or two nonzero digits. 2. Multiply the rounded factors. This is your estimate.	Estimate 279×52. $300 \times 50 = 15{,}000$
Estimate quotients [3.5]	To estimate quotients: 1. Think of the division as a fraction. 2. Round the numerator and denominator to one or two nonzero digits. 3. Divide the results of step 2. This is your estimate.	Estimate $93.4\overline{)345.26}$. $\dfrac{345.26}{93.4} \approx \dfrac{350}{100} = 3.5$

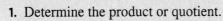

1. Determine the product or quotient.

   a. $-4 \cdot 38$

   b. $\dfrac{4}{9} \cdot -\dfrac{15}{14}$

   c. $-42 \div -6$

   d. $30.8 \div .002$

   e. $2\dfrac{4}{5} \div 2\dfrac{1}{10}$

   f. $-4.89(-.0008)$

2. Perform the indicated operations.

   a. $\left(-\dfrac{8}{13}\right)^2$

   b. -4^2

   c. $\sqrt{\dfrac{121}{144}}$

3. Determine the product of 13 factors of -1.

4. Explain the difference between -5^2 and $(-5)^2$.

5. Evaluate each expression.

   a. $-7.2 \cdot 0.06 + .81 \div (-0.9)$

   b. $\dfrac{10 - 6 \cdot 4 - 3^2}{6 - (2)^2}$

6. Evaluate each expression.

   a. $2x - 6(x - 3)$, where $x = -1\dfrac{1}{2}$

   b. $-3xy - x^2$, where $x = -2$ and $y = -6$

Answers to all Gateway exercises are included in the Selected Answers appendix.

c. $\pi r^2 h$, where $r = 2.4$ and $h = 0.9$

7. Solve for the unknown in each of the following.

a. $-12x = -72$

b. $\dfrac{-x}{6} = 14$

c. $-\dfrac{4}{9} = -18x$

d. $8n = 73.84$

e. $-\dfrac{5}{9} = \dfrac{20}{33}s$

f. $12.9 = 0.0387x$

8. Translate each of the following verbal statements into an equation and solve for the unknown value. Let x represent the unknown number.

a. The quotient of a number and -15 is -7.

b. $-\dfrac{11}{12}$ times a number is $2\dfrac{1}{16}$.

c. 1.08 is the product of a number and 0.2.

9. You have prepared $9\dfrac{1}{2}$ gallons of fruit punch for your friend's bridal shower. How many $\dfrac{3}{4}$-cup servings will you have for the guests?

10. According to the U.S. Bureau of the Census, the population of North Dakota in 1990 was 638,800. In 1930, North Dakota's population was 680,845. Determine the average population decrease per year since 1930.

11. There are 47,224 square miles of land in New York State. The population of the state is 18,196,601. If the land were divided equally among all people in New York State, approximately what part of a square mile would each person get? Round your answer to the nearest thousandth.

12. In 1820, there were approximately 2.9 million workers in the United States. Approximately 7 out of 10 of these workers were employed in farm-related occupations. How many people had farm occupations in 1820? (*Source*: U.S. Dept. of Agriculture)

13. You are trying to understand your electric bill. It looks like there are delivery charges for the electricity as well as supply charges. The basic charge for electricity for June 19 to July 17 was $13.79. In addition, you used 270 kWh of electricity. The delivery charge for 270 kWh was $.0059714 per kWh. The supply charge was $.0049600 per kWh. Determine your total electric bill before taxes.

14. There are 7318 air miles between London and New York City. If you are a passenger on a commercial plane, what is the average speed of the plane if the trip takes approximately $11\frac{3}{4}$ hours? Estimate your answer and then solve the equation.

15. You are making crafts to sell at an arts festival. There are two different types. The ceramic bowl sells for $15.85 and the candle holder sells for $9.95. Let *b* represent the number of bowls that you sell and *h* represent the number of candle holders.

   a. Write an expression that will determine the revenue from the sale of your crafts at the festival.

   b. If you sell 26 bowls and 13 holders, what would be the total revenue?

16. To help pay tuition, you take a part-time job at a fast-food restaurant. The job pays $6.75 per hour. Since you are going to a community college full-time, you need to determine how many hours you will work at the restaurant so you can balance your schoolwork and your job.

  a. Use the input/output table to calculate the total amount of salary (output) for different numbers of hours (input) worked.

NO. OF HOURS	12	18	24	30
TOTAL SALARY				

  b. Explain how you determined the total salary in the table.

  c. Write an equation to determine the number of hours you should work to receive $150 per week and solve.

17. You are planning a trip with your best friend from college. You have 4 days for your trip, and you plan to travel x hours per day. On the first day you drove 2 extra hours; the second day you doubled the number of hours you planned; on the third day you lost 4 hours due to fog; and on the fourth day you traveled only one-fourth of the planned time due to sightseeing. The table indicates the number of hours traveled per day in relationship to x hours per day.

DAY	1	2	3	4
NO. OF HOURS	Gained 2	double time	lost 4	$\frac{1}{4}$ of planned time

  a. Write an expression to show how many hours you traveled the first day.

  b. Write an expression to show the number of hours you traveled for the first 2 days.

  c. Write an expression to show the number of hours you traveled for the 4 days. Write in simplest form.

d. If you averaged 52 miles per hour over the 4 days, write an equation to determine the total distance traveled for the 4 days.

e. If 7 hours per day was your anticipated time traveling per day, determine the number of miles you would have traveled on your trip.

CHAPTER 4

PROBLEM SOLVING WITH RATIOS, PROPORTIONS, AND PERCENTS

When you deal with sales tax, mortgage and car payments, sales and discounts, salaries, and sports statistics, you use proportional reasoning.

When you work with drug doses in medicine, liquid solutions in chemistry, weights and volumes in physics, species identification in biology, and similar triangles in geometry, you use proportional reasoning. The list goes on and on.

Proportional reasoning is based on the idea of relative comparison of quantities. In this chapter you will learn about relative comparisons and how such comparisons lead to the use of fractions, decimals, and percents. When you have completed this chapter, you will have the basic mathematical tools you need for solving problems that require proportional reasoning.

ACTIVITY 4.1

Everything Is Relative

OBJECTIVES

1. Understand the distinction between actual and relative measure.

2. Write a ratio in its verbal, fraction, decimal, and percent formats.

In the 2005 National Basketball Association finals, the San Antonio Spurs defeated the Detroit Pistons. Among the outstanding players during the series were Tim Duncan and Tony Parker of the Spurs, and Chauncey Billups and Richard Hamilton of the Pistons. The data in the table represent each man's field goal totals for the five-game championship series.

PLAYER	FIELD GOALS MADE	FIELD GOALS ATTEMPTED
Billups	46	106
Duncan	54	129
Hamilton	49	127
Parker	44	96

1. Using *only* the data in column 2, Field Goals Made, rank the players from best to worst according to their field goal performance.

2. You can also rank the players by using the data from both column 2 and column 3. For example, Chauncey Billups made 46 field goals out of the 106 he attempted. The 46 successful baskets can be compared to the 106 attempts by *dividing* 46 *by* 106. You can represent that comparison numerically as the

fraction $\frac{46}{106}$, or, equivalently, as the decimal 0.434 (rounded to thousandths).

Complete the following table and use your results to determine another ranking of the four players from best to worst performance based on the ratio of goals made to goals attempted.

Key Players

PLAYER	FIELD GOALS MADE	FIELD GOALS ATTEMPTED	VERBAL	FRACTION	DECIMAL
Billups	46	106	46 out of 106	$\frac{46}{106}$	0.434
Duncan	54	129			
Hamilton	49	127			
Parker	44	96			

Actual and Relative Measure

The two sets of rankings in Problems 1 and 2 were based on two different points of view. The ranking in Problem 1 is from an **actual** viewpoint in which you just count the *actual* number of field goals made. The ranking in Problem 2 is from a **relative** perspective in which you take into account the number of successes relative to the number of attempts.

3. Which measure best describes field-goal performance: absolute or relative? Explain.

4. Identify which statements refer to an actual measure or a relative measure. Explain your answers.

   a. I got 7 answers wrong.

   b. I guessed on 4 answers.

   c. Two-thirds of the class failed.

d. I saved $10.

e. I saved 40%.

f. 4 out of 5 students work to help pay tuition.

g. Derek Jeter's batting average is 0.296.

h. Barry Bonds hit 73 home runs, a major league record, in 2001.

i. In 2005, 16 million Americans owned a Palm personal digital assistant.

j. By 2008, 40% of all physicians will rely on a personal digital assistant.

5. What mathematical notation or verbal phrases in Problem 4 indicated a relative measure?

DEFINITIONS

Relative measure is a term used to describe the comparison of two similar quantities.

Ratio is the term used to describe relative measure as a quotient of **two similar quantities,** often a "part" and a "total," where "part" is *divided by* the "total."

---

6. Use the free-throw statistics from the 2005 championship games to express each player's relative performance as a ratio in verbal, fraction, and decimal form. The ratios for Chauncey Billups are completed for you. Round decimals to the nearest thousandth.

Nothing but Net

PLAYER	FREE THROWS MADE	FREE THROW ATTEMPTS	VERBALLY	EXPRESSED AS A FRACTION	AS A DECIMAL
Billups	40	44	40 out of 44	$\frac{40}{44}$	0.909
Duncan	36	54			
Hamilton	18	24			
Parker	7	15			

7. a. Three friends, shooting baskets in the schoolyard, kept track of their performance. Andy made 9 out of 15 shots, Pat made 28 out of 40, and Val made 15 out of 24. Rank their relative performance.

   b. Which ratio form (fraction, decimal, or other) did you use to determine the ranking?

8. Describe how to determine if the two ratios "12 out of 20" and "21 out of 35" are equivalent?

9. a. Match each ratio from column A with the equivalent ratio in column B.

Column A	Column B
15 out of 25	84 out of 100
42 out of 60	65 out of 100
63 out of 75	60 out of 100
52 out of 80	70 out of 100

   b. Which set of ratios, those in column A or those in column B, is more useful in comparing and ranking the ratios? Why?

Percents

Relative measure based on 100 is familiar and natural. There are 100 cents in a dollar and 100 points on many tests. You have probably been using a ranking scale from 0 to 100 since childhood. You most likely have an instinctive understanding of ratios relative to 100. A ratio such as 40 out of 100 can be expressed as 40 **per** 100, or, more commonly, as 40 **percent**, 40%. Percent *always* indicates a ratio "out of 100."

10. Express each ratio in column B of Problem 9 as a percent, using the symbol "%."

Since each ratio in Problem 10 is already a ratio "out of 100," you replaced the phrase "out of 100" with the % symbol. But suppose you need to write a ratio such as 21 out of 25 in percent format. You may recognize that the denominator, 25, is a factor of 100 $(25 \cdot 4 = 100)$. Then the fraction $\frac{21}{25}$ can be written equivalently as

$$\frac{21 \cdot 4}{25 \cdot 4} = \frac{84}{100}, \text{ which is precisely } 84\%.$$

A more general method to convert the ratio 21 out of 25 into percent format is to first calculate the quotient, 21 divided by 25, by calculator or by long division.

On a calculator:

Key in ② ① ÷ ② ⑤ ＝
to obtain 0.84.

Using long division:

$$\begin{array}{r} 0.84 \\ 25\overline{)21.00} \\ 20.0 \\ \hline 100 \\ 100 \\ \hline 0 \end{array}$$

Next, you convert the decimal form of the ratio into percent format by multiplying the decimal by $\dfrac{100}{100} = 1$.

$$0.84 = 0.84 \cdot \frac{100}{100} = (0.84 \cdot 100) \cdot \frac{1}{100} = \frac{84}{100} = 84\%$$

Note that multiplying the decimal by 100 moves the decimal point in 0.84 two places to the right. This leads to a shortcut for converting a decimal to a percent.

PROCEDURE

Converting a Fraction or Decimal to a Percent

1. Convert the fraction to decimal form by dividing the numerator by the denominator.
2. Move the decimal point in the quotient from step 1 two places to the right, inserting placeholder zeros if necessary.
3. Then attach the % symbol to the right of the number.

Example: $\dfrac{4}{5} = 5\overline{)4} = .80 = 80\%$

---

11. Rewrite the following ratios in percent format.

    a. 35 out of 100   **b.** 16 out of 50

    c. 8 out of 20   **d.** 7 out of 8

In many applications, you will need to convert a percent into decimal format. The following examples demonstrate the process.

EXAMPLE 1   *Convert 73% to a decimal.*

SOLUTION

First locate the decimal point.

$$73.\%$$

Next, since percent means "out of 100,"

$$73.\% = \frac{73}{100}.$$

Finally, since division by 100 means moving the decimal point two places to the left,

$$\frac{73.}{100} = 0.73.$$

Therefore, 73% = 0.73.

EXAMPLE 2   *Convert 4.5% to a decimal.*

SOLUTION

$$4.5\% = \frac{4.5}{100} = 0.045$$

Note that it was necessary to insert a placeholding zero.

PROCEDURE

Converting a Percent to a Decimal

1. Locate the decimal point in the number attached to the % symbol.
2. Move the decimal point two places to the left, inserting place-holding zeros if needed, and write the decimal number without the % symbol.

12. Write the following percents in decimal format.

    a. 75%   **b.** 3.5%   **c.** 200%   **d.** 0.75%

13. Use the three-point shot statistics from the 2005 NBA championship series to express each player's relative performance as a ratio in verbal, fraction, decimal, and percent form. Round the decimal to the nearest hundredth. The ratios for the Piston's Chauncey Billups are completed for you.

PLAYER	THREE-POINT SHOTS MADE	THREE-POINT SHOTS ATTEMPTED	EXPRESSED			
			VERBALLY	AS A FRACTION	AS A DECIMAL	AS A PERCENT
C. Billups (Det)	11	34	11 out of 34	$\frac{11}{34}$	0.32	32%
M. Ginobili (SA)	12	31				
R. Horry (SA)	15	31				
R. Wallace (Det)	5	17				

SUMMARY
ACTIVITY 4.1

1. **Relative measure** is a term used to describe the comparison of two similar quantities.

2. **Ratio** is the term used to describe relative measure as a quotient of **two similar quantities,** often a "part" and a "total," where "part" is *divided by* the "total."

3. Ratios can be expressed in several forms: **verbally** (4 out of 5), as a **fraction** $\left(\frac{4}{5}\right)$, as a **decimal** (0.8), or as a **percent** (80%).

4. **Percent** always indicates a ratio out of 100.

5. **Converting a fraction or decimal to a percent**
   i. Convert the fraction to decimal form by dividing the numerator by the denominator.
   ii. Move the decimal point two places to the right, and then attach the % symbol.

6. **Converting a percent to a decimal**
   i. Locate the decimal point in the number attached to the % symbol.
   ii. Move the decimal point two places to the left, inserting place-holding zeros if needed, and write the decimal number without the % symbol.

7. Two ratios are **equivalent** if their decimal or reduced fraction forms are equal.

**EXERCISES
ACTIVITY 4.1**

1. Complete the following table by representing each ratio in all four formats. Round decimals to the thousandths place and percents to the tenths place.

Numerically Speaking...

VERBAL	REDUCED FRACTION	DECIMAL	PERCENT
1 out of 3			
2 out of 5			
18 out of 25			
8 out of 9			
3 out of 8			
25 out of 45			
120 out of 40			
3 out of 4			
27 out of 40			
3 out of 5			
2 out of 3			
4 out of 5			
1 out of 200			
2 out of 1			

2. **a.** Match each ratio from column 1 with the equivalent ratio in column 2.

Column 1	Column 2
12 out of 27	60 out of 75
28 out of 36	25 out of 40
45 out of 75	21 out of 27
64 out of 80	42 out of 70
35 out of 56	20 out of 45

b. Write each matched pair of equivalent ratios as a percent. If necessary, round to the nearest tenth of a percent.

3. Your biology instructor returned three quizzes today. On which quiz did you perform best? Explain how you determined the best score.

   Quiz 1: 18 out of 25   **Quiz 2:** 32 out of 40   **Quiz 3:** 35 out of 50

   $\dfrac{18}{25} = 72\%$ $\dfrac{32}{40} = 80\%$ $\dfrac{35}{50} = 70\%$

4. A baseball batting average is the ratio of hits to the number of times at bat. It is reported as a three-digit decimal. Determine the batting averages of three players with the given records.

   a. 16 hits out of 54 at bats

   b. 25 hits out of 80 at bats

   c. 32 hits out of 98 at bats

5. There are 1720 females among the 3200 students at the local community college. Express this ratio in each of the following forms.

   a. fraction   b. reduced   c. decimal   d. percent
                           fraction

6. At the state university campus near the community college in Exercise 5, there are 2304 females and 2196 males enrolled. In which school, the community college or university, is the relative number of females greater? Explain your reasoning.

7. In the 2005 Major League Baseball season, the world champion Chicago White Sox ended their regular season with a 99–63 win-loss record. During their playoff season, their win-loss record was 11–1. Did the White Sox play better in the regular season or in the playoff season? Justify your answer mathematically.

8. A random check of 150 Southwest Air flights last month identified that 113 of them arrived on time. What "on-time" percent does this represent?

9. A consumer magazine reported that of the 13,350 subscribers who owned brand A dishwasher, 2940 required a service call. Only 730 of the 1860 owners of brand B needed repairs. Which brand of dishwasher has the better repair record?

10. The admissions office in a local college has organized data in the following table listing the number of men and women who are currently enrolled. Admissions will use the data to help recruit students for the next academic year. Note that a student is matriculated if he or she is enrolled in a program that leads to a college degree.

School-Bound

	FULL-TIME MATRICULATED STUDENTS ($\geq$ 12 CREDITS)	PART-TIME MATRICULATED STUDENTS ($<$ 12 CREDITS)	PART-TIME NONMATRICULATED STUDENTS ($<$ 12 CREDITS)
MEN	214	174	65
WOMEN	262	87	29

a. How many men attend the college?

b. What percent of the men are full-time students?

c. How many women attend the college?

d. What percent of the women are full-time students?

e. How many students are enrolled full-time?

f. How many students are enrolled part-time?

g. What percent of the full-time students are women?

h. What percent of the part-time students are women?

i. How many students are nonmatriculated?

j. What percent of the student body is nonmatriculated?

ACTIVITY 4.2

The Devastation of AIDS in Africa

OBJECTIVES

1. Use proportional reasoning to apply a known ratio to a given piece of information.

2. Write an equation using the relationship "ratio · total = part" and then solve the resulting equation.

International public health experts are desperately seeking to stem the spread of the AIDS epidemic in sub-Saharan Africa, especially in the small nation of Botswana. According to United Nations officials, over 35% of Botswana's 800,000 adults (ages 15–49) are currently infected with the AIDS virus.

The data in the preceding paragraph is typical of the kind of numerical information you will find in reading virtually any printed document, report, or article.

1. What relative data (ratio) appears in the opening paragraph? What phrase or symbol identifies it as a relative measure?

2. Express the ratio in Problem 1 in fraction, decimal, and verbal form.

Proportional Reasoning

From the information given and your answers to Problems 1 and 2, you know that the adult population of Botswana is 800,000 and that 35% is the percentage of the adult population that has AIDS. The unknown quantity in this case is the number of adults that have AIDS. To determine the unknown quantity, take 35% of 800,000 as follows:

$$0.35 \cdot 800,000 = 280,000$$

Therefore, 280,000 adults in Botswana are infected with AIDS. Because the ratio $\frac{280,000}{800,000} = 0.35$, or 35%, you know that the calculation is correct.

This example illustrates a thought process called **proportional reasoning.** In this case, proportional reasoning is used to apply a known ratio to one piece of information (the total) to determine a related, but yet unknown, second piece of information (the part). The formula that was used,

$$ratio \cdot total = part$$

is equivalent to the formula

$$ratio = \frac{part}{total}.$$

A common procedure to apply a known ratio to a given piece of information is described as follows.

PROCEDURE

Setting Up and Solving ratio · total = part, When the Ratio Is Known

Step 1. Identify whether the given piece of information represents a *part* or a *total*.

Step 2. Substitute all the known information into the formula *ratio · total = part* to form an equation. The unknown may be represented by a letter.

Step 3. Solve the equation.

3. You do further research about this disturbing health problem and discover that by 2005 there were approximately 25,800,000 adults and children living in sub-Saharan Africa with HIV/AIDS. This represents 7.2% of the total population there.

   a. The ratio of the total population that is infected with AIDS is given in the preceding information. What is it? In what form is the ratio expressed?

   b. Identify the other given information.

   c. Identify the unknown piece of information.

   d. Use the formula *ratio* · *total* = *part* to estimate the total population.

4. It was estimated that 330,000 adults from Botswana were infected with HIV/AIDS in 2003, and that 190,000 of them were women. What percent of those infected were women? Use the formula $ratio = \dfrac{part}{total}$.

5. Africa has buried three-fourths of the 25 million people worldwide who have died from AIDS since the beginning of the AIDS epidemic. Calculate how many people from Africa have died from AIDS.

6. In the year 2005, 1.9 million sub-Saharan African children under the age of 15 were living with AIDS. This represents 80% of all children worldwide who were infected in 2005. Use the following steps to estimate the total number of all children worldwide who were infected.

   a. Identify the known ratio.

   b. Identify the given piece of information. Does this number represent a part or a total?

c. Identify the unknown piece of information. Does this number represent a part or a total?

d. Use the formula *ratio · total = part* to determine your estimate. Let the unknown quantity be represented by *x*.

7. In 2005, 4.9 million adults and children became newly infected with HIV. Sixty-five percent of these new cases occurred in sub-Saharan Africa and 20% of the new cases occurred in South and Southeast Asia.

a. Determine how many of these new cases of AIDS occurred in sub-Saharan Africa.

b. How many of these new cases of AIDS occurred in South and Southeast Asia?

8. Of the world's 6.5 billion people, 3 billion live on less than $2 per day. Calculate the percent of the world's population who live on less than $2 per day.

SUMMARY
ACTIVITY 4.2

Proportional reasoning is the process that uses the equation *ratio · total = part* to determine the unknown quantity when two of the quantities in the equation are known. This relationship is equivalently written as $ratio = \dfrac{part}{total}$.

Direct approach to solve for an unknown part or total:

Step 1. Identify whether the given piece of information represents a part or a total.

Step 2. Substitute all the known information into the formula *ratio · total = part* to form an equation. The unknown may be represented by a letter.

Step 3. Solve the equation.

Note that sometimes the unknown piece of information is the ratio. In this case, use the formula, $ratio = \dfrac{part}{total}$ to calculate the ratio directly.

EXERCISES
ACTIVITY 4.2

1. Determine the value of each expression.

   a. $12 \cdot \dfrac{2}{3}$

   b. $18 \div \dfrac{2}{3}$

   c. $\dfrac{3}{5}$ of 25

   d. $24 \div \dfrac{3}{4}$

   e. 30% of 60

   f. $150 \div 0.60$

   g. $45 \cdot \dfrac{4}{9}$

   h. 25% of 960

   i. $5280 \div 75\%$

   j. $2000 \div \dfrac{4}{5}$

   k. 80% of 225

   l. $30,000 \div 50\%$

2. Sub-Saharan Africa accounted for 77% of the 3.1 million adults and children who died of AIDS in the year 2005. How many sub-Saharan children died of AIDS that year?

   a. Identify the known ratio.

   b. Identify the given piece of information. Does this number represent a part or a total?

   c. How many sub-Saharan adults and children died of AIDS in 2005?

3. The 25.8 million sub-Saharan people (adults and children) currently living with AIDS account for 64% of the entire world population infected with the disease. How many people worldwide are infected with AIDS?

4. The customary tip on waiter service in New York City restaurants is approximately 20% of the food and beverage cost. This means that your server is counting on a tip of $0.20 for each dollar you spend on your meal. What is the expected tip on a dinner for two costing $65?

5. Your new car cost $22,500. The state sales tax rate is 8%. How much sales tax will you be paying on the car purchase?

6. You happened to notice that the 8% sales tax that your uncle paid on his new luxury car came to $3800. How much did the car itself cost him?

7. In your recent school board elections only 45% of the registered voters went to the polls. If 22,000 votes were cast, approximately how many voters are registered in your school district?

8. In 2005, new car and truck sales totaled approximately 16.9 million in the United States. The breakdown among the leading automobile manufacturers was

   General Motors   26.7%   Honda   8.6%
   Ford   11.8%   Toyota   13.4%
   Chrysler   13.6%

   Approximately how many new cars did each company sell that year?

9. In a very disappointing season, your softball team won only 40% of the games it played this year. If you won 8 games, how many games did you play? How many did you lose?

10. In a typical telemarketing campaign, 5% of the people contacted purchase the product. If your quota is to sign up 50 people, approximately how many phone calls do you anticipate making?

11. Approximately three-fourths of the teacher-education students in your college pass the licensing exam on their first attempt. This year, 92 students will sit for the exam. How many are expected to pass?

12. You paid $90 for your economics textbook. At the end of the semester, the bookstore will buy back your book for 20% of the original purchase price. The book sells used for $65. How much money does the bookstore earn on the resale?

● **ACTIVITY 4.3**

Fuel Economy

OBJECTIVES

1. Apply rates directly to solve problems.

2. Use unit analysis or dimensional analysis to solve problems that involve consecutive rates.

You are excited about purchasing a new car for commuting to college. Concerned about the cost of driving, you did some research on the Internet and came across the Web site, *http://www.fueleconomy.gov*. You found that this Web site listed fuel efficiency, in miles per gallons (mpg), for five cars that you are considering. You recorded the mpg for city and highway driving in the table after Problem 1.

1. a. For each of the cars listed in the table, how many city miles can you travel per week on 5 gallons of gasoline? Explain the calculation you will do to obtain the answers. Record your answers in the third column of the table.

b. The daily round-trip drive to your college is 38 city miles, which you do 4 days per week. Which of the cars would get you to school each week on 5 gallons of gas?

Every Drop Counts

FUEL ECONOMY GUIDE: MODEL YEAR 2006					
MAKE/MODEL	CITY MPG	CITY MILES ON 5 GALLONS OF GAS	HIGHWAY MPG	GALLONS NEEDED TO DRIVE 304 HIGHWAY MILES	FUEL TANK CAPACITY IN GALLONS
Chevrolet Aveo5	26		35		12.0
Ford Focus	26		34		14.0
Honda Civic	30		38		13.2
Hyundai Accent	32		35		11.9
Toyota Corolla	32		41		13.2

2. Suppose you plan to move and your round-trip commute to the college will be 304 highway miles each week. How many gallons of gas would each of the cars require? Explain the calculation you will do to obtain the answers. Record your answers to the nearest tenth in the fifth column of the table.

Miles per gallon (mpg) is an example of a rate. Mathematically, a rate is a comparison by division of two quantities that have different units of measurement. A rate such as 32 mpg expresses the number of miles that can be traveled per 1 gallon of gas. The word *per* signifies division.

Solving problems involving rates is similar to solving problems using ratios. The difference is that to solve rate problems you will use the units of measurement as a guide to set up the appropriate calculations. The problems that follow will guide you to do this efficiently.

Applying a Known Rate Directly by Multiplication/Division to Solve a Problem

In Problem 1, the known rate is miles per gallon for several cars. You can write the mpg in fraction form, $\dfrac{\text{number of miles}}{1 \text{ gallon}}$. In the case of the Chevrolet Aveo5, the mpg is $\dfrac{26 \text{ miles}}{1 \text{ gal}}$. To determine how many miles the Aveo5 can travel on 5 gallons, you notice that the units in the answer should be miles. So, you multiply the rate by 5 gallons.

$$5 \text{ g\cancel{al}.} \cdot \frac{26 \text{ mi.}}{1 \text{ g\cancel{al}.}} = 130 \text{ mi.}$$

Notice that gallon occurs in both a numerator and a denominator. You divide out common measurement units in the same way that you reduce a fraction by dividing out common numerical factors. Therefore, you can drive for 130 miles in the Chevrolet Aveo5 on 5 gallons of gas.

PROCEDURE

Multiplying and Dividing Directly to Solve Problems Involving Rates

- Identify the measurement unit of the answer to the problem.
- Set up the calculation so the appropriate units will divide out, leaving the measurement unit of the answer.
- Multiply or divide the numbers as usual to obtain the numerical part of the answer.
- Divide out the common units to obtain the measurement unit of the answer.

---

3. Solve each of the following problems involving rates.

   a. The gas tank of a Honda Civic holds 13.2 gallons. How many highway miles can you travel on a full tank of gas?

   b. The Hyundai Accent gas tank holds 11.9 gallons. Is it possible to travel as far in this car as in the Honda Civic on the highway?

4. After you purchase your new car, you would like to take a trip to see a good friend in another state. The highway distance is approximately 560 miles.

  a. If you bought the Hyundai Accent, how many gallons of gas would you need to make the round-trip?

  b. How many tanks of gas would you need for the trip?

Solving Rate Problems Using Measurement Units as a Guide

In Problem 2, you may have directly divided the total miles by the mpg. One way to decide that the calculation involves division is to consider the measurement units. From reading the problem, you identify that the measurement unit of the answer should be gallons. In the case of the Honda Civic, dividing 304 miles by 38 miles per gallon produces the correct unit for the answer, as the following calculation shows.

$$304 \text{ mi.} \div \frac{38 \text{ mi.}}{1 \text{ gal.}} = 304 \text{ mi.} \cdot \frac{1 \text{ gal.}}{38 \text{ mi.}} = \frac{304}{38} \text{ gal.} \approx 8 \text{ gal.}$$

Notice that the unit, miles, occurs in both the numerator and the denominator. You divide out miles to obtain gallons as the unit in the result. This is known as *unit analysis* or *dimensional analysis*.

  5. You decide to read a 15-page article that provides advice for negotiating the lowest price for a car. You read at the rate of 10 pages an hour. How long will it take you to read the article?

Unit Conversion

In many countries, distance is measured in kilometers (km) and gasoline in liters (ℓ). A kilometer is equivalent to 0.6214 miles and 1 liter is equivalent to 0.264 gallons. In general, the equivalence of two units can be treated as a rate written in fraction form. For example, the fact that a kilometer is equivalent to 0.6214 miles is written as

$$\frac{1 \text{ km}}{0.6214 \text{ mi.}} \quad \text{or} \quad \frac{0.6214 \text{ mi.}}{1 \text{ km}}$$

Using the fraction form, you can convert one unit to another by applying multiplication directly.

6. Your friend joins you on a trip through Canada where gasoline is measured in liters and distance in kilometers.

   a. Write the equivalence of liters and gallons in fraction form.

   b. If you bought 20 liters of gas, how many gallons did you buy?

Note that conversion equivalents are given on the inside front cover of this textbook.

7. To keep track of mileage and fuel needs in Canada your friend suggests that you convert your car's mpg into kilometers per liter. Your car's highway fuel efficiency is 45 mpg.

   a. Convert your car's fuel efficiency to *miles per liter.*

   b. Use the result you obtained in part a to determine your car's fuel efficiency in *kilometers per liter.*

Using Unit Analysis to Solve a Problem Involving Consecutive Rates

Problem 6 involved a one-step rate problem. In Problem 7, to convert the car's fuel efficiency from miles per gallon (mpg) to kilometers per liter (kpl) you were guided to do two one-step conversions. You may have observed that the two calculations could be done in a single chain of multiplications.

$$\frac{45 \text{ mi.}}{1 \text{ gal.}} \cdot \frac{0.264 \text{ gal.}}{1 \, \ell} \cdot \frac{1 \text{ km}}{0.6214 \text{ mi.}} = 19.1 \text{ km per liter (kpl)}$$

Note how the units given in the problem guide you to choose the appropriate equivalent fractions so the method becomes a single chain of multiplications.

8. You plan to buy 3 gallons of juice to serve guests at a breakfast rally that your local political group is hosting. How many cups would you have?

9. You are on a 1500-mile trip where gas stations are far apart. Your car is averaging 40 mpg and you are traveling at 60 miles per hour (mph). The fuel tank holds 12 gallons of gas and you just filled the tank. Use a chain of multiplications to determine how long it will be before you have to refill the tank.

PROCEDURE

Applying Consecutive Rates

- Identify the measurement unit of the answer.
- Set up the sequence of multiplications and/or divisions so the appropriate units divide out, leaving the appropriate measurement unit.
- Multiply and divide the numbers as usual to obtain the numerical part of the answer.
- Check that the appropriate measurement units divide out, leaving the expected measurement unit for the answer.

10. You have been driving for several hours and notice that your car's 13.2-gallon fuel tank registers half empty. How many more miles can you travel if your car is averaging 30 mpg?

SUMMARY
ACTIVITY 4.3

1. Multiplying/dividing directly by rates to solve problems:
  a. Identify the unit of the result.
  b. Set up the calculation so the appropriate units will divide out, leaving the unit of the result.
  c. Multiply or divide the numbers as usual to obtain the numerical part of the result.
  d. Divide out the common units to obtain the unit of the answer.

2. Applying several rates consecutively to solve problems:
  a. Identify the unit of the result.
  b. Set up the sequence of multiplications and/or divisions so the appropriate units divide out, leaving the unit of the result.
  c. Multiply and divide the numbers as usual to obtain the numerical part of the result.
  d. Check that the appropriate units divide out, leaving the expected unit of the result.

Use the conversion tables or formulas on the inside front cover of the textbook for conversion equivalencies.

1. The length of a football playing field is 100 yards between the opposing goal lines. What is the length of the football field in feet?

2. The distance between New York City, NY, and Los Angeles, CA, is approximately 4485 kilometers. What is the distance between these two major U.S. cities in miles?

3. As part of your job as a quality control worker in a factory you can check 16 parts in 3 minutes. How long will it take you to check 80 parts?

4. Your car averages about 27 miles per gallon on highways. With gasoline priced at $2.74 per gallon, how much will you expect to spend on gasoline during your 500-mile trip?

5. You currently earn $11.50 per hour. Assuming that you work fifty-two 40-hour weeks per year with no raises, what total gross salary will you earn over the next 5 years?

6. The aorta is the largest artery in the human body. The aorta attains a maximum diameter of about 1.18 inches where it adjoins the heart in the average adult. What is the maximum diameter of the aorta in terms of centimeters? In millimeters?

7. Mount Everest in the Himalaya mountain range along the border of Tibet and Nepal reaches upward to a record height of 29,035 feet. How high is Mt. Everest in miles? In kilometers? In meters?

8. The average weight of a mature human brain is approximately 1400 grams. What is the equivalent weight in kilograms? In pounds?

9. Approximately 4.5 liters of blood circulates in the body of the average human adult. How many quarts of blood does the average person have? How many pints?

10. How many seconds are in a day? In a week? In a non-leap year?

11. Lava flowing out of shield volcanoes has reached incredibly hot temperatures of about 1200°C. What is the Fahrenheit temperature of these lava flows?

12. The following places are three of the wettest locations on Earth. Determine the rainfall for each site in centimeters per year.

LOCATION	ANNUAL RAINFALL (INCHES)	ANNUAL RAINFALL (CENTIMETERS)
Mawsynram, Meghala, India	467 inches	
Tutenendo, Columbia	463.5 inches	
Mt. Waialeali, Kauai	410 inches	

13. The mass of diamonds is commonly measured in carats. Five carats is equivalent to 1 gram. How many grams are in a 24-carat diamond? How many ounces?

14. The tissue of Earth organisms contains carbon molecules known as proteins, carbohydrates, and fats. A healthy human body is approximately 18% carbon by weight. Determine how many pounds and kilograms of carbon your own body contains.

ACTIVITY 4.4

Four out of Five Dentists Prefer the Brooklyn Dodgers?

OBJECTIVES

1. Recognize that equivalent fractions lead to proportions.

2. Use proportions to solve problems involving ratios and rates.

Manufacturers of retail products often conduct surveys to see how well their products are selling compared to competing products. In some cases, they use the results in advertising campaigns.

One company, Proctor and Gamble, ran a TV ad in the 1970s claiming that "four out of five dentists surveyed preferred Crest toothpaste over other leading brands." The ad became a classic, and the phrase, *four out of five prefer*, has become a popular cliché in advertising, in appeals, and in one-line quips.

What does "four out of five prefer" mean in a survey? How does that lead to solving an equation called a proportion? Continue in this activity to find out.

1. Suppose Proctor and Gamble asked 250 dentists what brand toothpaste he or she preferred and 200 dentists responded that they preferred Crest.

   a. What is the ratio of the number of dentists who preferred Crest to the number who were asked the question? Write your answer in words, and as a fraction.

   b. Reduce the ratio in part a to lowest terms and write the result in words.

Note that part b of Problem 1 shows that the ratio $\frac{200}{250}$ is equivalent to the ratio $\frac{4}{5}$, or $\frac{200}{250} = \frac{4}{5}$. This is an example of a **proportion**.

DEFINITION

The mathematical statement that two ratios are equivalent is called a **proportion**. In fraction form, a proportion is written $\frac{a}{b} = \frac{c}{d}$.

If one of the component numbers, a, b, c, or d in a proportion is unknown and the other three are known, the equation can be solved for the unknown component. The next example shows how.

EXAMPLE 1 *Suppose that Proctor and Gamble had interviewed **600** dentists and reported that $\frac{4}{5}$ of the **600** dentists preferred Crest. However, the report did not say how many dentists in this survey preferred Crest. How can this number be determined from the given information?*

SOLUTION

At this point, the comparison ratio for all the dentists interviewed is $\frac{x}{600}$, where the variable x represents the unknown number of dentists who preferred Crest and 600 is the total number of dentists surveyed. According to the report, this ratio has to be equal to $\frac{4}{5}$, that is,

$$\frac{x}{600} = \frac{4}{5}.$$

The equation is solved for x by multiplying each fraction by 600 and simplifying:

$$600 \cdot \frac{x}{600} = \frac{4}{5} \cdot 600$$

$$\frac{\cancel{600}}{1} \cdot \frac{x}{\cancel{600}} = \frac{4}{\cancel{5}} \cdot \frac{\overset{120}{\cancel{600}}}{1}$$

$$x = 4 \cdot 120 = 480$$

Therefore, 480 dentists in the survey preferred Crest.

2. Suppose Proctor and Gamble surveyed another group of 85 dentists in Idaho. If $\frac{4}{5}$ of the group preferred Crest, how many of this group preferred Crest? Let x represent the number of dentists who preferred Crest.

3. The best season for the New York Mets baseball team was 1986 when they won $\frac{2}{3}$ of the games they played and won the World Series, beating the Boston Red Sox. If the Mets played 162 games, how many did they win?

Sometimes, the unknown in a proportion is in the denominator of one of the fractions. The next example shows a method of solving a proportion that is especially useful in this situation.

EXAMPLE 2   *The Los Angeles Dodgers were once the Brooklyn Dodgers team that made it to the World Series seven times from 1941 to 1956, each time opposing the New York Yankees. The Brooklyn Dodgers won only one World Series Championship against the Yankees and that was in 1955.*

In the 1955 season, the Dodgers won about 16 out of every 25 games that they played. They won a total of 98 games. How many games did they play during the season?

SOLUTION

Let x represent the total number of games that the Dodgers played in the 1955 season. To write a proportion, the units of the numerators in the proportion must be the same. Similarly, the units of the denominators must be the same. In this case, the proportion is

$$\frac{16 \text{ games won}}{25 \text{ total games played}} = \frac{98 \text{ games won}}{x \text{ total games played}} \quad \text{or} \quad \frac{16}{25} = \frac{98}{x}$$

This equation can be solved in three steps that will lead to a shortcut method. First follow the three steps.

Step 1.   Multiply each fraction by x and simplify.

$$\frac{16}{25} \cdot x = \frac{98}{x} \cdot x$$

$$\frac{16x}{25} = 98$$

Step 2.   Multiply each term of the equation by 25.

$$\frac{16x}{25} \cdot 25 = 98 \cdot 25$$

$$16x = 98 \cdot 25$$

Step 3.   Divide each term of the equation by 16 and calculate the value for x.

$$\frac{16x}{16} = \frac{98 \cdot 25}{16}$$

$$x = \frac{98 \cdot 25}{16} \approx 153.1$$

The Dodgers played 153 games in the 1955 season.

A Shortcut Method for Solving Proportions

In steps 1 and 2 of the solution in Example 2, the proportion $\frac{16}{25} = \frac{98}{x}$ was rewritten as $16x = 98 \cdot 25$. Observe that the denominator of each fraction is multiplied by the numerator of the other.

$$\frac{16}{25} = \frac{98}{x}$$

$$16x = 98 \cdot 25$$

Divide both terms in the equation by 16 to obtain the value for x.

$$x = \frac{98 \cdot 25}{16} \approx 153$$

The shortcut process just described is called *cross multiplication* because the numerator of the first fraction multiplies the denominator of the second, and vice versa.

PROCEDURE

Solving Proportions by Cross Multiplication Rewrite the proportion $\frac{a}{b} = \frac{c}{d}$ as $a \cdot d = b \cdot c$ and solve for the unknown quantity.

4. a. Solve the proportion $\dfrac{7}{10} = \dfrac{x}{24}$.

b. Solve the proportion $\dfrac{9}{x} = \dfrac{6}{50}$.

5. As a volunteer for a charity, you were given a job stuffing envelopes for an appeal for donations. After stuffing 240 envelopes, you were informed that you are two-thirds done. How many envelopes in total are you expected to stuff? Let x represent the number of envelopes to be stuffed.

6. You are feeding a group of 6 friends who are joining you to watch a figure skating competition and everyone wants soup. The information on a can of soup states that one can of soup contains about 2.5 servings. Use a proportion to determine the number of cans of soup to open so that all seven of you have one serving of soup. Let x represent the number of cans to be opened.

7. Solve each proportion for x.

a. $\dfrac{2}{3} = \dfrac{x}{48}$ **b.** $\dfrac{5}{8} = \dfrac{120}{x}$ **c.** $\dfrac{3}{20} = \dfrac{x}{3500}$

<table>
<tr><td>**SUMMARY**
ACTIVITY 4.4</td><td>

1. The mathematical statement that two ratios are equivalent is called a **proportion.** In fraction form, a proportion is written as $\dfrac{a}{b} = \dfrac{c}{d}$.

2. Shortcut (cross multiplication) procedure for solving proportions:

Rewrite the proportion $\dfrac{a}{b} = \dfrac{c}{d}$ as $a \cdot d = b \cdot c$ and solve for the unknown quantity.

</td></tr>
</table>

<table>
<tr><td>**EXERCISES**
ACTIVITY 4.4</td><td>

1. A company that manufactures optical products estimated that three out of five people in North America wore eyeglasses in 2006. The population estimate for North America in 2006 was about 334 million. Use a proportion to determine how many people in this part of the world were estimated to wear eyeglasses in 2006?

2. Solve each proportion for x.

   a. $\dfrac{2}{9} = \dfrac{x}{108}$ **b.** $\dfrac{8}{7} = \dfrac{120}{x}$ **c.** $\dfrac{x}{20} = \dfrac{70}{100}$

3. The Center for Education Reform is an organization founded in 1993 to help foster better education opportunities in American communities. It spends 4 cents out of every dollar in its spending budget for administrative expenses. In 2004, the center's spending budget was approximately 2.8 million dollars. Use a proportion to estimate the administrative expenses for 2004.

</td></tr>
</table>

4. Powdered skim milk sells for $6.99 a box in the supermarket. The amount in the box is enough to make 8 quarts of skim milk. What is the price for 12 quarts of skim milk prepared in this way?

5. A person who weighs 120 pounds on Earth would weigh 42.5 pounds on Mars. What would be a person's weight on Mars if she weighs 150 pounds on Earth?

6. You want to make up a saline (salt) solution in chemistry lab that has 12 grams of salt per 100 milliliters of water. How many grams of salt would you use if you needed 15 milliliters of solution for your experiment?

7. Tealeaf, a company that offers management solutions to companies that sell online, announced in a 2005 consumer survey that 9 out of 10 customers reported problems with transactions online. The survey sampled 1859 adults in the United States, 18 years and older, who had conducted an online transaction in the past year. How many of those adults reported problems with transactions online?

8. In 2005, the birth rate in the United States was estimated to be 14.14 births per 1000 persons. If the population estimate for the United States was 296.7 million, how many births were expected that year?

What Have I Learned?

1. On a 40-question practice test for this course, you answered 32 questions correctly. On the test itself, you correctly answered 16 out of 20 questions. Does this mean that you did better on the practice test than you did on the test itself? Explain your answer using the concepts of actual and relative comparison.

2. **a.** Ratios are often written as a fraction in the form $\frac{a}{b}$. List the other ways you can express a ratio.

   b. Thirty-three of the 108 colleges and universities in Michigan are 2-year institutions. Write this ratio in each of the ways you listed in part a.

3. Florida's total population, reported in the 2000 census, was 15,982,378 persons and 183 out of every 1000 residents were 65 years and older. Show how you would determine the actual number of Florida residents who are 65 years or older in 2000.

4. **a.** In conversion tables, conversions between two measurement units are usually given in an equation format. For example, 1 quart = 0.946 liters. Write this conversion in two different fraction formats.

b. Write the conversion 1 liter = 1.057 quarts in two different fraction formats.

c. Are the two conversions given in parts a and b equivalent? Explain.

How Can I Practice?

1. Write the following percents in decimal format.

   a. 25%   d. 3.5%

   b. 87.5%   e. 250%

   c. 6%   f. 0.3%

2. An error in a measurement is the difference between the measured value and the true value. The relative error in measurement is the ratio of the absolute value of the error to the true value. That is,

$$\text{relative error} = \frac{|\text{error}|}{\text{true value}}.$$

Determine the actual and relative errors in the following measurements.

MEASUREMENT	TRUE VALUE	ERROR	RELATIVE ERROR (AS A PERCENT)
107 inches	100 inches		
5.7 ounces	5.0 ounces		
4.3 grams	5.0 grams		
11.5 cm	12.5 cm		

3. You must interpret a study of cocaine-addiction relapse after three different treatment programs. The subjects were treated with the standard therapy, with an antidepressant, or with a placebo. They were tracked for 3 years.

TREATMENT	SUBJECTS WHO RELAPSED	SUBJECTS STILL SUBSTANCE FREE
Standard therapy	36	20
Antidepressant therapy	27	18
Placebo	30	9

Which therapy has proved most effective? Explain.

4. The 2619 female students on campus comprise 54% of the entire student body. What is the total enrollment of the college?

5. The Mariana Trench near the Mariana Islands in the South Pacific Ocean extends down to a maximum depth of 35,827 feet. How deep is this deepest point in miles? In kilometers? In meters?

6. Under the current union contract, you earn $22.50 per hour as a college laboratory technician. The contract is valid for the next 2 years. Assuming that you stay in this position and work 40 hours per week, 52 weeks a year, what will your total gross earnings be over the next 2 years?

7. As a nurse in a rehabilitation center, you have received an order to administer 60 milligrams of a drug. The drug is available at a strength of 12 milligrams per milliliter. How many milliliters would you administer?

8. Solve each proportion for x.

   a. $\dfrac{x}{8} = \dfrac{120}{320}$ b. $\dfrac{6}{13} = \dfrac{42}{x}$ c. $\dfrac{24}{x} = \dfrac{6}{5}$

9. A three-pound bag of rice cost $2.67. At that rate, what would a 20-pound bag of rice cost?

The bracketed numbers following each concept indicate the activity in which the concept is discussed.

CONCEPT / SKILL	DESCRIPTION	EXAMPLE
Ratio [4.1]	A quotient that compares two similar numerical quantities, such as part to total.	4 out of 5 is a ratio. It can be expressed as a fraction, $\frac{4}{5}$; a decimal, 0.8; and a percent, 80%.
Convert from decimal to percent format. [4.1]	Move the decimal place two places to the right and then attach the % symbol.	0.125 becomes 12.5%. 0.04 becomes 4%. 2.50 becomes 250%.
Convert from percent to decimal format. [4.1]	Drop the percent symbol and move the decimal point two places to the left.	35% becomes 0.35. 6% becomes 0.06. 200% becomes 2.00.
Apply a known ratio to a given piece of information. [4.2]	total · known ratio = unknown part	40% of the 350 children play an instrument. 40% is the known ratio; 350 is the total. 350 · 0.40 = 140 children play an instrument.
	part ÷ known ratio = unknown total	24 children, comprising 30% of the marching band, play the saxophone. 30% is the known ratio, 24 is the part. 24 ÷ 0.30 = 80, the total number of children in the marching band.
Use unit or dimensional analysis to solve conversion problems. [4.3]	1. Identify the measurement unit of the result. 2. Set up the sequence of multiplications and/or divisions so the appropriate measurement units cancel, leaving the measurement unit of the result. 3. Multiply and divide the numbers as usual to obtain the numerical part of the result. 4. Check that the appropriate measurement units divide out, leaving the expected measurement unit of the result.	To convert your height of 70 inches to centimeters, $70 \text{ in.} \cdot \dfrac{2.54 \text{ cm}}{1 \text{ in.}}$ $= 177.8 \text{ cm}$ Reading a 512-page book at the rate of 16 pages per hour will take how many 8-hour days? $512 \text{ pages} \div \dfrac{16 \text{ pages}}{1 \text{ hr.}} \cdot \dfrac{1 \text{ day}}{8 \text{ hr.}}$ $= 512 \text{ pages} \cdot \dfrac{1 \text{ hr.}}{16 \text{ pages}} \cdot \dfrac{1 \text{ day}}{8 \text{ hr}}$ $= 4 \text{ days}$
Proportion [4.4]	A mathematical statement that two ratios are equivalent. In fraction form a proportion is written as $\dfrac{a}{b} = \dfrac{c}{d}$	$\dfrac{2}{3} = \dfrac{50}{75}$ is a proportion because $\dfrac{50}{75}$ in reduced form equals $\dfrac{2}{3}$.

CONCEPT / SKILL	DESCRIPTION	EXAMPLE
Solve a proportion [4.4]	Rewrite $\dfrac{a}{b} = \dfrac{c}{d}$ as $a \cdot d = b \cdot c$ and solve for the unknown quantity.	$\dfrac{7}{30} = \dfrac{x}{4140}$ $30 \cdot x = 7 \cdot 4140$ $x = \dfrac{7 \cdot 4140}{30} = 966$

1. Determine the value of each expression.

   a. $20 \cdot \dfrac{7}{4}$ **b.** $\dfrac{4}{5} \div 2$ **c.** 27% of 44

   d. $1300 \div 20\%$ **e.** $45.7 \div 0.0012$ **f.** $\dfrac{1}{6} \cdot 37.34$

2. Solve the proportion for x.

   a. $\dfrac{4}{9} = \dfrac{x}{45}$ **b.** $\dfrac{x}{4} = \dfrac{5}{4}$ **c.** $\dfrac{1}{x} = \dfrac{2}{3}$

   d. $\dfrac{2.3}{1.7} = \dfrac{x}{4}$ **e.** $\dfrac{\frac{1}{2}}{7} = \dfrac{x}{6}$ **f.** $\dfrac{x}{3} = 4$

3. In a recent survey, 70% of the 1400 female students and 30% of the 1000 male students on campus indicated that shopping was their favorite leisure activity. How many students placed shopping at the top of their list? What percent of the entire student body does this represent?

4. The least-favorite responsibility in your summer job is to stuff and seal preaddressed envelopes. After sealing 600 envelopes you discover that you have only completed two-thirds of the job. How large is the entire mailing list?

Answers to all Gateway exercises are included in the Selected Answers appendix.

5. The size of an optical telescope is given by the diameter of its mirror, which is circular in shape. Currently, the world's largest optical telescope is the 10-meter Keck Telescope atop Mauna Kea, Hawaii. What is the diameter of the mirror in feet?

6. In the middle of a playing season, NBA players Kevin Garnet (Minn), Kobe Bryant (LA), and Shaquille O'Neal (MIA) had these respective field goal statistics:

   Garnet   87 field goals out of 167 attempts

   Bryant   170 field goals out of 342 attempts

   O'Neal   229 field goals out of 408 attempts

   Rank them according to their relative (%) performance.

7. Hybrid electric/gas cars seem to be friendlier to the environment than all-gas vehicles, and more models are being introduced each year in the United States. One model reports a 56 mpg for highway driving. How far can you travel on one tank of gas if the tank holds 10.6 gallons?

8. You run at the rate of 6 mph. Convert your rate to feet per second.

9. Solve each proportion for x.

   a. $\dfrac{x}{5} = \dfrac{120}{300}$

   b. $\dfrac{8}{15} = \dfrac{48}{x}$

   c. $\dfrac{18}{x} = \dfrac{3}{2}$

10. An eight-pound bag of flour cost $5.28. At that rate, what would a 100-pound bag of flour cost?

CHAPTER 5

PROBLEM SOLVING WITH GEOMETRY

Things around us come in different shapes and sizes and can be measured in a number of ways. A garden can be circular, a room is often rectangular, and a pool of water may be one of many interesting shapes. A fence around a garden is usually measured in terms of its perimeter, a carpet on the floor of a room in terms of its area, and a pool of water in terms of its volume. These ideas are all part of a field of mathematics called geometry. In this chapter you will determine the perimeters and areas of rectangles, triangles, circles, and figures composed of these shapes. You will also calculate the surface areas and volumes of prisms, cones, and spheres.

CLUSTER 1 | The Geometry of Two-Dimensional Plane Figures

● ACTIVITY 5.1

Walking around Bases, Gardens, Trusses, and Other Figures

OBJECTIVES

1. Recognize perimeter as a geometric property of plane figures.

2. Write formulas for, and calculate perimeters of, squares, rectangles, and triangles.

3. Use unit analysis to solve problems involving perimeter.

In this first cluster of activities, you will explore the properties of geometric figures or shapes that are two-dimensional. This means they exist in a **plane**—a surface like the floor at your feet or the walls in your classroom. To make sure you understand these various shapes, some preliminary definitions are needed.

┌─ **DEFINITION** ───

Parallel lines are lines in a plane that never intersect. No matter how far you extend the lines, in either direction, they will never meet.

Example:

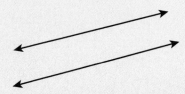

A **ray** is a portion of a line that starts from a point and continues indefinitely in one direction, much like a ray of light coming from the Sun.

Example:

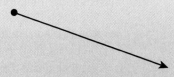

An **angle** is formed by two rays that have a common starting point. The common starting point is called the **vertex** of the angle.

Example:

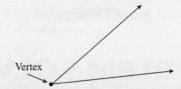

Vertex

Perpendicular lines are intersecting lines that form four angles of equal size. The resulting angles are defined to be **right angles**. Each right angle measures 90 degrees. In a diagram, right angles are usually designated by little squares at the point of intersection.

Example:

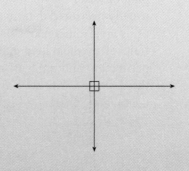

Squares

┌─ **DEFINITION** ─────────────────────────────────

A **square** is a closed plane figure whose four sides have equal length and are at right angles to each other.

Examples:

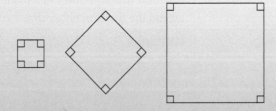

1. You are at bat in the middle of an exciting baseball game. You are a fairly good hitter and can run the bases at a speed of 15 feet per second. You know that the baseball diamond has the shape of a square, measuring 90 feet on each side.

   a. What is the total distance in feet you must run from home plate through the bases back to home? (See figure on next page.) Recall that the total distance around the square is called the *perimeter* of the square.

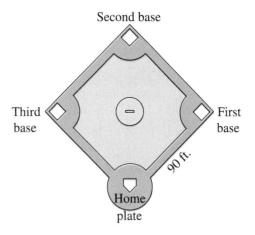

Second base

Third base

First base

90 ft.

Home plate

b. How many seconds will it take you to run this total distance?

2. Your niece plays Little League baseball. The square baseball diamond for Little League is 60 feet on each side. What is the total distance if she ran all of the bases?

DEFINITION

The **perimeter of a square** is the total distance around all its edges or sides.

PROCEDURE

Calculating the Perimeter of a Square The formula for the perimeter, P, of a square whose sides have length s has two equivalent forms.

$$P = s + s + s + s \quad \text{and} \quad P = 4s$$

Rectangles

DEFINITION

A **rectangle** is a closed plane figure whose four sides are at right angles to each other.

Examples:

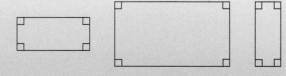

3. You are interested in planting a rectangular garden, 10 feet long by 15 feet wide. To protect your plants, you decide to purchase a fence to enclose your entire garden.

a. How many feet of fencing must you buy to enclose your garden?

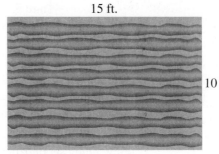

15 ft.

10 ft.

b. A friend suggests surrounding the garden with a 2-foot-wide path and then enclosing the garden and path with fencing. If you do this, how many feet of fencing must you buy? Explain by including a labeled sketch of the garden and path.

DEFINITION

The **perimeter of a rectangle** is the total distance around all its edges or sides.

PROCEDURE

Calculating the Perimeter of a Rectangle The formula for the perimeter, P, of a rectangle with length l and width w has three equivalent forms.

$$P = l + w + l + w$$
$$P = 2l + 2w \quad \text{and}$$
$$P = 2(l + w)$$

Triangles

DEFINITION

A **triangle** is a closed plane figure with three sides.

Examples:

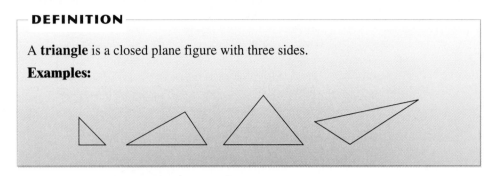

Many houses and garages have roofs supported by trusses, triangular structures usually made of wood. Trusses provide the greatest strength in building design. See the accompanying figure.

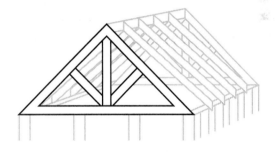

4. Why would a builder need to know about the perimeter of a triangular truss?

5. The dimensions of the three sides of a triangular truss are 13 feet, 13 feet, and 20 feet. What is the perimeter of the truss?

6. If the sides of a triangle measure a, b, and c, write a formula for the perimeter, P, of the following triangle.

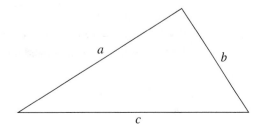

SUMMARY	Two-Dimensional	Labeled Sketch	Perimeter
ACTIVITY 5.1	Figure		Formula

	Two-Dimensional Figure	Labeled Sketch	Perimeter Formula
	Square	s (square with sides labeled s)	$P = 4s$
	Rectangle	l, w (rectangle labeled l and w)	$P = 2l + 2w$
	Triangle	a, b, c (triangle labeled a, b, c)	$P = a + b + c$

EXERCISES
ACTIVITY 5.1

1. You are interested in buying an older home. The first thing you learn about older homes is that they frequently have had additions over the years, and the floor plans often have the shape of a polygon.

   a. When the house you want to buy was built, 100 years ago, it had a simple rectangular floor plan.

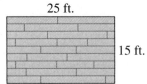

25 ft.

15 ft.

   Calculate the perimeter of the floor plan.

   b. Sixty years ago, a rectangular 10-foot by 25-foot garage was added to the original structure.

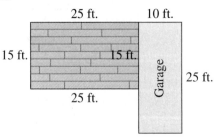

25 ft.   10 ft.

15 ft.   15 ft.   Garage   25 ft.

25 ft.

   Calculate the perimeter of the floor plan.

c. Twenty-five years ago, a new master bedroom, with the same size and shape as the garage, was added onto the other side of the original floor plan.

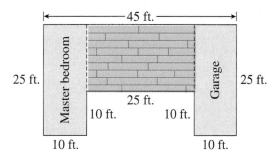

Calculate the perimeter of the remodeled floor plan.

d. You plan to add a family room with a triangular floor plan, as shown in the following floor plan.

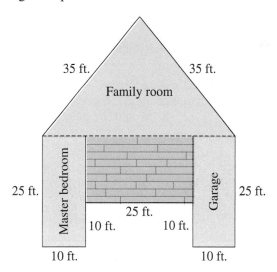

Calculate the perimeter of the floor plan of the house after the family room is added.

2. A standard basketball court has the following dimensions:

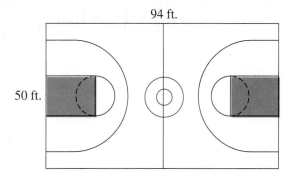

a. Calculate the perimeter of the court.

b. If you play a half-court game, calculate the perimeter of the half-court.

3. The Bermuda Triangle is an imaginary triangular area in the Atlantic Ocean in which there have been many unexplained disappearances of boats and planes. Public interest was aroused by the publication of a popular and controversial book, *The Bermuda Triangle*, by Charles Berlitz in 1974. The triangle starts at Miami, Florida, goes to San Juan, Puerto Rico (1038 miles), then to Bermuda (965 miles), and back to Miami (1042 miles).

   a. What is the perimeter of this triangle?

   b. If you were on a plane that was averaging 600 miles per hour, how long would it take you to fly the perimeter of the Bermuda Triangle?

4. Leonardo da Vinci's painting of the *Last Supper* is a 460-cm by 880-cm rectangle.

   a. Calculate its perimeter.

   b. Would the painting fit in your living room? Explain.

5. If a square has perimeter 64 feet, calculate the length of each side of the square.

6. A rectangle has a perimeter of 75 meters and a length of 10 meters. Calculate its width.

Objects in the shape of circles of varying sizes are found in abundance in everyday life. Coins, dartboards, and ripples made by a raindrop in a pond are just a few examples.

The size of a circle is customarily described by the length of a line segment that starts and ends on the circle's edge and passes through its center. This line segment is called the **diameter** of the circle. The **radius** of a circle is a line segment that starts at its center and ends on its edge. Therefore, the length of the radius is one-half the length of the diameter. The distance around the edge of the circle is the perimeter, more commonly called the **circumference**.

ACTIVITY 5.2

Circles Are Everywhere

OBJECTIVES

1. Measure lengths of diameters and circumferences of circles.

2. Develop and use formulas for calculating circumferences of circles.

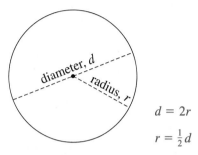

$$d = 2r$$
$$r = \tfrac{1}{2}d$$

1. The perimeter and diameter of four circular objects were measured and recorded in the following table. Some of these measurements are given in the metric system and others in the English system. From these measurements, you will develop formulas that relate the circumference of a circle to its diameter or radius.

COLUMN 1 CIRCULAR OBJECTS	COLUMN 2 MEASURED CIRCUMFERENCE, C	COLUMN 3 MEASURED DIAMETER, d	COLUMN 4 C/d, EXPRESSED AS A DECIMAL
Coin	7.62 cm	2.426 cm	
Salt Box	10.56 in.	3.37 in.	
Plate	69 cm	22 cm	
Can	12.38 in.	3.94 in.	

a. Use the data from columns 2 and 3 to determine the ratio $\frac{C}{d}$. Express each ratio as a decimal equivalent to the nearest thousandth and record it in column 4.

b. Are the four values in column 4 the same? How much do they vary?

c. Calculate the average of the four values in column 4, rounding to the hundredths place. What do you conclude?

In every circle, the ratio of the circumference, C, to the diameter, d, is always the same $\left(\text{approximately } 3.14, \text{ or } \frac{22}{7}\right)$. This ratio is represented by the Greek letter pi, or π. Most calculators have π keys.

PROCEDURE

Calculating the Circumference of a Circle The formula for the circumference, C, of a circle with diameter d is

$$\frac{C}{d} = \pi \quad \text{or} \quad C = \pi d.$$

Since $d = 2r$, where r is the radius of the circle, the circumference formula can also be written as

$$C = 2\pi r.$$

2. Use the circumference formulas to calculate the circumference of the following circles (not drawn to scale). Use π on your calculator and round your answers to the nearest hundredth.

a. The radius of the circle is 8 miles.

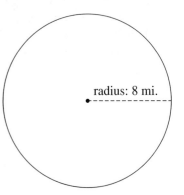

radius: 8 mi.

b. The diameter of the circle is 10 meters.

diameter: 10 m

c. The radius of the circle is 3 inches.

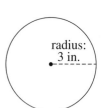

radius: 3 in.

SUMMARY ACTIVITY 5.2	**Two-Dimensional Figure**	**Labeled Sketch**	**Circumference (Perimeter) Formula**
	Circle		$C = \pi d \quad \text{or} \quad C = 2\pi r$

EXERCISES
ACTIVITY 5.2

For calculations in Exercises 1–5, use π on your calculator and round your answers to the nearest hundredths unless otherwise indicated.

1. You order a pizza in the shape of a circle with diameter 14 inches. Calculate the "length" of the crust (that is, find the circumference of the pizza).

2. You enjoy playing darts. You decide to make your own dartboard consisting of four concentric circles (that is, four circles with the same center). The smallest circle (the "bull's-eye") has radius 1 cm, the next largest circle has radius 3 cm, the third circle has radius 6 cm, and the largest circle has radius 10 cm. You decide to compare the circumferences of the circles. What are these circumferences?

3. United States coins are circular. Choose a quarter, dime, nickel, and penny.

   a. Use a tape measure (or ruler) to estimate the diameter of each coin in terms of centimeters. Record your results to the nearest tenth of a centimeter.

   b. Use a tape measure (or string and ruler) to estimate the circumference of each coin in terms of centimeters. Record your results to the nearest tenth of a centimeter.

c. Check your estimates by using the formulas derived in this activity. Record your results to the nearest tenth of a centimeter.

4. Use the appropriate geometric formulas to calculate the circumference, or fraction thereof, for each of the following circles. Round to the nearest tenth.

a.

diameter: 3 cm

b.

radius: 3 mi.

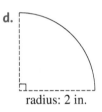

c.

radius: 5.3 ft.

d.

radius: 2 in.

5. If a circle has circumference 63 inches, approximate its radius.

Lance Armstrong and You

OBJECTIVES

1. Calculate perimeters of many-sided plane figures using formulas and combinations of formulas.

2. Use unit analysis to solve problems involving perimeters.

Inspired by Lance Armstrong's remarkable performance in the Tour de France, you decide to experiment with long-distance biking. You choose the route shown by the solid line path in the following figure, made up of rectangles and a quarter circle.

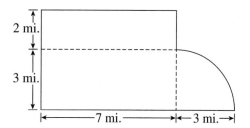

1. Calculate the total length of your bike trip in miles (that is, determine the perimeter of the figure). Use π on your calculator and round to the nearest thousandth.

2. If you can average 9 miles per hour on your bike, how long will it take you to complete the trip?

3. If your bike tires have a diameter of 2 feet, calculate the circumference of the tires to the nearest thousandth.

4. To analyze the wear on your tires, calculate how many rotations of the tires are needed to complete your trip. (*Note*: 1 mile = 5280 feet.)

5. Participants in the Tour de France bike 3454 kilometers (km). How many hours would it take you to complete the race if you average 9 miles per hour? (*Note*: 1 mile = 1.609 km.)

6. Compare your time with the 2005 time by Lance Armstrong: 86.25 hours.

SUMMARY
ACTIVITY 5.3

1. A many sided closed plane figure may be viewed as a combination of basic plane figures: squares, rectangles, parallelograms, triangles, trapezoids, and circles.

2. To calculate the perimeter of a many sided plane figure,

   i. Determine the length of each part that contributes to the perimeter.

   ii. Add the lengths to obtain the figure's total perimeter.

EXERCISES
ACTIVITY 5.3

1. You plan to fly from New York City to Los Angeles via Atlanta and return from Los Angeles to New York City via Chicago.

Use the data in the diagram to determine the total distance of your trip.

2. A Norman window is a rectangle with a semicircle on top. You decide to install a Norman window in your family room with the dimensions indicated in the diagram. What is its perimeter? Round to the nearest hundredth.

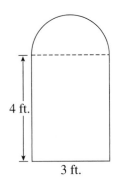

4 ft.

3 ft.

3. Stonehenge is an ancient site on the plains of southern England consisting of a collection of concentric circles (that is, circles with the same center) outlined with large sandstone blocks. Carbon dating has determined the age of the stones to be approximately 5000 years. Much curiosity and mystery has surrounded this site over the years. One theory about Stonehenge is that it was a ritualistic prayer site. However, even today, there is still controversy over what went on there. One thing everyone interested in Stonehenge can agree on is the mathematical description of the circles.

The diameters of the four circles are 288 feet for the largest circle, 177 feet for the next, 132 feet for the third, and 110 feet for the innermost circle.

a. For each time you walked around the outermost circle, how many times could you walk around the innermost circle? Round to the nearest hundredth.

b. How much longer is the trip around one of the two intermediate circles than around the other? Round to the nearset hundredth.

4. Calculate the perimeters of each of the following figures:

a.

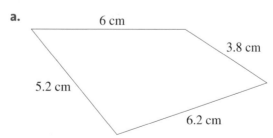

6 cm

3.8 cm

5.2 cm

6.2 cm

b.

3 ft.

Note: All sides of the star are equal length.

c.

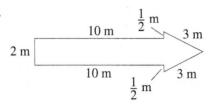

2 m

10 m

$\frac{1}{2}$ m

3 m

10 m

3 m

$\frac{1}{2}$ m

d.

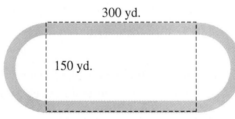

300 yd.

150 yd.

Note: The ends are semicircles.

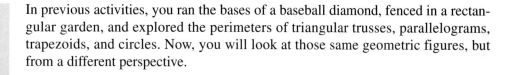

In previous activities, you ran the bases of a baseball diamond, fenced in a rectangular garden, and explored the perimeters of triangular trusses, parallelograms, trapezoids, and circles. Now, you will look at those same geometric figures, but from a different perspective.

Squares

As groundskeeper for the local baseball team, you need to guarantee good-quality turf for the baseball diamond. This is the square area enclosed by the baselines. To estimate the amount of sod to plant in the baseball diamond, you need to know the size of this area.

Recall that the area of a square is measured by determining the number of unit squares (squares that measure 1 unit in length on each side) that are needed to completely fill the inside of the square.

For example, the square pictured below has sides that are 4 units in length. As illustrated, it takes four rows of four unit squares to fill the inside of the square. You say the area, A, of the square is 16 square units.

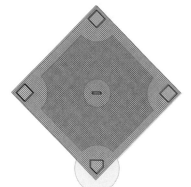

$A = 16$ square units

1. A regulation baseball diamond is a square with each side 90 feet long. How many square feet are needed to cover this baseball diamond? That is, how many 1-foot by 1-foot squares are inside the diamond?

PROCEDURE

Calculating the Area of a Square The formula for the area, A, of a square with sides of length s is

$$A = s \cdot s \text{ or } A = s^2$$

2. The Little League baseball diamond has sides measuring 60 feet. Use the formula to calculate the area of the Little League diamond.

DEFINITION

The **area** of a square, or any polygon, is the measure of the region enclosed by the sides of the polygon. Area is measured in square units.

Rectangles

Planting your rectangular 15-foot by 10-foot garden requires that you know how much space it contains.

3. How many square feet are required to cover your garden? Include a sketch to explain your answer.

PROCEDURE

Calculating the Area of a Rectangle The formula for the area of a rectangle with length l and width w is

$$A = lw.$$

---

4. Will doubling the length and width of your garden in Problem 3 double its area? Explain.

Parallelograms

Once you know the formula for the area of a rectangle, then you have the key for determining the formula for the area of a parallelogram. Recall that a parallelogram is formed by two intersecting pairs of parallel sides.

5. If you "cut off" a triangle and move it to the other side of the parallelogram forming the shaded rectangle, is the area different? Explain.

DEFINITION

The height of a parallelogram is the distance from one side (the base) to the opposite side, measured along a perpendicular line (see illustration).

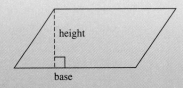

---

6. Use your observations from Problem 5 to calculate the area of the parallelogram with height 4 inches and base 7 inches.

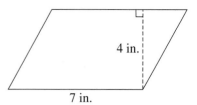

4 in.

7 in.

PROCEDURE

Calculating the Area of a Parallelogram The formula for the area of a parallelogram with base *b* (the length of one side) and height *h* (the perpendicular distance from the base *b* to its parallel side) is

$$A = bh.$$

Triangles

Every triangle can be pictured as one-half of a rectangle or parallelogram.

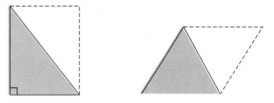

7. For each of the following triangles, draw a rectangle or parallelogram that encloses the triangle.

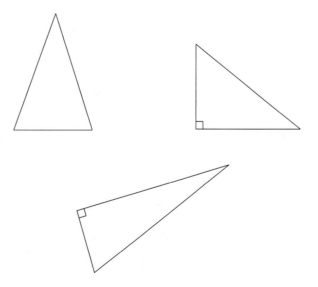

8. Use the idea that a triangle is one-half of a rectangle or parallelogram to write a formula for the area of a triangle in terms of its base *b* and height *h*. Explain how you obtained the formula.

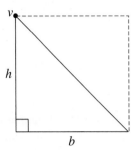 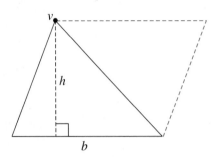

PROCEDURE

Calculating the Area of a Triangle The formula for the area of a triangle with base *b* (the length of one side) and height *h* (the perpendicular distance from the base *b* to the vertex opposite it) is

$$A = \tfrac{1}{2}bh.$$

9. Calculate the areas of the following triangles using a formula.

a.

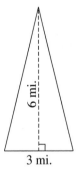

6 mi.

3 mi.

b.

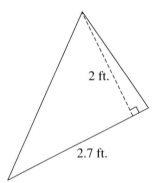

2 ft.

2.7 ft.

c.

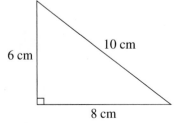

6 cm

10 cm

8 cm

d.

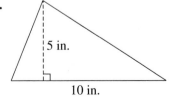

5 in.

10 in.

SUMMARY **ACTIVITY 5.4**	**Two-Dimensional Figure**	**Labeled Sketch**	**Area Formula**
	Square		$A = s^2$
	Rectangle		$A = lw$
	Triangle		$A = \dfrac{1}{2}bh$

---

1. You are carpeting your living room and sketch the following floor plan.

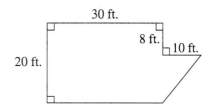

30 ft.

8 ft.

10 ft.

20 ft.

a. Calculate the area that you need to carpet.

b. Carpeting is sold in 10-foot-wide rolls. Calculate how much you need to buy. Explain.

2. You need to buy a solar cover for your 36-foot by 18-foot rectangular pool. A pool company advertises that solar covers are on sale for $1.77 per square foot. Determine the cost of the pool cover before sales tax.

3. How would you break up the following star to determine what dimensions you need to know in order to calculate its area? Explain.

4. A standard basketball court is a rectangle with length 94 feet and width 50 feet. How many square feet of flooring would you need to purchase in order to replace the court?

5. You are planning to build a new garage on your home and need to measure the length and width of your cars to help you estimate the size of the double garage. Your car measurements are

Car 1: 14 ft. 2 in. by 5 ft. 7 in.
Car 2: 14 ft. 6 in. by 5 ft. 9 in.

a. Based on these measurements, what would be a reasonable floor plan for your garage? Explain.

b. What is the area of your floor plan?

ACTIVITY 5.5

How Big Is That Circle?

OBJECTIVES

1. Develop a formula for the area of a circle.

2. Use the formula to determine areas of circles.

Determining the area of a circle becomes a challenge because there are no straight sides. No matter how hard you try, you cannot neatly pack unit squares inside a circle to completely cover the area of a circle. The best you can do in this way is to get an approximation of the area. In this activity you will explore methods for estimating the area of a circle and develop a formula to calculate the exact area.

DEFINITION

The **area of a circle** is the measure of the region enclosed by the circumference of the circle.

1. a. To help understand the formula for a circle's area, start by folding a paper circle in half, then in quarters, and finally halving it one more time into eighths.

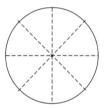

b. Cut the circle along the folds into eight equal pie-shaped pieces (called sectors) and rearrange these sectors into an approximate parallelogram (see accompanying figures).

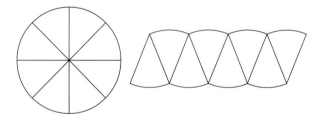

c. What measurement on the circle approximates the height of the parallelogram? Explain.

d. What measurement on the circle approximates the base of the parallelogram?

e. Recall that the area of a parallelogram is given by the product of its base and its height. Use the approximations from parts b and c to determine the approximate area of the parallelogram and the approximate area of the circle.

Imagine cutting a circle into more than eight equal sectors. Each sector would be thinner. When reassembled, as in Problem 1, the resulting figure will more closely approximate a parallelogram. Hence, the formula for the area of a circle, $A = \pi r^2$, is even more reasonable and accurate.

PROCEDURE

Calculating the Area of a Circle The formula for the area A of a circle with radius r is

$$A = \pi r^2.$$

---

2. You own a circular dartboard of radius 1.5 feet. To figure how much space you have as a target, calculate the area of the dartboard. Be sure to include the units of measurement in your answer.

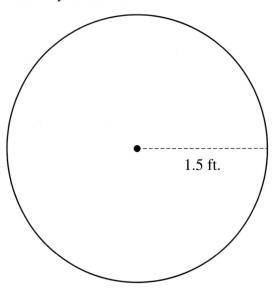

1.5 ft.

3. The diameter of a circle is twice its radius. Use this fact to rewrite the formula for the area of a circle using its diameter instead of the radius. Show the steps you took.

4. Calculate the areas of the following circles. Round to the nearest hundredth.

a.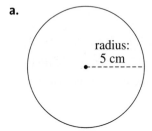

radius:
5 cm

b.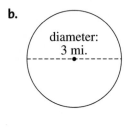

diameter:
3 mi.

5. As discussed in the introduction to this activity, you can estimate the area of a circle by counting the number of squares that come close to filling the inside of a circle. In the illustration, use the distance between grid lines as the basic unit of measurement. The steps in this problem show you how.

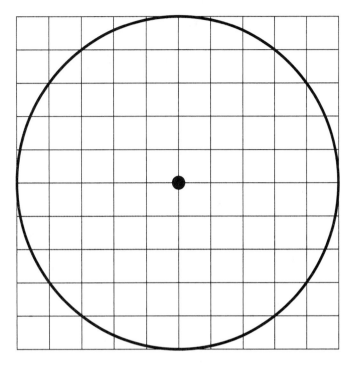

a. Count the number of small unit squares that are entirely inside the circle.

b. Now count the number of squares that are partly inside and partly outside the circle.

c. What is the total number of squares that are at least partly inside the square?

d. Your answer in part a is less than the actual area of the circle. Your answer in part c is more than the actual area of the circle. Find the average of these two numbers to get an estimate of the circle's area.

e. Determine the radius of the circle from the diagram.

f. Apply the formula $A = \pi r^2$ to determine the exact area of the circle. How far off was your estimate in part d?

g. A better estimate can be determined by using smaller squares. Note that in the following grid each square from the previous grid has been divided into four smaller squares. So when you count the squares, every four smaller squares will be the size of the unit square you used in parts a–f.

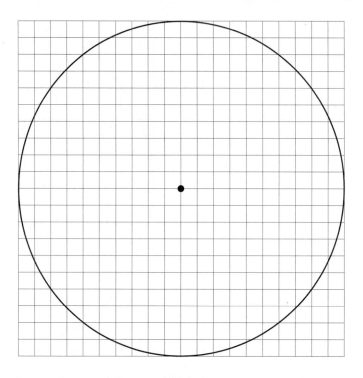

Follow the same procedure as before to estimate the area of the circle.

h. Divide the result in part g by 4 to obtain the area in terms of the larger squares.

i. How far is your new estimate from the actual area?

j. How much better is your new estimate than your estimate in part d?

SUMMARY ACTIVITY 5.5	Two-Dimensional Figure	Labeled Sketch	Area Formula
	Circle		$A = \pi r^2$ (involving the radius) $A = \dfrac{\pi d^2}{4}$ (involving the diameter)

EXERCISES ACTIVITY 5.5

1. You order a pizza with diameter 14 inches. Your friend orders a pizza with diameter 10 inches. Compare the areas of the two pizzas to estimate approximately how many of the smaller pizzas are equivalent to one larger pizza.

2. United States coins are circles of varying sizes. Choose a quarter, dime, nickel, and penny.

   a. Use a tape measure (or ruler) to estimate the diameter of each coin in centimeters.

   b. Calculate the area of each coin to the nearest hundredth.

3. Use an appropriate formula to calculate the area for each of the following figures. Round to the nearest hundredth.

   a.
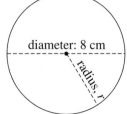
   diameter: 8 cm

   b.
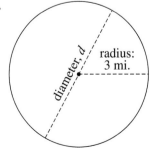
   radius: 3 mi.

c.

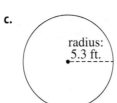

radius: 5.3 ft.

d.

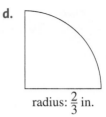

radius: $\frac{2}{3}$ in.

4. a. For each of the following three circles, estimate how many 1-cm by 1-cm unit squares and fractions of unit squares can fit in each circle by drawing these squares on the circles. Place these estimates in column 2 of the table in part c.

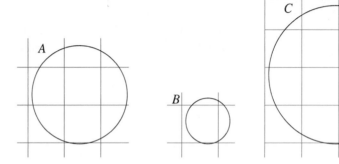

b. Measure the radius of each circle in centimeters, and record the results in column 3 of the table in part c.

c. Compute πr^2 for each circle and place your answers in column 4.

Measure for Measure

COLUMN 1 CIRCLE	COLUMN 2 ESTIMATED AREA	COLUMN 3 MEASURED RADIUS	COLUMN 4 CALCULATED πr^2
A			
B			
C			

d. Compare your answers in columns 2 and 4. What do you notice?

✳**ACTIVITY 5.6**

**A New Pool and
Other Home
Improvements**

OBJECTIVES

1. Solve problems in
context using geometric
formulas.

2. Distinguish between
problems that require
area formulas and those
that require perimeter
formulas.

You are the proud owner of a new circular swimming pool with a diameter of 25 feet and are eager to dive in. However, you quickly discover that having a new pool requires making many decisions about other purchases.

1. Your first concern is a solar pool cover. You do some research and find that circular pool covers come in the following sizes: 400, 500, and 600 square feet. Friends recommend that you buy a pool cover with very little overhang. Which size is best for your needs? Explain.

2. You decide to build a concrete patio around the circumference of your pool. It will be 6 feet wide all the way around. Provide a diagram of your pool with the patio. Show all the distances you know on the diagram. What is the area of the patio alone? Explain how you determined this area.

3. State law requires that all pools be enclosed by a fence to prevent accidents. You decide to completely enclose your pool and patio with a stockade fence. How many feet of fencing do you need? Explain.

4. Next, you decide to stain the new fence. The paint store recommends a stain that covers 500 square feet per gallon. If the stockade fence has a height of 5 feet, how many gallons of stain should you buy? Explain.

5. Lastly, you decide to plant a circular flower garden near the pool and patio but outside the fence. You determine that a circle of circumference 30 feet would fit. What is the length of the corresponding diameter of the flower garden?

Other Home Improvements

Now that you have a new pool, patio, and flower garden, you want to do some other home improvements in anticipation of enjoying your new pool with family and friends.

You have $1000 budgeted for this purpose and the list looks like this:

- Replace the kitchen floor.
- Add a wallpaper border to the third bedroom.
- Paint the walls in the family room.

To stay within your budget, you need to determine the cost of each of these projects. You expect to do this work yourself, so the only monetary cost will be for materials.

6. The kitchen floor is divided into two parts. The first section is rectangular and measures 12 by 14 feet. The second section is a semicircular breakfast area that extends off the 14-foot side. The cost of vinyl flooring is $21 per square yard plus 6% sales tax. The vinyl is sold in 12-foot widths.

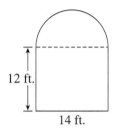

a. How long a piece of vinyl flooring will you need to purchase if you want only one seam, where the breakfast area meets the main kitchen, as shown? Remember that the vinyl is 12 feet wide.

b. How many square feet of flooring must you purchase? How many square yards is that (9 square feet = 1 square yard)?

c. How much will the vinyl flooring cost, including tax?

d. How many square feet of flooring will be left over after you're done? Explain.

7. The third bedroom is rectangular in shape and has dimensions of $8\frac{1}{2}$ by 13 feet. On each 13-foot side, there is a window that measures 3 feet 8 inches wide. The door is located on an $8\frac{1}{2}$-foot side and measures 3 feet wide from edge to edge. You are planning to put up a decorative horizontal wallpaper stripe around the room about halfway up the wall.

a. How many feet of wallpaper stripe will you need to purchase?

b. The border comes in rolls 5 yards in length. How many rolls will you need to purchase?

c. The wallpaper border costs $10.56 per roll plus 6% sales tax. Determine the cost of the border.

d. How many feet of wallpaper will be left over after you're done?

8. Your family room needs to be painted. It has a cathedral ceiling with front and back walls that measure the same, as shown in the diagram. The two side walls are 14 feet long and 12 feet high. Each of the walls will need two coats of paint. The ceiling will not be painted. For simplicity, ignore the fact that there are windows.

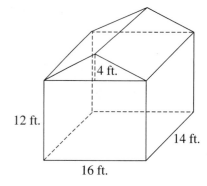

a. How many square feet of wall surface will you be painting? (Remember, all walls will need two coats.)

b. Each gallon of paint covers approximately 400 square feet. How many gallons of paint will you need to purchase?

c. The paint costs $19.81 per gallon plus 6% sales tax. What is the total cost of the paint you need for the family room?

9. What is the cost for all your home-improvement projects (not including the new pool, patio, and flower garden)?

10. Additional costs for items such as paint rollers and wallpaper paste amount to approximately $30. Can you afford to do all the projects? Explain.

SUMMARY
ACTIVITY 5.6

1. Area formulas are used when you are measuring the amount of space *inside* a figure.

2. Perimeter or circumference formulas are used when you are measuring the length *around* a figure.

EXERCISES
ACTIVITY 5.6

1. Your driveway is rectangular in shape and measures 15 feet wide and 25 feet long. Calculate the area of your driveway.

2. A flower bed in the corner of your yard is in the shape of a right triangle. The perpendicular sides of the bed measure 6 feet 8 inches and 8 feet 4 inches. Calculate the area of the flower bed. What are the units of this area?

3. You live in a small, one-bedroom apartment. The bedroom is 10 by 12 feet, the living room is 12 by 14 feet, the kitchen is 8 by 6 feet, and the bathroom is 5 by 9 feet. Calculate the total floor space (area) of your apartment.

4. In your living room, there is a large rectangular window with dimensions of 10 feet by 6 feet. You love the sunlight but would like to redesign the window so that it admits the same amount of light but is only 8 feet wide. How tall should your redesigned window be?

36.2 in.

15 in.

5. A stop sign is in the shape of a regular octagon (an eight-sided polygon with equal sides and angles). A regular octagon can be created using eight triangles of equal area. One triangle that makes up a stop sign has a base of 15 inches and a height of approximately 18.1 inches. Calculate the area of the stop sign.

6. How does the area of the stop sign in Exercise 6 compare with the area of a circle of radius 18.1 inches? Explain.

7. You are buying material to make drapes for your Norman window (in the shape of a rectangle with a semicircular top). So you need to calculate the area of the window. If the rectangular part of the window is 4 feet wide and 5 feet tall, what is the area of the entire window? Explain.

8. The diameter of Earth is 12,742 kilometers; the diameter of the Moon is 3476 kilometers.

a. If you flew around Earth by following the equator at a height of 10 kilometers, how many trips around the Moon could you take in the same amount of time, at the same height from the Moon, and at the same speed? Explain.

b. The circle whose circumference is the equator is sometimes called the "great circle" of Earth or of the Moon. Compare the areas of the great circles of Earth and the Moon.

**How Big Is
That Angle?**

OBJECTIVES

1. Measure sizes of angles
with a protractor.

2. Classify triangles as
equiangular, equilateral,
right, isosceles, or
scalene.

EQUIPMENT

In this laboratory activity,
you will need the following
equipment:

1. A 12-inch ruler.

2. A protractor.

You may have wondered why a right angle measures 90 degrees. Why not 100 degrees? As with much of the mathematics that we use today, the measurement of angles has a rich history, going back to ancient times when navigation of the oceans and surveying the land were priorities. The ancient Babylonian culture used a base 60 number system, which at least in part led to the circle being divided into 360 equal sectors. The angle of each sector was simply defined to measure 1 degree and so today we say there are 360 degrees (abbreviated 360°) in a circle. In this activity you will be using degrees to measure angles. The illustration shows a sector having an angle of 20 degrees ($\frac{1}{18}$ of a circle).

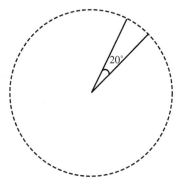

In the following diagram, the circle is divided into four equal sectors by two perpendicular lines. The angles of the four sectors must add up to 360 degrees. Since the angles are equal, dividing 360° by 4 results in each angle measuring 90°. Recall that 90° angles are called *right* angles.

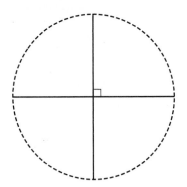

1. How many degrees are in the angle of a sector that is exactly half of a circle? Such an angle is called a *straight angle*.

Measuring Angles

PROCEDURE

Measuring Angles with a Protractor A protractor is a device for measuring the size of angles in degrees. Place the vertex of the angle at the center of the protractor (often a hole in the center of the baseline) and place one side of the angle along the baseline of the protractor. Where the other side of the angle meets the appropriate scale on the semicircle is the measure of the angle in degrees.

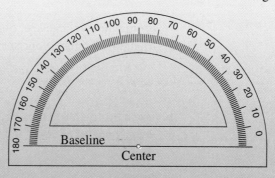

EXAMPLE 1   *The following angle measures 75°.*

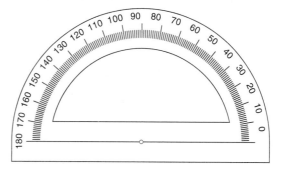

2. Use a protractor to measure the size of each of the following angles.

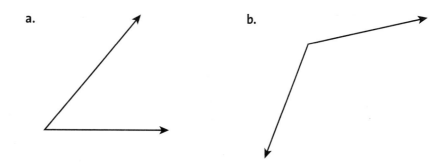

a.

b.

DEFINITIONS

An **acute angle** is any angle that is smaller than a right angle. Its degree measure is less than 90°.

An **obtuse angle** is any angle that is larger than a right angle. Its degree measure is greater than 90°.

3. Cut out a triangle from a piece of paper. Label the three angles X, Y, and Z.

    a. Tear off two of the corners. Place the three vertices (plural for vertex) together at a single point so the three angles are next to each other. (See the illustration.)

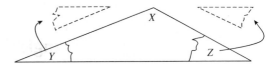

    From what you can see, estimate the sum of the three angles of your triangle. Compare your answer to those of your classmates.

    b. Use a protractor to measure each angle of your paper triangle, to the nearest degree. Record the sum of these three angles.

It is a well-known theorem in geometry that the sum of the measures of the angles of a triangle must equal 180°.

4. Verify this theorem by carefully measuring the angles of each of the following triangles, recording the results in the table on page 363. You will have to extend the sides of each triangle to use your protractor effectively.

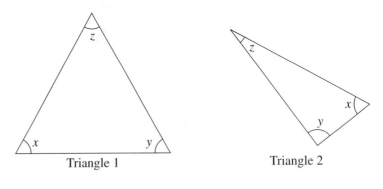

Triangle 1   Triangle 2

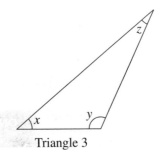

Triangle 3

	ANGLE *X*	ANGLE *Y*	ANGLE *Z*	SUM
TRIANGLE 1				
TRIANGLE 2				
TRIANGLE 3				

Classifying Triangles

Sometimes, it is useful to classify triangles in terms of special properties of their sides or angles. These classifications are summarized in the following table.

TRIANGLE CLASSIFICATIONS	DEFINITION
Equilateral	All three sides have the same length.
Isosceles	Exactly two sides have the same length. The two angles opposite the equal sides will also have the same measure.
Scalene	None of the sides have the same length.
Equiangular	All three angles have the same measure. An equiangular triangle is also an equilateral triangle.
Right	One angle measures 90°.
Acute	All angles measure less than 90°.
Obtuse	One angle measures greater than 90°.

5. Use your protractor to measure the acute angles in the following right triangles, recording your results in the table. What is the sum of the two acute angles in each triangle?

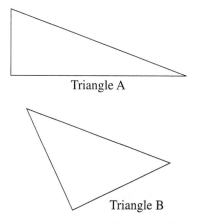

Triangle A

Triangle B

	ONE NONRIGHT ANGLE	OTHER NONRIGHT ANGLE	SUM
TRIANGLE A			
TRIANGLE B			

6. In a right triangle, what must be true about the two angles which are not right angles? Explain your answer.

7. a. In an equiangular triangle, what is the measure of each angle?

  b. In an isosceles triangle, if one angle measures 110°, what is the measure of the other two equal angles?

  c. Consider the following three triangles:

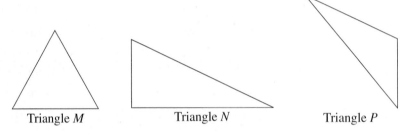

  Triangle *M*   Triangle *N*   Triangle *P*

  i. Choose the triangles that are scalene, and explain why. Then use a protractor to measure the angles.

  ii. Choose the triangle(s) which is(are) obtuse and explain why.

  iii. Choose the triangle(s) which is(are) acute and explain why.

SUMMARY **ACTIVITY 5.7**	**Concept/Skill**	**Description**	**Example**
	1. Using a protractor	Place the vertex of the angle to be measured at the center of the protractor and line up one side with the base line. Read the protractor scale to measure the angle.	See Example 1, page 361

2. Equilateral triangle

A triangle in which all three sides have the same length (also equiangular).

3. Isosceles triangle

A triangle in which two sides have the same length. The two angles opposite the equal sides will also have the same measure.

4. Scalene triangle

A triangle in which all the sides have different lengths.

5. Equiangular triangle

A triangle in which all three angles are the same measure (also equilateral).

6. Right triangle

A triangle in which one angle measures 90°.

7. Acute triangle

A triangle in which all angles measure less than 90°.

8. Obtuse triangle

A triangle in which one angle measures greater than 90°.

9. Angle sum of a triangle

The sum of the measures of the angles of a triangle equals 180°.

EXERCISES
ACTIVITY 5.7

1. Use a protractor to measure the angles in this triangle. Verify that the sum of the angles is 180°.

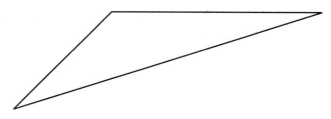

2. In a right triangle, one of the acute angles measures 47°. What is the size of the other acute angle?

3. In an isosceles triangle one of the angles measures 102°. What is the size of the other two angles?

4. What is true about the sizes of the three angles in a scalene triangle?

5. Give an example of the possible sizes of the three angles in a scalene triangle which is also an acute triangle.

6. What must be the sum of the four angles in a parallelogram? (*Hint:* Consider dividing the parallelogram into two triangles.)

7. a. Extend the idea of Exercise 6 to a pentagon (a five-sided polygon) to determine the sum of all 5 angles by dividing the pentagon into 3 triangles that all meet at one point on the pentagon.

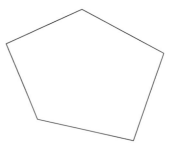

b. Extend the idea of part a to determine the sum of all eight angles in an octagon (an eight-sided polygon).

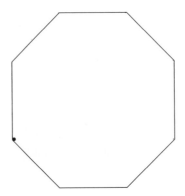

In this activity you will experimentally verify a very important formula of geometry. The formula is used by surveyors, architects, and builders to check whether or not two lines are perpendicular, or if a corner truly forms a right angle.

A right triangle is simply a triangle that has a right angle. In other words, one of the angles formed by the triangle measures 90°. The two sides that are perpendicular and form the right angle are called the **legs** of the right triangle. The third side, opposite the right angle, is called the **hypotenuse**.

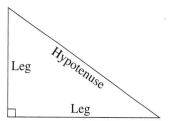

LAB ACTIVITY 5.8

How About Pythagoras?

OBJECTIVES

1. Develop and use the Pythagorean Theorem for right triangles.

2. Calculate the square root of numbers other than perfect squares.

3. Apply the Pythagorean Theorem in context.

EQUIPMENT

In this laboratory activity, you will need the following equipment:

1. A 12-inch ruler.

2. A protractor.

3. A 12-inch piece of string.

1. Use a protractor to construct three right triangles, one with legs of length 1 inch and 5 inches, a second with legs of length 3 inches and 4 inches, and a third with legs of length 2 inches each.

Triangle 1

Triangle 2

Triangle 3

Pythagorean Theorem

2. For each triangle in Problem 1, complete the following table. The first triangle was done for you as an example. Note that the lengths of the legs of the triangles are represented by a and b. The letter c represents the length of the hypotenuse.

   a. Use a ruler to measure the length of each hypotenuse, in inches. Record the lengths in column c.

   b. Square each length a, b, and c and record in the table.

	a	b	c	a^2	b^2	c^2
Triangle 1	1	5	5.1	1	25	26.0
Triangle 2	3	4				
Triangle 3	2	2				

3. There does not appear to be a relationship between a, b, and c, but investigate further. What is the relationship between a^2, b^2, and c^2?

The relationship demonstrated in Problem 2 has been known since antiquity. It was known by many cultures, but has been attributed to the Greek mathematician Pythagoras, who lived in the sixth century B.C.

The **Pythagorean theorem** states that, in a right triangle, the sum of the squares of the leg lengths is equal to the square of the hypotenuse length.

Symbolically, the Pythagorean theorem is written as

$$c^2 = a^2 + b^2 \quad \text{or} \quad c = \sqrt{a^2 + b^2},$$

where a and b are leg lengths and c is the hypotenuse length.

Note that this relationship is true for any right triangle. Also, if this relationship is true for a triangle, then the triangle is a right triangle.

EXAMPLE 1   *If a right triangle has legs a = 4 centimeters and b = 7 centimeters, you can calculate the length of the hypotenuse as follows:*

$$c = \sqrt{a^2 + b^2} = \sqrt{(4 \text{ cm})^2 + (7 \text{ cm})^2}$$
$$= \sqrt{16 \text{ cm}^2 + 49 \text{ cm}^2} = \sqrt{65 \text{ cm}^2} \approx 8.06 \text{ cm}$$

DEFINITION

The **square root** of a non-negative number, N, written $\sqrt{N}$, is the non-negative number M whose square is N, that is,

$$\sqrt{N} = M \text{ provided } M^2 = N.$$

Example: $\sqrt{25} = 5$ because $5^2 = 25$.

The number 25 is an example of a *perfect square* since the square root of 25 can be determined exactly.

PROCEDURE

Calculating a Square Root If N is not a perfect square, then estimating the square root of N by hand involves "guess and check." You can determine a square root more efficiently by using a calculator with a square root key.

EXAMPLE 2   *Estimate $\sqrt{10}$ by guess and check.*

Determining the square root of 10 involves finding a number whose square is 10. Note that 3 is too small, since $3^2 = 9$ and 4 is too large, since $4^2 = 16$. So, $3 < \sqrt{10} < 4$, and $\sqrt{10}$ is closer to 3. Try $3.1^2 = 9.61$ and $3.2^2 = 10.24$. Therefore, $3.1 < \sqrt{10} < 3.2$. Continuing in this manner, one can estimate that $\sqrt{10} \approx 3.16$, easily confirmed on your calculator.

4. Estimate the square root of 53, written $\sqrt{53}$. Then use your calculator to check the answer.

5. A right triangle has legs measuring 5 centimeters and 16 centimeters. Use the Pythagorean theorem to calculate the length of the hypotenuse.

6. A popular triangle with builders and carpenters has dimensions 3 units by 4 units by 5 units.

   a. Use the Pythagorean theorem to show that this triangle is a right triangle.

   b. Builders use this triangle by taking a 12-unit-long rope and marking it in lengths of 3 units, 4 units, and 5 units (see graphic).

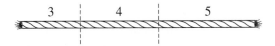

   Then, by fitting this rope to a corner, they can quickly tell if the corner is a true right angle. Another special right triangle has legs of length 5 units and 12 units. Determine the perimeter of this right triangle. Explain how a carpenter can use this triangle to check for a right angle.

7. Suppose you wish to measure the distance across your pond but don't wish to get your feet wet! By being clever, and knowing the Pythagorean theorem, you can estimate the distance by taking two measurements on dry land, as long as your two distances lie along perpendicular lines. (See the illustration.)

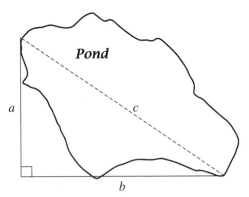

   If your measurements for legs a and b are 260 feet and 310 feet, respectively, what is the distance, c, across the pond?

SUMMARY
ACTIVITY 5.8

Concept/Skill	Description	Example
1. Pythagorean theorem	In a right triangle, $c^2 = a^2 + b^2$.	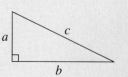
2. Determining a square root	If $N \geq 0$, then $\sqrt{N} = M$ provided $M^2 = N$; use a calculator to obtain an approximation.	

EXERCISES
ACTIVITY 5.8

1. New cell phone towers are being constructed on a daily basis throughout the country. Typically, they consist of a tall, thin tower supported by several guy wires. Assume the ground is level in the following. Round answers to the nearest foot.

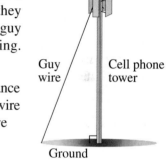

   a. The guy wire is attached on the ground at a distance of 100 feet from the base of the tower. The guy wire is also attached to the phone tower 300 feet above the ground. What is the length of the guy wire?

   b. You move the base of the guy wire so that it is attached 120 feet from the base of the tower. Now how much wire do you need for the one guy wire?

   c. Another option is to attach the base of the guy wire 100 feet from the base of the tower and to the phone tower 350 feet above the ground. How much wire do you need for this option?

2. A building inspector needs to determine if two walls in a new house are built at right angles, as the building code requires. He measures and finds the following information. Wall 1 measures 12 feet, wall 2 measures 14 feet, and the distance from the end of wall 1 to the end of wall 2 measures 18 feet. Do the walls meet at right angles? Explain.

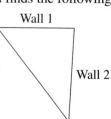

3. Trusses used to support the roofs of many structures can be thought of as two right triangles placed side by side.

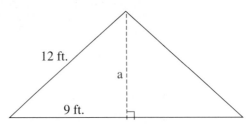

12 ft.

a

9 ft.

a. If the hypotenuse in one of the right triangles of a truss measures 12 feet and the horizontal leg in the same right triangle measures 9 feet, how high is the vertical leg of the truss?

b. To make a steeper roof, you may increase the vertical leg to 10 feet. Keeping the 9-foot horizontal leg, how long will the hypotenuse of the truss be now?

4. You can consider the truss in Exercise 3 as a single triangle. In this case, it is a good example of an isosceles triangle.

a. If the top angle of the truss is 120°, then what are the measures of the other two angles?

b. If you wish to have a steeper roof, with the base angles of the isosceles truss each measuring 42°, what is the measure of the top angle?

5. For the following right triangles, use the Pythagorean theorem to compute the length of the third side of the triangle:

a.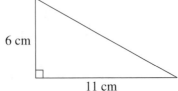

6 cm

11 cm

b.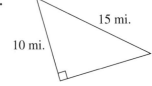

15 mi.

10 mi.

6. You are buying a ladder for your 30-foot-tall house. For safety, you would always like to ensure that the base of the ladder be placed at least 8 feet from the base of the house. What is the shortest ladder you can buy in order to be able to reach the top of your house?

7. Pythagorean triples are three positive integers that could be the lengths of three sides of a right triangle. For example, 3, 4, 5 is a Pythagorean triple since $5^2 = 3^2 + 4^2$.

   a. Is 5, 12, 13 a Pythagorean triple? Why or why not?

   b. Is 5, 10, 15 a Pythagorean triple? Why or why not?

   c. Is 1, 1, 2 a Pythagorean triple? Why or why not?

   d. Name another Pythagorean triple. Explain.

8. You own a summer home on the east side of Lake George in New York's Adirondack Mountains. To drive to your favorite restaurant on the west side of the lake, you must go directly south for 7 miles and then directly west for 3 miles. If you could go directly to the restaurant in your boat, how far is the boat trip?

9. You are decorating a large evergreen tree in your yard for the holidays. The tree stands 25 feet tall and 15 feet wide. You want to hang strings of lights from top to bottom draped on the outside of the tree. How long should the strings of lights be? Explain.

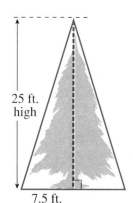

25 ft. high

7.5 ft.

10. Is it possible to have a right triangle with sides measuring 7 inches, 10 inches, and 15 inches?

ACTIVITY 5.9

**Moving Up
with Math**

OBJECTIVES

1. Recognize the geometric
properties of similar
triangles.

2. Use similar triangles in
indirect measurement.

Imagine you live on the twelfth floor of an apartment building. Looking out your window, you wonder how high you are above the ground. Measuring directly would be difficult. But applying a basic formula from geometry will allow you to determine the height indirectly. By walking outside, to a point 100 feet away from your building, a right triangle is formed with the wall of your building and your line of sight to the twelfth-floor window (see illustration).

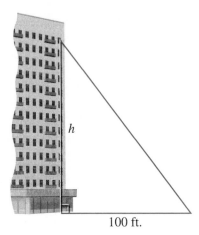

100 ft.

The Pythagorean theorem does not help since you only know the length of one side of the right triangle. The problem can be solved, however, by applying a result involving similar triangles.

DEFINITION

Two triangles are **similar** when they are exactly the same shape, meaning their angles are the same size. The pairs of matching angles are called **corresponding angles**. The two sides that are opposite corresponding angles are called **corresponding sides**.

The two triangles shown here are similar because the pairs of angles A and X, B and Y, and C and Z are the same size. Note that the pairs of corresponding sides are a and x, b and y, and c and z.

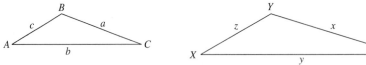

An important theorem that relates similar triangles involves the ratios of the corresponding sides of the triangles.

THEOREM

The ratio of the lengths of corresponding sides in similar triangles are equal. Using the similar triangles illustrated,

$$\frac{a}{x} = \frac{b}{y} = \frac{c}{z}.$$

The corresponding sides of similar triangles are said to be in **proportion**.

You can use this theorem and a simple drinking straw to determine the height of your twelfth-floor apartment.

After walking 100 feet away from your building, you use a drinking straw to get the line of sight to your twelfth-floor window. Your straw is 10 inches long. With your window in view through the straw, a horizontal distance of 6 inches can be measured from your eye to the end of the straw. The height of the end of the straw above your eye will measure 8 inches. The illustration shows this small right triangle.

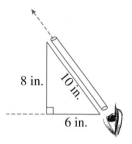

1. Do the lengths of the sides of this small triangle satisfy the Pythagorean theorem?

2. Explain why the small drinking straw triangle is similar to the large triangle involving your apartment building.

3. Use the information from Problems 1 and 2 to determine the height of your window.

   a. Set up the proportion involving the corresponding legs of the similar triangles (not the hypotenuse). Let h represent the unknown height of your window, in the large triangle.

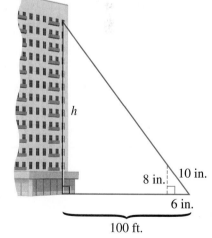

   b. Solve the proportion for h.

   c. Is your answer reasonable if each floor of your apartment building is approximately 10 to 12 feet high? Explain.

4. You have a friend who lives on the twentieth floor. Go through the same procedure as in Problem 3 to determine the height of your friend's window from the ground. The dimensions of the small "drinking straw triangle" are shown in the diagram.

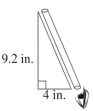

9.2 in.

4 in.

SUMMARY
ACTIVITY 5.9

1. Two triangles are **similar** provided they have equal corresponding angles.

2. For all similar triangles, the ratios of the lengths of corresponding sides are equal. In other words, corresponding sides of similar triangles are in **proportion**.

EXERCISES
ACTIVITY 5.9

1. You and your friends decide to set up an experiment to estimate the height of the math building on your campus. You wait until dark and then use a flashlight to project shadows onto the building. One of your friends sets the flashlight on the ground 50 feet from the building and shines it at you. You walk away from the flashlight and towards the building. Another friend tells you to stop when the height of your shadow reaches the top of the building. You have walked 12 feet. Because you know you are 6 feet tall, it is possible to determine the height of the building.

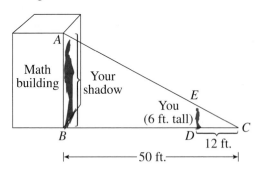

a. Where do you see two similar right triangles in the diagram? Explain.

b. Use the properties of similar right triangles to estimate the height of the math building.

2. You measure an isosceles triangle and label the lengths, as shown. In a similar isosceles triangle the longest side is 14 feet. Sketch the similar triangle and compute the lengths of its two equal sides.

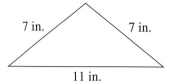

7 in.　　　7 in.

11 in.

3. On campus, there is a very tall tree. Your math professor challenges the class to devise a way to use similar triangles to indirectly measure the height of the tree. Be specific in explaining your best strategy.

4. A triangle has sides that measure 3 feet, 5 feet, and 6 feet.

   a. Calculate the dimensions of a similar triangle whose longest side measures 15 inches.

   b. Calculate the dimensions of a similar triangle whose shortest side measures 2 meters.

CLUSTER 1   # What Have I Learned?

1. What are the differences and similarities between the area and perimeter of a figure? Explain.

2. If the perimeter of a figure is measured in feet, then what are the usual units of the area of that figure? Explain.

3. If the area of a circular figure is measured in square centimeters, then what are the usual units of the diameter of that circle? Explain.

4. A racetrack can be described as a long rectangle with semicircles on the ends.

  a. At a racetrack, who would be interested in its perimeter? Why?

  b. At a racetrack, who would be interested in knowing its area? Why?

5. If different figures have the same perimeter, must their areas be the same? Explain.

6. If different figures have the same area, must their perimeters be the same? Explain.

7. Construct a nonright triangle, measure the sides, and show that the square of the length of the longest side is not equal to the sum of the squares of the lengths of the shorter sides.

8. True or false: If you double the diameter of a circle, then the area of the circle will also double. Give a reason for your answer.

9. The number π has an extraordinary place in the history of mathematics. Many books and articles have been written about this curious number. Research π and report on your findings.

1. Calculate the area and the perimeter for each of the following figures.

    a. Rectangle topped by a semicircle.

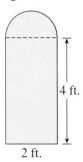

    b. Rectangle topped by a right triangle.

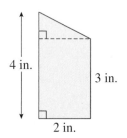

    c. Three-quarters of a circle with a square "corner."

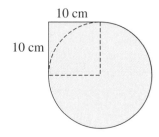

2. Determine the area of the shaded region in each of the following:

    a.

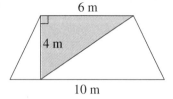

    b.

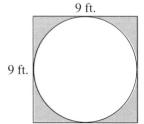

3. Consider the right triangle with dimensions as shown.

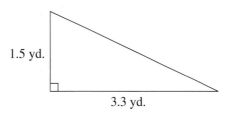

1.5 yd.

3.3 yd.

a. Determine the length of the third side of the triangle. Round to the nearest tenth.

b. Determine the perimeter of the triangle.

c. Determine the area of the triangle.

d. Give an example of another right triangle that is similar to the given triangle.

4. A triangle has two angles measuring 42° and 73°.

a. Make a sketch of the triangle.

b. Calculate the third angle of the triangle.

c. Give the angle measurements of a triangle similar to this triangle.

5. You intend to put in a 4-foot-wide concrete walkway along two sides of your house, as shown.

    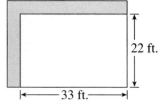

    a. Determine the area covered by the walkway only.

    b. If you decide to place a narrow flower bed along the outside of the walkway, how many feet of flowers should you plan for?

6. Triangle *A* has sides measuring 3 feet, 5 feet, and 7 feet; triangle *B* has sides measuring 4 feet, 4 feet, and 5 feet; triangle *C* has sides measuring 5 inches, 12 inches, and 13 inches.

    a. Which of the three triangles is a right triangle? Explain.

    b. A fourth triangle, *D*, is similar to triangle *B* but not identical to it. What are some possibilities for the lengths of the sides of triangle *D*? Explain.

    c. If 2 feet is added to the lengths of each side of triangle *A*, will the resulting triangle be similar to triangle *A*? Explain.

    d. If the length of each side of triangle *C* is tripled, will the resulting triangle be similar to triangle *C*?

    e. Which of the three triangles, *A*, *B*, or *C*, are scalene? Explain.

7. Answer the following questions about right triangles.

   a. Is it possible for a right triangle to be isosceles? Scalene? Equilateral? Explain.

   b. Is it possible for a right triangle to be acute? Obtuse? Equiangular? Explain.

8. If you measure the circumference of a circle to be 20 inches, estimate the length of its radius.

9. You want to know how much space is available between a basketball and the rim of the basket. One way to find out is to measure the circumference of each and then use the circumference formula to determine the corresponding diameters. The distance you want to determine is the difference between the diameter of the rim and the diameter of the ball. Try it!

The bracketed numbers following each concept indicate the activity in which the concept is discussed.

CONCEPT / SKILL	DESCRIPTION	EXAMPLE
Perimeter formulas [5.1]	Perimeter measures the length around the edge of the figure.	

Square [5.1]

$P = 4s$

$P = 4 \cdot 1 = 4$ ft.

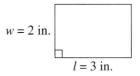

Rectangle [5.1]

$P = 2l + 2w$

$P = 2 \cdot 2 + 2 \cdot 3 = 10$ in.

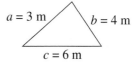

Triangle [5.1]

$P = a + b + c$

$P = 3 + 4 + 6 = 13$ m

Circle [5.2]

$C = 2\pi r$

For circles, perimeter is usually called *circumference*.

$C = 2\pi \cdot 3 = 6\pi \approx 18.85$ ft.

$C = \pi d$

$C = \pi \cdot 5 \approx 15.71$ m

CONCEPT / SKILL	DESCRIPTION	EXAMPLE
Area formulas [5.4]	Area is the measure of the space inside the figure.	
Square [5.4]	$A = s \cdot s$ or $A = s^2$	$A = 3 \cdot 3 = 9$ sq. ft. 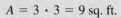
Rectangle [5.4]	$A = lw$	$A = 2 \cdot 3 = 6$ sq. in. 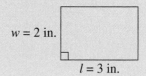
Triangle [5.4]	$A = \frac{1}{2}bh$	$A = \frac{1}{2} \cdot 4 \cdot 6 = 12$ sq. m 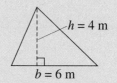
Circle [5.5]	$A = \pi r^2$	$A = \pi \cdot 3^2 = 9\pi \approx 28.27$ sq. ft.
Circle [5.5]	$A = \pi\left(\dfrac{d}{2}\right)^2$ or $A = \dfrac{\pi d^2}{4}$	$A = \pi\left(\dfrac{5}{2}\right)^2 = \dfrac{\pi \cdot 5^2}{4} \approx 19.63$ sq. m

Using a protractor [5.7]	Place the vertex of the angle to be measured at the center of the protractor and one side of the angle along the baseline of the protractor. Where the other side of the angle meets the appropriate scale (smaller than 90° or larger than 90°) is the measure of the angle in degrees.	

CONCEPT / SKILL	DESCRIPTION	EXAMPLE
Classification of triangles [5.7]		
Equilateral [5.7]	All three sides have the same length.	
Isosceles [5.7]	Two sides have the same length. (The two angles opposite the equal sides are also the same size.)	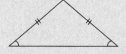
Scalene [5.7]	Each side has a different length.	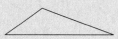
Equiangular [5.7]	All three angles have the same measure.	
Right [5.7]	One angle measures 90°.	
Acute [5.7]	All angles measure less than 90°.	
Obtuse [5.7]	One angle measures greater than 90°.	

The sum of the angles of a triangle [5.7]

The sum of the angles of a triangle is 180°.

$$a + b + c = 180°$$

Pythagorean theorem [5.8]

$c^2 = a^2 + b^2$

This important formula for right triangles is useful for indirect measurement.

$13^2 = 5^2 + 12^2$, since $169 = 169$

CONCEPT / SKILL	DESCRIPTION	EXAMPLE

Taking square roots [5.8]

If $N \geq 0$, then $\sqrt{N} = M$ providing $M^2 = N$.

Calculators can be very useful in estimating square roots. Use $\sqrt{N}$.

$\sqrt{64} = 8$

$\sqrt{70} \approx 8.37$

Similar triangles [5.9]

Two triangles are similar provided their corresponding angles are equal; the lengths of their corresponding sides must be proportional (that is, their ratios must be equal).

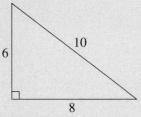

$$\frac{3}{6} = \frac{4}{8} \quad \text{and} \quad \frac{3}{6} = \frac{5}{10}$$

1. Consider the following two-dimensional figures.

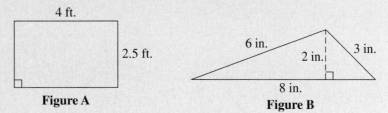

Figure A   **Figure B**

a. The area of Figure A = _____

b. The perimeter of Figure B = _____

c. The area of Figure B = _____

2. If a circle has area 23 square inches, what is the length of its radius?

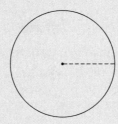

3. You buy a candy dish with a 2-inch by 2-inch square center surrounded on each side by attached semicircles.

a. Draw the candy dish described above and label its dimensions.

Answers to all Gateway exercises are included in the Selected Answers appendix.

389

b. Determine its perimeter and area.

c. If you place the dish on a 1-foot by 1-foot square table, how much space is left on the table for other items? Explain.

4. You buy a kite in the shape shown. When you open the box, you discover a tear in the kite's fabric. You decide to buy new fabric to place over the entire frame.

   a. How much fabric do you need to buy?

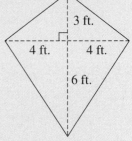

   b. You also decide to buy gold ribbon to line the perimeter of the kite. How much ribbon must you buy?

5. You are in the process of building a new home and the architect sends you the following floor plan for your approval.

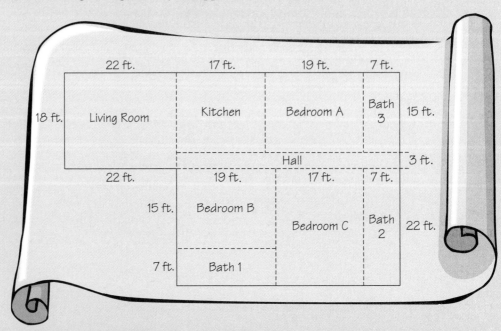

a. What is the perimeter of this floor plan?

b. What is the floor space, in square feet, of the floor plan?

c. Which bedroom has the largest area?

d. If you decide to double the area of the living room, what change in dimensions should you mark on the floor plan that you send back to the architect?

6. Your home is located in the center of a 300-foot by 200-foot rectangular plot of land. You are interested in measuring the diagonal of that plot. Use the Pythagorean theorem to make that indirect measurement.

7. Calculate the volumes of the following three-dimensional figures.

a.

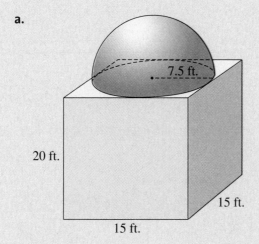

b.

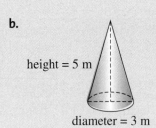

height = 5 m

diameter = 3 m

c.

diameter = 5 in.

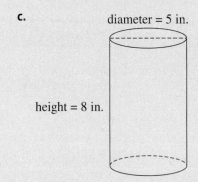

height = 8 in.

CHAPTER 6

VARIABLE SENSE

Arithmetic is the branch of mathematics that deals with counting, measuring, and calculating. Algebra is the branch that deals with variables and the relationships between and among variables. Variables and their relationships, expressed in table, graph, verbal, and symbolic forms, will be the central focus of this chapter.

| CLUSTER 1 | Interpreting and Constructing Tables and Graphs |

✳ ACTIVITY 6.1

Blood-Alcohol Levels

OBJECTIVES

1. Identify input and output in situations involving two variable quantities.

2. Use a table to numerically represent a relationship between two variables.

3. Represent a relationship between two variables graphically.

4. Identify trends in data pairs that are represented numerically and graphically.

Suppose you are asked to give a physical description of yourself. What categories might you include? You probably would include gender, ethnicity, and age. Can you think of any other categories? Each of these categories represents a distinct variable.

DEFINITION

A **variable**, usually represented by a letter, is a quantity or quality that may change in value from one particular instance to another.

The particular responses are the **values** of each variable. The first category, or variable, gender, has just two possible values: male or female. The second variable, ethnicity, has several possible values: Caucasian, African American, Hispanic, Asian, Native American, and so on. The third variable, age, has a large range of possible values: from 17 years up to possibly 100 years. Note that the values of the variable age are numerical but the values of gender and ethnicity are not. The variables you will deal with in this text are numerical.

In many situations, you are not just interested in analyzing data pertaining to individual variables. Often you will look for **relationships** between two or more variables. One way that you can represent a relationship between two variables is by means of a **table** of paired data values. Typically, one variable is designated the *input*, and the other is called the *output*.

The **input** is the value that is considered first. The **output** is the number that corresponds to or is matched with the input. The **input/output** designation may represent a cause-and-effect relationship, but this is not always the case.

This activity presents a variety of common input/output relationships.

Blood-Alcohol Concentration—Numerical Representation

In 2000, the U.S. Congress moved to reduce highway funding to states that did not implement a national standard of 0.08% blood-alcohol concentration as the minimum legal limit for drunk driving. By 2004, every state plus the District of Columbia had adopted the 0.08% legal limit. The following table presents a numerical description of the relationship between the number of beers consumed in an hour by a 200-pound person (input) and his corresponding blood-alcohol concentration (output). You may symbolically represent the input variable, the number of beers consumed in an hour, by the letter n. Similarly, you may represent the output variable, blood-alcohol concentration (%), by B.

NUMBER OF BEERS IN AN HOUR, n	1	2	3	4	5	6	7	8	9	10
BLOOD-ALCOHOL CONCENTRATION (%),* B	0.018	0.035	0.053	0.070	0.087	0.104	0.121	0.138	0.155	0.171

*Based on body weight of 200 pounds

1. Why is it reasonable in this situation to designate the number of beers consumed in an hour as the input and the blood-alcohol concentration as the output?

2. What is the blood-alcohol concentration for a 200-pound person who has consumed four beers in 1 hour? nine beers in 1 hour?

3. What is the blood-alcohol concentration when eight beers are consumed in an hour?

Notice that a table can reveal *numerical* patterns and relationships between the input and output variables. You can also describe these patterns and relationships *verbally* using such terms as *increases*, *decreases*, or *remains the same*.

4. According to the preceding table, as the number of beers consumed in 1 hour increases, what happens to the blood-alcohol concentration?

5. From the preceding table, determine the number of beers a 200-pound person can consume in 1 hour without exceeding the recommended legal measure of drunk driving.

Graphical Representation

A visual display (**graph**) of data on a **rectangular coordinate system** is often helpful in detecting trends or other information not apparent in a table.

On a graph, the input is referenced on the **horizontal axis**, and the output is referenced on the **vertical axis**.

The following graph provides a visual description of the beer consumption and blood-alcohol level data from the preceding table. Note that each of the 10 input/output data pairs in that table corresponds to a plotted point on the graph. For example, drinking seven beers in an hour is associated with a blood-alcohol concentration of 0.121%. If you read across to 7 along the input (horizontal) axis and move up to 0.121 on the output (vertical) axis, you locate the point that represents the ordered pair of numbers (7, 0.121). Similarly, you would label the other points on the graph by ordered pairs of the form (n, B), where n is the input value and B is the output value.

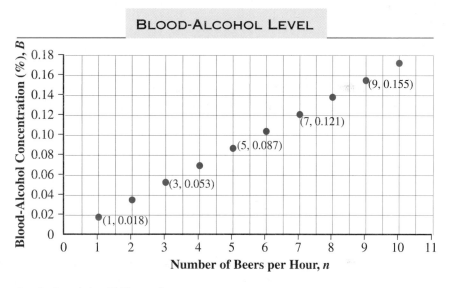

Based on body weight of 200 pounds

6. a. From the graph, approximate the blood-alcohol concentration of a 200-pound person who consumes two beers in an hour.

Write this input/output correspondence using ordered-pair notation.

b. Estimate the number of beers that a 200-pound person must consume in 1 hour to have a blood-alcohol concentration of 0.104.

Write this input/output correspondence using ordered-pair notation.

c. When $n = 4$, what is the approximate value of B from the graph?

Write this input/output correspondence using ordered-pair notation.

d. As the number of beers consumed in an hour increases, what happens to the blood-alcohol concentration?

7. What are some advantages and disadvantages of using a graph when you are trying to describe the relationship between the number of beers consumed in an hour and blood-alcohol concentration?

8. What advantages and disadvantages do you see in using a table?

Effect of Weight on Blood-Alcohol Concentration

You know that weight is a determining factor in a person's blood-alcohol concentration. The following table presents a numerical description of the relationship between the number of beers consumed in an hour by a 130-pound person (input) and her corresponding blood-alcohol concentration (output). Other factors may influence blood-alcohol concentration, such as the rate at which the individual's body processes alcohol, the amount of food eaten prior to drinking, and the concentration of alcohol in the drink, but these effects are not considered here.

NUMBER OF BEERS, n	1	2	3	4	5	6	7	8	9	10
BLOOD-ALCOHOL CONCENTRATION (%),* B	0.027	0.054	0.081	0.108	0.134	0.160	0.187	0.212	0.238	0.264

*Based on body weight of 130 pounds

9. According to the preceding table, how many beers can a 130-pound person consume in an hour without exceeding the recommended legal limit for driving while intoxicated?

10. Use the data in the previous two tables to explain how body weight affects the blood-alcohol concentration for a given number of beers consumed in an hour.

SUMMARY
ACTIVITY 6.1

1. A **variable**, usually represented by a letter, is a quantity or quality that may change in value from one particular instance to another.

2. The **input** is the value that is given first in an input/output relationship.

3. The **output** is the second number in an input/output situation. It is the number that corresponds to or is matched with the input.

4. An input/output relationship can be represented **numerically** by a table of paired data values.

5. An input/output relationship can be represented **graphically** as plotted points on a rectangular coordinate system.

6. The input variable is referenced on the **horizontal axis**.

7. The output variable is referenced on the **vertical axis**.

EXERCISES
ACTIVITY 6.1

1. Medicare is a government program that helps senior citizens pay for medical expenses. As the U.S. population ages and greater numbers of senior citizens join the Medicare rolls each year, the expense and quality of health service becomes an increasing concern. The following graph presents Medicare expenditures from 1967 through 2004. Use the graph to answer the following questions.

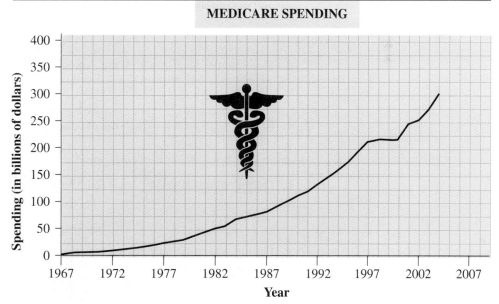

MEDICARE SPENDING

Source: Centers for Medicare and Medicaid Services

a. Identify the input variable and the output variable in this situation.

b. Use the graph to estimate the Medicare expenditures for the years in the following table.

The Cost of Care

YEAR, y	MEDICARE EXPENDITURES, e (IN BILLIONS OF DOLLARS)
1967	
1972	
1977	
1984	
1989	
1994	
1999	
2001	
2003	
2004	

c. What letters in the table in part b are used to represent the input variable and the output variable?

d. Estimate the year in which the expenditures reached $100 billion.

e. Estimate the year in which the expenditures reached $25 billion.

f. During which 10-year period did Medicare expenditures change the least?

g. During which 10-year period was the change in Medicare expenditures the greatest?

h. For which time period does the graph indicate the most rapid increase in Medicare expenditures?

i. In what period was there no change in Medicare expenditures?

j. From the graph, predict the Medicare expenditures in 2009.

k. What assumptions are you making about the change in Medicare expenditures from 2004 to 2009?

2. When the input variable is measured in units of time, the relationship between input (time) and output indicates how the output *changes* over time. For example, the U.S. oil-refining industry has undergone many changes since the Middle East oil embargo of the 1970s. Among the factors that have had a major impact on the industry are changing crude oil prices, changing demand, increased imports, economics, and quality control. Since 1981, 168 U.S. oil refineries have been dismantled. Most were small and inefficient. The following graph shows the fluctuations in the number of U.S. refineries from 1974 to 2004.

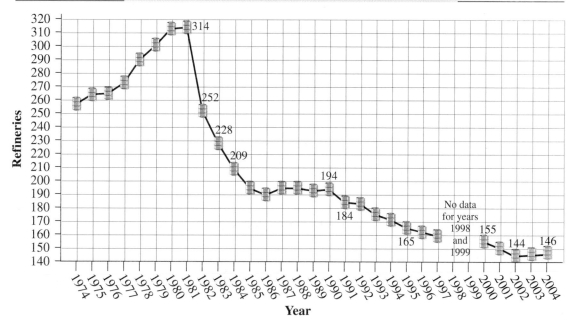

OPERATING U.S. REFINERIES: 1974–2004

Source: Energy Information Administration

a. Identify the input variable.

b. Which axis represents the input variable?

c. Identify the output variable.

d. Which axis represents the output variable?

e. Complete the table below, listing the number of refineries (output) in operation each given year (input).

YEAR	NUMBER OF OPERATING REFINERIES	YEAR	NUMBER OF OPERATING REFINERIES
1974		1985	
1976		1990	
1978		1995	
1980		2002	

f. Summarize the changes that the U.S. oil-refining industry has undergone since the 1970s. Include specific information. For example, indicate the intervals during which the number of U.S. oil refineries increased, decreased, and remained about the same. Also, indicate the years in which the number of refineries increased and decreased the most.

Living on Earth's surface, you experience a relatively narrow range of temperatures. You may know what $-20°$ F (or $-28.9°$ C) feels like on a bitterly cold winter day. Or you may have sweated through $100°$ F (or $37.8°$ C) during summer heat waves. If you were to travel below Earth's surface and above Earth's atmosphere, you would discover a wider range of temperatures. The following graph displays a relationship between the altitude (input) and temperature (output). Note that the altitude is measured from Earth's surface. That is, Earth's surface is at altitude 0.

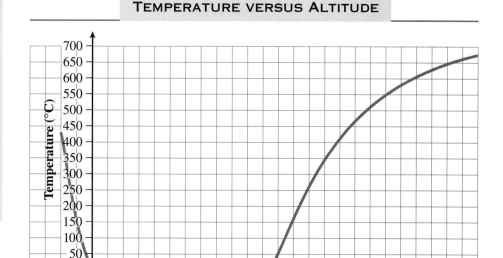

TEMPERATURE VERSUS ALTITUDE

This graph uses a rectangular coordinate system, also known as a Cartesian coordinate system. It contains both a horizontal axis and a vertical axis. Recall that the input variable is referenced on the horizontal axis. The output variable is referenced on the vertical axis.

1. **a.** With what variable and units of measure is the horizontal axis labeled?

   b. What is the practical significance of the positive values of this quantity?

   c. What is the practical significance of the negative values of this quantity?

   d. How many kilometers are represented between the tick marks on the horizontal axis?

2. a. With what variable and units of measure is the vertical axis labeled?

b. What is the practical significance of the positive values of this quantity?

c. What is the practical significance of the negative values of this quantity?

d. How many degrees Celsius are represented between the tick marks on the vertical axis?

3. Consult the graph to determine at which elevations or depths the temperature is high enough to cause water to boil.

Observations

- The distance represented by space between adjacent tick marks on an axis is determined by the range of particular replacement values for the variable represented on that axis. The process of determining and labeling an appropriate distance between tick marks is called **scaling**.
- The axes are often labeled and scaled differently. The way axes are labeled and scaled depends on the context of the problem. Note that the tick marks to the left of zero on the horizontal axis are negative; similarly, the tick marks below zero on the vertical axis are negative.
- On each axis, equal distance between adjacent pairs of tick marks must be maintained.

Rectangular Coordinate System

In the rectangular (Cartesian) coordinate system, the horizontal axis (commonly called the *x*-**axis**) and the vertical axis (commonly called the *y*-**axis**) are number lines that intersect at their respective zero values at a point called the **origin**. The two perpendicular coordinate axes divide the plane into four **quadrants**. The quadrants are labeled counterclockwise, using Roman numerals, with quadrant I being the upper-right quadrant.

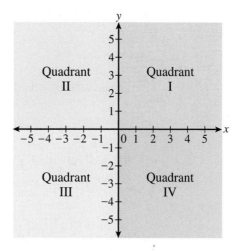

Each point in the plane is identified by an **ordered pair** of numbers (x, y) that can be thought of as the point's "address" relative to the origin. The ordered pair representing the origin is $(0, 0)$. The first number, x, of an ordered pair (x, y) is called the **horizontal coordinate** because it represents the point's horizontal distance (to the right if x is positive, to the left if x is negative) from the y-axis. Similarly, the second number, y, is called the **vertical coordinate** because it represents the point's vertical distance (up if y is positive, down if y is negative) from the x-axis.

> In contextual situations involving relationships between two variables, the input value is written first in the ordered pair, and the corresponding output value is written second (input value, corresponding output value).

4. The following graph displays eight points selected from the temperature graph on page 401.

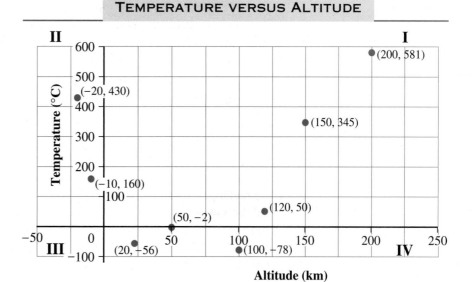

TEMPERATURE VERSUS ALTITUDE

a. What is the practical meaning of the point with coordinates (150, 345)?

b. What is the practical meaning of the point with coordinates $(100, -78)$?

c. What is the practical meaning of the point with coordinates $(-20, 430)$?

d. In which quadrant are the points $(120, 50)$, $(150, 345)$, and $(200, 581)$ located?

e. In which quadrant are the points $(-10, 160)$ and $(-20, 430)$ located?

f. In which quadrant are the points $(20, -56)$ and $(100, -78)$ located?

g. Are there any points located in quadrant III? What is the significance of your answer?

5. Consider ordered pairs of the form (x, y). Determine the sign (positive or negative) of the x- and y-coordinates of a point in each quadrant. For example, any point located in quadrant I has a positive x-coordinate and a positive y-coordinate.

QUADRANT	SIGN (+ OR −) OF x-COORDINATE	SIGN (+ OR −) OF y-COORDINATE
I		
II		
III		
IV		

6. In the following coordinate system, the horizontal axis is labeled the x-axis, and the vertical axis is labeled the y-axis. Determine the coordinates (x, y) of points A to N. For example, the coordinates of A are $(30, 300)$.

A _____	B _____	C _____
D _____	E _____	F _____
G _____	H _____	I _____
J _____	K _____	L _____
M _____	N _____	

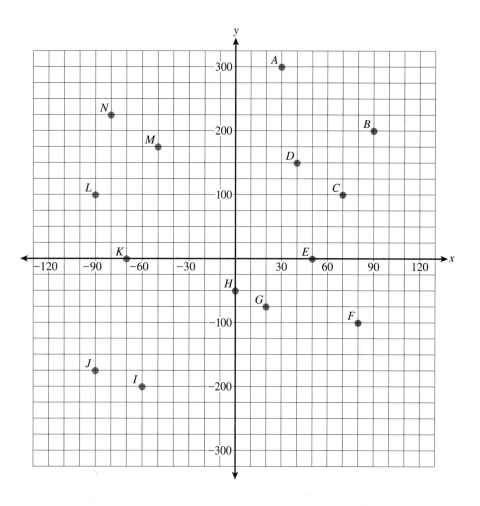

7. Which points (*A* to *N*) from Problem 6 are located

   a. in the first quadrant?

   b. in the second quadrant?

   c. in the third quadrant?

   d. in the fourth quadrant?

8. **a.** Which points (*A* to *N*) from Problem 6 are on the horizontal axis? What are their coordinates?

   b. What is the *y*-value of any point located on the *x*-axis?

c. Which points are on the vertical axis? What are their coordinates?

d. What is the *x*-value of any point located on the *y*-axis?

Additional Relationships Represented Graphically

9. You work for the National Weather Service and are asked to study the average daily temperatures in Fairbanks, Alaska. You calculate the mean of the average daily temperatures for each month. You decide to place the information on a graph in which the date is the input and the temperature is the output. You also decide that January 1980 will correspond to the month zero as indicated by the dot on the input scale. Determine the quadrant in which you would plot the points that correspond to the following data.

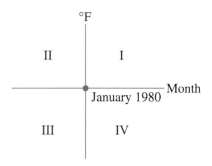

a. The average daily temperature for January 1966 was $-15°$ F.

b. The average daily temperature for July 1993 was 63°F.

c. The average daily temperature for July 1940 was 59° F.

d. The average daily temperature for January 2002 was $-6°$ F.

10. Measurements in wells and mines have shown that the temperatures within Earth generally increase with depth. The following table shows average temperatures for several depths below sea level.

A Hot Topic

DEPTH (km) BELOW SEA LEVEL	0	25	50	75	100	150	200
TEMPERATURE (°C)	20	600	1000	1250	1400	1700	1800

a. Represent the data from the table graphically on the grid following part d. Place depth (input) along the horizontal axis and temperature (output) along the vertical axis.

b. How many units does each tick mark on the horizontal axis represent?

c. How many units does each tick mark on the vertical axis represent?

d. Explain your reasons for selecting the particular scales that you used.

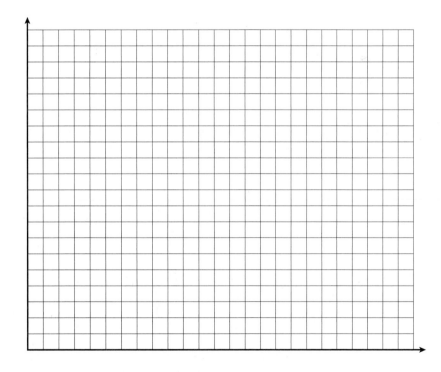

e. Which representation (table or graph) presents the information and trends in this data more clearly? Explain your choice.

SUMMARY
ACTIVITY 6.2

1. Input/output data pairs can be represented graphically as plotted points on a grid called a **rectangular coordinate system**.

2. The rectangular coordinate system consists of two perpendicular number lines (called **coordinate axes**) that intersect at their respective zero values. The point of intersection is called the **origin** and has coordinates (0, 0).

3. The **input variable** is referenced on the horizontal axis. The **output variable** is referenced on the vertical axis.

4. Each point in the plane is identified by its horizontal and vertical directed distance from the axes. The distances are listed as an **ordered pair** of numbers (x, y) in which the horizontal coordinate, x, is written first and the vertical coordinate, y, second.

5. The two perpendicular coordinate axes divide the plane into four **quadrants**. The quadrants are labeled counterclockwise, using Roman numerals, with quadrant I being the upper-right quadrant.

6. The distance represented by the space between adjacent tick marks on an axis is determined by the particular replacement values for the variable represented on the axis. This is called **scaling**. On each axis, equal distance between adjacent pairs of tick marks must be maintained.

EXERCISES
ACTIVITY 6.2

Points in a coordinate plane lie in one of the four quadrants or on one of the axes. In Exercises 1–18, place the letter corresponding to the phrase that best describes the location of the given point.

a. The point lies in the first quadrant.   **b.** The point lies in the second quadrant.

c. The point lies in the third quadrant.   **d.** The point lies in the fourth quadrant.

e. The point lies at the origin.   **f.** The point lies on the positive x-axis.

g. The point lies on the negative x-axis.   **h.** The point lies on the positive y-axis.

i. The point lies on the negative y-axis.

1. $(2, -5)$ **2.** $(-3, -1)$ **3.** $(-4, 0)$

4. $(0, 0)$ **5.** $(0, 3)$ **6.** $(-2, 4)$

7. $(8, 6)$ **8.** $(0, -6)$ **9.** $(5, 0)$

10. $(4, -6)$ **11.** $(2, 0)$ **12.** $(0, 6)$

13. $(-7, -7)$ **14.** $(12, 5)$ **15.** $(0, -2)$

16. $(12, 0)$ **17.** $(-10, 2)$ **18.** $(-13, 0)$

19. The following table presents the average recommended weights for given heights for 25- to 29-year-old medium-framed women (wearing 1-inch heels and 3 pounds of clothing). Consider height to be the input variable and weight to be the output variable. As ordered pairs, height and weight take on the form (h, w). Designate the horizontal (input) axis as the h-axis, and the vertical (output) axis as the w-axis. Since all values of the data are positive, the points will lie in quadrant I only.

h, HEIGHT (in.)	58	60	62	64	66	68	70	72
w, WEIGHT (lb.)	115	119	125	131	137	143	149	155

Plot the ordered pairs in the height-weight table on the following grid. Note the consistent spacing between tick marks on each axis. The distance between tick marks on the horizontal axis represents 2 inches. On the vertical axis the distance between tick marks represents 5 pounds.

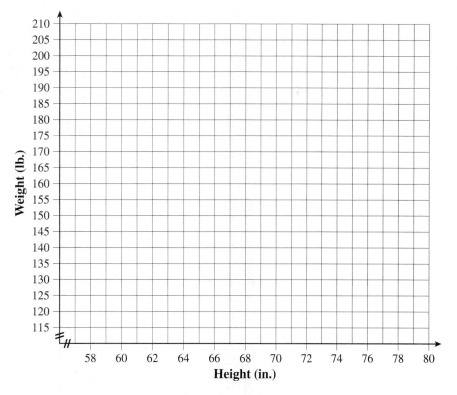

Note: The slash marks (//) near the origin indicate that the interval from 0 to 56 on the horizontal axis and the interval from 0 to 115 on the vertical axis are not shown. That is, only the part of the graph containing the plotted points is shown.

※ **ACTIVITY 6.3**

College Expenses

OBJECTIVES

1. Identify input variables and output variables.

2. Determine possible replacement values for the input.

3. Write verbal rules that represent relationships between input and output variables.

4. Construct tables of input/output values.

5. Construct graphs from input/output tables.

You are considering taking some courses at your local community college on a part-time basis for the upcoming semester. For a student who carries fewer than 12 credits (the full-time minimum), the tuition is $143 for each credit hour taken. You have a limited budget, so you need to calculate the total cost based on the number of credit hours.

Whenever you use a letter or symbol to represent a variable in the process of solving a problem, you must state what quantity (with units of measure) the variable represents and what collection of numbers are meaningful replacement values for the variable.

1. **a.** Describe in words the input variable and the output variable in the college tuition situation. Remember, the inputs are the values that are given or considered first. The outputs are the values that are matched or determined from the given input values.

   b. Choose a letter or symbol to represent the input variable and a letter or symbol to represent the output variable.

   c. Would a replacement value of zero be reasonable for the input? Explain.

   d. Would a replacement value of 15 be reasonable for the input? Explain.

   e. What are reasonable replacement values for the input?

   f. What is the tuition bill if you only register for a 3-credit-hour accounting course?

g. Use the replacement values you determined in part e to complete the following table.

A Matter of Course

NUMBER OF HOURS	1	2	3	4	5	6	7	8	9	10	11
TUITION ($)											

h. Write a rule in words (called a **verbal rule**) that describes how to calculate the total tuition bill for a student carrying fewer than 12 credit hours.

i. What is the change in the tuition bill as the number of credit hours increases from 2 to 3? Is the change in the tuition bill the same amount for each unit increase in credit hours?

Additional College Expenses

Other possible college expenses include parking fines, library fines, and food costs. Students whose first class is later in the morning often do not find a parking space and park illegally. Campus police have no sympathy and readily write tickets. Last semester, your first class began at 11:00 A.M.

2. a. The following table shows your cumulative number of tickets as the semester progressed and the total in fines you owed the college at that time. Use the given data pairs to determine how you can calculate the total fine, given your cumulative number of tickets. Describe this relationship in words (write a verbal rule).

Feeling Fine

CUMULATIVE NUMBER OF TICKETS LAST SEMESTER	2	3	5	8	10	12
TOTAL FINES	$25	$37.50	$62.50			

b. Use the verbal rule to complete the table in part a.

c. Graph the information from the preceding table. Choose a scale for each axis that will enable you to plot all six points. Label the horizontal axis to represent the cumulative number of tickets received and the vertical axis to represent the total in fines owed to the college at that time.

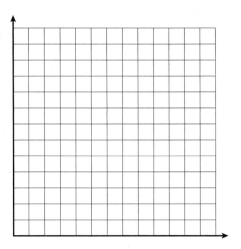

3. The college library fine for an overdue book is $0.25 per day with a maximum charge of $10.00 per item. You leave a library book at a friend's house and totally forget about it.

a. The number of days the book is overdue represents the input. What are the possible replacement values?

b. Determine the total fine (output) for selected values of the input given in the following table.

NUMBER OF DAYS OVERDUE	TOTAL FINE
2	
5	
8	
10	
14	

c. Write a verbal rule describing the arithmetic relationship between the input variable and the output variable.

d. Graph the information from the table in part b.

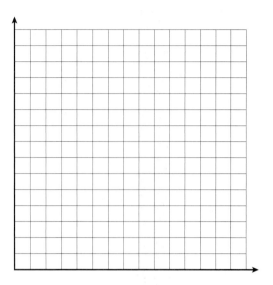

4. At the beginning of the semester, you buy a cafeteria meal ticket worth $150. The daily lunch special costs $4 in the college cafeteria.

a. Fill in the following table. Use the number of lunch specials you purchase as the input variable.

NUMBER OF LUNCH SPECIALS PURCHASED	REMAINING BALANCE ON YOUR MEAL TICKET
0	
10	
20	
30	
35	

b. Write a verbal rule describing the relationship between the input variable, number of lunch specials, and the output variable, remaining balance.

c. What are possible replacement values for the input variable? Explain.

d. Graph the information from the table in part a.

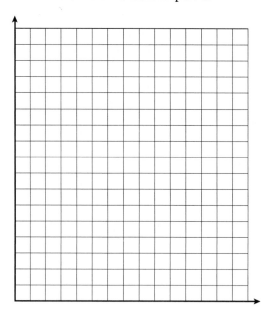

SUMMARY
ACTIVITY 6.3

1. A **verbal rule** is a statement that describes (in words) the arithmetic steps used to calculate the output corresponding to any input value.

2. The set of **replacement values** for the input is the collection of all numbers for which a meaningful output value can be determined.

3. Input/output data can be visually presented as points on an appropriately scaled rectangular coordinate system. Input is referenced along the horizontal axis and output along the vertical axis.

EXERCISES
ACTIVITY 6.3

1. Suppose the variable n represents the number of notebooks purchased by a student in the college bookstore for the semester.

   a. Can n be reasonably replaced by a negative value, such as -2? Explain.

   b. Can n be reasonably replaced by the number zero? Explain.

   c. What is a possible collection of replacement values for the variable n in this situation?

2. Determine the arithmetic relationship common to all input and output pairs in each of the following tables. For each table, write a verbal rule that describes how to calculate the output from its corresponding input. Then complete the tables.

a.

INPUT	OUTPUT
2	4
4	8
6	12
8	16
10	
20	
25	

b.

INPUT	OUTPUT
2	4
3	9
4	16
5	
6	
7	
8	

c.

INPUT	OUTPUT
−2	−4
0	−2
2	0
4	2
6	
8	
10	

d. Graph the input/output data from part a.

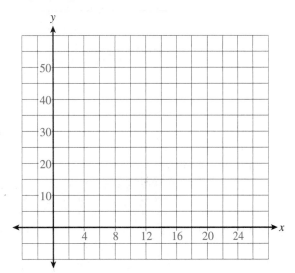

e. Graph the input/output data from part b.

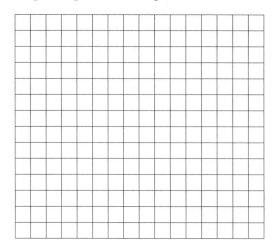

f. Graph the input/output data from part c.

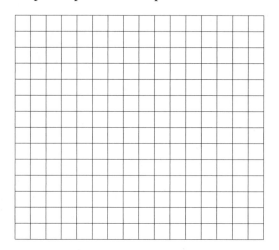

3. Complete the following tables using the verbal rule in column 2.

a.

INPUT	OUTPUT IS 10 MORE THAN THE INPUT
1	
3	
5	
7	
9	
12	
14	

b.

INPUT	OUTPUT IS 3 TIMES THE INPUT, PLUS 2
−5	
−4	
−3	
−2	
−1	
0	
1	
2	

c. Graph the information in the completed table in part a.

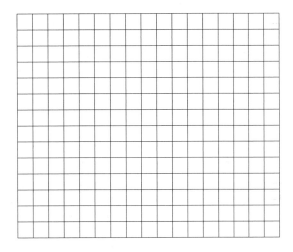

d. Graph the information in the completed table in part b.

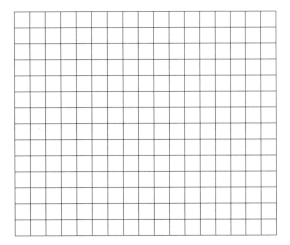

4. Suppose the variable n represents the number of DVDs a student owns.

   a. Can n be reasonably replaced by a negative value, such as -2? Explain.

   b. Can n be reasonably replaced by the number 0? Explain.

   c. What is a possible collection of replacement values for the variable n in this situation?

5. Suppose the variable t represents the average daily Fahrenheit temperature in Oswego, a city in upstate New York, during the month of February in any given year.

   a. Can t be reasonably replaced with a temperature of $-3°$ F? Explain.

   b. Can t be reasonably replaced with a temperature of $-70°$ F? Explain.

   c. Can t be reasonably replaced with a temperature of $98°$ F? Explain.

   d. What is a possible collection of replacement values for the variable t that would make this situation realistic?

6. You are considering taking a part-time job at McDonald's. The job pays $7.25 per hour.

   a. What would be your gross pay if you work 22 hours one week?

   b. Write a verbal rule that describes how to determine your gross weekly pay based on the number of hours worked.

c. Complete the following table using the rule in part b.

NUMBER OF HOURS WORKED (INPUT)	WEEKLY PAY (OUTPUT)
9	
12	
15	
20	
22	
28	
30	

d. What are realistic replacement values for the input variable, the number of hours worked?

e. Graph the information given in the table in part c. Make sure you use properly scaled and labeled axes.

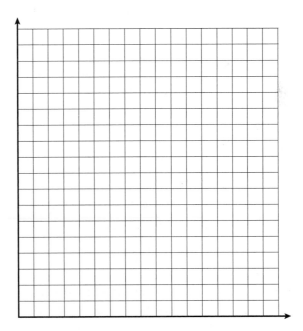

f. Explain your reasons for selecting the particular scales that you used.

g. Which representation (table or graph) presents the information and trends more clearly? Explain your choice.

ACTIVITY 6.4

The Write Way to Learn Algebra

OBJECTIVES

1. Translate verbal phrases into symbolic (algebraic) expressions.

2. Distinguish between a factor and a term in an algebraic expression.

3. Evaluate algebraic expressions for specified input values.

To communicate in a foreign language, you must learn the language's alphabet, grammar, and vocabulary. You must also learn to translate between your native language and the foreign language you are learning. The same is true for algebra, which, with its symbols and grammar, is the language of mathematics. To become confident and comfortable with algebra, you must practice speaking and writing it and translating between it and the natural language you are using (English, in this book).

For example, in Activity 6.3 (College Expenses, Problem 4), you purchased a meal ticket at the beginning of the semester for $150. The daily lunch special costs $4 in the college cafeteria. You want to be able to determine the balance on your meal ticket after you have purchased a given number of lunch specials.

1. a. Identify the input and output variables in the meal ticket situation.

b. Write a verbal description of the sequence of operations that you must perform on the input value to obtain the corresponding output value.

c. Translate the verbal description in part b to a symbolic expression using x to represent the input.

Algebraic Expressions

The symbolic expression $150 - 4x$ is called an **algebraic expression in the variable x**. Such an expression is a shorthand code for a sequence of operations that is to be performed on x.

EXAMPLE 1 *In the table below each algebraic expression is paired with its corresponding translation into a verbal phrase.*

ALGEBRAIC EXPRESSION	VERBAL DESCRIPTION
1. $3x$	1. Three times the input
2. $x + 5$	2. Five added to the input
3. x^2	3. The input squared
4. $2x - 10$	4. Ten less than twice the input

2. Let x represent the input variable. Translate each of the following phrases into an algebraic expression.

a. The product of 3 and the input   **b.** Four times the input

c. The input increased by 5   **d.** Ten less than the input

e. The input squared

In any algebraic expression in which x (or any other variable) is *multiplied* by a constant number, the constant is called the **coefficient** of x. Several examples are $3 \cdot x$, $-2 \cdot x$, $\frac{5}{6} \cdot x$. It is not necessary to include the multiplication symbol when multiplying a variable by a constant number. Because the arithmetic operation between a variable and its coefficient is always understood to be multiplication, the expressions above are usually written as $3x$, $-2x$, and $\frac{5}{6}x$, respectively. The coefficients of each of these terms are, respectively, 3, -2, and $\frac{5}{6}$.

3. Determine the coefficient of each of the following expressions.

    a. $-3x$ **b.** x **c.** $-x$ **d.** $5x^2$

    e. $\frac{3}{4}x$ **f.** $\frac{x}{3}$ **g.** $\frac{2x}{5}$

4. a. In Problem 2c, the phrase "the input increased by 5" could be translated as $x + 5$ or $5 + x$. Explain why. (*Hint:* What property of addition does this demonstrate?)

    b. In Problem 2d, can the phrase "ten less than the input" be correctly translated as $10 - x$ and as $x - 10$? Explain why or why not.

In the expression $3x$, the 3 and x are called **factors.** Factors are numbers, variables, or expressions multiplied together to form a product. In the expression $x + 5$, the x and 5 are called **terms.** Terms are the parts of an overall expression separated by addition and subtraction symbols.

5. Identify the factors of each expression.

    a. $7y$ **b.** πr^2 **c.** $3(x - 2)(x + 5)$ **d.** $\frac{1}{2}h(a + b)$

6. Identify the terms in each expression.

    a. $2x - 3y$ **b.** $2w^2 + 3wl - 5l^2$ **c.** $4x(x - 1) + 8(x - 1)$

7. a. Let n represent the input. The output is determined by the following verbal phrase.

    Five times the square of the input, increased by twice the input and then decreased by seven

    Translate the above phrase into an algebraic expression.

b. How many terms are in this expression?

c. List the terms in the expression from part a.

8. The area of a triangle is represented by the algebraic expression $\frac{1}{2}bh$, where b represents the base of the triangle and h represents its height.

a. How many terms are in the expression $\frac{1}{2}bh$?

b. How many factors are in the expression $\frac{1}{2}bh$?

Evaluating an Algebraic Expression

9. Suppose you have purchased 16 lunch specials so far in the semester. Use the algebraic expression $150 - 4x$ from Problem 1c to determine the remaining balance.

In Problem 9, the remaining balance (output) was determined by replacing the input variable x with a given numerical value (namely 16) and then performing the arithmetic operations. This process is known as **evaluating** the algebraic expression for a given value of the variable.

10. a. The markdown of every piece of clothing in the college bookstore is 20% of the original price of the item. If p represents the original price, write an algebraic expression that can be used to determine the markdown.

b. Complete the following table by evaluating the expression in part a with the given input values.

INPUT PRICE, p	50	100	150	200
OUTPUT MARKDOWN				

11. a. The perimeter of a rectangle is twice the length plus twice the width. If l represents the length and w represents the width, write an algebraic expression that represents the perimeter.

b. Calculate the perimeter of a rectangle with length 10 inches and width 17 inches.

c. The area of a rectangle is the product of its length and width. Write an algebraic expression in *l* and *w* that represents its area.

d. Calculate the area of a rectangle with length 10 inches and width 17 inches.

12. Evaluate each of the following algebraic expressions for the given value.

a. $3x - 10$, for $x = -2.5$

b. $5 - 2.7x$, for $x = 10.25$

c. $\frac{1}{2}bh$, for $b = 10$ and $h = 6.5$

13. a. Do the expressions x^2 and $2x$ produce the same output for a given input value for x? Explain why or why not.

b. In the expression $2x$, the 2 is called the _____.

c. In the expression x^2, the 2 is called the _____.

<table>
<tr><td>

SUMMARY
ACTIVITY 6.4

</td><td>

1. An **algebraic expression** is a shorthand code for a sequence of operations to be performed on an input value to produce a corresponding output value.

2. A **variable** is a quantity, usually presented by a letter or symbol, that changes in value.

3. A **constant** is a quantity that does not change in value (e.g., the number 2).

4. A **numerical coefficient** is a number that multiplies a variable or expression.

5. **Factors** are numbers, variables, and/or expressions that are multiplied together to form a product.

6. **Terms** are parts of an expression that are separated by plus or minus signs.

</td></tr>
</table>

Let x represent the input variable. Translate each of the phrases in Exercises 1–6 into an algebraic expression.

1. The input decreased by 7

2. Five times the difference between the input and 6

3. Seven increased by the quotient of the input and 5

4. Twelve more than one-half of the square of the input

5. Twenty less than the product of the input and -2

6. The sum of three-eighths of the input and five

7. Determine the coefficient of x in the following expressions:

a. $7x$ b. x c. $-x$ d. $\dfrac{3}{4}x$

e. $\dfrac{2x}{3}$ f. $\dfrac{x}{5}$

8. Identify the factors in each of the following algebraic expressions.

a. $5x$ b. $\dfrac{x}{2}$ c. $-2x^3$

d. $2(x + 3)$ e. $\pi r^2 h$

9. Identify the terms in each of the following expressions.

a. $x + 10$ b. $2x - 3$

c. $x^2 + 2x + 5$ **d.** $3x$

10. Consider the algebraic expression $8x^2 - 10x + 9y - z + 7$.

  a. How many terms are in this expression?

  b. What is the coefficient of the first term?

  c. What is the coefficient of the fourth term?

  d. What is the coefficient of the second term?

  e. What is the constant term?

  f. What are the factors in the first term?

11. a. Translate each of the following phrases into an algebraic expression. Let x represent the input variable.

    i. The input divided by 2

    ii. Two divided by the input

  b. Do the expressions in parts a (i) and a (ii) produce the same output? Complete the following table to help justify your answer.

x	INPUT DIVIDED BY 2	2 DIVIDED BY INPUT
−4		
−2		
2		
4		

  c. Is the operation of division commutative?

d. Is zero a possible replacement value for the input in part a (i)? If yes, what is the output value?

e. Is zero a possible replacement value for the input in part a (ii)? Explain.

12. Evaluate each of the following algebraic expressions for the given value.

   a. $5x - 7$, for $x = -2.5$ **b.** $55 - 6.7x$, for $x = 10$

   c. $\frac{1}{2}bh$, for $b = 5$ and $h = 5$ **d.** $\frac{1}{2}h(b + B)$, for $h = 10, b = 5, B = 7$

In this lab, you will stack and measure the heights of disposable Styrofoam or plastic cups placed inside one another. With a centimeter ruler, measure and record the height (to the nearest tenth of a centimeter) of stacks containing increasing numbers of cups.

LAB ACTIVITY 6.5

How Many Cups Are in That Stack?

OBJECTIVES

1. Collect input/output data.

2. Represent input/output data numerically in tables.

3. Construct tables of data pairs for graphing.

4. Graph input/output data pairs.

Heightened Importance

NUMBER OF CUPS	1	2	3	4	5	6	7	8
HEIGHT OF STACK (cm)								

1. Graph the data with the inputs (number of cups) on the horizontal axis and the outputs (height of stack) on the vertical axis.

2. Use the information you have gathered to *estimate* the height (to the nearest tenth of a centimeter) of 10 stacked cups.

3. Now construct a stack of 10 cups. Measure the stack and compare it with your estimate. Was your estimate reasonable? If not, why not?

4. Estimate the height of 16 cups. Is a stack of 16 cups twice as tall as a stack of 8 cups? Justify your answer.

5. Estimate the height of 20 cups. Is a stack of 20 cups twice as tall as a stack of 10 cups? Justify your answer.

6. Describe the formula or method you used to estimate the height of a stack of cups.

7. If your shelf has clearance of 40 centimeters, how many cups can you stack to fit on the shelf? Explain how you obtained your answer.

Variables arise in many common measurements. Your height is one measurement that has probably been recorded frequently from the day you were born. In this project, you are asked to pair up and measure five lengths associated with your body: height (*h*); arm span (*a*), the distance between the tips of your two middle fingers with arms outstretched; wrist circumference (*w*); foot length (*f*); and neck circumference (*n*). For consistency, measure the lengths in inches.

1. Gather the data for your entire class, and record it in the following table.

 Inch by Inch

STUDENT	HEIGHT *h*	ARM SPAN *a*	WRIST *w*	FOOT *f*	NECK *n*

2. What are some relationships you can identify, based on eyeballing the data? For example, how do the heights relate to the arm spans?

3. Graph one relationship, such as that between height (*h*) and wrist circumference (*w*). Make sure you label your axes and indicate the scales for each axis.

What Have I Learned?

1. Describe several ways that relationships between variables may be represented. What are the advantages and disadvantages of each?

2. Obtain a graph from a local newspaper, magazine, or textbook in your major field. Identify the input and output variables. The input variable is referenced on which axis? Describe any trends in the graph.

3. You will be graphing some data from a table in which the input values range from 0 to 150 and the output values range from 0 to 2000. Assume that your grid is a square with 16 tick marks across and up.

   a. Will you use all four quadrants? Explain.

   b. How many units does the distance between tick marks on the horizontal axis represent?

   c. How many units does the distance between tick marks on the vertical axis represent?

4. Describe the difference between terms and factors in the algebraic expression $3a + 2b$.

1. You are a scuba diver and plan a dive in the St. Lawrence River. The water depth in the diving area does not exceed 150 feet. Let x represent your depth in feet *below* the surface of the water.

   a. What are the possible replacement values to represent your depth from the surface?

   b. Would a replacement value of zero feet be reasonable? Explain.

   c. Would a replacement value of -200 be reasonable? Explain.

   d. Would a replacement value of 12 feet be reasonable? Explain.

2. You bought a company in 2003 and have tracked the company's profits and losses from its beginning in 1993 to the present. You decide to graph the information where the number of years since 2003 is the input variable and profit or loss for the year is the output variable. Note that the year 2003 corresponds to zero on the horizontal axis. Determine the quadrant or axis on which you would plot the points that correspond to the following data. If your answer is on an axis, indicate between which quadrants the point is located.

   a. The loss in 1995 was $1500.

   b. The profit in 2006 was $6000.

   c. The loss in 2005 was $1000.

d. In 2004, there was no profit or loss.

e. The profit in 2001 was $500.

f. The loss in 2003 was $800.

3. Fish need oxygen to live, just as you do. The amount of dissolved oxygen (D.O.) in water is measured in parts per million (ppm). Trout need a minimum of 6 ppm to live.

The data in the table shows the relationship between the temperature of the water and the amount of dissolved oxygen present.

TEMP (°C)	11	16	21	26	31
D.O. (in ppm)	10.2	8.6	7.7	7.0	6.4

a. Represent the data in the table graphically. Place temperature (input) along the horizontal axis and dissolved oxygen (output) along the vertical axis.

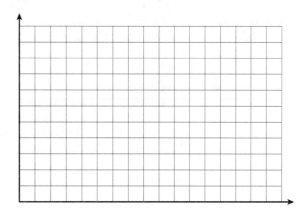

b. What general trend do you notice in the data?

c. In which of the 5-degree temperature intervals given in the table does the dissolved oxygen content change the most?

d. Which representation (table or graph) presents the information and trends more clearly?

4. When you were born, your uncle invested $1000 for you in a local bank. The following graph shows how your investment grows.

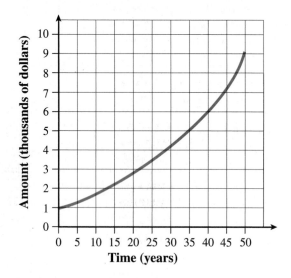

a. Which variable is the input variable?

b. How much money did you have when you were 10 years old?

c. Estimate in what year your original investment will have doubled.

d. If your college bill is estimated to be $3000 in the first year of college, will you have enough to pay the bill with these funds? (Assume that you attend when you are 18.) Explain.

e. Assume that you expect to be married when you are 30 years old. You figure that you will need about $5000 for your share of the wedding and honeymoon expenses. Assume also that you left the money in the bank and did not use it for your education. Will you have enough money to pay your share of the wedding and honeymoon expenses? Explain.

5. Consider the expression $5x^3 + 4x^2 - x - 3$.

   a. How many terms are there?

   b. What is the coefficient of the first term?

   c. What is the coefficient of the third term?

   d. If there is a constant term, what is its value?

   e. What are the factors of the second term?

6. Let x represent the input variable. Translate each of the following phrases into an algebraic expression.

   a. 20 less than twice the input

   b. the sum of half the input and 6

7. a. Let n represent the input. The output is described by the following verbal phrase.

   Six times the square of the input, decreased by twice the input and then increased by eleven

   Translate the above phrase into an algebraic expression.

   b. How many terms are in this expression?

   c. List the terms in the expression from part a.

8. Evaluate each algebraic expression for the given value(s).

   a. $2x + 7$, for $x = -3.5$

   b. $8x - 3$, for $x = 1.5$

   c. $2k + 3h$, for $k = -2.5, h = 9$

| **CLUSTER 2** | **Solving Equations Numerically, Graphically, and Algebraically** |

ACTIVITY 6.7

Fund-Raiser

OBJECTIVES

1. Translate verbal rules (statements using words) to symbolic rules (equations).

2. Distinguish an algebraic expression from an equation and from a symbolic rule.

3. Solve an equation numerically and graphically.

4. Distinguish between a graph of distinct points and a graph of a continuous line.

As part of a community service project at your college, you are organizing a fund-raiser at the neighborhood roller rink. Money raised will benefit a summer camp for children with special needs. The admission charge is $10.00 per person, $7.50 of which is used to pay the rink's rental fee. The remainder is donated to the summer camp fund.

1. What are the variables that naturally arise from the description of the summer camp fund-raiser?

2. On what variable does the total amount donated depend?

3. **a.** Which variable can best be designated as the input variable?

   b. What are the possible replacement values for the input? Note that the capacity of the rink is 200 skaters.

   c. What are its units of measurement?

4. **a.** Which variable can best be designated as the output variable?

   b. What are its units of measurement?

5. **a.** Create a table to represent the relationship between input and output in the fund-raiser situation.

INPUT	OUTPUT ($)
1	
2	
3	
4	
5	
6	
7	
8	

b. Graph the data pairs in part a. Recall that the input axis is horizontal and the output axis is vertical. Label and scale each axis appropriately.

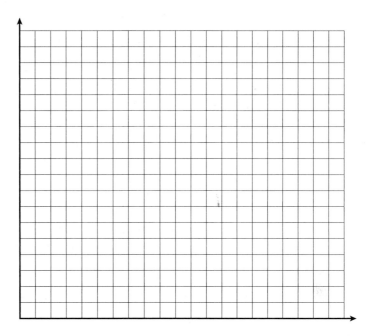

If the input/output pairs on the graph were connected, they would all lie on a single straight line. However, the points of this line do *not* all represent legitimate input/output pairs of the fund-raising relationship. Only the points with integer-valued inputs, such as (3, 7.50) or (8, 20), represent actual data pairs of the relationship. A point such as (4.4, 11), although on the line, has no practical meaning in this situation, because you can not sell exactly 4.4 tickets.

6. What difficulty would you encounter in using your table or graph to determine the amount of money raised if 84 tickets are sold?

Symbolic Rule of an Input/Output Relationship

DEFINITION

A **symbolic rule** is a mathematical statement that defines an **output** variable as an algebraic expression in terms of the **input** variable. The symbolic rule is essentially a recipe that describes how to determine the output value corresponding to a given input value.

7. a. For any input value in the fund-raiser project, explain in your own words how to determine the corresponding output value. Recall that this description is called a *verbal rule*.

b. Let x represent the input, the number of admission tickets sold.
Let y represent the output, the amount of money donated to the summer camp fund. Write a *symbolic rule* describing the input/output relationship given in part a.

The symbolic rule $y = 2.50x$ is an example of an equation that is written using variables, constants, and algebraic symbols. The symbol "=" indicates that the two sides of an equation have the same value. The equation $y = 2.50x$ is a recipe for determining the output y for any given input value for x. Since the variable y is written by itself (isolated) on one side, you say the equation is "solved for y."

Evaluating an Algebraic Expression

To determine the output value corresponding to any input value using a symbolic rule, replace the input symbol, commonly x, with its assigned value, and perform the arithmetic operation(s) to obtain the output value. Recall that this process is known as **evaluating** the expression for a given input value.

EXAMPLE 1 *Use the symbolic rule $y = 2.5x$ to determine the amount of money raised if 84 tickets are sold. Stated another way, determine the output y for an input value of $x = 84$.*

SOLUTION:

Step 1: Substitute 84 for x in the equation $y = 2.5x$:

$$y = 2.50\,(84).$$

Step 2: Perform the arithmetic operations on the right-hand side to obtain the output value:

$$y = \$210.$$

Note that the expression $2.50x$ has been **evaluated** for $x = 84$ to obtain the output value.

8. Use the symbolic rule $y = 2.50x$ to complete the table.

x, NUMBER OF TICKETS SOLD	y, AMOUNT RAISED ($)
26	
94	
178	

Solving Equations Numerically and Graphically

9. Suppose the goal is to raise $200 for the summer camp fund. Is 200 an input value or an output value? (Note its units.)

You can determine how many tickets to sell to raise $200 by replacing y with 200 in the rule $y = 2.50x$ to produce the **equation**

$$200 = 2.50x.$$

The problem now is to solve the equation for x. There are three different methods for solving such equations: numerical, graphical, and algebraic. Although the algebraic methods of solution are fundamental mathematical skills, the numerical and graphical methods are often quite useful, but frequently overlooked. Problems 10 and 11 will illustrate the numerical and graphical solution techniques. The algebraic method is explored in the next activity.

10. **a.** Use a table of values to estimate how many tickets must be sold to raise $200. Begin by estimating a value for x so that the expression $2.50x$ is close to 200. For example, $x = 100$ tickets produces a value of 250. Increase or decrease your guesses for x until you obtain 200 for y.

x, NUMBER OF TICKETS SOLD	y, AMOUNT RAISED ($)

This approach, consisting of a guess, check, and repeat, is a **numerical method** for solving the equation $200 = 2.50x$ for x.

b. List at least one disadvantage of solving an equation numerically.

11. Recall that the collection of replacement values for the input (number of tickets sold) of the summer camp situation is 0, 1, 2, 3, . . ., 200. Some of the input/output pairs are shown in the following graph.

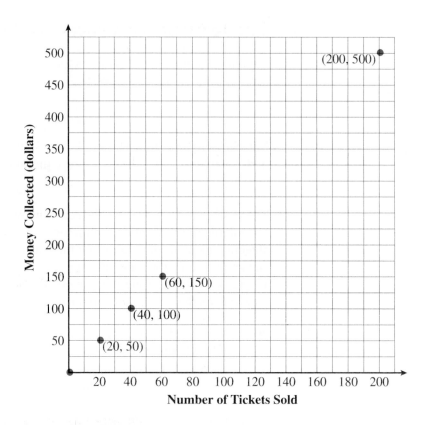

a. The point (60, 150) lies on the graph. Interpret the meaning of the coordinates 60 and 150 in the fund-raiser situation.

b. Connect the points on the graph above to form a line. Use this line to estimate how many tickets must be sold to raise $200. Remember, you need to determine x when $y = 200$.

c. Explain the process you used in part b.

The approach in part b is the **graphical method** for solving the equation $200 = 2.50x$ for x.

---

d. List at least one disadvantage to using a graphing approach to solving an equation.

12. Consider the general equation $y = 2.50x$ where x is not restricted to whole numbers as it is for number of tickets sold.

a. What is the replacement set for the input variable x?

b. Complete the following table for selected input values.

x	y = 2.50x
−100	
−75	
−50	
−25	
0	
25	
50	
75	
100	

c. The points from the table in part b are plotted on the following grid and a straight line is drawn through them. Compare the graph with the graph of $y = 2.50x$ in Problem 5b where the input x represents the number of tickets sold.

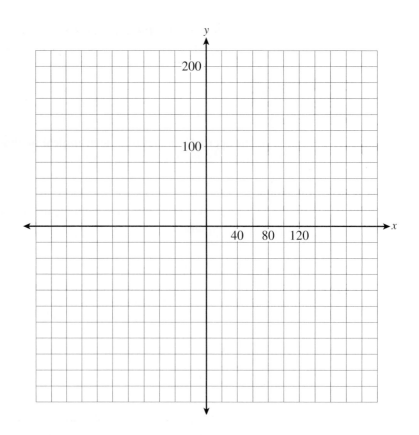

 A graphing calculator is also an excellent tool for graphing symbolic rules. Instructions for graphing on the TI-83/TI-84 Plus are given in Appendix E.

Additional Practice

13. a. An output is determined by adding three to an input. If x represents the input and y represents the output, translate the verbal rule into a symbolic rule.

   b. Determine y if $x = -5$.

   c. Write an equation that can be used to determine x when $y = 9$. Solve the equation using a numerical approach.

d. Solve the equation in part c using a graphical approach. A graph of the symbolic rule $y = x + 3$ is provided below.

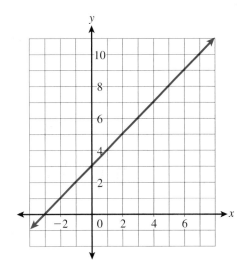

SUMMARY
ACTIVITY 6.7

SUMMARY
ACTIVITY 6.7

1. A **symbolic rule** is a mathematical statement that defines an **output** variable as an algebraic expression in terms of the **input** variable. The symbolic rule is essentially a recipe that describes how to determine the output value corresponding to a given input value.

2. For a given input value, **evaluate** the symbolic rule to obtain the corresponding output value.

3. For a given output value, you must **solve** the resulting equation to obtain the corresponding input value.

   a. To solve the equation **numerically**, use a guess and check method.

   b. To solve the equation **graphically**, graph the symbolic rule and read the appropriate coordinates from the graph.

EXERCISES
ACTIVITY 6.7

1. At one time, your favorite gas station listed the price of regular unleaded gasoline as $2.459 per gallon.

   a. Let x be the input variable representing the number of gallons purchased. Let C be the output variable representing the total cost of the fuel. Write a symbolic rule relating x and C.

   b. What is the replacement set for the input x?

c. Use the equation from part a to complete the following table.

x, NUMBER OF GALLONS PURCHASED	5	10	15	20
C, TOTAL COST OF THE PURCHASE ($)				

d. You have only $10 with you. Use the symbolic rule from part a to write an equation that can be used to determine how many gallons you can purchase.

e. Use a numerical approach to solve your equation from part d.

f. The graph of the equation determined in part a is given below. Use the graph to estimate the number of gallons you can purchase with $10.

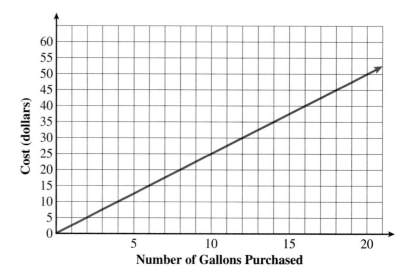

g. Which approach is more accurate?

2. You are president of the band booster club at your local college. You have arranged for the college's jazz band to perform at a local bookstore for 3 hours. In exchange for the performance, the Booster Club will receive three-quarters of the store's gross receipts during that 3-hour period.

a. Let x be the input variable representing the gross receipts of the bookstore during the performance. Let y be the output variable representing the share of the gross receipts that the bookstore will donate to the band boosters. Write a symbolic rule relating x and y.

b. Use the symbolic rule from part a to complete the following table.

x, TOTAL GROSS RECEIPTS ($)	250	500	750	1000
y, BOOSTERS' SHARE ($)				

c. If the bookstore presents you with a check for $650, what were the gross receipts during the performance? Use a numerical approach to estimate your answer.

d. The graph of the equation determined in part a is given below. Use a graphical approach to estimate the gross receipts from part c.

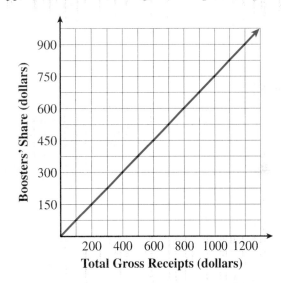

3. A tennis ball is dropped from the top of the Empire State Building in New York City. The following table gives the ball's distance (output) from ground level at a given time (input) after it is dropped.

TIME (sec.)	1	2	3	4	5	6	7
DISTANCE (ft.)	1398	1350	1270	1158	1014	838	630

The Empire State Building is 1414 feet tall. Use the information in the table to approximate the time when the ball will have fallen half the height of the building.

4. a. If $y = -2x$, determine y when $x = -5$.

b. If $y = x - 10$, determine y when $x = -7.5$.

In each of Exercises 5 and 6, write the equation that results after replacing y by the given value. Solve this equation in two ways, numerically (by completing the table) and graphically. The graph of each symbolic rule is shown.

5. If $y = x + 4$, determine x when $y = 7$.

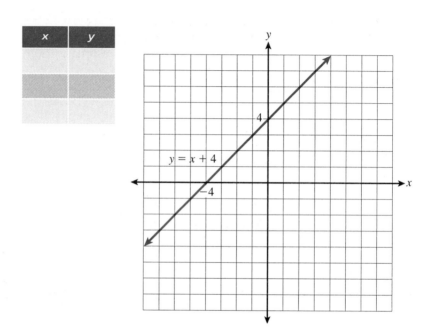

6. If $y = 3x$, determine x when $y = -12$.

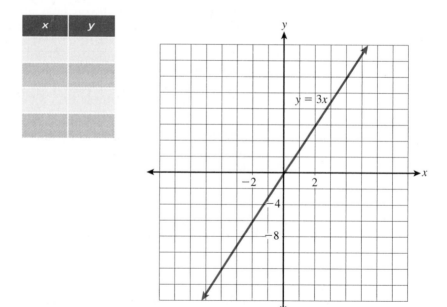

Let's Go Shopping

OBJECTIVES

1. Translate verbal rules into symbolic rules.

2. Solve an equation of the form $ax = b$, $a \neq 0$, for x using an algebraic approach.

3. Solve an equation of the form $x + a = b$ for x using an algebraic approach.

The sales tax collected on taxable items in Allegany County in western New York, is 8.5%. The tax you must pay depends on the price of the item you are purchasing.

1. What is the sales tax on a dress shirt that costs $20?

2. **a.** Because you are interested in determining the sales tax given the price of an item, which variable is the input?

   b. What are its units of measurement?

3. **a.** Which variable is the output?

   b. What are its units of measurement?

4. Determine the sales tax you must pay on the following items.

Power Shopping

ITEM	PRICE ($)	SALES TAX ($)
Calculator	12.00	
Shirt	25.00	
Microwave Oven	200.00	
Car	15,000.00	

5. **a.** Write a verbal rule that describes how to determine the sales tax for a given price of an item.

   b. Translate the verbal rule in part a into a symbolic rule, with x representing the input (price) and y representing the output (sales tax).

Solving Equations of the Form $ax = b$, $a \neq 0$, Using an Algebraic Approach

You can diagram the symbolic rule $y = 0.085x$ in the following way.

Start with x (price) ⟶ multiply by 0.085 ⟶ to obtain y (sales tax).

How might you determine the price of a fax machine for which you paid a sales tax of $21.25? In this situation you know the sales tax (output), and want to determine the price (input). To accomplish this, "reverse the direction" in the preceding diagram, and replace the operation (multiplication) by its inverse (division).

Start with y (sales tax) ⟶ divide by 0.085 ⟶ to obtain x (price).

Start with 21.25   ⟶ 21.25 ÷ 0.085 ⟶   to obtain 250.

Therefore, the price of a fax machine for which you paid $21.25 sales tax is $250.

6. Use this reverse process to determine the price of a color scanner for which you paid a sales tax of $61.20.

The reverse process illustrated above can also be done in a more common and formal way as demonstrated in Example 1.

EXAMPLE 1   *The sales tax for the fax machine was $21.25. In the symbolic rule $y = 0.085x$, replace y by 21.25 and proceed as follows:*

$21.25 = 0.085x$ This is the equation to be solved.

$\dfrac{21.25}{0.085} = \dfrac{0.085x}{0.085}$ Divide both sides of the equation by 0.085 or, equivalently, multiply by $\dfrac{1}{0.085}$

$250 = x$

The approach demonstrated in Example 1 is the **algebraic method** of solving the equation $21.25 = 0.085x$. Note that this process is completed when the variable, x, has been isolated on one side of the equation and its coefficient is 1. In this situation, you needed to undo the multiplication of x by 0.085 by dividing each side of the equation by 0.085. The value obtained for x (here, 250) is called the **solution** of the equation.

7. Use the symbolic rule $y = 0.085x$ to determine the price of a DVD player for which you paid a sales tax of $34.85.

Solving Equations of the Form $x + a = b$ Using an Algebraic Approach

8. Suppose you have a $15 coupon that can be used on any purchase over $100 at your favorite clothing store.

a. Determine the discount price of a sports jacket having a retail price of $116.

b. Identify the input variable and the output variable.

c. Let x represent the input and y represent the output. Write a symbolic rule that describes the relationship between the input and output. Assume that your total purchase will be greater than $100.

d. Complete the following table using the symbolic rule determined in part c.

x, RETAIL PRICE ($)	y, DISCOUNT PRICE ($)
105	
135	
184	
205	

You can also diagram this symbolic rule in the following way:

Start with x (retail price) ⟶ subtract 15 ⟶ to obtain y (discount price).

9. Suppose you are asked to determine the retail price if the discount price of a suit is $187.

a. Is 187 an input value or an output value?

b. Reverse the direction in the diagram above, replacing the operation (subtraction) with its inverse (addition).

Start with $y = 187$ (output) ⟶ _____ ⟶ to obtain x (input).

c. Use this reverse process to determine the retail price of the suit.

The equation in Problem 9 can be solved using an algebraic approach.

EXAMPLE 2 *Solve the equation $187 = x - 15$ for x. To isolate the variable x on one side, undo the subtraction of 15 from x by adding 15 to each side of the equation.*

$$187 = x - 15 \qquad \text{Equation to be solved.}$$
$$\underline{+15 \qquad + 15} \qquad \text{Add 15 to each side.}$$
$$202 = x$$

10. Use the symbolic rule $y = x - 15$ to determine the retail price, x, of a trench coat whose discounted price is $203.

In this activity, you solved equations using an algebraic approach. Your strategy in each case was to isolate the input variable, x, on one side of the equation by applying the appropriate inverse operation. To undo a multiplication, you divided. To undo a subtraction, you added.

11. Use an algebraic approach to determine the input x for the given output value. That is, set up and solve the appropriate equation.

a. $y = 7.5x$

Determine x when $y = 90$.

b. $z = -5x$

Determine x when $z = -115$.

c. $y = \dfrac{x}{4}$

Determine x when $y = 2$.

d. $p = \dfrac{2}{3}x$

Determine x when $p = -18$.

12. Use an algebraic approach to determine the input x for the given output value.

a. $y = x - 10$

Determine x when $y = -13$.

b. $y = 13 + x$

Determine x when $y = 7$.

c. $p = x + 4.5$

Determine x when $p = -10$.

d. $x - \dfrac{1}{3} = s$

Determine x when $s = 8$.

13. Consider the symbolic rule $y = 7.5x$ where x represents the input and y represents the output.

   a. Suppose $y = 26$. Use an algebraic approach to determine the corresponding value of x.

   b. Suppose $x = 10$. Use an algebraic approach to determine the corresponding value of y.

   c. Describe the difference and similarities in determining your results in parts a and b.

SUMMARY
ACTIVITY 6.8

1. A **solution** of an equation containing one variable is a replacement value for the variable that produces equal values on both sides of the equation.

2. An **algebraic approach** to solving an equation for a given variable is complete when the variable (such as x) is isolated on one side of the equation with coefficient 1. To isolate the variable, you apply the appropriate inverse operation, as follows.

   a. Multiplication and division are inverse operations. Therefore,

   i. to undo multiplication of the input by a numerical nonzero coefficient, divide each side of the equation by that coefficient

   ii. to undo division of the input by a number, multiply each side of the equation by that number

   b. Addition and subtraction are inverse operations. Therefore,

   i. to undo addition of a value to the input, subtract that value from each side of the equation

   ii. to undo subtraction of a value from the input, add that value to each side of the equation

1. You've decided to enroll in a local college as a part-time student (taking fewer than 12 credit hours). Full-time college work does not fit into your present financial or personal situation. The cost per credit hour at your college is $175.

   a. What is the cost of a 3-credit-hour literature course?

   b. Write a symbolic rule to determine the total tuition for a given number of credit hours. Let n represent the number of credit hours taken (input) and y represent the total tuition paid (output).

   c. Complete the following table.

CREDIT HOURS	TUITION PAID ($)
1	
2	
3	
4	

   d. Suppose you have enrolled in a psychology course and a computer course, each of which is 3 credit hours. Use the symbolic rule in part b to determine the total tuition paid.

   e. Use the symbolic rule from part b to determine algebraically the number of credit hours carried by a student with the following tuition bill.

   i. $875   ii. $1400

2. a. The average amount, A, of precipitation in Boston during March is four times the average amount, P, of precipitation in Phoenix. Translate the verbal rule into a symbolic rule.

b. What is the amount of precipitation in Boston if there are 2 inches in Phoenix?

c. What is the amount of precipitation in Phoenix if there are 24 inches in Boston?

3. a. The depth (inches) of water that accumulates in the spring soil from melted snow can be determined by dividing the cumulative winter snowfall (inches) by 12. Translate the verbal statement into a symbolic rule, using I for the accumulated inches of water and n for the inches of fallen snow.

b. Determine the amount of water that accumulates in the soil if 25 inches of snow falls.

c. Determine the total amount of winter snow that accumulates 6 inches of water in the soil.

4. Have you ever played a game based on the popular TV game show *The Price Is Right*? The idea is to guess the price of an item. You win the item by coming closest to the correct price without going over. If your opponent goes first, a good strategy is to overbid her regularly by a small amount, say, $15. Then your opponent can win only if the item's price falls in that $15 region between her bid and yours.

You can model this strategy by defining two variables: The input, x, will represent your opponent's bid, and the output, y, will represent your bid.

a. Write a symbolic rule to represent the input/output relationship in this strategy.

b. Determine your bid if your opponent's bid is $475.

c. Complete the following table.

OPPONENT'S BID	YOUR BID
$390	
$585	
$1095	

d. Use the symbolic rule determined in part a to calculate your opponent's bid if you have just bid $605. Stated another way, determine x if $y = 605$.

5. a. Profit is always calculated as revenue minus expenses. If a company's expenses were $10 million, write a symbolic rule that expresses profit, P (in millions of dollars), in terms of revenue, R (in millions of dollars).

   b. Determine the profit when revenue is $25 million.

   c. Determine the revenue that will produce a profit of $5 million.

For part a of Exercises 6–11, determine the output when you are given the input. For part b, use an algebraic approach to solve the equation for the input when you are given the output.

6. $3.5x = y$

   a. Determine y when $x = 15$.   b. Determine x when $y = 144$.

7. $z = -12x$

   a. Determine z when $x = -7$.   b. Determine x when $z = 108$.

8. $y = 15.3x$

    a. Determine y when $x = -13$.   **b.** Determine x when $y = 351.9$.

9. $y = x + 5$

    a. Determine y when $x = -11$.   **b.** Determine x when $y = 17$.

10. $y = x + 5.5$

    a. Determine y when $x = -3.7$.   **b.** Determine x when $y = 13.7$.

11. $z = x - 11$

    a. Determine z when $x = -5$.   **b.** Determine x when $z = -4$.

✺ ACTIVITY 6.9

Are They the Same?

OBJECTIVES

1. Translate verbal rules into symbolic (algebraic) rules.

2. Write algebraic expressions that involve grouping symbols.

3. Evaluate algebraic expressions containing two or more operations.

4. Identify equivalent algebraic expressions by examining their outputs.

A major road-construction project in your neighborhood is forcing you to take a 3-mile detour each way when you leave and return home. To compute the round-trip mileage for a routine trip, you will have to double the usual one-way mileage, adding in the 3-mile detour.

Does it matter in which order you perform these operations? That is, to determine the round-trip mileage (output), do you

a. double the usual one-way mileage (input) and then add 3, or

b. add 3 to the usual one-way mileage (input) and then double the result?

Complete the following table to determine whether there is a difference in the results from using these two methods.

0 4 2 9 5 1 ⅔ Mile After Mile

USUAL MILEAGE (INPUT)	RULE 1: TO OBTAIN THE OUTPUT, DOUBLE THE INPUT, THEN ADD 3.	RULE 2: TO OBTAIN THE OUTPUT, ADD 3 TO THE INPUT, THEN DOUBLE.
8		
15		
24		

1. Do rules 1 and 2 generate the same output values (round-trip mileage)?

2. From which sequence of operations do you obtain the correct round-trip mileage? Explain why.

3. For each of the rules given in the preceding table, let x represent the input and y represent the output. Translate each verbal rule into a symbolic rule.

Rule 1:

Rule 2:

4. The graphs of rules 1 and 2 are given on the same axes. Compare the graphs. What do you observe?

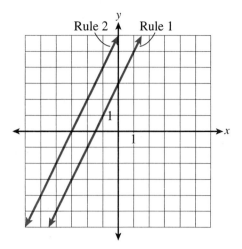

Equivalent Expressions

Algebraic expressions are said to be **equivalent** if identical inputs always produce the same output. The expressions $2x + 3$ (from rule 1) and $(x + 3) \cdot 2$ (from rule 2) are not equivalent. The table preceding Problem 1 shows that an input such as $x = 8$ produces different outputs.

5. a. For each of the following, translate the verbal rule into a symbolic rule. Let x represent the input and y the output. Then, complete the given table.

Rule 3: To obtain y, multiply x by 2, and then add 10 to the product.

x	y
−1	
0	
2	
5	
10	

Rule 4: To obtain y, add 5 to x, and then multiply the sum by 2.

b. What do you notice about the outputs generated by rules 3 and 4?

x	y
−1	
0	
2	
5	
10	

c. The graphs of rules 3 and 4 are given on the same axes. Compare the graphs. What do you observe?

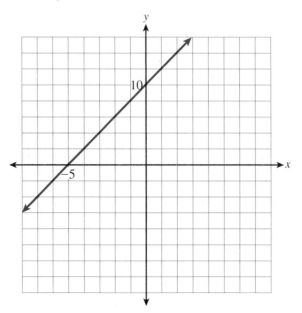

d. Is the expression $2x + 10$ equivalent to the expression $2(x + 5)$?

6. a. For each of the following rules, translate the given verbal rule into a symbolic rule. Let x represent the input and y the output. Then, complete the tables.

Rule 5: To obtain y, square the sum of x and 3.

x	y
−1	
0	
2	
5	
10	

Rule 6: To obtain y, add 9 to the square of x.

b. What do you notice about the outputs generated by rules 5 and 6?

x	y
−1	
0	
2	
5	
10	

c. Is the expression $(x + 3)^2$ equivalent to the expression $x^2 + 9$? Explain.

d. If you were to graph rule 5 and rule 6, how would you expect the graphs to compare?

SUMMARY
ACTIVITY 6.9

1. Algebraic expressions are said to be **equivalent** if identical inputs always produce the same output.

2. The order in which arithmetic operations are performed on the input affects the output.

3. The graphs of rules that contain equivalent expressions are identical.

EXERCISES
ACTIVITY 6.9

Let x represent the input variable and y represent the output variable. Translate each of the verbal rules in Exercises 1–6 into a symbolic rule.

1. The output is the input decreased by ten.

2. The output is three times the difference between the input and four.

3. The output is nine increased by the quotient of the input and six.

4. The output is seven more than one-half of the square of the input.

5. The output is fifteen less than the product of the input and -4.

6. The output is the sum of one-third of the input and ten.

7. a. Complete the following table.

x	x · 3	3x
−4	−12	
−1	−3	
0	0	
3	6	

b. Do the expressions $x \cdot 3$ and $3x$ produce the same output value when given the same input value?

c. In part b, the input value times 3 gives the same result as 3 times the input value. What property of multiplication does this demonstrate?

 d. Use a graphing calculator to sketch a graph of $y_1 = x \cdot 3$ and $y_2 = 3x$ on the same coordinate axes. How do the graphs compare?

8. a. Is the expression $x - 3$ equivalent to $3 - x$? Complete the following table to help justify your answer.

x	x − 3	3 − x
−5	−8	8
−3	−6	4
0	−3	3
1	2	2
3	0	0

b. What correspondence do you observe between the output values in columns 2 and 3? How is the expression $3 - x$ related to the expression $x - 3$?

c. Is the operation of subtraction commutative?

d. Use your graphing calculator to sketch a graph of $y_1 = x - 3$ and $y_2 = 3 - x$. How do the graphs compare? Why does this show that $x - 3$ and $3 - x$ are not equivalent expressions?

9. a. Is the algebraic expression $3x$ equivalent to the expression x^3? Explain.

b. In the expression $2x$, the number 2 is called the _____ .

c. In the expression x^2, the number 2 is called the _____ .

10. a. Write a verbal rule that describes the sequence of operations indicated by the given symbolic rule. Then complete the tables.

i. $y_1 = x^2$

x	y_1
−2	
−1	
0	
2	
3	

ii. $y_2 = -x^2$

x	y_2
−2	
−1	
0	
2	
3	

iii. $y_3 = (-x)^2$

x	y_3
−2	
−1	
0	
2	
3	

b. Which, if any, of the expressions $x^2, -x^2,$ and $(-x)^2$ are equivalent? Explain.

The symbolic rules in the following exercises each contain two or more arithmetic operations. In each exercise, diagram the rule, complete the table, and then answer the question about your results.

11.

x	$y_1 = 2x + 1$	$y_2 = 2(x + 1)$
−1		
0		
2		
5		

Are the expressions $2x + 1$ and $2(x + 1)$ equivalent? Why or why not?

12.

x	$y_5 = 1 + x^2$	$y_6 = (1 + x)^2$
−1		
0		
2		
5		

Are the expressions $1 + x^2$ and $(1 + x)^2$ equivalent? Why or why not?

13.

x	$y_7 = 2x^2 - 4$	$y_8 = 2(x^2 - 2)$
-3		
-1		
0		
1		
3		

Are the expressions $2x^2 - 4$ and $2(x^2 - 2)$ equivalent? Why or why not?

14.

x	$y_9 = 3x^2 + 1$	$y_{10} = (3x)^2 + 1$
-1		
0		
2		
5		

Are the expressions $3x^2 + 1$ and $(3x)^2 + 1$ equivalent? Why or why not?

ACTIVITY 6.10

Sherlock Holmes

OBJECTIVE

1. Recognize the conceptual basis for solving equations algebraically.

As a warm-up to this activity, try the following.

Given the rule $y = 2x$, determine x when $y = 12$.

Given the rule $y = \frac{x}{4}$, determine x when $y = 17$.

Given the rule $y = \frac{3}{5}x$, determine x when $y = 18$.

Given the rule $y = x + 9$, determine x when $y = 6$.

Your instructor (or any brave student volunteer) leaves the classroom. The rest of the class will choose a number, although a positive integer would be the kindest. Place a question mark in place of this number on the blackboard. Then record a sequence of any number of arithmetic operations (addition, subtraction, multiplication, division) in any order you choose. Record this sequence on the board together with the final result of the calculations.

For example, suppose you decide to choose 33 as your number and select the following sequence of operations:

add 5, subtract 2, divide by 3, multiply by 4, add 17, and divide by 5

Here is how you write this on the board (do not include the column of partial results shown in parentheses).

$$
\begin{array}{rll}
? & (33) & \text{mystery input} \\
+\ 5 & (38) & \\
-2 & (36) & \\
\div\ 3 & (12) & \\
\cdot\ 4 & (48) & \\
+\ 17 & (65) & \\
\div\ 5 & (13) & \text{final output} \\
\end{array}
$$

Result: **13**

Call the volunteer back into the classroom, and ask her to find the mystery input the class chose and to explain how she was able to determine it.

1. As a class, create an activity similar to the sample just described.

2. Individually, make up a similar activity on a separate sheet of paper. Trade papers with a classmate and determine his original number.

An equation that results from an algebraic rule containing a sequence of arithmetic operations is solved by reversing the sequence and replacing each operation by its inverse.

Determine the mystery input in each of the following exercises.

1. ?

   + 4

   − 6

   · 3

   ÷ 11

   The output is **6**.

2. ?

   ÷ − 3

   − 7

   + 3

   · 4

   ÷ − 2

   The output is **18**.

3. ?

   · 2

   − 8

   + 5

   ÷ 3

   The output is **−9**.

⊛**ACTIVITY 6.11**

Leasing a Copier

OBJECTIVES

1. Model contextual situations with symbolic rules of the form $y = ax + b, a \neq 0$.

2. Solve equations of the form $ax + b = c, a \neq 0$.

As part of your college program, you are a summer intern in a law office. You are asked by the office manager to gather some information about leasing a copy machine for the office. The sales representative at Eastern Supply Company recommends a 50-copy/minute copier to satisfy the office's copying needs. The copier leases for $455 per month, plus 1.5 cents a copy. Maintenance fees are covered in the monthly charge. The lawyers would own the copier after 39 months.

1. a. The total monthly cost depends upon the number of copies made. Identify the input and output variables.

b. Write a verbal rule to determine the total monthly cost in terms of the number of copies made during the month.

c. Complete the following table.

The Lease You Can Do

NUMBER OF COPIES	5000	10,000	15,000	20,000
MONTHLY COST ($)				

d. Translate the verbal rule in part b into a symbolic rule. Let n represent the number of copies (input) made during the month and c represent the total monthly cost (output).

2. a. Use the symbolic rule obtained in Problem 1d to determine the monthly cost if 12,000 copies are made.

b. Is 12,000 a replacement value for the input or for the output variable?

In Problem 2, you determined the cost by evaluating the symbolic rule $c = 0.015n + 455$ for $n = 12,000$. This was accomplished by performing the sequence of operations shown in the diagram.

Start with n ⟶ multiply by 0.015 ⟶ add 455 ⟶ to obtain c.

3. Suppose the monthly budget for leasing the copier is $800.

a. Is 800 an input value for n or an output value for c?

b. To determine the input, n, for a given output value of c, reverse the sequence of operations in the preceding diagram and replace each operation with its inverse. Recall that addition and subtraction are inverse operations and that multiplication and division are inverse operations. Complete the following:

Start with c ⟶ _____ ⟶ _____ ⟶ to obtain n.

c. Use the sequence of operations in part b to determine the number of copies that can be made for a monthly budget of $c = 800$.

Solving Equations Algebraically

Once you understand the concept of using the reverse process to solve equations (see Problem 3), you will want a more systematic algebraic procedure to follow.

4. Use the symbolic rule in Problem 1 to write an equation that can be used to determine the number, n, of copies that can be made with a monthly budget of $c = 800$.

Notice in Problem 4 that n is not isolated on one side of the equation. To isolate n, you need to undo two operations: the addition of 455 and the multiplication by 0.015. To do this, reverse the sequence of operations, and replace each operation by its inverse.

EXAMPLE 1 *The following example illustrates a systematic algebraic procedure by undoing two operations to solve an equation.*

Solve for x: $120 = 3x + 90$

$$120 = 3x + 90$$
$$\underline{-90 \qquad -90}$$
$$30 = 3x$$

Step 1: To undo the addition of 90, subtract 90 from each side of the equation.

$$\frac{30}{3} = \frac{3x}{3}$$
$$10 = x$$

Step 2: To undo the multiplication by 3, divide each side of the equation by 3.

The variable x has been isolated on the right side; the solution is 10.

Check: $120 \overset{?}{=} 3(10) + 90$

$120 \overset{?}{=} 30 + 90$

$120 = 120$

Note that the algebraic procedure emphasizes that an equation can be thought of as a scale whose arms are in balance. The equal sign can be thought of as the balancing point.

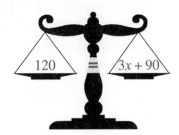

As you perform the appropriate inverse operation to solve the equation $120 = 3x + 90$ for x, you must maintain the balance as you perform each step in the process. If you subtract 90 from one side of the equal sign, then you must subtract 90 from the other side. Similarly, if you divide one side of the equation by 3, then you must divide the other side by 3.

5. Use the algebraic procedure outlined in Example 1 to solve the equation in Problem 4.

6. For each of the following, substitute the given value of y and use an algebraic approach to solve the resulting equation for x.

   a. If $y = 3x - 5$ and $y = 10$, determine x.

   b. If $y = 30 - 2x$ and $y = 24$, determine x.

   c. If $y = \frac{3}{4}x - 21$ and $y = -9$, determine x.

d. If $-2x + 15 = y$ and $y = -3$, determine x.

7. Complete the following tables.

a. $y = 4x - 11$

x	y
6	
	53

b. $y = -5x - 80$

x	y
12	
	35

**SUMMARY
ACTIVITY 6.11**

1. The goal of **solving an equation** of the form $ax + b = c$, where $a \neq 0$, for the variable x is to isolate the variable x on one side of the equation.

2. Use **inverse operations** to isolate the variable. Apply the inverse operations in the following order.

Step 1: Undo the addition of b by subtracting b from each side of the equation; undo the subtraction of b by adding b to each side of the equation.

Step 2: Undo the multiplication of the variable x by the nonzero coefficient a by dividing each side of the equation by a.

**EXERCISES
ACTIVITY 6.11**

1. A long-distance telephone plan costs $2.00 a month, plus 4 cents per minute, or part thereof, for any long-distance call made during the month.

a. Write a verbal rule to determine the total monthly cost for your long-distance calls for the month.

b. Translate the verbal rule in part a into a symbolic rule. Use c to represent the total monthly cost and n to represent the total number of long-distance minutes for the month.

c. Determine the monthly cost if 250 minutes of long-distance calls are made.

d. If you budget $50 per month for long-distance calls, how many minutes can you call in the month?

2. You are considering taking some courses at your local community college on a part-time basis for the upcoming semester. For a student who carries fewer than 12 credits (the full-time minimum), the tuition is $175 for each credit hour taken. All students, part-time or full-time, must pay a $50 parking fee for the semester. This fixed fee is added directly to your tuition and is included in your total bill.

a. Complete the following table, where t represents the total bill and n represents the number of credit hours taken.

NUMBER OF CREDIT HOURS, n	1	2	3	4	5	6
TOTAL TUITION, t ($)						

b. Write a symbolic rule to determine the total bill, t, for a student carrying fewer than 12 credit hours. Use n to represent the number of hours taken for the semester.

c. Determine the total bill if you take 9 credit hours.

d. Suppose you have $1650 to spend on the total bill. How many credit hours can you carry for the semester?

3. The social psychology class is organizing a campus-entertainment night to benefit charities in the community. You are a member of the budget committee for the class project. The committee suggests a $10 per person admission donation for food, nonalcoholic beverages, and entertainment. The committee determines that the fixed costs for the event (food, drinks, posters, tickets, etc.) will total $2100. The college is donating the use of the gymnasium for the evening.

a. The total revenue (gross income before expenses are deducted) depends on the number, *n*, of students who attend. Write an expression in terms of *n* that represents the total revenue if *n* students attend.

b. Profit is the net income after expenses are deducted. Write a symbolic rule expressing the profit, *p*, in terms of the number, *n*, of students who attend.

c. If the gymnasium holds a maximum of 700 people, what is the maximum amount of money that can be donated to charity?

d. Suppose that the members of the committee want to be able to donate at least $1500 to community charities. How many students must attend in order to have a profit of $1500?

4. The value of most assets, such as a car, computer, or house, depreciates, or drops, over time. When an asset depreciates by a fixed amount per year, the depreciation is called straight-line depreciation. Suppose a car has an initial value of $12,400 and depreciates $820 per year.

a. Let *v* represent the value of the car after *t* years. Write a symbolic rule that expresses *v* in terms of *t*.

b. What is the value of the car after four years?

c. How long will it take for the value of the car to decrease to $2000?

5. The cost, *c*, in dollars, of mailing a priority overnight package weighing 1 pound or more is given by the formula $c = 2.085x + 15.08$, where *x* represents the weight of the package in pounds.

a. Determine the cost of mailing a package that weighs 10 pounds.

b. Determine the weight of a package that costs $56.78 to mail.

6. Archaeologists and forensic scientists use the length of human bones to estimate the height of individuals. A person's height, h, in centimeters, can be determined from the length of the femur, f (the bone from the knee to the hip socket), in centimeters, using the following formulas:

Man: $h = 69.089 + 2.238f$

Woman: $h = 61.412 + 2.317f$

a. A partial skeleton of a man is found. The femur measures 50 centimeters. How tall was the man?

b. What is the length of the femur for a woman who is 150 centimeters tall?

7. Let p represent the perimeter of an isosceles triangle that has two equal sides of length a, and a third side of length b. The formula for the perimeter is $p = 2a + b$. Determine the length of the equal side of an isosceles triangle having perimeter of $\frac{3}{4}$ yard and a third side measuring $\frac{1}{3}$ yard.

8. The recommended weight of an adult male is given by the formula $w = \frac{11}{2}h - 220$, where w represents his recommended weight in pounds and h represents his height in inches. Determine the height of a man whose recommended weight is 165 pounds.

9. Housing prices in your neighborhood have been increasing steadily since you bought your home in 1995. The relationship between the market value of your home and the length of time you have been living there can be expressed algebraically by the rule

$$V = 130{,}000 + 3500x,$$

where x is the length of time (in years) in your home and V is the market value (in dollars).

a. Complete the following table.

YEAR	x	MARKET VALUE
1995		
2000		
2003		

b. Determine the value of your home in 2010.

c. In which year will the value of your home reach $193,000?

10. Use an algebraic approach to solve each of the following equations for x.

a. $10 = 2x + 12$

b. $-27 = -5x - 7$

c. $3x - 26 = -14$

d. $24 - 2x = 38$

e. $5x - 15 = 15$

f. $-4x + 8 = 8$

g. $12 + \dfrac{1}{5}x = 9$

h. $\dfrac{2}{3}x - 12 = 0$

i. $0.25x - 14.5 = 10$ **j.** $5 = 2.5x - 20$

11. Complete the following tables using algebraic methods. Indicate the equation that results when you replace x or y with its assigned value.

a. $y = 2x - 10$

x	y
4	
	14

b. $y = 20 + 0.5x$

x	y
3.5	
	-10

c. $y = -3x + 15$

x	y
$\frac{2}{3}$	
	-3

d. $y = 12 - \frac{3}{4}x$

x	y
-8	
	-6

e. $y = \frac{x}{5} - 2$

x	y
24	
	18

✳ ACTIVITY 6.12

How Long Can You Live?

OBJECTIVES

1. Represent sets of data by a regression equation of the form $y = ax + b, a \neq 0$.

2. Solve equations of the form $ax + b = c, a \neq 0$.

3. Solve problems involving equations of the form $ax + b = c, a \neq 0$.

Life expectancy in the United States has been steadily increasing. The number of Americans aged 100 or older could exceed 850,000 by the middle of this century. Medical advancements have been a primary reason for Americans living longer. Another factor is the increased awareness and practice of a healthy lifestyle.

The following table shows the life expectancies at birth of men and women in the United States born in various years. For convenience, t, the number of years since 1975, has been inserted into the table. Note that for several years the life expectancy for women has been greater than that of men.

Year By Year

BIRTH YEAR	1975 $t = 0$	1980 $t = 5$	1985 $t = 10$	1990 $t = 15$	1995 $t = 20$	2000 $t = 25$
Women	76.6	77.4	78.2	78.8	78.9	80.0
Men	68.8	70.0	71.1	71.8	72.5	73.0

Source: U.S. Bureau of the Census

1. a. Plot the data for the life expectancy of women. The horizontal axis (input) is represented by t, where t is the number of years since 1975 ($t = 0$ corresponds to 1975, $t = 5$ corresponds to 1980, etc.). The vertical axis (output) is represented by E, the life expectancy in years.

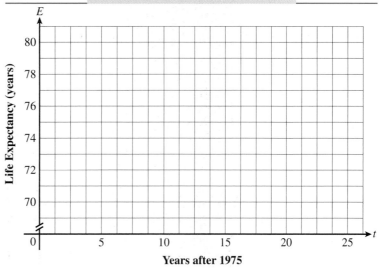

LIFE EXPECTANCY OF U.S. WOMEN 1975–2000

Years after 1975

b. Do the plotted points in the graph follow any kind of pattern?

The plotted points do form a somewhat linear pattern. In such a situation, an equation of a line can be determined (using a statistical technique) that approximates the *life expectancy*, E, for any given value of t. The equation is called a **linear regression equation**. The equation and its graph are said to model the relationship between the two variables.

A linear regression equation is a formula or algebraic equation that can be formed from actual data. The regression equation can be used to represent or model the relationship between two variables.

2. a. The data in the preceding table can be modeled by the linear regression equation $E = 0.126t + 76.74$, where E is the life expectancy for women born t years after 1975.

Use the equation to complete the following table.

As Time Goes By

NUMBER OF YEARS SINCE 1975, t	(1975) 0	(1980) 5	(1985) 10	(1990) 15	(1995) 20	(2000) 25
LIFE EXPECTANCY FOR WOMEN, E						

b. How do the values of E obtained from the regression equation compare to the actual values of E in the first life-expectancy table?

3. According to the model relating the variables E and t, how long would a woman born in 1983 expect to live? Keep in mind that the input value of t is the number of years since 1975.

4. a. Use the formula $E = 0.126t + 76.74$ to predict the birth year of a woman who can expect to live 85 years.

b. Predict the birth year of a woman who can expect to live 100 years.

c. For which prediction, in part a or b, do you have the greater confidence? Explain.

5. A mathematical model for the life expectancy of men born *t* years after 1975 is $E = 0.167t + 69.11$.

a. According to the model, how long would a man born in 1983 expect to live?

b. Predict the birth year of a man who can expect to live 100 years.

SUMMARY
ACTIVITY 6.12

1. A **linear regression equation** is a formula or algebraic equation that can be formed from actual data. The regression equation can be used to represent or model the relationship between two variables.

EXERCISES
ACTIVITY 6.12

1. In 1966, the U.S. Surgeon General's health warnings began appearing on cigarette packages. The following data seems to demonstrate that public awareness of the health hazards of smoking has had some effect on consumption of cigarettes.

Heading in the Right Direction

YEAR	1965	1974	1979	1983	1985	1990	1995	2000	2004
% OF TOTAL POPULATION 18 AND OLDER WHO SMOKE	42.4	37.1	33.5	32.1	30.1	25.5	24.7	23.3	20.9

Source: U.S. National Center for Health Statistics

Exercise numbers appearing in color are answered in the Selected Answers appendix.

The percentage, p, of the total population (18 and older) who smoke t years after 1965 can be approximated by the model $p = -0.555t + 41.67$, where t is the number of years after 1965. Note that $t = 0$ corresponds to the year 1965, $t = 9$ corresponds to 1974, etc.

a. Determine the percentage of the population who smoked in 1981 ($t = 16$).

b. Using the formula, in what year would the percentage of smokers be 15% ($p = 15$)?

2. In 1965, 51.9% of all men (18 or older) smoked. The percentage, p, of men who smoke in t years after 1965 is modeled by the formula $p = -0.89t + 51.1$.

a. Determine the percentage of men smoking in the year 2000.

b. In what year would the percentage of male smokers 18 or older be 25%?

3. As you might guess, medical-related expenses tend to increase with age. The average annual per capita expense for health care in America can be modeled by the formula

$$E = 136A - 1116,$$

where E is the average per capita expense (dollars) associated with a person of age A (years).

a. Determine the average per capita health care expenses for a 30-year-old.

b. At approximately what age will a person typically incur annual health care expenses of $8000?

4. Medical researchers have determined that, for exercise to be beneficial, a person's desirable heart rate, R, in beats per minute, can be approximated by the formulas

$$R = 143 - 0.65a \text{ for women}$$

$$R = 165 - 0.75a \text{ for men,}$$

where a (years) represents the person's age.

a. If the desirable heart rate for a woman is 130 beats per minute, how old is she?

b. If the desirable heart rate for a man is 135 beats per minute, how old is he?

5. The basal energy rate is the daily amount of energy (measured in calories) needed by the body at rest to maintain body temperature and the basic life processes of respiration, cell metabolism, circulation, and glandular activity. As you may suspect, the basal energy rate differs for individuals, depending on their gender, age, height, and weight. The formula for the basal energy rate for men is

$$B = 655.096 + 9.563W + 1.85H - 4.676A,$$

where B is the basal energy rate (in calories), W is the weight (in kilograms), H is the height (in centimeters), and A is the age (in years).

a. A male patient is 70 years old, weighs 55 kilograms, and is 172 centimeters tall. A total daily calorie intake of 1000 calories is prescribed for him. Determine if he is being properly fed.

b. A man is 178 centimeters tall and weighs 84 kilograms. If his basal energy rate is 1500 calories, how old is the man?

✳ACTIVITY 6.13

The Algebra of Weather

OBJECTIVES

1. Evaluate formulas for specified input values.

2. Solve a formula for a specified variable.

Windchill

On Monday morning you listen to the news and weather before going to class. The meteorologist reports that the temperature is 25°F, a balmy February day on the campus of SUNY Oswego in New York State, but he adds that a 30 mph wind makes it feel like 8°F.

Curious, you do some research and learn that windchill is the term commonly used to describe how cold your skin feels if it is exposed to the wind. You also find the following chart that reports windchill as a temperature relative to air temperature and wind speed.

Wind Chill Chart

Air Temperature (°F)

Wind (mph)	40	35	30	25	20	15	10	5	0	−5	−10	−15	−20	−25	−30	−35	−40	−45
5	36	31	25	19	13	7	1	−5	−11	−16	−22	−28	−34	−40	−46	−52	−57	−63
10	34	27	21	15	9	3	−4	−10	−16	−22	−28	−35	−41	−47	−53	−59	−66	−72
15	32	25	19	13	6	0	−7	−13	−19	−26	−32	−39		−51	−58	−64	−71	−77
20	30	24	17	11	4	−2	−9	−15	−22	−29	−35	−42	−48	−55	−61	−68	−74	−81
25	29	23	16	9	3	−4	−11	−17	−24	−31	−37	−44	−51	−58	−64	−71	−78	−84
30	28	22	15	8	1	−5	−12	−19	−26	−33	−39	−46	−53	−60	−67	−73	−80	−87
35	28	21	14	7		−7	−14	−21	−27	−34		−48	−55	−62		−76	−82	−89
40	27	20	13	6	−1	−8	−15	−22	−29	−36	−43	−50	−57	−64	−71	−78	−84	−91
45	26	29	12	5	−2	−9	−16	−23		−37	−44	−51	−58	−65	−72	−79	−86	−93
50	26	19	12	4	−3	−10	−17	−24	−31	−38	−45	−52	−60	−67	−74	−81	−88	−95
55	25	18	11	4	−3	−11	−18	−25	−32	−39	−46	−54	−61	−68	−75	−82	−89	−97
60	25	17	10		−4	−11	−19	−26	−33	−40	−48	−55	−62	−69	−76	−84	−91	−98

Frostbite Times   ▢ 30 minutes   ▧ 10 minutes   ■ 5 minutes

Wind Chill (°F) = $35.74 + 0.6215T - 35.75(V^{0.16}) + 0.4275T(V^{0.16})$

where, T = Air Temperature (°F) V = Wind Speed (mph)

Note: Wind speeds above 40 mph have little additional chilling affect

To use the chart, find the approximate temperature on the top of the chart. Read down until you are opposite the appropriate wind speed. The number that appears at the intersection of the temperature and wind speed is the windchill index.

1. **a.** The chart has several windchill temperatures missing. Use the patterns that you observe in the chart to fill in the missing windchills with reasonable estimates. Then, describe some of the patterns that you observe in the rows of the chart.

   b. On an earlier not-so-balmy day in Oswego, the air temperature was 15 degrees but the wind made it feel like −2°F. Use the chart to determine the wind speed.

2. Windchill temperature, w (°F), produced by a 30-mph wind at various air temperatures, t (°F), can be modeled by the formula

$$w = 1.36t - 26.$$

a. Complete the following table using the given formula.

AIR TEMPERATURE, t (°F)	−15	5	30
WINDCHILL TEMPERATURE, w (°F) (30-MPH WIND)			

b. How do the windchill temperatures in the preceding table compare to the values given in the chart for a 30-mph wind?

3. a. Use the formula $w = 1.36t - 26$ to determine the windchill temperature if the air temperature is 7°F.

b. On a cold day in New York City, the wind is blowing at 30 mph. If the windchill temperature is reported to be −18°F, then what is the air temperature on that day? Use the formula $w = 1.36t - 26$.

The formula $w = 1.36t - 26$ is said to be solved for w in terms of t because the variable w is isolated on one side of the equation. To determine the windchill temperature, w, for air temperature $t = 7$°F (Problem 3a), you substitute 7 for t in $1.36t - 26$ and do the arithmetic:

$$w = 1.36(7) - 26 = -16.48° \text{ F}$$

In Problem 3b, you were asked to determine the air temperature, t, for a windchill temperature of −18°F. In this case, you replaced w by −18 and solved the resulting equation

$$-18 = 1.36t - 26$$

for t.

Each time you are given a windchill temperature and asked to determine the air temperature you need to set up and solve a similar equation. Often it is more convenient and efficient to solve the original formula $w = 1.36t - 26$ for t symbolically and then evaluate the new rule to determine values of t.

EXAMPLE 1   *Solving the formula $w = 1.36t - 26$ for t is similar to solving the equation $-18 = 1.36t - 26$ for t.*

$$-18 = 1.36t - 26$$
$$\underline{+26 = \qquad +26}$$
$$8 = 1.36t$$
$$\frac{8}{1.36} = \frac{1.36t}{1.36}$$
$$6 \approx t$$

$$w = 1.36t - 26$$
$$\underline{+26 = \qquad +26}$$
$$w + 26 = 1.36t$$
$$\frac{w + 26}{1.36} = \frac{1.36t}{1.36}$$
$$\frac{w + 26}{1.36} = t$$

The new formula is $t = \dfrac{w + 26}{1.36}$ or $t = \dfrac{w}{1.36} + \dfrac{26}{1.36}$, which is equivalent to $t = 0.735w + 19.12$.

> To solve the equation $w = 1.36t - 26$ for t means to isolate the variable t on one side of the equation, with all other terms on the opposite side.

4. Redo Problem 3b using the new formula derived in Example 1 that expresses t in terms of w.

5. **a.** If the wind speed is 15 mph, the windchill can be approximated by the formula $w = 1.28t - 19$, where t is the air temperature in degrees Fahrenheit. Solve the formula for t.

   b. Use the new formula from part a to determine the air temperature, t, if the windchill temperature is $-10°F$.

Weather Balloon

A weather balloon is launched at sea level. The balloon is carrying instruments that measure temperature during the balloon's trip. After the balloon is released, the data collected shows that the temperature dropped 0.0117°F for each meter that the balloon rose.

6. a. If the temperature at sea level is 50°F, determine the temperature at a distance of 600 meters above sea level.

   b. Write a verbal rule to determine the temperature at a given distance above sea level on a 50°F day.

   c. If t represents the temperature (°F) a distance of m meters above sea level, translate the verbal rule in part b into a symbolic rule.

   d. Complete the following table.

METERS ABOVE SEA LEVEL, m	500	750	1000
TEMPERATURE, t (50°F DAY)			

7. a. Solve the formula $t = 50 - 0.0117m$ for m.

   b. Water freezes at 32°F. Determine the distance above sea level at which water will freeze on a 50°F day. Use the formula from part a.

Crickets and Temperature

During the summer, one of the more familiar late-evening sounds is the rhythmic chirping of a male cricket. Of particular interest is the snowy tree cricket, sometimes called the temperature cricket. It is very sensitive to temperature, speeding up or slowing down its chirping as the temperature rises or falls.

Data shows that the number, n, of chirps per minute of the snowy tree cricket is related to the temperature t (°F) by the formula

$$t = \frac{1}{4}n + 40.$$

8. a. If a cricket chirps 60 times in 1 minute, what is the temperature?

b. Solve the equation $t = \frac{1}{4}n + 40$ for n.

c. If the temperature is 80°F, use the formula from part b to determine the expected number of chirps made by the cricket in 1 minute.

9. Solve each of the following formulas for the indicated letter.

a. $A = lw$, for w **b.** $p = c + m$, for m

c. $P = 2l + 2w$, for l **d.** $R = 165 - 0.75a$, for a

e. $V = \pi r^2 h$, for h

SUMMARY **ACTIVITY 6.13**	To solve a **formula** for a variable, isolate that variable on one side of the equation with all other terms on the "opposite" side.

EXERCISES **ACTIVITY 6.13**	**1.** The following formula is used by the National Football League (NFL) to calculate quarterback ratings:

$$R = \frac{250C + 12.5Y + 1000T - 1250I + 6.25A}{3A},$$

where

$R = $ quarterback rating
$A = $ passes attempted
$C = $ passes completed
$Y = $ passing yardage
$T = $ touchdown passes
$I \ = $ number of interceptions.

In the 2005–2006 regular season, Tom Brady, quarterback for the New England Patriots, and Brett Favre, for the Green Bay Packers, had the following player statistics:

Take a Pass

PLAYER	PASSES ATTEMPTED	PASSES COMPLETED	PASSING YARDAGE	NUMBER OF TOUCHDOWN PASSES	NUMBER OF INTERCEPTIONS
Tom Brady	530	334	4110	26	14
Brett Favre	607	372	3881	20	29

a. Determine the quarterback rating for Tom Brady for the 2005–2006 NFL football season.

b. Determine the quarterback rating for Brett Favre.

c. Visit www.nfl.com and select stats to obtain the rating of your favorite quarterback.

2. The profit that a business makes is the difference between its revenue (the money it takes in) and its costs.

a. Write a formula that describes the relationship between the profit, p, revenue, r, and costs, c.

b. It costs a publishing company $85,400 to produce a textbook. The revenue from the sale of the textbook is $315,000. Determine the profit.

c. The sales from another textbook amount to $877,000, and the company earns a profit of $465,000. Use your formula from part a to determine the cost of producing the book.

3. The distance traveled is the product of the rate (speed) at which you travel and the amount of time you travel at that rate.

   a. Write a symbolic rule that describes the relationship between the distance, d, rate, r, and time, t.

   b. A gray whale can swim 20 hours a day at an average speed of approximately 3.5 mph. How far can the whale swim in a day?

   c. A Boeing 747 flies 1950 miles at an average speed of 575 mph. Use the formula from part a to determine the flying time.

   d. Solve the formula in part a for the variable t. Then use this new formula to rework part c.

4. The speed, s, of an ant (in centimeters per second) is related to the temperature, t (in degrees Celsius), by the formula

$$s = 0.167t - 0.67.$$

   a. If an ant is moving at 4 centimeters per second, what is the temperature?

   b. Solve the equation $s = 0.167t - 0.67$ for t.

   c. Use the new formula from part b to answer part a.

5. The National Weather Service reports the daily temperature in degrees Fahrenheit. The scientific community, as well as Canada and most of Europe, reports temperature in degrees Celsius. The Celsius, C, and Fahrenheit, F, temperature readings are related by the formula

$$F = 1.8C + 32$$

a. Determine the Fahrenheit reading corresponding to the temperature at which water boils, 100°C.

b. Solve the formula $F = 1.8C + 32$ for C.

c. Use the new formula from part b to answer part a.

6. The number of women enrolled in college has steadily increased. The following table gives the enrollment, in millions, of women in a given year.

Women in College

YEAR	1970	1975	1980	1985	1990	1995	2000	2001
NUMBER ENROLLED IN MILLIONS	3.54	5.04	6.22	6.43	7.54	7.92	8.59	8.97

Source: U.S. Department of Education, National Center for Education Statistics

Let t represent the number of years since 1970. The number N (in millions) of women enrolled in college can be modeled by the formula

$$N = 0.158t + 4.092.$$

a. Estimate in what year women's college enrollment will reach 10 million.

b. Solve the equation $N = 0.158t + 4.092$ for t.

c. Use the new formula in part b to estimate the year in which women's enrollment will reach 11 million.

7. The pressure, p, of water (in pounds per square foot) at a depth of d feet below the surface is given by the formula

$$p = 15 + \frac{15}{33}d.$$

a. On November 14, 1993, Francisco Ferreras reached a record depth for breath-held diving. During the dive, he experienced a pressure of 201 pounds per square foot. What was his record depth?

b. Solve the equation $p = 15 + \frac{15}{33}d$ for d.

c. Use the formula from part b to determine the record depth and compare your answer to the one you obtained in part a.

Solve each of the following formulas for the specified variable.

8. $E = IR$, for I **9.** $C = 2\pi r$, for r

10. $P = 2a + b$, for b **11.** $P = 2l + 2w$, for w

12. $R = 143 - 0.65a$, for a **13.** $A = P + Prt$, for r

14. $y = mx + b$, for m **15.** $m = g - vt^2$, for g

16. a. You want to invest in order to receive the best return on your money. You have two options:

Option 1:   Invest at 6% simple annual interest for 10 years;

Option 2:   Invest at 5% interest compounded annually.

The following table models the growth of $2000 over the 10-year period using the two options.

 Interesting Choices

NUMBER OF YEARS	1	2	3	4	5	6	7	8	9	10
6% simple annual interest	2120	2240	2360	2480	2600	2720	2840	2960	3080	3200
5% compounded annually	2100	2205	2315.30	2431	2552.60	2680.20	2814.20	2954.90	3102.70	3257.80

Describe any trends or patterns that you observe in the data.

b. The amount of your investment in Option 1 can be determined by the following formula:

$$A = P + Prt,$$

where

A = amount of the investment

P = principal or amount invested

r = annual percentage rate (expressed as a decimal)

t = number of years invested.

Use the formula to determine the amount of your $2000 investment in Option 1 after 20 years. What is the total amount of interest earned?

c. The amount of your investment in Option 2 can be determined by

$$A = P(1 + r)^t,$$

where

A = amount of the investment

P = principal

r = annual percentage rate (expressed as a decimal)

t = number of years invested.

Use the formula to determine the amount of your $2000 investment in Option 2 after 20 years. What is the total amount of interest earned?

d. Which option would you choose? Explain.

CLUSTER 2 | **What Have I Learned?**

1. Describe how solving the equation $4x - 5 = 11$ for x is similar to solving the equation $4x - 5 = y$ for x.

2. In the formula $d = rt$, assume that the rate, r, is 60 mph. The formula then becomes the equation $d = 60t$.

   a. Which variable is the input variable?

   b. Which is the output variable?

   c. Which variable from the original formula is now a constant?

   d. Discuss the similarities and differences in the equations $d = 60t$ and $y = 60x$.

3. Describe in words what operation(s) must be performed to isolate the variable x in each of the following.

   a. $10 = x - 16$ 　　　　　　　　　　 **b.** $-8 = \dfrac{1}{2}x$

   c. $-2x + 4 = -6$ 　　　　　　　　 **d.** $ax - b = c$

4. The area, A, of a triangle is given by the formula $A = \frac{1}{2}bh$, where b represents the base and h represents the height. The formula can be rewritten as $b = \frac{2A}{h}$ or $h = \frac{2A}{b}$. Which formula would you use to determine the base, b, of a triangle, given its area, A, and height, h? Explain.

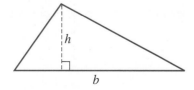

CLUSTER 2

5. You are designing a cylindrical container as new packaging for a popular brand of coffee. The current package is a cylinder with a diameter of 4 inches and a height of 5.5 inches. The volume of a cylinder is given by the formula

$$V = \pi r^2 h,$$

where V is the volume (in cubic inches), r is the radius (in inches), and h is the height (in inches).

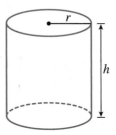

How much coffee does the current container hold? Round your answer to the nearest tenth of a cubic inch.

6. You have been asked to alter the dimensions of the container in Problem 5 so that the new package will contain less coffee. To save money, the company plans to sell the new package for the same price as before.

You will do this in one of two ways:

i. By increasing the diameter and decreasing the height by $\frac{1}{2}$-inch each (resulting in a slightly wider and shorter can), or

ii. By decreasing the diameter and increasing the height by $\frac{1}{2}$-inch each (resulting in a slightly narrower and taller can).

a. Determine which new design, if either, will result in a package that holds less coffee than the current one.

b. By what percent will you have decreased the volume?

1. Let x represent the input variable. Translate each of the following phrases into an algebraic expression.

   a. input increased by 10

   b. the input subtracted from 10

   c. twelve divided by the input

   d. eight less than the product of the input and -4

   e. the quotient of the input and 4, increased by 3

   f. one-half of the square of the input, decreased by 2

2. **a.** Write a symbolic rule that represents the relationship in which the output variable y is 35 less than the input variable x.

   b. What is the output corresponding to an input value of 52?

   c. What is the input corresponding to an output value of 123?

3. **a.** Write a symbolic rule that represents the relationship in which the output variable t is 10 more than 2.5 times the input variable r.

   b. What is the output corresponding to an input of 8?

Exercise numbers appearing in color are answered in the Selected Answers appendix.

    c. What is the input corresponding to an output of -65?

4. Use an algebraic approach to solve each of the following equations for x.

    a. $x + 5 = 2$ **b.** $2x = -20$

    c. $x - 3.5 = 12$ **d.** $-x = 9$

    e. $13 = x + 15$ **f.** $4x - 7 = 9$

    g. $10 = -2x + 3$ **h.** $\frac{3}{5}x - 6 = 1$

5. The cost of printing a brochure to advertise your lawn-care business is a flat fee of \$10 plus \$0.08 per copy. Let C represent the total cost of printing and x represent the number of copies you order.

    a. Write a symbolic rule that expresses the relationship between C and x.

    b. Organize the data into a table of values. Begin with 1000 copies, increase by increments of 1000, and end with 5000 copies.

NUMBER OF COPIES, x	TOTAL COST (\$), C

c. Graph the data obtained in part b. Use a straightedge to connect the points and extend the graph. Scale the axes appropriately so that you can plot the ordered pair corresponding to 10,000 copies.

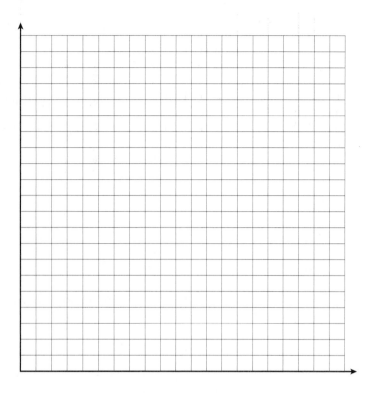

d. What is the total cost of printing 8000 copies?

e. You have $500 to spend on advertising. How many copies can you have printed for that amount?

6. Your car needs a few new parts to pass inspection. The labor cost is $68 an hour, charged by the half hour, and the parts cost a total of $148. Whether you can afford these repairs depends on how long it will take the mechanic to install the parts.

a. Write a verbal rule that will enable you to determine a total cost for repairs.

b. Write the symbolic form of this verbal rule, letting x be the input variable and y be the output variable. What does x represent? (Include its units.) What does y represent? (Include its units.)

c. Use the symbolic rule in part b to create a table of values.

HOURS, x	TOTAL COST ($), y

d. How much will it cost if the mechanic works 4 hours?

e. You have $350 available in your budget for car repair. Determine if you have enough money if the mechanic says that it will take him $3\frac{1}{2}$ hours to install the parts.

f. You decide that you can spend an additional $100. How long can you afford to have the mechanic work?

g. Solve the symbolic rule from part b for the input variable x. Why would it ever be to your advantage to do this?

7. a. The formula used to convert a temperature in degrees Fahrenheit to a temperature in degrees Celsius is $C = \frac{5}{9}(F - 32)$. Use this formula to determine the Celsius temperature when the Fahrenheit temperature is 59°.

b. Solve the formula in part a for F.

c. Use your result from part b to determine the Fahrenheit temperature corresponding to a Celsius temperature of 15°.

8. Solve each of the following equations for the given variable.

a. $d = rt$, for r

b. $P = a + b + c$, for b

c. $A = P + Prt$, for r

d. $y = 4x - 5$, for x

e. $w = \frac{4}{7}h + 3$, for h

CLUSTER 3   Mathematical Modeling and Problem Solving

ACTIVITY 6.14

Do It Two Ways

OBJECTIVES

1. Apply the distributive property.

2. Use areas of rectangles to interpret the distributive property geometrically.

3. Identify equivalent expressions.

1. You earn \$8 per hour at your job and are paid every other week. You work 25 hours the first week and 15 hours the second week. Use two different approaches to compute your gross salary for the pay period. Explain in a sentence each of the approaches you used.

Problem 1 demonstrates the **distributive property** of multiplication over addition. In the problem, the distributive property asserts that adding the hours first and then multiplying the sum by \$8 produces the same gross salary as does multiplying separately each week's hours by \$8 and then adding the weekly salaries.

> The **distributive property** is expressed algebraically as
>
> $$\underbrace{a \cdot (b + c)}_{\text{factored form}} = \underbrace{a \cdot b + a \cdot c}_{\text{expanded form}}$$
>
> Note that in factored form, you add first, and then multiply. In the expanded form, you calculate the individual products first, and then add the results.

Geometric Interpretation of the Distributive Property

The distributive property can also be interpreted geometrically. Consider the following diagram:

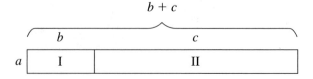

2. **a.** Write an expression for the area of rectangle I in the diagram.

   b. Write an expression for the area of rectangle II in the diagram.

   c. Write an expression for the area of the rectangle having width a and total top length $b + c$.

   d. Explain in terms of the areas in the geometric diagram why $a(b + c)$ equals $ab + ac$.

Application of the Distributive Property

The distributive property is frequently used to transform one algebraic expression into an equivalent expression.

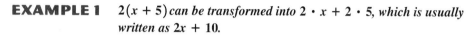

EXAMPLE 1   *$2(x + 5)$ can be transformed into $2 \cdot x + 2 \cdot 5$, which is usually written as $2x + 10$.*

The *factored form*, $2(x + 5)$, indicates that you start with x, add 5, and then multiply by 2. The *expanded form*, $2x + 10$, indicates that you start with x, multiply by 2, and then add 10.

   3. a. Complete the following table to demonstrate numerically that the expression $2(x + 5)$ is equivalent to the expression $2x + 10$:

INPUT	OUTPUT 1	OUTPUT 2
x	$y_1 = 2(x + 5)$	$y_2 = 2x + 10$
1		
2		
4		
10		

   b. Explain how the table illustrates the equivalence of the two expressions.

   c. Use your graphing calculator to sketch the graphs of both symbolic rules. How are the graphs related? What does this indicate about the expressions in the two symbolic rules?

There are two ways in which you can visualize the process of writing an expression such as $4(3x - 5)$ in expanded form using the distributive property.

First, you can make a diagram that looks very similar to a rectangular area problem. (See next page.) Place the factor 4 on the left of the diagram. Place the terms of the expression $3x - 5$ along the top. Multiply each term along the top by 4, and then add the resulting products. Note that the terms do not actually represent lengths of the sides of the rectangle. The diagram is an organizational tool to help you apply the distributive property properly.

	$3x$	-5
4	$12x$	-20

Therefore, $4(3x - 5) = 12x - 20$.

Second, you can draw arrows to emphasize that each term within the parentheses is multiplied by the factor 4:

$$4(3x - 5) = 4(3x) - 4(5) = 12x - 20.$$

4. Use the distributive property to write each of the following expressions in expanded form.

   a. $5(x + 6)$

   b. $-10x(y + 11)$

   c. Note: A negative sign preceding parentheses indicates multiplication by -1. Use this fact to expand $-(2x - 7)$.

   d. $3x(4 - 2x)$

Extension of the Distributive Property

The distributive property can be extended to sums of more than two terms within the parentheses. For example, it can be used to multiply $5(3x - 2y + 6)$.

To help you apply the distributive property, you can use the diagram approach,

	$3x$	$-2y$	6
5	$15x$	$-10y$	30

or you can use the arrows approach,

$$5(3x - 2y + 6) = 5 \cdot 3x + 5 \cdot (-2y) + 5 \cdot 6 = 15x - 10y + 30.$$

5. Verbally describe the procedure used to multiply $5(3x - 2y + 6)$.

6. Use the distributive property to write each of the expressions in expanded form.

a. $-3(2x^2 - 4x - 5)$

b. $2x(3a + 4b - x)$

Applications

7. For exercise to be the most beneficial, it should increase a person's heart rate to a target level. The symbolic rule

$$T = 0.6(220 - a)$$

describes how to calculate an individual's target heart rate, T, measured in beats per minute, in terms of age, a, in years.

a. Use the distributive property to rewrite the right-hand side of symbolic rule in expanded form.

b. Use both the factored and expanded rules to determine the target heart rate for an 18-year-old person during aerobics.

8. The manager of a clothing store decides to reduce the price of a leather jacket by $25.

a. Use x to represent the regular cost of the jacket, and write an expression that represents the discounted price of the leather jacket.

b. If eight jackets are sold at the reduced price, write an expression in factored form that represents the total receipts for the jackets.

c. Write the expression in part b as an equivalent expression without parentheses (expanded form).

SUMMARY
ACTIVITY 6.14

1. The **distributive property** is expressed algebraically as
   $a \cdot (b + c) = a \cdot b + a \cdot c$, where a, b, and c are any real numbers.

2. The **distributive property** can be extended to sums of more than two terms, as follows: $a \cdot (b + c + d) = a \cdot b + a \cdot c + a \cdot d$.

EXERCISES
ACTIVITY 6.14

1. Use the distributive property to expand the algebraic expression $10(x - 8)$. Then evaluate the factored form and the expanded form for these values of x: 5, -3, and $\frac{1}{2}$. What do you discover about these two algebraic expressions? Explain.

Use the distributive property to expand each of the algebraic expressions in Exercises 2–13.

2. $6(4x - 5)$

3. $-7(t + 5.4)$

4. $2.5(4 - 2x)$

5. $3(2x^2 + 5x - 1)$

6. $-(3p - 17)$

7. $-(-2x - 3y)$

8. $-3(4x^2 - 3x + 7)$

9. $-(4x + 10y - z)$

10. $\frac{5}{6}\left(\frac{3}{4}x + \frac{2}{3}\right)$

11. $-\frac{1}{2}\left(\frac{6}{7}x - \frac{2}{5}\right)$

12. $3x(5x - 4)$

13. $4a(2a + 3b - 6)$

Exercise numbers appearing in color are answered in the Selected Answers appendix.

14. Expand the expression $4(a + b + c)$ and simplify the expression $4(abc)$. Are the results the same? Explain.

15. In chemistry, the ideal gas law is given by the equation $PV = n(T + 273)$, where P is the pressure, V the volume, T the temperature, and n the number of moles of gas. Write the right-hand side of the equation in expanded form (without parentheses).

16. In business, an initial deposit of P dollars, invested at a simple interest rate, r (in decimal form), will grow after t years, to amount A given by the formula

$$A = P(1 + rt).$$

Write the right side of the equation in expanded form (without parentheses).

17. a. The width, w, of a rectangle is increased by 5 units. Write an expression that represents the new width.

  b. If l represents the length of the rectangle, write a product that represents the area of the new rectangle.

  c. Use the distributive property to write the expression in part b in expanded form (without parentheses).

18. A rectangle has width w and length l. If the width is increased by 4 units and the length is decreased by 2 units, write a formula in expanded form that represents the perimeter of the new rectangle.

19. The manager of a local discount store reduces the regular retail price of a certain cell phone brand by $5.

  a. Use y to represent the regular retail price and write an expression that represents the discounted price of the cell phone.

  b. If 12 of these phones are sold at the reduced price, write an expression in expanded form (without parentheses) that represents the store's total receipts for the 12 phones.

✳ACTIVITY 6.15

Ring It Up!

OBJECTIVES

1. Identify the greatest common factor in an expression.

2. Factor out the greatest common factor in an expression.

3. Recognize like terms.

4. Simplify an expression by combining like terms.

You and your friends vacation in Cancun, Mexico, during spring break. International calls are not included in your regular cell phone plan. Calls from Cancun are billed at a rate of $0.69 per minute. You make four phone calls for 12, 7, 8, and 10 minutes in duration.

1. One way to determine the phone bill is to multiply the number of minutes of each call by $0.69 and then add the results. Complete the following calculation.

$$0.69(12) + 0.69(7) + 0.69(8) + 0.69(10)$$

2. Another way to calculate your share of the phone bill is to add the number of minutes first and then multiply the sum by $0.69. Complete the following calculation.

$$0.69(12 + 7 + 8 + 10)$$

3. Compare your results in Problems 1 and 2. Are they equal? Why should they be?

In Problem 3, you determined that the numerical expressions in Problems 1 and 2 are equivalent by the distributive property. That is,

$$\underbrace{0.69(12 + 7 + 8 + 10)}_{\text{product}} = \underbrace{0.69(12) + 0.69(7) + 0.69(8) + 0.69(10)}_{\text{sum}}.$$

The equation shows how the distributive property allows the product (factored form) to be expanded as an equivalent sum of terms (expanded form). When each term in a sum contains a common factor, the distributive property can be used to reverse the expansion process and write the sum as a product. To write a sum as a product, you

1. divide each term by the common factor to remove it from the term, and

2. place the common factor outside parentheses that contain the sum of the remaining factors.

In the example from the preceding problems, the equation

$$\underbrace{0.69(12) + 0.69(7) + 0.69(8) + 0.69(10)}_{\text{sum}} = \underbrace{0.69(12 + 7 + 8 + 10)}_{\text{product}}$$

shows that 0.69 is a factor of each term on the left. It is called a **common factor**. The process of writing a sum equivalently as a product is called **factoring**. The process of dividing each term by a common factor and placing it outside parentheses containing the sum of the remaining factors is called **factoring out the common factor**.

4. a. One of your friends used your cell phone to make calls that were 11, 9, 6, and 5 minutes in duration. Use this data to describe in words the procedure you would use to write the sum

$$0.69(11) + 0.69(9) + 0.69(6) + 0.69(5)$$

in equivalent factored form as the product

$$0.69(11 + 9 + 6 + 5).$$

b. Use the procedure from part a to write the sum $23(5) + 16(5) - 4(5)$ as a product. What is the common factor?

Greatest Common Factor

A common factor is called a **greatest common factor** if there are no additional factors common to the terms in the expression. In the expression $12x + 30$, the numbers 2, 3, and 6 are common factors, but 6 is the greatest common factor. When an expression is written in factored form and the remaining terms in parentheses have no factors in common, the expression is said to be in **completely factored form**. Therefore, $12x + 30$ is written in completely factored form as $6(2x + 5)$.

5. a. What is the greatest common factor of $8x + 20$? Rewrite the expression in completely factored form.

b. What are common factors in the sum $10x + 6x$? What is the greatest common factor? Rewrite the expression as an equivalent product.

PROCEDURE

Factoring a Sum of Terms Containing a Common Factor

1. Identify the common factor.
2. Divide each term of the sum by the common factor. (Factor out the common factor.)
3. Place the sum of the remaining factors inside the parentheses, and place the common factor outside the parentheses.

6. Factor each of the following completely by factoring out the greatest common factor.

a. $2a + 6$ **b.** $5x + 3x - 7x$ **c.** $3x + 12$

d. $6x + 18y - 24$ **e.** $2xy - 5x$ **f.** $5x^2 - 3x^2$

Like Terms

7. a. Suppose you do not know the cost per minute for your four calls from Cancun of 12, 7, 8, and 10 minutes in duration, so you represent the cost per minute by the letter x. Write four distinct algebraic expressions, each representing the cost of one of your calls.

b. Your phone bill for the calls from Cancun is the sum of these four expressions. Write this sum.

c. What is the common factor?

d. Factor out the common factor from each term to write the expression as a product.

e. Rewrite the expression in part d by summing the values contained within the parentheses.

f. Recall that terms are parts of an algebraic expression that are separated by plus or minus signs. How many terms are there in the expression in Problem 7b? In Problem 7e?

Because the number of terms in the expression $12x + 7x + 8x + 10x$ has been reduced from four terms to one term in Problem 7e, the expression is said to have been simplified to $37x$.

The terms in the expression $12x + 7x + 8x + 10x$ are called **like terms**. They differ only by their numerical coefficients.

DEFINITION

Like terms are terms that contain identical variable factors, including exponents.

EXAMPLE 1

    a. $4x$ and $6x$ are like terms.   **b.** $4xy$ and $-10xy$ are like terms.

    c. x^2 and $-10x^2$ are like terms.   **d.** $4x$ and $9y$ are not like terms.

    e. $-3x^2$ and $-3x$ are not like terms.

Combining Like Terms

The distributive property provides a way to combine like terms. You will investigate this in more detail in the following problems.

8. a. Your friend has a different cell phone plan. He has two different rates per minute (a U.S. overage rate and a Cancun rate). His overage calls were 4, 8, and 13 minutes long, and his Cancun calls were 25, 2, 9, and 14 minutes long. Represent the overage rate by x cents per minute and the Cancun rate by y cents per minute. Write an expression in terms of x and y that represents the total cost of your friend's calls by forming a sum of the individual costs of the seven calls.

b. How many terms does the algebraic expression in part a contain?

c. Are there any like terms in the expression written in part a? If so, list them.

d. Combine the like terms in part c to simplify the algebraic expression.

Like terms can be combined by adding or subtracting their coefficients. This is a direct result of the distributive property.

EXAMPLE 2   *$15xy$ and $-8xy$ are like terms with coefficients 15 and -8, respectively. Thus, $15xy - 8xy = (15 - 8)xy = 7xy$.*

9. Identify the like terms, if any, in each of the following expressions, and combine them.

a. $3x - 5y + 2z - 2x$

b. $13s^2 + 6s - 4s^2$

c. $2x + 5y - 4x + 3y - x$

d. $3x^2 + 2x - 4x^2 - (-4x)$

When there is no coefficient written immediately to the left of a set of parentheses, the number 1 is understood to be the coefficient of the expression in parentheses. For example, $45 - (x - 7)$ can be understood as $45 - 1(x - 7)$. Therefore, you can use the distributive property to multiply each term inside the parentheses by -1 and then combine like terms:

$$45 - 1(x - 7) = 45 - x + 7 = 52 - x.$$

10. Professor Sims brings calculators to class each day. There are 30 calculators in the bag she brings. She never knows how many students will be late for class on a given day. Her routine is to first remove 15 calculators and then to remove one additional calculator for each late arrival. If x represents the number of late arrivals on any given day, then the expression $30 - (15 + x)$ represents the number of calculators left in the bag after the late arrivals remove theirs.

   a. Simplify the expression for Professor Sims so that she can more easily keep track of her calculators.

   b. Suppose there are four late arrivals. Evaluate both the original expression and the simplified expression. Compare your two results.

11. Use the distributive property to simplify and combine like terms.

   a. $20 - (10 - x)$ b. $4x - (-2x + 3)$

   c. $2x - 5y - 3(5x - 6y)$ d. $2(x - 3) - 4(x + 7)$

SUMMARY
ACTIVITY 6.15

1. The process of writing a sum equivalently as a product is called **factoring**.

2. A factor common to each term of an algebraic expression is called a **common factor**.

3. The process of dividing each term by a common factor and placing it outside parentheses containing the sum of the remaining terms is called **factoring out a common factor**.

4. A common factor of an expression involving a sum of terms is called a **greatest common factor** if the terms remaining inside the parentheses have no factor in common other than 1.

5. An algebraic expression is said to be in **completely factored form** when it is written in factored form and none of its factors can themselves be factored any further.

6. Procedure for factoring a sum of terms containing a common factor:

   a. Identify the common factor.

   b. Divide each term of the sum by the common factor. (Factor out the common factor.)

   c. Place the sum of the remaining factors inside the parentheses, and place the common factor outside the parentheses.

7. Like terms are terms that contain identical variable factors, including exponents. They differ only in their numerical coefficients.

8. To combine like terms of an algebraic expression, add or subtract their coefficients.

EXERCISES
ACTIVITY 6.15

In Exercises 1–8, factor out the greatest common factor, and write the result in factored form as a product.

1. $3x + 15$

2. $5w - 10$

3. $3xy - 7xy + xy$

4. $6x + 20xy - 10x$

5. $4 - 12x$

6. $2x^2 + 3x^2y$

7. $4srt^2 - 3srt^2 + 10st$

8. $10abc + 15abd + 35ab$

9. a. How many terms are in the expression $2x^2 + 3x - x - 3$ as written?

   b. How many terms are in the simplified expression $2x^2 + 2x - 3$?

10. Are $3x^2$ and $3x$ like terms? Explain.

In Exercises 11–21, simplify the following expressions by combining like terms.

11. $5a + 2ab - 3b + 6ab$

12. $3x^2 - 6x + 7$

13. $100r - 13s^2 + 4r - 18s^3$

14. $3a + 7b - 5a - 10b$

15. $2x^3 - 2y^2 + 4x^2 + 9y^2$

16. $7ab - 3ab + ab - 10ab$

17. $xy^2 + 3x^2y - 2xy^2$

18. $9x - 7x + 3x^2 + 5x$

19. $2x - 2x^2 + 7 - 12$

20. $3mn^3 - 2m^2n + m^2n - 7mn^3 + 3$

21. $5r^2s - 6rs^2 + 2rs + 4rs^2 - 3r^2s + 6rs - 7$

22. Simplify the expression $2x - (4x - 8)$.

In Exercises 23–34, use the distributive property, and then combine like terms to simplify the expressions.

23. $30 - (x + 6)$

24. $18 - (x - 8)$

25. $2x - 3(25 - x)$

26. $27 - 6(4x + 3y)$

27. $12.5 - (3.5 - x)$

28. $3x + 2(x + 4)$

29. $x + 3(2x - 5)$

30. $4(x + 2) + 5(x - 1)$

31. $7(x - 3) - 2(x - 8)$

32. $11(0.5x + 1) - (0.5x + 6)$

33. $2x^2 - 3x(x + 3)$

34. $y(2x - 2) - 3y(x + 4)$

35. You will be entering a craft fair with your latest metal wire lawn ornament. It is metal around the exterior and hollow in the middle, in the shape of a bird, as illustrated. However, you can produce different sizes, and all will be in proportion, depending on the length of the legs, x.

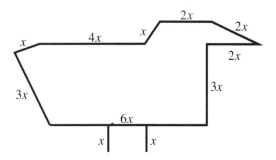

a. Write an algebraic expression that would represent the amount of wire you would need to create the bird. Be sure to include its legs.

b. Simplify the expression by combining like terms.

c. The amount of wire you need for each lawn ornament is determined from the expression in part b plus an extra 2 inches for the eye. If you have a spool containing 400 inches of metal wire, write an expression showing how much wire you will have left after completing one ornament.

d. Exactly how much wire is needed for an ornament whose legs measure 3 inches? How much wire will be left on the spool?

LAB ACTIVITY 6.16

Math Magic

OBJECTIVES

1. Recognize an algebraic expression as a code of instruction.

2. Simplify algebraic expressions.

Algebraic expressions arise every time a sequence of arithmetic operations (instructions) is applied to a variable. For example, if your instructions are to double a variable quantity and then add 5, you would express this algebraically as $2x + 5$. If, however, you start with an algebraic expression, say $3x - 2$, you can "decode" the expression to determine the sequence of operations that is applied to x:

Multiply by 3, and then subtract 2.

Perhaps you have seen magicians on TV who astound their audiences by guessing numbers that a volunteer has secretly picked. Consider the following examples of "math magic" and see if you can decode the tricks.

Select a number, preferably an integer for ease of calculation. Don't tell anyone your number. Perform the following sequence of operations using the number you selected:

Add 1 to the number.

Triple the result.

Subtract 6.

Divide by 3.

Tell your instructor your result.

You might be very surprised that your instructor, a "math magician" of sorts, can tell you the number that you originally selected. There is a hidden pattern in the sequence of operations that causes the number selected and the result of the sequence of operations to always have the same relationship.

1. One way to guess the relationship hidden in a number trick is to use the code of instructions on several different numbers. The following table lists results from this trick for four selected numbers. What relationship do you observe between the number selected and the result? How did your instructor know the number you selected?

Pick a Number

NUMBER SELECTED	RESULT OF SEQUENCE OF OPERATIONS
0	−1
2	1
5	4
10	9

2. **a.** To show how and why this trick works, you first generalize the situation by choosing a variable to represent the number selected. Use x as your variable and translate the first instruction into an algebraic expression. Then simplify it by removing parentheses (if necessary) and combining like terms.

b. Now, use the result from part a and translate the second instruction into an algebraic expression, and simplify where possible. Continue until you complete all the steps.

c. Use your result from part b to interpret verbally (in words) the relationship between the number selected and the result. Also explain how to obtain the original number.

3. Rather than simplifying after each step, you can wait until after you have written a single algebraic expression using all the steps. As in Problem 2, the resulting expression will represent the algebraic code for the number trick.

a. Write all the steps for this number trick as a single algebraic expression without simplifying at each step.

b. Simplify the expression you obtained in part a. How does this simplified expression compare with the result you obtained in Problem 2b?

4. Here is another trick you can try on a friend. The instructions for your friend are:

Think of a number.
Double it.
Subtract 5.
Multiply by 3.
Add 9.
Divide by 6.
Add 1.
Tell me your result.

a. Try this trick with a friend several times. Record the result of your friend's calculations and the numbers he or she originally selected.

   i. Start with 5:

   ii. Start with 8:

   iii. Start with 10:

b. Explain how you know your friend's numbers.

c. Show how your trick works no matter what number your friend chooses. Use an algebraic approach as you did in either Problem 2 or Problem 3.

5. You are a magician, and you need a new number trick for your next show at the Magic Hat Club. Make up a trick like the ones in Problems 1 and 4. Have a friend select a number and do the trick. Explain how you figured out the number. Show how your trick will work using any number.

6. Your magician friend had a show to do tonight but was suddenly called out of town due to an emergency. She asked you and some other magician friends to do her show for her. She wanted you to do the mind trick, and she left you the instructions in algebraic code. Translate the code into a sequence of arithmetic operations to be performed on a selected number. Try the trick on a friend before the show. Write down how you will figure out any chosen number.

Code: $[2(x - 1) + 8] \div 2 - 5$

7. Here are more codes you can use in the show. Try them out as you did in Problem 6. State what the trick is.

a. Code: $[(3n + 8) - n] \div 2 - 4$

b. Code: $\dfrac{(4x - 5) + x}{5} + 2$

8. Simplify the algebraic expressions.

a. $[3 - 2(x - 3)] \div 2 + 9$

b. $[3 - 2(x - 1)] - [-4(2x - 3) + 5] + 4$

c. $\dfrac{2(x - 6) + 8}{2} + 9$

SUMMARY
ACTIVITY 6.16

Procedure for simplifying algebraic expressions:

1. Simplify the expression from the innermost parentheses outward using the order of operations convention.

2. Use the distributive property when it applies.

3. Combine like terms.

EXERCISES
ACTIVITY 6.16

1. You want to boast to a friend about the stock that you own without telling him how much money you originally invested in the stock. Let your original stock value be represented by x dollars. You watch the market once a month for 4 months and record the following.

MONTH	1	2	3	4
STOCK VALUE	Increased $50	Doubled	Decreased $100	Tripled

a. Use x to represent the value of your original investment, and write an algebraic expression to represent the value of your stock after the first month.

b. Use the result from part a to determine the value at the end of the second month, simplifying when possible. Continue until you determine an expression that represents the value of your stock at the end of the fourth month.

c. Do you have good news to tell your friend? Explain to him what has happened to the value of your stock over 4 months.

d. Instead of simplifying expressions after each step, write a single algebraic expression that represents the 4-month period.

e. Simplify the expression in part d. How does the simplified algebraic expression compare with the result in part b?

2. a. Write a single algebraic expression for the following sequence of operations. Begin with a number represented by n.

Multiply by -2.

Add 4.

Divide by 2.

Subtract 5.

Multiply by 3.

Add 6.

b. Simplify the algebraic expression $3(-n + 2 - 5) + 6$.

c. Your friend in Alaska tells you that if you replace n with the value 10 in your answer to Problem 2b, you will discover the average Fahrenheit temperature in Alaska for the month of December. Does that seem reasonable? Explain.

3. Show how you would simplify the expression $2\{3 - [4(x - 7) - 3] + 2x\}$.

4. Simplify the following algebraic expressions.

a. $5x + 2(4x + 9)$

b. $2(x - y) + 3(2x + 3) - 3y + 4$

c. $-(x - 4y) + 3(-3x + 2y) - 7x$

d. $2 + 3[3x + 2(x - 3) - 2(x + 1) - 4x]$

e. $6[3 + 2(x - 5)] - [2 - (x + 1)]$

f. $\dfrac{5(x - 2) - 2x + 1}{3}$

You have hired an architect to design a home. She gives you the following information regarding the installation and operating costs of two types of heating systems: solar and electric.

Some Like It Hot

TYPE OF HEATING SYSTEM	INSTALLATION COST	OPERATING COST PER YEAR
Solar	$25,600	$200
Electric	$5500	$1600

1. a. Determine the total cost of the solar heating system after 5 years of use.

b. Write a verbal rule for the total cost of the solar heating system (output) in terms of the number of years of use (input).

c. Let x represent the number of years of use and c represent the total cost of the solar heating system. Translate the verbal rule in part b into a symbolic rule.

d. Use the formula from part c to complete the following table:

NUMBER OF YEARS IN USE, x	5	10	15	20
TOTAL COST, c ($)				

2. a. Determine the total cost of the electric heating system after 5 years of use.

b. Write a verbal rule for the total cost of the electric heating system (output) in terms of the number of years of use (input).

c. Let x represent the number of years of use and c represent the total cost of the electric heating system. Translate the verbal rule in part b into a symbolic rule.

d. Use the equation from part c to complete the following table:

NUMBER OF YEARS IN USE, x	5	10	15	20
TOTAL COST, c ($)				

The installation cost of solar heating is much more than that of the electric system, but the operating cost per year of the solar system is much lower. Therefore, it is reasonable to think that the total cost for the electric system will eventually "catch up" and surpass the total cost of the solar system.

3. Compare the table values for total heating costs in Problems 1d and 2d. Estimate in what year the total cost for electric heating will "catch up" and surpass the total cost for solar heating. Explain.

4. The year in which the total costs of the two heating systems are equal can be determined algebraically. Set the expressions in the symbolic rules in Problems 1c and 2c equal to each other to write an equation you can solve to determine when the total heating costs are the same.

The following example demonstrates a systematic algebraic procedure that you can use to solve equations similar to the equation in Problem 4. Remember that your goal is to isolate the variable on one side of the equation by applying the appropriate inverse operations.

EXAMPLE 1　　*Solve for x: 2x + 14 = 8x + 2.*

SOLUTION

First, add and/or subtract terms appropriately so that all terms involving the variable are on one side of the equal sign and all other terms are on the other side.

$$\begin{aligned}
2x + 14 &= 8x + 2 \qquad &&\text{Subtract } 8x \text{ from both sides and combine like terms.}\\
\underline{-8x \qquad\quad -8x} &\\
-6x + 14 &= 2 \\
\underline{-14 = -14} & &&\text{Subtract 14 from each side and combine like terms.}\\
-6x \qquad &= -12 \\
\frac{-6x}{-6} &= \frac{-12}{-6} &&\text{Divide each side by } -6, \text{ the coefficient of } x.\\
x &= 2
\end{aligned}$$

Check: $2(2) + 14 = 8(2) + 2$

$$4 + 14 = 16 + 2$$

$$18 = 18$$

5. In Example 1, the variable terms are combined on the left side of the equation. To solve the equation $2x + 14 = 8x + 2$, combine the variable terms on the right side.

6. a. Solve the equation in Problem 4 for x.

b. Interpret what your answer in part a represents in the context of the heating system situation.

Purchasing a Car

You are interested in purchasing a new car and have narrowed the choice to a Honda Accord LX (4 cylinder) and a Passat GLS (4 cylinder). Being concerned about the value of the car depreciating over time, you search the Internet and obtain the following information:

Driven Down...

MODEL OF CAR (2005)	MARKET SUGGESTED RETAIL PRICE (MSRP) ($)	ANNUAL DEPRECIATION ($)
Accord LX	20,925	1730
Passat GLS	24,995	2420

Data: Kelley Blue Book

7. a. Complete the following table:

YEARS THE CAR IS OWNED	VALUE OF ACCORD LX ($)	VALUE OF PASSAT GLS ($)
1		
2		
3		

b. Will the value of the Passat GLS ever be lower than the value of the Accord LX? Explain.

c. Let v represent the value of the car after x years of ownership. Write a symbolic rule to determine v in terms of x for the Accord LX.

d. Write a symbolic rule to determine v in terms of x for the Passat GLS.

e. Write an equation to determine when the value of the Accord LX will equal the value of the Passat GLS.

f. Solve the equation in part e.

NBA Basketball Court

You and your friend are avid professional basketball fans and discover that your mathematics instructor shares your enthusiasm for basketball. During a mathematics class, your instructor tells you that the perimeter of an NBA basketball court is 288 feet and the length is 44 feet more than its width. He challenges you to use your algebra skills to determine the dimensions of the court. To solve the problem, you and your friend use the following plan.

8. a. Let w represent the width of the court. Write an expression for the length in terms of the width, w.

b. Use the formula for the perimeter of a rectangle, $P = 2l + 2w$, and the information given to obtain an equation containing just the variable w.

c. To solve the equation you obtained in part b, first apply the distributive property and then combine like terms in the expression involving w.

d. What are the dimensions of an NBA basketball court?

9. Solve each of the following formulas for the specified variable.

a. $P = 2l + 2w$ for w

b. $V(P + a) = k$ for P

c. $w = 110 + \frac{11}{2}(h - 60)$ for h

10. Solve each of the following equations for x. Remember to check your result in the original equation.

a. $2x + 9 = 5x - 12$

b. $21 - x = -3 - 5x$

c. $2(x - 3) = -8$

d. $2(x - 4) + 6 = 4x - 7$

11. Three friends worked together on a homework assignment that included two equations to solve. Although they are certain that they solved the equations correctly, they are puzzled by the results they obtained. Here they are.

a. $3(x + 4) + 2x = 5(x - 12)$

$3x + 12 + 2x = 5x - 60$

$5x + 12 = 5x - 60$

$5x - 5x = -12 - 60$

$0 = -72?$

 Graph the equations $y_1 = 3(x + 4) + 2x$ and $y_2 = 5(x - 12)$. Do the graphs intersect?

What does this indicate about the solution to the original equation?

b. $2(x + 3) + 4x = 6(x + 1)$

$2x + 6 + 4x = 6x + 6$

$6x + 6 = 6x + 6$

$6x - 6x = 6 - 6$

$0 = 0?$

 Graph the equations $y_1 = 2(x + 3) + 4x$ and $y_2 = 6(x + 1)$. Do the graphs intersect?

What does this indicate about the solution to the original equation?

12. Solve the following equations, if possible.

a. $12x - 9 = 4(6 + 3x)$ **b.** $2(8x - 4) + 10 = 22 - 4(5 - 4x)$

In the process of solving these equations in Problems 11 and 12, the identical variable term appeared on each side of the simplified equation. Subtracting this term from both sides eliminated the variable completely. Two outcomes are possible:

1. The final line of the solution is an equation that is true. For example, $0 = 0$. When this occurs, the equation is called an **identity**. **All real numbers** are solutions to the original equation.

2. The final line of the solution is an equation that is false. For example, $0 = 30$. When this occurs, the equation is called a **contradiction**. There is **no solution** to the original equation.

SUMMARY
ACTIVITY 6.17

General strategy for solving equations for an unknown quantity, such as x:

1. If necessary, apply the distributive property to remove parentheses.

2. Combine like terms that appear on the same side of the equation.

3. Isolate x so that only a single term in x remains on one side of the equation and all other terms, not containing x, are moved to the other side. This is generally accomplished by adding (or subtracting) appropriate terms to both sides of the equation.

4. Solve for x by dividing each side of the equation by its coefficient.

5. Check your result by replacing x by this value in the original equation. A correct solution will produce a true statement.

EXERCISES
ACTIVITY 6.17

1. Finals are over, and you are moving back home for the summer. You need to rent a truck to move your possessions from the college residence hall back to your home. You contact two local rental companies and acquire the following information for the 1-day cost of renting a truck:

   Company 1: $25.95 per day, plus $0.49 per mile
   Company 2: $19.95 per day, plus $0.69 per mile

   Let x represent the number of miles driven in 1 day and C represent that total daily rental cost ($).

   a. Write a symbolic rule that represents the total daily rental cost from company 1 in terms of the number of miles driven.

   b. Write a symbolic rule that represents the total daily rental cost from company 2 in terms of the number of miles driven.

   c. Write an equation to determine for what mileage the 1-day rental cost would be the same.

   d. Solve the equation you obtained in part c.

   e. For which mileages would company 2 have the lower price?

2. You are considering installing a security system in your new house. You gather the following information about similar security systems from two local home security dealers:

   Dealer 1: $3560 to install and $15 per month monitoring fee

   Dealer 2: $2850 to install and $28 per month for monitoring

   You see that the initial cost of the security system from dealer 1 is much higher than that of the system from dealer 2, but that the monitoring fee is lower. You want to determine which is the better system for your needs.

   Let x represent the number of months that you have the security system and C represent the cumulative cost ($).

   a. Write a symbolic rule that represents the total cost of the system from dealer 1 in terms of the number of months you have the system.

   b. Write a symbolic rule that represents the total cost of the system from dealer 2 in terms of the number of months you have the system.

   c. Write an equation to determine the number of months for which the total cost of the systems will be equal.

   d. Solve the equation in part c.

   e. If you plan to live in the house and use the system for 10 years, which system would be less expensive?

3. You are able to get three summer jobs to help pay for college expenses. In your job as a cashier, you work 20 hours per week and earn $8.00 per hour. Your second and third jobs are both at a local hospital. There you earn $9.50 per hour as a payroll clerk and $7.00 per hour as an aide. You always work 10 hours less per week as an aide than you do as a payroll clerk. Your total weekly salary depends on the number of hours that you work at each job.

a. Determine the input and output variables for this situation.

b. Explain how you calculate the total amount earned each week.

c. If x represents the number of hours that you work as a payroll clerk, represent the number of hours that you work as an aide in terms of x.

d. Write a symbolic rule that describes the total amount you earn each week. Use x to represent the input variable and y to represent the output variable. Simplify the expression as much as possible.

e. If you work 12 hours as a payroll clerk, how much will you make in 1 week?

f. What are realistic replacement values for x? Would 8 hours at your payroll job be a realistic replacement value? What about 50 hours?

g. When you don't work as an aide, what is your total weekly salary?

h. If you plan to earn a total of $500 in 1 week from all jobs, how many hours would you have to work at each job? Is the total number of hours worked realistic? Explain.

    i. Solve the equation in part d for x in terms of y. When would it be useful to have the equation in this form?

4. A florist sells roses for $1.50 each and carnations for $0.85 each. Suppose you purchase a bouquet of 1 dozen flowers consisting of roses and carnations.

    a. Let x represent the number of roses purchased. Write an expression in terms of x that represents the number of carnations purchased.

    b. Write an expression that represents the cost of purchasing x roses.

    c. Write an expression that represents the cost of purchasing the carnations.

    d. What does the sum of the expressions in parts b and c represent?

    e. Suppose you are willing to spend $14.75. Write an equation that can be used to determine the number of roses that can be included in a bouquet of 1 dozen flowers consisting of roses and carnations.

    f. Solve the equation in part e to determine the number of roses and the number of carnations in the bouquet.

5. The viewing window of a certain calculator is in the shape of a rectangle.

    a. Let w represent the width of the viewing window in centimeters. If the window is 5 centimeters longer than it is wide, write an expression in terms of w for the length of the viewing window.

    b. Write a symbolic rule that represents the perimeter, P, of the viewing window in terms of w.

c. If the perimeter of the viewing window is 26 centimeters, determine the dimensions of the window.

Solve the equations in Exercises 6–19.

6. $5x - 4 = 3x - 6$

7. $3x - 14 = 6x + 4$

8. $0.5x + 9 = 4.5x + 17$

9. $4x - 10 = -2x + 8$

10. $0.3x - 5.5 = 0.2x + 2.6$

11. $4 - 0.025x = 0.1 - 0.05x$

12. $5t + 3 = 2(t + 6)$

13. $3(w + 2) = w - 14$

14. $21 + 3(x - 4) = 4(x + 5)$

15. $2(x + 3) = 5(2x + 1) + 4x$

16. $500 = 0.75x - (750 + 0.25x)$ **17.** $1.5x + 3(22 - x) = 70$

18. $18 + 2(4x - 3) = 8x + 12$ **19.** $3 - 2(x - 4) = 5 - 2x$

20. You are asked to grade some of the questions on a skills test. Here are five results you are asked to check. If an example is incorrect, find the error and show the correct solution.

a. $34 = 17 - (x - 5)$

$34 = 17 - x - 5$

$34 = 12 - x$

$22 = -x$

$x = -22$

b. $-47 = -6(x - 2) + 25$

$-47 = -6x + 12 + 25$

$-47 = -6x + 37$

$-6x = 84$

$x = 14$

c. $-93 = -(x - 5) - 13x$

$-93 = -x + 5 - 13x$

$-93 = -14x + 5$

$-14x = -98$

$x = 7$

d. $3(x + 1) + 9 = 22$

$3x + 4 + 9 = 22$

$3x + 13 = 22$

$3x = 9$

$x = 3$

e. $83 = -(x + 19) - 41$

$83 = -x - 19 - 41$

$83 = -x - 50$

$133 = -x$

$x = -133$

21. Explain how to solve for y in terms of x in the equation $2x + 4y = 7$.

22. Solve each formula for the specified variable.

a. $y = mx + b$, for x

b. $A = \dfrac{B + C}{2}$, for B

c. $A = 2\pi r^2 + 2\pi rh$, for h

d. $F = \dfrac{9}{5}C + 32$, for C

e. $3x - 2y = 5$, for y

f. $12 = -x + \frac{y}{3}$, for y

g. $A = P + Prt$, for P

h. $z = \dfrac{x - m}{s}$, for x

PROJECT ACTIVITY 6.18

Summer Job Opportunities

OBJECTIVE

1. Use critical-thinking skills to make decisions based on solutions of systems of two linear equations.

It can be very difficult keeping up with college expenses, so it is important for you to find a summer job that pays well. Luckily, the classified section of your newspaper lists numerous summer job opportunities in sales, road construction, and food service. The advertisements for all these positions welcome applications from college students. All positions involve the same 10-week period from early June to mid-August.

Sales

A new electronics store opened recently. There are several sales associate positions that pay an hourly rate of $7.25 plus a 5% commission based on your total weekly sales. You would be guaranteed at least 30 hours of work per week, but not more than 40 hours.

Construction

Your state's highway department hires college students every summer to help with road construction projects. The hourly rate is $13.50 with the possibility of up to 10 hours per week in overtime, for which you would be paid time and a half. Of course, the work is totally dependent on good weather, and so the number of hours that you would work per week could vary.

Restaurants

Local restaurants experience an increase in business during the summer. There are several positions for wait staff. The hourly rate is $3.60, and the weekly tip total ranges from $300 to $850. You are told that you can expect a weekly average of approximately $520 in tips. You would be scheduled to work five dinner shifts of 6.5 hours each for a total of 32.5 hours per week. However, on slow nights you might be sent home early, perhaps after working only 5 hours. Thus, your total weekly hours might be fewer than 32.5.

All of the jobs would provide an interesting summer experience. Your personal preferences might favor one position over another. Keep in mind that you have a lot of college expenses.

1. At the electronics store, sales associates average $8000 in sales each week.

   a. Based on the expected weekly average of $8000 in sales, calculate your gross weekly paycheck (before any taxes or other deductions) if you worked a full 40-hour week in sales.

   b. Use the average weekly sales figure of $8000 and write a symbolic rule for your weekly earnings, s, where x represents the total number of hours you would work.

c. What would be your gross paycheck for the week if you worked 30 hours and still managed to sell $8000 in merchandise?

d. You are told that you would typically work 35 hours per week if your total electronic sales do average $8000. Calculate your typical gross paycheck for a week.

e. You calculate that to pay college expenses for the upcoming academic year, you need to gross at least $675 a week. How many hours would you have to work in sales each week? Assume that you would sell $8000 in merchandise.

2. In the construction job, you would average a 40-hour workweek.

   a. Calculate your gross paycheck for a typical 40-hour workweek.

   b. Write a symbolic rule for your weekly salary, s, for a week with no overtime. Let x represent the total number of hours worked.

   c. If the weather is ideal for a week, you can expect to work 10 hours in overtime (over and above the regular 40-hour workweek). Determine your total gross pay for a week with 10 hours of overtime.

   d. The symbolic rule in part b can be used to determine the weekly salary, s, when x, the total number of hours worked, is less than or equal to 40 (no overtime). Write a symbolic rule to determine your weekly salary, s, if x is greater than 40 hours.

e. Suppose it turns out to be a gorgeous summer and your supervisor says that you can work as many hours as you want. If you are able to gross $800 a week, you will be able to afford to buy a computer. How many hours would you have to work each week to achieve your goal?

3. The restaurant job involves working a maximum of five dinner shifts of 6.5 hours each.

a. Calculate what your gross paycheck would be for an exceptionally busy week of five 6.5-hour dinner shifts and $850 in tips.

b. Calculate what your gross paycheck would be for an exceptionally slow week of five 5-hour dinner shifts and only $300 in tips.

c. Calculate what your gross paycheck would be for a typical week of five 6.5-hour dinner shifts and $520 in tips.

d. Use $520 as your typical weekly total for tips, and write a symbolic rule for your gross weekly salary, s, where x represents the number of hours.

e. Calculate what your gross paycheck would be for a 27-hour week and $520 in tips.

f. During the holiday week of July 4, you would be asked to work an extra dinner shift. You are told to expect $280 in tips for that night alone. Assuming a typical workweek for the rest of the week, would working that extra dinner shift enable you to gross at least $950?

4. You would like to make an informed decision in choosing one of the three positions. Based on all the information you have about the three jobs, fill in the following table.

Totally Gross

	LOWEST WEEKLY GROSS PAYCHECK	TYPICAL WEEKLY GROSS PAYCHECK	HIGHEST WEEKLY GROSS PAYCHECK
SALES ASSOCIATE			
CONSTRUCTION WORKER			
WAIT STAFF			

5. Money may be the biggest factor in making your decision. But it is summer, and it would be nice to enjoy what you are doing. Discuss the advantages and disadvantages of each position. What would your personal choice be? Why?

6. You decide that you would prefer an indoor job. Use the algebraic rules you developed for the sales job in Problem 1b and for the restaurant position in Problem 3d to calculate how many hours you would have to work in each job to receive the same weekly salary.

CLUSTER 3   # What Have I Learned?

1. The following table presents three symbolic rules. Select any three input values and then complete the table. Use the numerical results to determine which symbolic rules are equivalent. Then confirm this algebraically.

x	$y_1 = 3x + 2$	$y_2 = 3(x + 2)$	$y_3 = 3x + 6$

2. **a.** Explain the difference between the two expressions $-x^2$ and $(-x)^2$. Use an example to illustrate your explanation.

   b. What role does the negative sign to the left of the parentheses play in simplifying the expression $-(x - y)$? Simplify this expression.

3. **a.** Are $2x$ and $2x^2$ like terms? Why or why not?

   b. A student simplified the expression $6x^2 - 2x + 5x$ and obtained $9x^2$. Is he correct? Explain.

4. Can the distributive property be used to simplify the expression $3(2xy)$? Explain.

5. a. Is the expression, $2x(5y + 15x)$ completely factored? Explain.

b. One classmate factored the expression $12x^2 - 18x + 12$ as $2(6x^2 - 9x + 6)$ and another factored it as $6(2x^2 - 3x + 2)$. Which is correct?

6. Another algebraic code of instructions you can use in your number trick show is

$$\frac{4x + 4(x - 1)}{4} + 1.$$

a. Write all the steps you will use to figure out any chosen number. (Hint: See Activity 6.16 Math Magic.)

b. Simplify the original expression and state how you will determine the chosen number when given a resulting value.

7. For extra credit on exams, your mathematics instructor permits you to locate and circle your errors and then correct them. To get additional points, you are to show all correctly worked steps alongside the incorrect ones. On your last math test, the following problem was completed incorrectly. Show the work necessary to obtain the extra points.

$$2(x - 3) = 5x + 3x - 7(x + 1)$$
$$2x - 5 = 8x - 7x + 7$$
$$2x - 5 = x + 7$$
$$3x = 12$$
$$x = 4$$

How Can I Practice?

1. Complete the following table. Then determine numerically and algebraically which of the following expressions are equivalent.

   a. $13 + 2(5x - 3)$ **b.** $10x + 10$ **c.** $10x + 7$

x	$13 + 2(5x - 3)$	$10x + 10$	$10x + 7$
1			
5			
10			

2. Use the distributive property to expand each of the following algebraic expressions.

   a. $6(x - 7)$ **b.** $3x(x + 5)$ **c.** $-(x - 1)$

   d. $-2.4(x + 1.1)$ **e.** $4x(a - 6b - 1)$ **f.** $-2x(3x + 2y - 4)$

3. Write each expression in completely factored form.

   a. $5x - 30$ **b.** $6xy - 8xz$

   c. $-6y - 36$ **d.** $2xa - 4xy + 10xz$

   e. $2x^2 - 6x$

Exercise numbers appearing in color are answered in the Selected Answers appendix.

4. Combine like terms to simplify the following expressions.

 a. $5x^3 + 5x^2 - x^3 - 3$

 b. $xy^2 - x^2y + x^2y^2 + xy^2 + x^2y$

 c. $3ab - 7ab + 2ab - ab$

5. For each of the following algebraic expressions, list the specific operations indicated, in the order in which they are to be performed.

 a. $10 + 3(x - 5)$ b. $(x + 5)^2 - 15$

 c. $(2x - 4)^3 + 12$

6. Simplify the following algebraic expressions.

 a. $4 - (x - 2)$ b. $4x - 3(4x - 7) + 4$

 c. $x(x - 3) + 2x(x + 3)$ d. $2[3 - 2(a - b) + 3a] - 2b$

 e. $3 - [2x + 5(x + 3) - 2] + 3x$ f. $\dfrac{7(x - 2) - (2x + 1)}{5}$

7. You own 25 shares of a certain stock. The share price at the beginning of the week is *x* dollars. By the end of the week, the share's price doubles and then drops $3. Write a symbolic rule that represents the total value, *V*, of your stock at the end of the week.

8. A volatile stock began the last week of the year worth *x* dollars per share. The following table shows the changes during that week. If you own 30 shares, write a symbolic rule that represents the total value, *V*, of your stock at the end of the week.

DAY	1	2	3	4	5
CHANGE IN VALUE/SHARE	Doubled	Lost 10	Tripled	Gained 12	Lost half its value

9. You planned a trip with your best friend from college. You had only 4 days for your trip and planned to travel *x* hours each day.

The first day, you stopped for sightseeing and lost 2 hours of travel time. The second day, you gained 1 hour because you did not stop for lunch. On the third day, you traveled well into the night and doubled your planned travel time. On the fourth day, you traveled only a fourth of the time you planned because your friend was sick. You averaged 45 miles per hour for the first 2 days and 48 miles per hour for the last 2 days.

a. How many hours, in terms of *x*, did you travel the first 2 days?

b. How many hours, in terms of *x*, did you travel the last 2 days?

c. Express the total distance, *D*, traveled over the 4 days as a symbolic rule in terms of *x*. Simplify the rule.
Recall that distance = average rate · time.

d. Write a symbolic rule that expresses the total distance, *y*, you would have traveled had you traveled exactly *x* hours each day at the average speeds indicated above. Simplify the rule.

e. If you had originally planned to travel 7 hours each day, how many miles did you actually travel?

f. How many miles would you have gone had you traveled exactly 7 hours each day?

10. You read about a full-time summer position in sales at the Furniture Barn. The job pays $280 per week plus 20% commission on sales over $1000.

a. Explain how you would calculate the total amount earned each week.

b. Let x represent the dollar amount of sales for the week. Write a symbolic rule that expresses your earnings, E, for the week in terms of x.

c. Write an equation to determine how much furniture you must sell to have a gross salary of $600 for the week.

d. Solve the equation in part c.

e. Is the total amount of sales reasonable?

11. As a prospective employee in a furniture store, you are offered a choice of salary. The following table shows your options.

OPTION 1	$200 per week	Plus 30% of all sales
OPTION 2	$350 per week	Plus 15% of all sales

a. Write a symbolic rule to represent the total salary, S, for option 1 if the total sales are x dollars per week.

b. Write a symbolic rule to represent the total salary, S, for option 2 if the total sales are x dollars per week.

c. Write an equation that you could use to determine how much you would have to sell in a week to earn the same salary under both plans.

d. Solve the equation in part c. Interpret your result.

e. What is the common salary for the amount of sales found in part d?

f. Graph the two symbolic rules from parts a and b on the following grid. Locate the point of the common salary and use the graph to determine which option provides the larger salary for furniture sales more than $1000 per week.

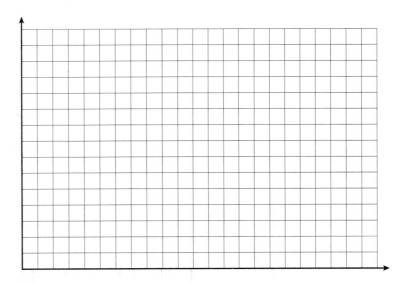

12. A triathlon includes swimming, long-distance running, and cycling.

a. Let x represent the number of miles the competitors swim. If the long-distance run is 10 miles longer than the distance swum, write an expression that represents the distance the competitors run in the event.

b. The distance the athletes cycle is 55 miles longer than they run. Use the result in part a to write an expression in terms of x that represents the cycling distance of the race.

c. Write an expression that represents the total distance of all three phases of the triathlon. Simplify the expression.

d. If the total distance of the triathlon is 120 miles, write and solve an equation to determine x. Interpret the result.

e. What are the lengths of the running and cycling portions of the race?

The bracketed numbers following each concept indicate the activity in which the concept is discussed.

CONCEPT / SKILL	DESCRIPTION	EXAMPLE
Variable [6.1]	A quantity or quality that may change in value from one particular instance to another, usually represented by a letter. When a variable describes an actual quantity, its values must include the unit of measurement of that quantity.	The number of miles you drive in a week is a variable. Its value may (and usually does) change from one week to the next. x and y are commonly used to represent variables.
Input [6.1]	The value that is given first in an input/output relationship.	Your weekly earnings depend on the number of hours you work. The two variables in this relationship are hours worked (input) and total earnings (output).
Output [6.1]	The second number in an input/output relationship. It is the number that corresponds to or is matched with the input.	

| Input/output relationship [6.1] | Relationship between two variables that can be represented numerically by a table of values (data pairs) or graphically as plotted points in a rectangular coordinate system. |

NUMBER OF HOURS WORKED	EARNINGS
15	$90
25	$150

| Horizontal axis [6.1] | In graphing an input/output relationship, the input is referenced on the horizontal axis. |
| Vertical axis [6.1] | In graphing an input/output relationship, the output is referenced on the vertical axis. |

| Rectangular coordinate system [6.1] and [6.2] | Allows every point in the plane to be identified by an ordered pair of numbers, determined by the distance of the point from two perpendicular number lines (called coordinate axes) that intersect at their respective 0 values, the origin. |

| Scaling [6.2] | Setting the same distance between each pair of adjacent tick marks on an axis. |

CONCEPT / SKILL	DESCRIPTION	EXAMPLE
Quadrants [6.2]	Two perpendicular coordinate axes divide the plane into four quadrants, labeled counterclockwise with Quadrant I being the upper-right quadrant.	
Point in the plane [6.2]	Points are identified by an ordered pair of numbers (x, y) in which x represents the horizontal distance from the origin and y represents the vertical distance from the origin.	$(2, 30)$ are the coordinates of a point in the first quadrant located 2 units to the right and 30 units above the origin.
Verbal rule [6.3]	A statement that describes in words the arithmetic relationship between the input and output variables.	Your payment (in dollars) for mowing a lawn is 8 times the number of hours worked.
Set of replacement values for the input [6.3]	The set of replacement values for the input is the collection of all numbers for which a corresponding output value can be determined.	The amount of lawn you can mow depends on whether you can mow for 2, 3, or 4 hours. The set of input values is $\{2, 3, 4\}$.
Algebraic expression [6.4]	An algebraic expression is a shorthand code for a sequence of arithmetic operations to be performed on a variable.	The algebraic expression $2x + 3$ indicates that you start with a value of x, multiply by 2, and then add 3.
Constant [6.4]	A constant is a quantity that does not change in value within the context of a problem.	A number, such as 2, or a symbol, such as k, that is understood to have a constant value within a problem.
Numerical coefficient [6.4]	A numerical coefficient is a number that multiplies a variable or expression.	The number 8 in $8x$.
Factors [6.4]	Factors are numbers, variables, and/or expressions that are multiplied together to form a product.	$2 \cdot x \cdot (x - 1)$ Here, 2, x, and $(x - 1)$ are all factors.
Terms [6.4]	Terms are parts of an expression that are separated by plus or minus signs.	The expression $3x + 6y - 8z$ contains three terms.
Equation [6.7]	An equation is a statement that two algebraic expressions are equal.	$2x + 3 = 5x - 9$

CONCEPT / SKILL	DESCRIPTION	EXAMPLE
Symbolic rule [6.7]	A symbolic rule is a mathematical statement that defines an output variable as an algebraic expression in terms of the input variable. The symbolic rule is essentially a recipe that describes how to determine the output value corresponding to a given input value.	The symbolic rule $y = 3x - 5$ indicates that the output, y, is obtained by multiplying x by 3 and then subtracting 5.
Solution of an equation [6.8]	The solution of an equation is a replacement value for the variable that makes both sides of the equation equal in value.	3 is a solution of the equation $4x - 5 = 7$.
Solve an equation using a numerical approach [6.7]	To solve an equation using a numerical approach, use a guess, check, and repeat process. This process can be automated using the table feature of a graphing calculator.	$4x - 7 = 5$ Try $x = 2$: $4(2) - 7 = 1$ too low. Try $x = 4$: $4(4) - 7 = 9$ too high. Try $x = 3$: $4(3) - 7 = 5$. This is it!
Solve an equation graphically [6.7]	To solve an equation graphically, first graph the input/output symbolic rule. Then locate the point that has the desired value as its output coordinate. The value of the input coordinate of that point is the solution of the equation.	Solve $-2x + 3 = 5$. The output value is 5 when the input value is -1. Therefore, -1 is the solution.
Evaluate an algebraic expression [6.7]	To evaluate an algebraic expression, replace the variable(s) by its (their) assigned value(s) and perform the indicated arithmetic operation(s).	Evaluate $3x^2 - 2x + 4$ when $x = 2$. $3(2)^2 - 2(2) + 4$ $3 \cdot 4 - 4 + 4$ $12 - 4 + 4$ 12
Equivalent expressions [6.9] and [6.14]	Equivalent expressions are two algebraic expressions that always produce the same output for identical inputs.	$4(x + 6)$ and $4x + 24$ are equivalent expressions. For any value of x, adding 6 and then multiplying by 4 *always* gives the same result as multiplying by 4 and then adding 24.

CONCEPT / SKILL	DESCRIPTION	EXAMPLE
Solve equations of the form $ax + b = c$ algebraically [6.10] and [6.11]	Solve equations containing more than one arithmetic operation by performing the inverse operations in reverse order of the operations shown in the equation.	To solve $3x - 6 = 15$ for x, add 6, then divide by 3 as follows: $$3x - 6 = 15$$ $$3x - 6 + 6 = 15 + 6$$ $$3x = 21$$ $$\frac{3x}{3} = \frac{21}{3}$$ $$x = 7$$
Algebraic goal of solving an equation [6.11]	The goal of solving an equation is to isolate the variable on one side of the equation.	$$3x - 5 = x - 2$$ $$2x = 3$$ $$x = \frac{3}{2}$$
Linear regression equation [6.12]	A linear regression equation is a formula or algebraic rule that can be calculated from ordered pairs of actual input/output data. The regression equation and its linear graph, when they provide good estimates of the data, are called mathematical models of the relationship between the two variables.	A linear regression equation for the life expectancy, E, of men born t years after 1975 is $E = 0.169t + 69.11$.
How to isolate a specified variable in a symbolic rule [6.13] and [6.17]	Rewrite the equation so that the variable you are isolating is contained in a single term on one side and all other numbers and variable terms are on the other side.	The x-variable term has been isolated in the following symbolic rule: $$3x - 6y = 15$$ $$3x = 6y + 15$$ $$x = 2y + 5$$
Solve a literal equation for a given variable [6.13] and [6.17]	To solve a literal equation, isolate the term containing the variable of interest on one side of the equation, with all other expressions on the other side. Then, divide both sides of the equation by the coefficient of the variable.	$$2(a + b) = 8 - 5a, \text{ for } a$$ $$2a + 2b = 8 - 5a$$ $$2a + 5a = 8 - 2b$$ $$7a = 8 - 2b$$ $$a = \frac{8 - 2b}{7}$$
Distributive property [6.14]	$\underbrace{a \cdot (b + c)}_{\text{factored form}} = \underbrace{a \cdot b + a \cdot c}_{\text{expanded form}}$	$$4(x + 6) = 4 \cdot x + 4 \cdot 6$$ $$= 4x + 24$$
Geometric interpretation of the distributive property [6.14]	The area of the large rectangle is equal to the sum of the areas of the two smaller rectangles.	$a \cdot (b + c)$ equals $a \cdot b + a \cdot c$

CONCEPT / SKILL	DESCRIPTION	EXAMPLE
Factored form of an algebraic expression [6.14]	An algebraic expression is in factored form when it is written as a product of factors.	The expression $4(x + 6)$ is in factored form. The two factors are 4 and $x + 6$.
Expanded form of an algebraic expression [6.14]	An algebraic expression is in expanded form when it is written as a sum of distinct terms.	The expression $4x + 24$ is in expanded form. The two distinct terms are $4x$ and 24.
Extension of the distributive property [6.14]	The distributive property extended to sums or differences of more than two terms is $$a(b + c + d) = a \cdot b + a \cdot c + a \cdot d.$$	$4(3x + 5y - 6)$ $= 4 \cdot 3x + 4 \cdot 5y - 4 \cdot 6$ $= 12x + 20y - 24$
Factoring [6.15]	Factoring is the process of writing a sum of distinct terms equivalently as a product of factors.	$10xy + 15xz = 5x(2y + 3z)$
Common factor [6.15]	The common factor is one that is a factor contained in every term of an algebraic expression.	In the expression $12abc + 3abd - 21ab$, 3, a, and b are common factors.
Factoring out a common factor [6.15]	This is the process of dividing each term by a common factor and placing this factor outside parentheses containing the sum of remaining terms.	$12abc + 3abd - 21ab$ $= 3b(4ac + ad - 7a)$
Greatest common factor [6.15]	A common factor such that there are no additional factors (other than 1) common to the terms in the expression is the greatest common factor.	The greatest common factor in the expression $12abc + 3abd - 21ab$ is $3ab$.
Completely factored form [6.15]	An algebraic expression is in completely factored form when none of its factors can themselves be factored any further.	$4x(2y + 10z)$ is not in completely factored form because the expression in the parentheses has a common factor of 2. $8x(y + 5z)$ is the completely factored form of this expression.
Procedure for factoring an algebraic expression whose terms contain a common factor [6.15]	The procedure for factoring an algebraic expression whose terms contain a common factor: a. Identify the common factor. b. Divide each term by the common factor. c. Place the sum of the remaining factors inside the parentheses, and place the common factor outside the parentheses.	Given $20x + 35y - 45$: The common factor of the terms in this expression is 5. Dividing each term by 5 yields remaining terms $4x, 7y, -9$. The factored form is therefore $5(4x + 7y - 9)$.

CONCEPT / SKILL	DESCRIPTION	EXAMPLE
Like terms [6.15]	Like terms are terms that contain identical variable factors, including exponents. They differ only in their numerical coefficients.	$5y^2$ and $5y$ are not like terms. $7xy$ and $-3xy$ are like terms.
Combining like terms [6.15]	To combine like terms into a single term, add or subtract the coefficients of like terms.	$12cd^2 - 5c^2d + 10 +$ $3cd^2 - 6c^2d$ $= 15cd^2 - 11c^2d + 100$
Procedure for simplifying algebraic expressions [6.16]	Steps for simplifying algebraic expressions: 1. Simplify the expression from the innermost grouping outward using the order of operations convention. 2. Use the distributive property when applicable. 3. Combine like terms.	$[5 - 2(x - 7)] + 5(3x - 10)$ $[5 - 2x + 14] + 5(3x - 10)$ $-2x + 19 + 5(3x - 10)$ $-2x + 19 + 15x - 50$ $13x - 31$
General strategy for solving equations algebraically [6.17]	General strategy for solving an equation algebraically: 1. Simplify the expressions on each side of the equation (as discussed above). 2. Isolate the variable term on one side of the equation. 3. Divide each side of the equation by the coefficient of the variable. 4. Check your result in the original equation.	$3(2x - 5) + 2x = 9$ $6x - 15 + 2x = 9$ $8x - 15 = 9$ $8x = 24$ $x = 3$ Check: $3(2 \cdot 3 - 5) + 2 \cdot 3$ $= 3(6 - 5) + 6$ $= 3 \cdot 1 + 6$ $= 9$
Identity [6.17]	An equation that is true for all real number replacement values is called an identity. This occurs algebraically when both sides of the equation become identical in the process of solving.	Solve $2x - (6x - 5) = 5 - 4x$. $2x - 6x + 5 = 5 - 4x$ $-4x + 5 = 5 - 4x$ $0 = 0$ *all real numbers*
Contradiction [6.17]	An equation that is never true for any real number replacement value is called a contradiction. This occurs algebraically when the variable terms are eliminated from both sides of the equation in the process of solving it and the resulting equation is a false statement.	Solve $3(2x + 4) = 6x - 5$. $6x + 12 = 6x - 5$ $12 = -5$ *no solution*

1. Scale each axis on the Cartesian coordinate plane below, and plot the points whose coordinates are given in parts a–g.

   a. $(1, 2)$ **b.** $(3, -4)$ **c.** $(-2, 5)$ **d.** $(-4, -6)$

   e. $(0, 4)$ **f.** $(-5, 0)$ **g.** $(0, 0)$

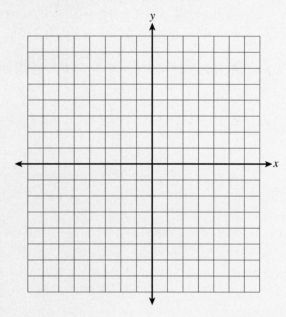

2. Let x represent any number. Translate each of the following phrases into an algebraic expression.

   a. 5 more than x

   b. x less than 18

   c. Double x

   d. Divide 4 by x

   e. 17 more than the product of 3 and x

   f. 12 times the sum of 8 and x

Answers to all Gateway exercises are included in the Selected Answers appendix.

549

g. 11 times the difference of 14 and x

h. 49 less than the quotient of x and 7

3. Determine the values requested in the following.

a. If $y = 2x$ and $y = 18$, what is the value of x?

b. If $y = -8x$ and $x = 3$, what is the value of y?

c. If $y = 15$ and $y = 6x$, what is the value of x?

d. If $y = -8$ and $y = 4 + x$, what is the value of x?

e. If $x = 19$ and $y = x - 21$, what is the value of y?

f. If $y = -71$ and $y = x - 87$, what is the value of x?

g. If $y = 36$ and $y = \dfrac{x}{4}$, what is the value of x?

h. If $x = 5$ and $y = \dfrac{x}{6}$, what is the value of y?

i. If $y = \dfrac{x}{3}$ and $y = 24$, what is the value of x?

4. Tiger Woods had scores of 63, 68, and 72 for three rounds of a golf tournament.

a. Let x represent his score on the fourth round. Write a symbolic rule that expresses his average score after four rounds of golf.

b. To be competitive in the tournament, Tiger must maintain an average of about 66. Use the symbolic rule from part a to determine what he must score on the fourth round to achieve a 66 average for the tournament.

5. Determine the values requested in the following.

   a. If $y = 2x + 8$ and $y = 18$, what is the value of x?

   b. If $x = 14$ and $y = 6x - 42$, determine the value of y.

   c. If $y = -33$ and $y = -5x - 3$, determine the value of x.

   d. If $y = -38$ and $y = 24 + 8x$, what is the value of x?

   e. If $x = 72$ and $y = -54 - \dfrac{x}{6}$, what is the value of y?

   f. If $y = 66$ and $y = \dfrac{2}{3}x - 27$, what is the value of x?

   g. If $y = 39$ and $y = -\dfrac{x}{4} + 15$, what is the value of x?

   h. If $y = 32.56x + 27$ and $x = 0$, what is the value of y?

6. You must drive to Syracuse to take care of some legal matters. The cost of renting a car for a day is \$25, plus 15 cents per mile.

   a. Identify the input variable.

   b. Identify the output variable.

   c. Use x to represent the input and y to represent the output. Write a symbolic rule that describes the daily rental cost in terms of the number of miles driven.

   d. Complete the following table.

INPUT, x	100	200	300	400	500
OUTPUT, y					

e. Plot the points from the table in part d. Then draw the line through all five points. (Make sure you label your axes and use appropriate scaling.)

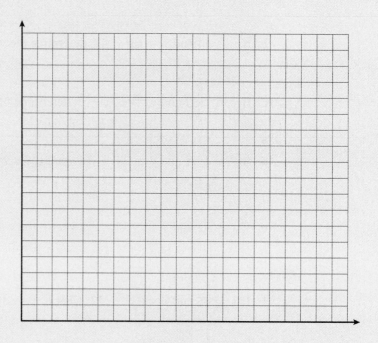

f. The distance from Buffalo to Syracuse is 153 miles. Estimate from the graph in part e how much it will cost to travel from Buffalo to Syracuse and back.

g. Use the symbolic rule in part c to determine the exact cost of this trip.

h. You have budgeted $90 for car rental for your day trip. Use your graph to estimate the greatest number of miles you can travel in the day and not exceed your allotted budget. Estimate from your graph.

i. Use the symbolic rule in part c to determine the exact number of miles you can travel in the day and not exceed $90.

j. What are realistic replacement values for the input if you rent the car for only 1 day?

7. As a real estate salesperson, you earn a small salary, plus a percentage of the selling price of each house you sell. If your salary is $100 a week, plus 3.5% of the selling price of each house sold, what must your total annual home sales be for you to gross $30,000 in 1 year? Assume that you work 50 weeks per year.

8. Use the formula $I = Prt$ to evaluate I, given the following information.

   a. $P = \$2000, r = 5\%, t = 1$

   b. $P = \$3000, r = 6\%, t = 2$

9. Use the formula $P = 2(w + l)$, to evaluate P for the following information.

   a. $w = 2.8$ and $l = 3.4$

   b. $w = 7\frac{1}{3}$ and $l = 8\frac{1}{4}$

10. Complete the table below and use your results to determine numerically which, if any, of the following expressions are equivalent.

    a. $(4x - 3)^2$ **b.** $4x^2 - 3$ **c.** $(4x)^2 - 3$

x	$(4x - 3)^2$	$4x^2 - 3$	$(4x)^2 - 3$
−1			
0			
3			

11. Simplify the following expressions.

    a. $3(x + 1)$ **b.** $-6(2x^2 - 2x + 3)$

    c. $x(4x - 7)$ **d.** $6 - (2x + 14)$

    e. $4 + 2(6x - 5) - 19$ **f.** $5x - 4x(2x - 3)$

12. Factor the following expressions completely.

   a. $4x - 12$

   b. $18x^2 + 60x - xy$

   c. $-12x - 20$

13. Simplify the following expressions.

   a. $4x^2 - 3x - 2 + 2x^2 - 3x + 5$

   b. $(3x^2 - 7x + 8) - (2x^2 - 4x + 1)$

14. Use the distributive property to expand each of the algebraic expressions.

   a. $5(2x - 7y)$

   b. $\dfrac{1}{3}(6a + 3b - 9)$

   c. $-10(x - 2w + z)$

   d. $4\left(\dfrac{1}{2}c - \dfrac{1}{4}\right)$

15. Solve the given equations, and check your results.

   a. $4(x + 5) - x = 80$

   b. $-5(x - 3) + 2x = 6$

   c. $38 = 57 - (x + 32)$

   d. $-13 + 4(3x + 5) = 7$

   e. $5x + 3(2x - 8) = 2(x + 6)$

   f. $-4x - 2(5x - 7) + 2 = -3(3x + 5) - 4$

   g. $-32 + 6(3x + 4) = -(-5x + 38) + 3x$

   h. $4(3x - 5) + 7 = 2(6x + 7)$

   i. $2(9x + 8) = 4(3x + 4) + 6x$

16. You have just found the perfect dress for a wedding. The price of the dress is reduced by 30%. You are told that there will be a huge sale next week, so you wait to purchase it. When you go to buy the dress, you find that it has been reduced again by 30% of the already reduced price.

   a. If the original price of the dress is $400, what is the price of the dress after the first reduction?

   b. What is the price of the dress after the second reduction?

   c. Let x represent the original price (input). Determine an expression that represents the price of the dress after the first reduction. Simplify this expression.

   d. Use the result from part c to write an expression that represents the price of the dress after the second reduction. Simplify this expression.

   e. Use the result from part d to determine the price of the dress after the two reductions if the original price is $400. How does this compare with your answer to part b?

   f. You see another dress that is marked down to $147 after the same two reductions. You want to know the original price of the dress. Write and solve the equation to determine the original price.

17. The proceeds from your college talent show to benefit a local charity totaled $1550. Since the seats were all taken, you know that 500 people attended. The cost per ticket was $2.50 for students and $4.00 for adults. Unfortunately, you misplaced the ticket stubs that would indicate how many students and how many adults attended. You need this information for accounting purposes and future planning.

   a. Let n represent the number of students who attended. Write an expression in terms of n to represent the number of adults who attended.

   b. Write an expression in terms of n that will represent the proceeds from the student tickets.

c. Write an expression in terms of n that will represent the proceeds from the adult tickets.

d. Write an equation that indicates that the total proceeds from the student and adult tickets totaled $1550.

e. How many student tickets and how many adult tickets were sold?

18. You have an opportunity to be the manager of a day camp for the summer. You know that your fixed costs for operating the camp are $1200 per week, even if there are no campers. Each camper who attends costs the management $25 per week. The camp charges each camper $60 per week.

Let x represent the number of campers.

a. Write a symbolic rule in terms of x that represents the total cost, C, of running the camp per week.

b. Write a symbolic rule in terms of x that represents the total income (revenue), R, from the campers per week.

c. Write a symbolic rule in terms of x that represents the total profit, P, from the campers per week.

d. How many campers must attend for the camp to break even with revenue and costs?

e. The camp would like to make a profit of $620. How many campers must enroll to make that profit?

f. How much money would the camp lose if only 20 campers attend?

556

g. Use your graphing calculator to graph the revenue and cost equations. Compare the break-even point from the graph (point of intersection) with your answer in part d.

19. Solve each of the following equations for the specified variable.

    a. $I = Prt$, for P

    b. $f = v + at$, for t

    c. $2x - 3y = 7$, for y

20. You contact the local print shop to produce a commemorative booklet for your college theater group. It is the group's twenty-fifth anniversary, and in the booklet you want a short history plus a description of all the theater productions for the past 25 years. It costs $750 to typeset the booklet and 25 cents for each copy produced.

    a. Write a symbolic rule that gives the total cost, C, in terms of the number, x, of booklets produced.

    b. Use the symbolic rule from part a to determine the total cost of producing 500 booklets.

    c. How many booklets can be produced for $1000?

    d. Suppose the booklets are sold for 75 cents each. Write a symbolic rule for the total revenue, R, from the sale of x booklets.

    e. How many booklets must be sold to break even? That is, for what value of x is the total cost of production equal to the total amount of revenue?

f. How many booklets must be sold to make a $500 profit?

21. You live 7.5 miles from work, where you have free parking. Some days, you must drive to work. On other days, you can take the bus. It costs you 30 cents per mile to drive the car and $2.50 round-trip to take the bus. Assume that there are 22 working days in a month.

   a. Let x represent the number of days that you take the bus. Express the number of days that you drive in terms of x.

   b. Express the cost of taking the bus in terms of x.

   c. Express the cost of driving in terms of x.

   d. Express the total cost of transportation in terms of x.

   e. How many days can you drive if you budget $70 a month for transportation?

   f. How much should you budget for the month if you would like to take the bus only half of the time?

FUNCTION SENSE AND LINEAR FUNCTIONS

Chapter 7 continues the study of relationships between input and output variables. The focus here is on functions, which are special relationships between input and output variables. You will learn how functions are represented verbally, numerically, graphically, and symbolically. You will also study a special type of function—the linear function.

CLUSTER 1	Function Sense

ACTIVITY 7.1

Graphs Tell Stories

OBJECTIVES

1. Describe in words what a graph tells you about a given situation.

2. Sketch a graph that best represents a situation that is described in words.

3. Identify increasing, decreasing, and constant parts of a graph.

4. Identify minimum and maximum points on a graph.

5. Define a function.

6. Use the vertical line test to determine whether a graph represents a function.

"A picture is worth a thousand words" may be a cliché, but nonetheless, it is frequently true. Numerical relationships are often easier to understand when presented in visual form. Understanding graphical pictures requires practice going in both directions—from graphs to words and from words to graphs.

Graphs are always constructed so that as you read the graph from left to right, the input variable increases in value. The graph shows the change (increasing, decreasing, or constant) in the output values as the input values increase.

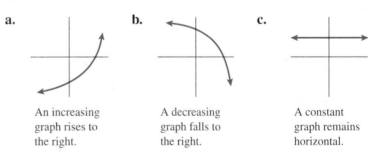

a. An increasing graph rises to the right.

b. A decreasing graph falls to the right.

c. A constant graph remains horizontal.

Graphs to Stories

The graphs in Problems 1–4 present visual images of several situations. Each graph shows how the outputs change in relation to the inputs. In each situation, identify the input variable and the output variable. Then, interpret the situation; that is, describe, in words, what the graph is telling you about the situation. Indicate whether the graph rises, falls, or is constant and whether the graph reaches either a minimum (smallest) or maximum (largest) output value.

1. A person's core body temperature (°F) in relation to time of day

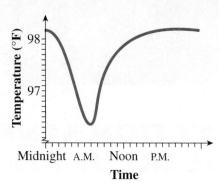

   a. Input: _____   Output: _____

   b. Interpretation:

2. Performance of a simple task in relation to interest level

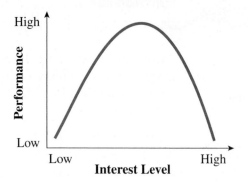

   a. Input: _____   Output: _____

   b. Interpretation:

3. Net profit of a particular business in relation to time

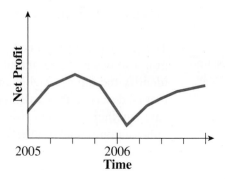

a. Input: _____   Output: _____

b. Interpretation:

4. Annual gross income in relation to number of years

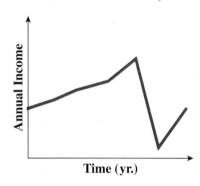

a. Input: _____   Output: _____

b. Interpretation:

Stories to Graphs

In Problems 5 and 6, sketch a graph that best represents the situation described. Note that in many cases, the actual values are unknown, so you will need to estimate what seems reasonable to you.

5. You drive to visit your parents, who live 100 miles away. Your average speed is 50 miles per hour. On arrival, you stay for 5 hours and then return home, again at an average speed of 50 miles per hour. Graph your distance in miles from home, from the time you leave until you return home.

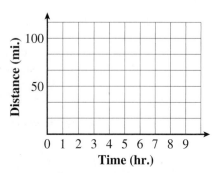

6. You just started a new job that pays 8 dollars per hour, with a raise of 2 dollars per hour every 6 months. After one-and-a-half years, you receive a promotion that gives you a wage increase of 5 dollars per hour, but your next raise won't come for another year. Sketch a graph of your wage over your first *two-and-a-half* years.

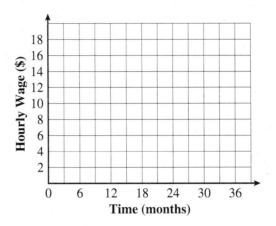

Introduction to Functions

Although the graphs in Problems 1–6 have different shapes and different properties, they all reflect a special relationship between the input and output variables. In the following problem, you will explore this special relationship or correspondence, which is called a **function**.

7. a. Use the graph in Problem 1 to complete the following table. Estimate the temperature for each value of time.

TIME OF DAY	1 A.M.	5 A.M.	7 A.M.	10 A.M.	12 NOON	1 P.M.
BODY TEMPERATURE (°F)						

b. How many corresponding temperatures (output) are assigned to any one particular time (input)?

The relationship or correspondence between the time of day and the corresponding body temperature is an example of a function. For any specific time of day, there is one and only one corresponding temperature. In such a case, you say that the body temperature (output) is a function of the time of day (input).

DEFINITION

A **function** is a rule relating an input variable and an output variable in a way that assigns one and only one output value to each input value.

8. The following graph shows the distance from home over a 9-hour period as described in Problem 5.

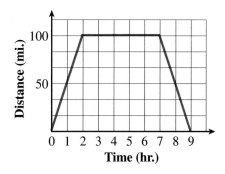

a. Use the graph to complete the following table.

TIME (hr.)	1	3	4	8	9
DISTANCE FROM HOME (mi.)					

b. Is the distance from home a function of the time on the trip? Explain.

9. The following graph shows the height of a roller coaster as it moves away from its starting point and goes through its first loop.

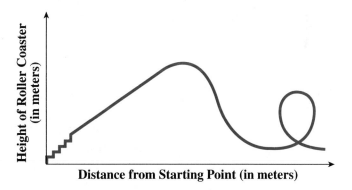

Is the height of the roller coaster a function of the distance of the coaster from the starting point?

Vertical Line Test

You can determine directly from a graph whether or not the output is a function of the input.

10. a. Refer to the graph in Problem 1, and select any specific time of day along the horizontal (input) axis. Then, move straight up or down (vertically) from that value of time to locate the corresponding point on the graph. How many points do you locate for any given time?

b. If you locate only one point on the graph in part a for each value of time you select, explain why this would mean that body temperature is a function of the time of day.

c. If you had located more than one point on the graph in part a, explain why this would mean that body temperature is not a function of time.

The procedure in Problem 10 is referred to as the **vertical line test**.

DEFINITION

In the **vertical line test**, a graph represents a function if any vertical line drawn through the graph intersects the graph no more than once.

---

11. Use the vertical line test on the graphs in Problems 2 through 4 to verify that each graph represents the output as a function of the input.

12. Use the vertical line test to determine which of the following graphs represent functions. Explain.

a.

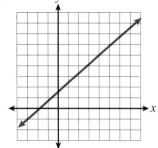

b.

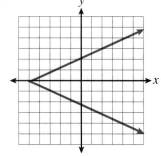

c.
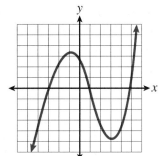

d.
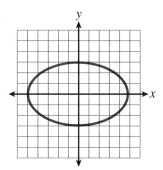

SUMMARY
ACTIVITY 7.1

1. A **function** is a rule relating an input variable and an output variable in a way that assigns one and only one output value to each input value.

2. In the **vertical line test**, a graph represents a function if any vertical line drawn through the graph intersects the graph no more than once.

EXERCISES
ACTIVITY 7.1

1. You are a technician at the local power plant, and you have been asked to prepare a report that compares the output and efficiency of the six generators in your sector. Each generator has a graph that shows output of the generator as a function of time over the previous week, Monday through Sunday. You take all the paperwork home for the night (your supervisor wants this report on his desk at 7:00 A.M.), and to your dismay your feisty cat scatters your pile of papers out of the neat order in which you left them. Unfortunately, the graphs for generators A through F were not labeled (you will know better next time!). You recall some information and find evidence elsewhere for the following facts.

   - Generators A and D were the only ones that maintained a fairly steady output.
   - Generator B was shut down for a little more than 2 days during midweek.
   - Generator C experienced a slow decrease in output during the entire week.
   - On Tuesday morning, there was a problem with generator E that was corrected in a few hours.
   - Generator D was the most productive over the entire week.

Match each graph with its corresponding generator. Explain in complete sentences how you arrived at your answers.

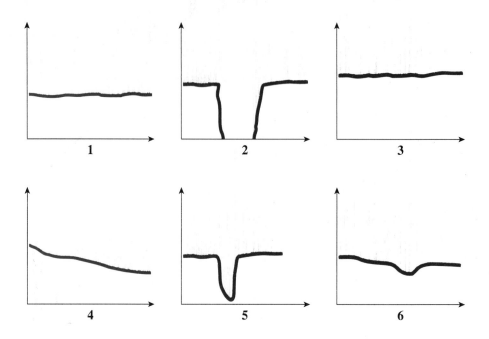

In Exercises 2 and 3, identify the input variable and the output variable. Then interpret the situation being represented. Indicate whether the graph rises, falls, or is constant and whether the graph reaches either a minimum (smallest) or maximum (largest) output value.

2. Time required to complete a task in relation to number of times the task is attempted

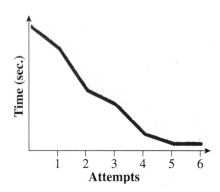

a. Input: _____   Output: _____

b. Interpretation:

3. Number of units sold in relation to selling price

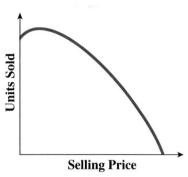

a. Input: _____   Output: _____

b. Interpretation:

4. In baseball, a .300 batting average is considered quite good. Consider a player who struggles his first few years but is a consistently good hitter throughout the rest of his 20 years in the majors. His lifetime average is around .300, and he retires before his skills fall off too noticeably. Sketch a graph that roughly shows his batting average as a function of time (years in the majors).

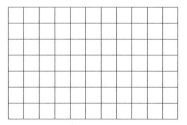

5. The following graph gives the time of day in relation to one's core body temperature.

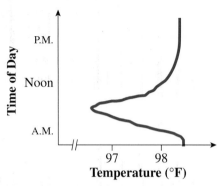

Is the time of day a function of body temperature?

6. Use the vertical line test to determine which of the following graphs represents a function. Explain your answer.

a.

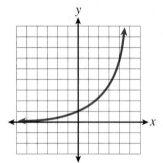

b.

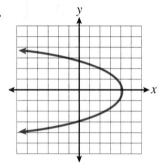

c.

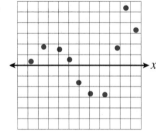

The semester is drawing to a close, and you are concerned about your grade in your anthropology course. During the semester, you have already taken four exams and scored 82, 75, 85, and 93. Your score on exam 5 will determine your final average for the anthropology course.

1. a. Identify the input and output variables.

b. Four possible exam 5 scores are listed in the following table. Calculate the final average corresponding to each one, and record your answers.

EXAM 5 SCORE, input	FINAL AVERAGE, output
100	
85	
70	
60	

Recall from Activity 7.1 that a function relates the input to the output in a special way. For any specific input value, there is one and only one output value.

c. Explain how the table of data in part b fits the definition of a function.

2. a. Plot the (input, output) pairs from the preceding table.

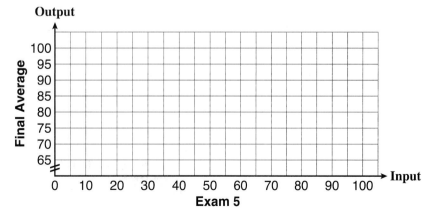

Note: Use a double slash (//) to indicate that the vertical axis has been compressed between 0 and 65.

b. Draw a smooth line through the plotted points. Does the graph represent a function? Explain.

   c. Use the graph to estimate what your final average will be if you score a 95 on exam 5.

   d. Use the graph to estimate what score you will need on exam 5 to earn a final average of 85.

In the context of Problems 1 and 2, you can write that

the final average is a *function* of the score on exam 5.
output   input

In general, you write that the *output* is a function of the *input*.

Representing Functions Verbally and Symbolically

There are several ways to represent a function. So far, you have seen that a function may be presented *numerically* by a table, as in Problem 1, and *graphically* on a grid, as in Problem 2. A function can also be given *verbally* by stating how the output value is obtained for a given input value.

3. a. Describe in words how to obtain the final average for any given score on the fifth exam.

   b. Let *A* represent the final average and *s* represent the score on the fifth exam. Translate the verbal rule in part a into a symbolic rule that expresses *A* in terms of *s*.

4. a. The symbolic rule in Problem 3b represents a fourth way to represent a function. Use the symbolic rule to determine the final average for a score of 75 on exam 5.

   b. Use the symbolic rule to determine the score you will need on exam 5 to earn a final average of 87.

Function Notation

Often you want to emphasize the functional relationship between input and output. You do this symbolically by writing $A(s)$, which you read as "A is a function of s." The letter within the parentheses always represents the input variable, and the letter outside the parentheses is the function name.

The formula that defines the "final average" function is then written as

$$A(s) = \frac{335 + s}{5}.$$

To denote the final average corresponding to a specific input, you would write the desired input value in the parentheses. For example, the symbol $A(100)$ denotes the final average for a score of 100 on the fifth exam, and is pronounced "A of 100." To determine the value of $A(100)$, substitute 100 for s in the expression $\frac{335 + s}{5}$, and evaluate the expression:

$$A(100) = \frac{335 + 100}{5} = \frac{435}{5} = 87$$

You interpret the symbolic statement $A(100) = 87$ as "The final average for a fifth exam score of 100 is 87."

Notice that the symbolic way of defining a function is very useful because it clearly shows the rule for determining an output no matter what the input might be.

5. a. In the final average statement $A(75) = 82$, identify the input value and output value.

   b. Interpret the practical meaning of $A(75) = 82$. Write your answer as a complete sentence.

6. a. Use the symbolic formula for the final average function to determine the missing coordinate in each input/output pair.

   i. (78, _____)   **ii.** (_____, 67)

   b. Evaluate $A(95)$ in the final average function.

   c. Write a sentence that interprets the practical meaning of $A(95)$ in the final average function.

Function Notation—A Word of Caution

In **function notation**, the parentheses *do not* indicate multiplication. If the letter *f* is the function name, and *x* represents the input variable, then the symbol $f(x)$ represents the output value corresponding to the input value *x*. Function notation such as $f(x)$ is used to emphasize the input/output relationship.

EXAMPLE 1   *Given the symbolic rule $f(x) = x^2 + 3$, identify the name of the function and translate the rule into a verbal rule. Illustrate the rule for a given input value.*

SOLUTION

The symbolic statement $f(x) = x^2 + 3$ tells you that the function name is f and that you must square the input and then add 3 to obtain the corresponding output. For example, if $x = 4$, $f(4) = (4)^2 + 3 = 19$. This means that $(4, 19)$ is one (input, output) pair associated with the function f and $(4, 19)$ is one point on the graph of f. An (input, output) pair may also be referred to as an **ordered pair**.

7. For the function defined by $H(a) = 2a + 7$,

   a. identify the function name

   b. identify the input variable

   c. state the verbal rule for determining the output value for a given input value

   d. determine $H(-5)$

   e. write the ordered pair that represents the point on the graph of H corresponding to the fact that $H(4) = 15$

   f. determine the value of a for which $H(a) = 3$.

Domain and Range

> **DEFINITION**
>
> The collection of all possible replacement values of the input variable is called the **domain** of the function. The **practical domain** is the collection of replacement values of the input variable that makes practical sense in the context of a particular problem.

8. **a.** Determine the practical domain of the final average function. Assume that no fractional part of a point can be given and that the exam has a total of 100 points.

   b. What is the domain of the function defined by $W(s) = \frac{335 + s}{5}$, where neither W nor s has any contextual significance?

DEFINITION

The collection of all possible values of the output variable is the **range** of the function. The collection of all possible values of the output variable using the practical domain is the **practical range**.

---

9. Show or explain how you would determine the practical range of the final average function, and interpret the meaning of this range.

10. You are on your way to the college to take the fifth exam in the anthropology course. The gas gauge on your car indicates that you are almost out of gas. You stop to fill your car with gas.

a. Identify a reasonable input and output variable in this situation.

b. Write a verbal rule to determine the cost for any given number of gallons pumped. Assume that the price of regular-grade gasoline is $2.86 $\frac{9}{10}$ per gallon.

c. Let C represent the cost of the gas purchased and g represent the number of gallons pumped. Translate the verbal rule in part b into a symbolic rule (equation) for C in terms of g.

d. What is the practical domain for the cost function? Assume that your gas tank has a maximum capacity of 17 gallons.

e. What is the practical range for the cost function?

f. Represent the output, cost, by $C(g)$. Rewrite the equation in part c using the function notation.

g. Determine $C(15)$. Interpret the answer within the context of the situation.

SUMMARY
ACTIVITY 7.2

1. A **function** is a rule relating an input variable and output variable that assigns one and only one output value to each input value. Stated another way, for each input value, there is *one and only one* corresponding output value.

2. A function can be defined **numerically** as a list of **ordered pairs**, often listed in a table format. A function can also be defined as a set of ordered pairs.

3. When a function is defined **graphically**, the input variable is referenced on the horizontal axis and the output variable is referenced on the vertical axis.

4. Functions can also be defined by a **verbal rule** (in words) or **symbolically** (by an equation).

5. A function can be expressed symbolically using the **function notation** $f(x)$, where f is the name of the function and x is the input variable. The notation $f(x)$ represents the output value corresponding to a given x. If the output variable is denoted by y, you can write $y = f(x)$ and say that the output y is a function of x.

6. Associated with any function is a specific set of input values. The collection of all possible input values is called the **domain** of the function. In functions that result from contextual situations, the domain consists of input values that make sense within the context. Such a domain is often called a **practical domain**.

7. In a function, the collection of all possible values of the output variable is called the **range**. In functions that result from contextual situations, the **practical range** is the set of output values assigned to each element of the practical domain.

EXERCISES
ACTIVITY 7.2

1. The following input/output table shows the cost of a history club trip defined by the symbolic rule $y = 2x + 78$, where x represents the number of students (input) and y represents the cost of the trip (output).

NUMBER OF STUDENTS	COST OF TRIP ($)
10	98
15	108
20	118
25	128

a. Rewrite the symbolic rule in function notation that defines the input/output relationship. Use n to represent the number of students and C to represent the name of the cost function for the trip.

    b. Use function notation to write a symbolic statement for "The total cost is $108 if 15 students go on the trip."

    c. Choose another (input, output) pair for the cost function *C*. Write this pair in both ordered-pair notation and in function notation.

    d. What is the practical domain if the club's transportation is a school bus?

    e. Determine $C(37)$.

    f. Describe, in words, what information about the cost of the trip is given by the statement $C(24) = 126$.

2. Each of the following tables defines a relationship between an input and an output. Which of the relationships represent functions? Explain your answers.

    a.

INPUT	−8	−3	0	6	9	15	24	38	100
OUTPUT	24	4	9	72	−14	−16	53	29	7

    b.

INPUT	−8	−5	0	6	9	15	24	24	100
OUTPUT	24	4	9	72	14	−16	53	29	7

    c.

INPUT	−8	−3	0	6	9	15	24	38	100
OUTPUT	24	4	9	72	4	−16	53	24	7

3. Identify the input and output variables in each of the following. Then determine if the statement is true. Give a reason for your answer.

   a. Your letter grade in a course is a function of your numerical grade.

   b. Your numerical grade is a function of your letter grade.

4. A table is often used to define a function that has a finite number of inputs and outputs. Consider the function f defined by the following table and assume that these points are the only input/output pairs that belong to the function f.

x	−3	−2	−1	0	1	2	3	4
$f(x)$	5	4	2	−1	1	3	5	6

   a. What is the domain of f?

   b. What is the range of f?

   c. For which set of consecutive x-values is f increasing?

   d. Determine the maximum output value of f and the input for which it occurs.

   e. Determine the minimum output value of f and the input for which it occurs.

   f. Write f as a set of ordered pairs. You should have eight ordered pairs.

   g. Determine $f(3)$.

   h. For what value of x is $f(x) = 2$?

5. a. Suppose that all you know about a function f is that $f(2) = -4$. Use this information to complete the following.

    i. If the input value for f is 2, then the corresponding output value is

    _____ .

    ii. One point on the graph of f is _____ .

b. The statement in part a indicates that $f(x) = -4$ for $x = 2$. Is it possible for f to have an output of -4 for another value of x, such as $x = 5$? Explain.

6. Let $f(x) = 2x - 1$. Evaluate $f(4)$.

7. Let $g(n) = 3n + 5$. Evaluate $g(-3)$.

8. Let $h(m) = 2m^2 + 3m - 1$. Evaluate $h(-2)$.

9. Let $p(x) = 3x^2 - 2x + 4$. Evaluate $p(5)$.

10. Let f be a function defined by $f(x) = x + 1$. Determine the value of x for which $f(x) = 3$.

11. Let g be a function defined by $g(x) = 5x - 4$. Determine the value of x for which $g(x) = 11$.

12. Let h be a function defined by $h(t) = \frac{t}{4}$. Determine the value of t for which $h(t) = 12$.

13. Let k be a function defined by $k(w) = 0.4w$. Determine the value of w for which $k(w) = 12$.

14. Give at least two examples of functions from your daily life. Explain how each fits the description of a function. Be sure to identify the input variable and output variable.

ACTIVITY 7.3

**How Fast Did
You Lose?**

OBJECTIVE

1. Determine the average
rate of change of an out-
put variable with respect
to the input variable.

You are a member of a health and fitness club. The club's registered dietitian and your personal trainer helped you develop a special 8-week diet and exercise program. The data in the following table represents your weight, w, as a function of time, t, over an 8-week period.

Time Weights for No One

TIME (wk.)	0	1	2	3	4	5	6	7	8
WEIGHT (lb.)	140	136	133	131	130	127	127	130	126

1. a. Plot the data points using ordered pairs of the form (t, w). For example, $(3, 131)$ is a data point that represents your weight at the end of the third week.

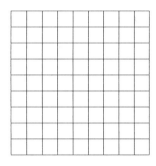

b. What is the practical domain of this function?

c. What is the practical range of this function?

2. a. What is your weight at the beginning of the program?

b. What is your weight at the end of the first week?

3. To see how the health program is working for you, you analyze your weekly weight changes during the 8-week period.

   a. During which week(s) does your weight increase?

   b. During which week(s) does your weight decrease?

   c. During which week(s) does your weight remain unchanged?

Average Rate of Change

4. Your weight decreases during each of the first 5 weeks of the program.

   a. Determine the actual change in your weight, the output value, over the first 5 weeks of the program by subtracting your initial weight from your weight at the end of the first 5 weeks.

   b. What is the sign (positive or negative) of your answer? What is the significance of this sign?

   c. Determine the change in the input value over the first 5 weeks, that is, from $t = 0$ to $t = 5$.

   d. Write the ratio of the change in weight from part a to the change in time in part c. Interpret the meaning of this ratio.

The change in weight describes how much weight you have gained or lost, but it does not tell how quickly you shed those pounds. That is, a loss of 3 pounds in 1 week is more impressive than a loss of 3 pounds over a month's time. Dividing the change in weight by the change in time gives an average rate at which you have lost weight over this period of time. The units for this rate are output units per input unit—in this case, pounds per week.

The ratio in Problem 4d,

$$\frac{-13 \text{ lb.}}{5 \text{ wk.}} = -2.6 \text{ pounds per week,}$$

is called the **average rate of change** of weight with respect to time over the first 5 weeks of the program. It can be interpreted as an average loss of 2.6 pounds each week for the first 5 weeks of the program.

The **average rate of change** is the ratio

$$\frac{\text{change in output}}{\text{change in input}}$$

where

  i. change in output is calculated by subtracting the first (initial) output value from the second (final) output value

  ii. change in input is calculated by subtracting the first (initial) input value from the second (final) input value

Graphical Interpretation of the Average Rate of Change

5. a. On the graph in Problem 1, connect the points $(0, 140)$ and $(5, 127)$ with a line segment. Does the line segment rise, fall, or remain horizontal as you follow it from left to right?

b. Recall that the average rate of change over the first 5 weeks was -2.6 pounds per week. What does the average rate of change tell you about the line segment drawn in part a?

6. a. Determine the average rate of change of your weight over the time period from $t = 5$ to $t = 7$ weeks. Include the appropriate sign and units.

b. Interpret the rate in part a with respect to your diet.

c. On the graph in Problem 1, connect the points $(5, 127)$ and $(7, 130)$ with a line segment. Does the line segment rise, fall, or remain horizontal as you follow it from left to right?

d. How is the average rate of change of weight over the given 2-week period related to the line segment you drew in part c?

7. a. At what rate is your weight changing during the 6th week of your diet, that is, from $t = 5$ to $t = 6$?

   b. Interpret the rate in part a with respect to your diet.

   c. Connect the points (5, 127) and (6, 127) on the graph with a line segment. Does the line segment rise, fall, or remain horizontal as you follow it from left to right?

   d. How is the average rate of change in part a related to the line segment drawn in part c?

8. a. What is the average rate of change of your weight over the period from $t = 4$ to $t = 7$ weeks?

   b. Explain how the rate in part a reflects the progress of your diet over those 3 weeks.

Delta Notation

The rate of change in output with respect to a corresponding change in input is so important that special symbolic notation has been developed to denote it.

The uppercase Greek letter delta, Δ, is used with a variable's name to represent a change in the value of the variable from a starting point to an ending point.

For example, in Problem 4 the notation Δw represents the change in value of the output variable weight, w. It is calculated by subtracting the initial value of w, denoted by w_1, from the final value of w, denoted by w_2. Symbolically, this change is represented by

$$\Delta w = w_2 - w_1.$$

In the case of Problem 4a, the change in weight over the first 5 weeks can be calculated as

$$\Delta w = w_2 - w_1 = 127 - 140 = -13 \text{ lb}.$$

In the same way, the change in value of the input variable time, t, is written as Δt and is calculated by subtracting the initial value of t, denoted by t_1, from the final value of t, denoted by t_2. Symbolically, this change is represented by

$$\Delta t = t_2 - t_1.$$

In Problem 4c, the change in the number of weeks can be written using Δ notation as follows:

$$\Delta t = t_2 - t_1 = 5 - 0 = 5 \text{ wk}.$$

The average rate of change of weight over the first 5 weeks of the program can now be symbolically written as follows:

$$\frac{\Delta w}{\Delta t} = \frac{-13}{5} = -2.6 \text{ pounds per week}$$

Note that the symbol Δ for delta is the Greek version of d, for difference, the result of a subtraction that produces the change in value.

9. a. Use Δ notation and determine the average rate of change of weight over the last 4 weeks of the program.

b. Rewrite your solution to Problem 6a using delta notation.

c. Rewrite your solution to Problem 7a using delta notation.

1. Let y_1 represent the corresponding output value for the input x_1, and y_2 represent the corresponding output value for the input x_2. As the variable x changes in value from x_1 to x_2,

   a. the change in input is represented by $\Delta x = x_2 - x_1$

   b. the change in output is represented by $\Delta y = y_2 - y_1$

2. The quotient $\dfrac{\Delta y}{\Delta x} = \dfrac{y_2 - y_1}{x_2 - x_1}$ is called the **average rate of change** of y (output) with respect to x (input) over the x-interval from x_1 to x_2. The units of measurement of the quantity $\dfrac{\Delta y}{\Delta x}$ are *output units* per *input unit*.

3. The line segment connecting the points (x_1, y_1) and (x_2, y_2)

   a. rises from left to right if $\dfrac{\Delta y}{\Delta x} > 0$

   b. falls from left to right if $\dfrac{\Delta y}{\Delta x} < 0$

   c. remains constant if $\dfrac{\Delta y}{\Delta x} = 0$

1. For the years between 1900 and 2000, the following table presents the median ages (output) of U.S. men at the time when they first married.

INPUT, year	1900	1910	1920	1930	1940	1950	1960	1970	1980	1990	2000
OUTPUT, age	25.9	25.1	24.6	24.3	24.3	22.8	22.8	23.2	24.7	26.1	27.1

a. During which decade(s) did the median age at first marriage increase for men?

b. During which decade(s) did the median age at first marriage decrease?

c. During which decade(s) did the median age at first marriage remain unchanged?

d. During which decade(s) was the change in median age at first marriage the greatest?

2. Graph the data from Exercise 1, and connect consecutive points with line segments. Then answer the following questions using the graph.

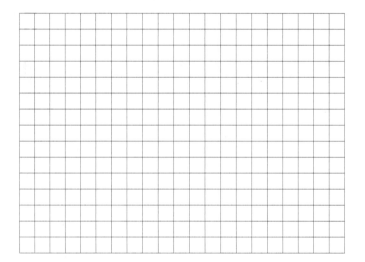

a. During which decade(s) is your graph rising?

b. During which decade(s) is the graph falling?

c. During which decade(s) is your graph horizontal?

d. During which decade(s) is the graph the steepest?

e. Compare the answers of the corresponding parts (a–d) of Exercises 1 and 2. What is the relationship between the sign of the output change for a given input interval and the direction (rising, falling, horizontal) of the graph in that interval?

3. a. Refer to the data in Exercise 1 to determine the average rate of change per year of first-marriage age for men from 1900 through 1950.

b. On the graph, plot the points (1900, 25.9) and (1950, 22.8). Connect the points with a line segment. Does the line segment rise, fall, or remain horizontal as you follow it from left to right?

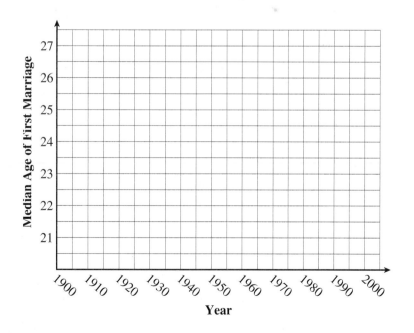

c. What does the average rate in part a tell you about the line segment drawn in part b?

d. Compare the average rate of change in part a to the average rate of change prior to World War II (period 1900 to 1940).

e. On the graph in part b, plot the points (1900, 25.9) and (1940, 24.3). Connect the points with a line segment. Is this line segment falling more or less rapidly than the line segment in part a? Explain by comparing the average rates of change.

4. The National Weather Service recorded the following temperatures one February day in Chicago.

TIME OF DAY	10 A.M.	12 NOON	2 P.M.	4 P.M.	6 P.M.	8 P.M.	10 P.M.
TEMPERATURE (°F)	30	35	36	36	34	30	28

a. Determine the average rate of change (including units and sign) of temperature with respect to time over the entire 12-hour period given in the table.

b. Over which period(s) of time is the average rate of change zero? What, if anything, can you conclude about the actual temperature fluctuation within this period?

c. What is the average rate of change of temperature with respect to time over the evening hours from 6 P.M. to 10 P.M.? Interpret this value (including units and sign) in a complete sentence.

d. Write a brief paragraph describing the temperature and its fluctuations during the 12-hour period in the table.

1. Can the graph of a function have more than one vertical intercept? Explain.

2. What is the mathematical definition of a function? Give a real-life example, and explain how this example satisfies the definition of a function.

3. Describe how you can tell from its graph when a function is increasing and when it is decreasing.

4. Explain the meaning of the symbolic statement $H(5) = 100$.

5. Describe how you would determine the domain and range of a function defined by a continuous graph (one with no breaks or holes). Assume that the graph you see includes all the points of the function.

6. Give an example of a function from your major field of study or area of interest.

7. Identify four different ways that a function can be defined. Give an example of each.

COST OF ITEM (dollars)										
SALES TAX										

8. A function is defined by the rule $f(x) = 5x - 8$. What does $f(1)$ refer to on the graph of f?

9. The notation $g(t)$ represents the weight (in grams) of a melting ice cube t minutes after being removed from the freezer. Interpret the meaning of $g(10) = 4$.

10. What must be true about the average rate of change between any two points on the graph of an increasing function?

11. You are told that the average rate of change of a particular function is always negative. What can you conclude about the graph of that function and why?

12. Describe a step-by-step procedure for determining the average rate of change between any two points on the graph of a function. Use the points represented by (85, 350) and (89, 400) in your explanation.

1. Students at one community college in New York State pay $129 per credit hour when taking fewer than 12 credits, provided they are New York State residents. For 12 or more credit hours, they pay $1550 per semester.

   a. Determine the tuition cost for a student taking the given number of credit hours.

NUMBER OF CREDIT HOURS	TUITION COST ($)
3	
6	
10	
12	
16	
18	

   b. Is the tuition cost a function of the number of credit hours for the values in your completed table from part a? Explain. Be sure to identify the input and output variables in your explanation.

   c. What is the practical domain of the tuition cost function? Assume there are no half-credit courses. However, there are 1- and 2- credit courses available.

   d. Use the table in part a to help graph the tuition cost at this college as a function of the number of credit hours taken.

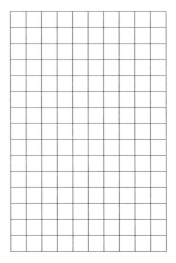

e. Suppose you have saved $700 for tuition. Use the graph to estimate the most credit hours you can take.

f. Does the graph of the tuition cost function pass the vertical line test?

g. Let h represent the number of credit hours (input) and C represent the tuition cost (output). Write a symbolic rule for the cost of part-time tuition in terms of the number of credit hours taken.

h. Use your equation from part g to verify the tuition cost for the credit hours given in the table in part a.

2. Let f be defined by the set of two ordered pairs $\{(2, 3), (0, -5)\}$.

a. List the set of numbers that constitute the domain of f.

b. List the set of numbers that constitute the range of f.

3. You decide to lose weight and will cut down on your calories to lose 2 pounds per week. Suppose that your present weight is 180 pounds. Sketch a graph covering 20 weeks showing your projected weight loss. Describe your graph. If you stick to your plan, how much will you weigh in 3 months (13 weeks)?

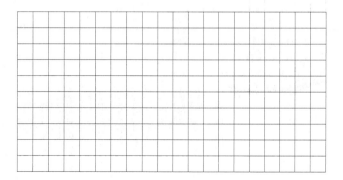

4. A taxicab driver charges a flat rate of $2.50 plus $2.20 per mile. The fare F (in dollars) is a function of the distance driven, x (in miles). The driver wants to display a table for her customers to show approximate fares for different locations within the city.

   a. Write a symbolic rule for F in terms of x.

   b. Use the symbolic rule to complete the following table.

x	0.25	0.5	0.75	1.0	1.5	2.0	3.0	5.0	10.0
$F(x)$									

5. Let $f(x) = -3x + 4$. Determine $f(-5)$.

6. Let $g(x) = (x + 3)(x - 2)$. Determine $g(-4)$.

7. Let $m(x) = 2x^2 + 6x - 7$. Determine $m(3)$.

8. Let $h(s) = (s - 1)^2$. Determine $h(-3)$.

9. Let $s(x) = \sqrt{x + 3}$. Determine $s(6)$.

10. Let f be a function defined by $f(x) = x - 6$. Determine the value of x for which $f(x) = 10$.

11. Let g be a function defined by $g(x) = 0.8x$. Determine the value of x for which $g(x) = 16$.

12. Let h be a function defined by $h(x) = 2x + 1$. Determine the value of x for which $h(x) = 13$.

13. Let k be a function defined by $k(x) = \dfrac{x}{6}$. Determine the value of x for which $k(x) = -3$.

14. Interpret each situation represented by the following graphs. That is, describe, in words, what the graph is saying about the input/output relationship. Indicate what occurs when the function reaches either a minimum or maximum value.

a. Hours of daylight per day in relation to time of year

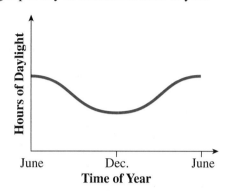

b. Population of fish in a pond in relation to the number of years since stocking

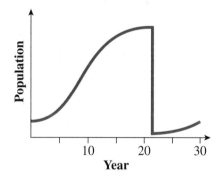

c. Distance from home (in miles) in relation to driving time (in hours)

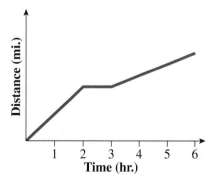

d. Amount of money saved per year in relation to amount of money earned

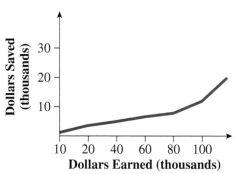

15. In the following situations, determine the input and output variables, and then sketch a graph that best describes the situation. Remember to label the axes with the names of the variables.

a. Sketch a graph that approximates average temperatures where you live as a function of the number of months since January.

   Input variable: _____

   Output variable: _____

b. If you don't study, you would expect to do poorly on the next test. If you study several hours, you should do quite well, but if you study for too many more hours, your test score will probably not improve. Sketch a graph of your test score as a function of study time.

   Input variable: _____   Output variable: _____

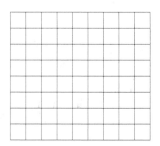

16. As part of your special diet and exercise program, you record your weight at the beginning of the program and each week thereafter. The following data gives your weight, w, over a 5-week period.

TIME, t (wk.)	0	1	2	3	4	5
WEIGHT, w (lb.)	196	183	180	177	174	171

a. Sketch a graph of the data on appropriately scaled and labeled axes.

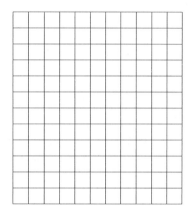

b. Determine the average rate of change of your weight during the first 3 weeks. Be sure to include the units of measurement of this rate.

c. Determine the average rate of change during the 5-week period.

d. On the graph in part a, connect the points (0, 196) and (3, 177) with a line segment. Does the line segment rise, fall, or remain horizontal as you follow the line left to right?

e. What is the practical meaning of the average rate of change in this situation?

f. What can you say about the average rate of change of weight during any of the time intervals in this situation?

17. Between 1960 and 2003 automobiles in the United States changed size and shape almost annually. The amount of fuel consumed by these vehicles also changed. The following table describes the average number of gallons of gasoline consumed per year per passenger car.

YEAR	1960	1970	1980	1990	1995	1997	1998	1999	2000	2001	2002	2003
AVERAGE GALLONS OF GASOLINE CONSUMED PER PASSENGER CAR (gal.)	668	760	576	520	530	538	544	552	546	534	551	583

a. Determine the average rate of change, of gallons of gasoline per year, from 1960 to 1970.

b. Suppose you connected the points (1960, 668) and (1970, 760) on a graph of the data points with a line segment. Would the line segment rise, fall, or remain horizontal as you follow the line left to right?

c. Determine the average rate of change, in gallons of gasoline per year, from 1960 to 1990.

d. Determine the average rate of change, of gallons of gasoline per year, from 2000 to 2002.

e. Determine the average rate of change, of gallons of gasoline per year, between 1960 and 2003.

CLUSTER 2	Introduction to Linear Functions

**ACTIVITY 7.4**

The Snowy Tree Cricket

OBJECTIVES

1. Identify linear functions by a constant rate of change of the output variable with respect to the input variable.

2. Determine the slope of the line drawn through two points.

3. Identify increasing linear functions using slope.

One of the more familiar late-evening sounds during the summer is the rhythmic chirping of a male cricket. Of particular interest is the snowy tree cricket, sometimes called the temperature cricket. It is very sensitive to temperature, speeding up or slowing down its chirping as the temperature rises or falls. The following data shows how the number of chirps per minute of the snowy tree cricket is related to temperature.

 Timely Noise

t, TEMPERATURE (°F)	$N(t)$, NUMBER OF CHIRPS/MINUTE
55	60
60	80
65	100
70	120
75	140
80	160

1. Crickets are usually silent when the temperature falls below 55°F. What is a possible practical domain for the snowy tree cricket function?

2. a. Determine the average rate of change of the number of chirps per minute with respect to temperature as the temperature increases from 55°F to 60°F.

b. What are the units of measure of this rate of change?

3. a. How does the average rate of change determined in Problem 2 compare with the average rate of change as the temperature increases from 65°F to 80°F?

b. Determine the average rate of change of number of chirps per minute with respect to temperature for the temperature intervals given in the following table. The results from Problems 1 and 2 are already recorded. Add several more of your own choice. List all your results in the table.

TEMPERATURE INCREASES	AVERAGE RATE OF CHANGE (number of chirps/minute per degree F)
From 55° to 60°F	4
From 60° to 80°F	4
From 55° to 75°F	
From 65° to 80°F	

c. What can you conclude about the average rate of increase in the number of chirps per minute for any particular increase in temperature?

4. For any 7° increase in temperature, what is the expected increase in chirps per minute?

5. Plot the data pairs (temperature, chirps per minute) from the table preceding Problem 1. What type of graph is suggested by the pattern of points?

Note: Use a double slash (//) to indicate that the horizontal axis has been compressed between 0 and 50 and the vertical axis between 0 and 60.

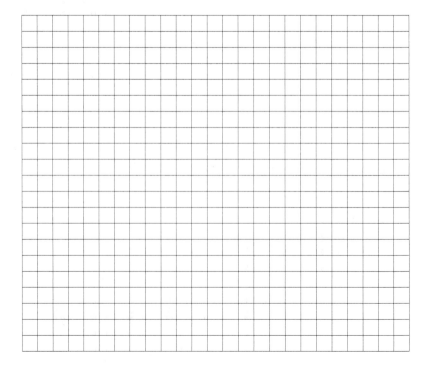

Linear Functions

If the average rate of change in output with respect to input remains constant (stays the same) for *any* two points in a data set, the points will lie on a straight line. That is, the output is a **linear** function of the input. Conversely, if all the points of a data set lie on a straight line when graphed, the average rate of change of output with respect to input will be constant for any two data points.

    6. From the graph in Problem 5, would you conclude that the number of chirps per minute is a linear function of the temperature? Explain.

Slope of a Line

You have seen that the average rate of change between any two points on a line is always the same constant value. This value has a geometric interpretation as well—it describes the "steepness" of the line and is called the **slope** of the line. The larger the absolute value of the slope, the steeper the line.

    7. a. What is the slope of the line in the snowy tree cricket situation?

       b. Because the slope of this line is positive, what can you conclude about the direction of the line as the input variable (temperature) increases in value?

       c. What is the practical meaning of slope in this situation?

The slope of a line is often denoted by the letter *m*. It can be determined by selecting *any* two points on the line and calculating the rate of change between them. That is, if (x_1, y_1) and (x_2, y_2) represent two points on a line, then the slope of the line is calculated by the following formula:

$$m = slope = \frac{\Delta y}{\Delta x} = \frac{y_2 - y_1}{x_2 - x_1}, \text{ where } x_1 \neq x_2$$

EXAMPLE 1   *Determine the slope of the line containing the points* **(1, −2)** *and* **(3, 8).**

SOLUTION

Let $x_1 = 1$, $y_1 = -2$, $x_2 = 3$, and $y_2 = 8$, so

$$m = \frac{\Delta y}{\Delta x} = \frac{y_2 - y_1}{x_2 - x_1} = \frac{8 - (-2)}{3 - 1} = \frac{10}{2} = \frac{5}{1} = 5.$$

8. Use delta notation and determine the slope of the line in the snowy tree cricket situation. Select any two points from the table preceding Problem 1 for (x_1, y_1) and (x_2, y_2).

On a graph, slope is the ratio of two distances. For example, in the snowy tree cricket situation, the slope of the line between the points (55, 60) and (56, 64) as well as between (56, 64) and (57, 68) is $\frac{4}{1}$, as shown on the following graph. The change in the input, 1, represents a horizontal distance (the run) in going from one point to another point on the same line. The change in the output, 4, represents a vertical distance (the rise) between the same points. The graph on the right illustrates that a horizontal distance (run) of 2 and a vertical distance (rise) of 8 from (55, 60) will also locate the point (57, 68) on the line.

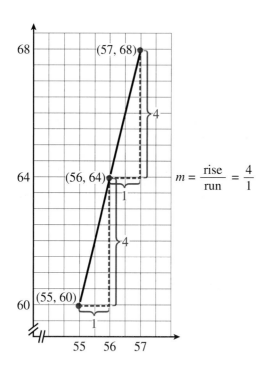
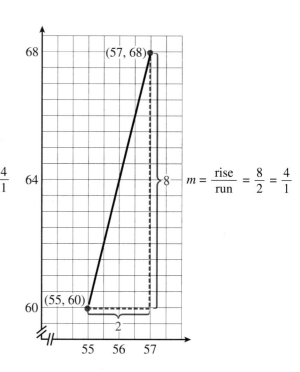

DEFINITION

From its geometric meaning, slope may be determined from a graph by the formula

$$m = \text{slope} = \frac{\text{rise}}{\text{run}} = \frac{\text{distance up } (+) \text{ or down } (-)}{\text{distance right } (+) \text{ or left } (-)}.$$

The slope can be used to locate additional points on a graph.

Note that a positive slope of $\frac{5}{3}$ can be interpreted as $\frac{+5}{+3} = \frac{\text{up } 5}{\text{right } 3}$ or $\frac{-5}{-3} = \frac{\text{down } 5}{\text{left } 3}$ or any multiple of either, such as $\frac{-10}{-6}$.

EXAMPLE 2 *Use the geometric interpretation of slope to locate two additional points in the snowy cricket situation.*

a. Locate a point below (55, 60).

$$m = 4 = \frac{4}{1} = \frac{-4}{-1} = \frac{-12}{-3} = \frac{down\ 12}{left\ 3}$$

Moving down 12 and left 3 from (55, 60) locates the point (52, 48).

b. Locate a point between (55, 60) and (56, 64).

$$m = 4 = \frac{4}{1} = \frac{+2}{+0.5} = \frac{up\ 2}{right\ 0.5}$$

Moving right 0.5 and up 2 from (55, 60) locates the point (55.5, 62)

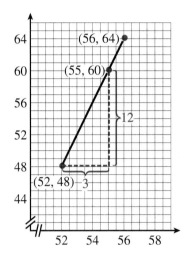 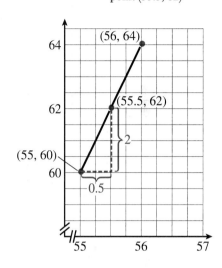

9. a. Suppose a line contains the point $(1, 2)$ and has slope $\frac{3}{1}$. Plot the point and then use the geometric interpretation of slope to determine two additional points on the line. Draw the line containing these three points.

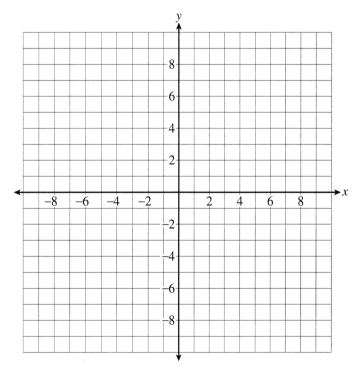

b. Consider the line containing the point $(-6, 4)$ and having slope $\frac{3}{4}$. Plot the point and then determine two additional points on the line. Draw a line through these points.

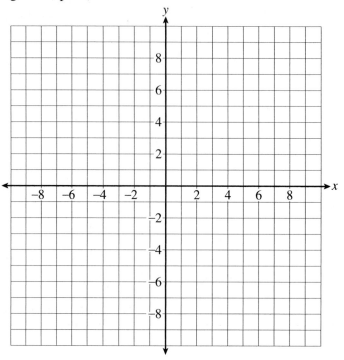

c. Which one of the lines in parts a and b increases more rapidly? Explain.

SUMMARY
ACTIVITY 7.4

1. A **linear function** is one whose average rate of change of output with respect to input from any one data point to any other data point is always the same (constant) value.

2. The **graph** of a linear function is a line whose slope is the constant rate of change of the function.

3. The **slope of a line segment** joining two points (x_1, y_1) and (x_2, y_2) is denoted by m and can be calculated using the formula $m = \dfrac{\Delta y}{\Delta x} = \dfrac{y_2 - y_1}{x_2 - x_1}$.

Geometrically, Δy represents a vertical distance (rise), and Δx represents a horizontal distance (run).

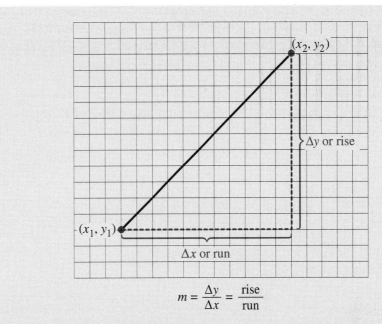

$$m = \frac{\Delta y}{\Delta x} = \frac{\text{rise}}{\text{run}}$$

Therefore, $m = \dfrac{\Delta y}{\Delta x} = \dfrac{\text{rise}}{\text{run}}$

4. The graph of every linear function with **positive slope** is an increasing line, rising to the right. The function is then said to be an **increasing function**.

EXERCISES
ACTIVITY 7.4

1. Consider the following data regarding the growth of the U.S. national debt from 1940 to 2000.

NUMBER OF YEARS SINCE 1940	0	10	20	30	40	50	60
NATIONAL DEBT (billions of dollars)	51	257	291	381	909	3113	5674

a. Compare the average rate of increase in the national debt from 1940 to 1950 with that from 1980 to 1990. Is the average rate of change constant? Explain, using the data.

b. Plot the data points. If the points are connected to form a smooth curve, is the graph a straight line? Are the input and output variables in this problem related linearly?

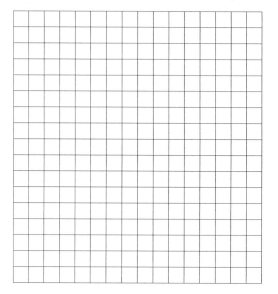

c. Compare the graph in part b with the graph of the snowy tree cricket data in Problem 5. What must be true about the average rate of change between any two data points in order for all the data points to lie on a straight line?

2. Your friend's parents began to give her a weekly allowance of 4 dollars on her 4th birthday. On each successive birthday her allowance increased, so that her weekly allowance in dollars was equal to her age in years.

a. List your friend's allowance for the ages in the table.

AGE (years)	WEEKLY ALLOWANCE ($)
4	
5	
6	
7	

b. Is her allowance a linear function of her age? Explain.

3. Calculate the average rate of change between consecutive data points to determine whether the output in each table is a linear function of the input.

a.

INPUT	−4	0	3	5
OUTPUT	−23.8	1	19.6	32

b.

INPUT	2	7	12	17
OUTPUT	0	10	16	18

c.

INPUT	−5	0	5	8
OUTPUT	−45	−5	35	59

4. For each of the following, determine three additional points on the line. Then sketch a graph of the line.

a. A line contains the point $(-5, 10)$ and has slope $\frac{2}{3}$.

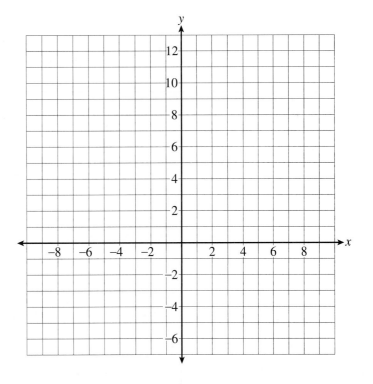

b. A line contains the point $(3, -4)$ and has slope 5.

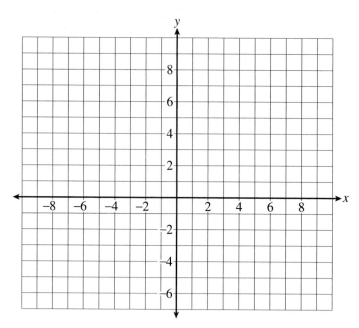

5. The concept of slope arises in many practical applications. When designing and building roads, engineers and surveyors need to be concerned about the grade of the road. The grade, usually expressed as a percent, is one way to describe the steepness of the finished surface of the road. For example, a 5% grade means that the road has a slope (rise over run) of $0.05 = \dfrac{5}{100}$.

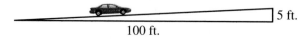

100 ft.

5 ft.

a. If a road has a 5% upward grade over a 1000-foot run, how much higher will you be at the end of that run than at the beginning?

b. What is the grade of a road that rises 26 feet over a distance of 500 feet?

6. The American National Standards Institute (ANSI) requires that the slope for a wheelchair ramp not exceed $\frac{1}{12}$.

   a. Does a ramp that is 160 inches long and 10 inches high meet the requirements of ANSI? Explain.

   b. A ramp for a wheelchair must be 20 inches high. Determine the minimum horizontal length of the ramp so that it meets the ANSI requirement.

ACTIVITY 7.5

Descending in an Airplane

OBJECTIVES

1. Identify lines as having negative, zero, or undefined slopes.

2. Identify a decreasing linear function from its graph or slope.

3. Determine horizontal and vertical intercepts of a linear function from its graph.

4. Interpret the meaning of horizontal and vertical intercepts of a line.

While on a trip, you notice that the video screen on the airplane, in addition to showing movies and news, records your altitude (in kilometers) above the ground. As the plane starts its descent (at time $t = 0$), you record the following data.

Cleared for a Landing

TIME, t (min)	ALTITUDE, $A(t)$ (km)
0	12
2	10
4	8
6	6
8	4
10	2

1. a. What is the average rate of change in the altitude of the plane from 2 to 6 minutes into the descent? Pay careful attention to the sign of this rate of change.

b. What are the units of measurement of this average rate of change?

2. a. Determine the average rate of change over several other input intervals.

b. What is the significance of the signs of these average rates of change?

c. Based on your calculation in Problems 1a and 2a, do you think that the data lie on a single straight line? Explain.

d. What is the practical meaning of slope in this situation?

3. By how much does the altitude of the plane change for each 3-minute change in time during the descent?

4. a. Plot the data points from the table preceding Problem 1, and verify that the points lie on a line. What is the slope of the line?

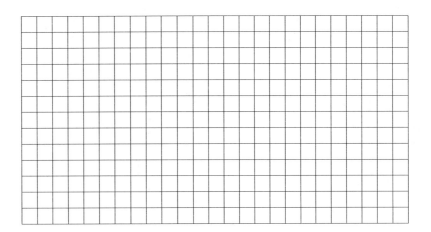

b. Explain to a classmate the method you used to determine the slope in part a.

c. Describe another method to determine the slope (other than the one you used in part a).

5. a. The slope of the line for the descent function in this activity is negative. What does this tell you about how the outputs change as the input variable (time) increases in value?

b. Is the descent function an increasing or decreasing function?

6. Suppose another airplane was descending at the rate of 1.5 kilometers every minute.

a. Complete the following table.

TIME	0	1	2	3
ALTITUDE	12			

b. Plot the data points, and verify that the points lie on a line. What is the slope of the line?

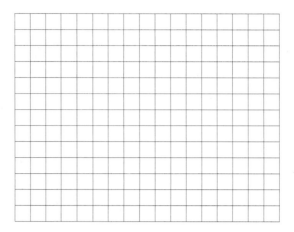

Horizontal and Vertical Intercepts

7. a. From the time the plane (in Problems 1–5) begins its descent, how many minutes does it take to reach the ground?

b. Use a straightedge to connect the data points on your graph in Problem 4a. Extend the line so that it crosses both axes.

> **DEFINITION**
>
> A **horizontal intercept** of a graph is a point where the graph crosses the horizontal (input) axis. It is clearly identified by its second (vertical) coordinate, which is always equal to 0. The ordered-pair notation for a horizontal intercept has the form $(a, 0)$, where a is the input value.

8. a. Identify the horizontal intercept of the line in Problem 4a from the graph.

b. How is the horizontal intercept related to the answer you obtained in Problem 7a? That is, what is the practical meaning of the horizontal intercept?

> **DEFINITION**
>
> A **vertical intercept** of a graph is a point where the graph crosses the vertical (output) axis. It is clearly identified by its first (horizontal) coordinate, which is always equal to 0. The ordered-pair notation for a vertical intercept has the form $(0, b)$, where b represents the output value.

9. a. Identify the vertical intercept of the descent function from its graph in Problem 4a.

   b. What is the practical meaning of this intercept?

10. Determine the slope and the horizontal and vertical intercepts for each of the following lines.

   a.

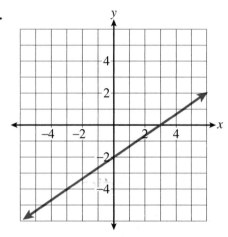

   b.

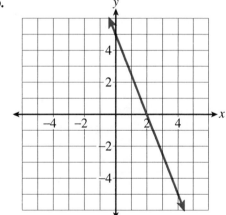

Horizontal Line

11. a. You found a promotion for unlimited access to the Internet for $20 per month. Complete the following table of values, where t is the number of hours a subscriber spends online during the month and c is the monthly access cost for that subscriber.

t, TIME (hr.)	1	2	3	4	5
c, COST ($)					

b. Sketch a graph of the data points.

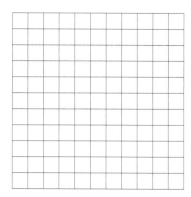

c. What is the slope of the line drawn through the points?

d. What single word best describes a line with zero slope?

e. Determine the horizontal and vertical intercepts (if any).

f. What can you say about the output value of every point on a horizontal line?

> The slope, m, of a horizontal line is 0 and the output of each of its points is the same constant value, c. The equation of the line is $y = c$.

EXAMPLE 1   *Write a symbolic rule that expresses the relationship in Problem 11—the monthly cost for unlimited access to the Internet in terms of the number of hours spent online.*

SOLUTION

Let t represent the number of hours spent online during the month and $c(t)$ the monthly access cost for a subscriber.

$c(t) = 20$ The cost $c(t)$ is $20 no matter how many hours are spent online.

12. a. Describe another situation (or give a data collection) in which the slope or average rate of change is zero.

b. Write a symbolic rule for this situation.

Vertical Line

13. To cover your weekly expenses while going to school, you work as a part-time aide in your college's health center and earn $100 each week. Complete the following table, where x represents your weekly salary and y represents your weekly expenses for a typical month.

x, WEEKLY SALARY ($)				
y, WEEKLY EXPENSES ($)	50	70	90	60

a. Sketch a graph of the data points. Do the points lie on a line? Explain.

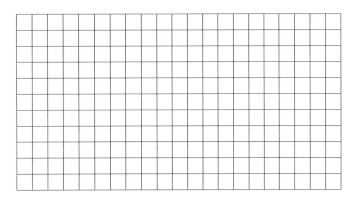

b. Explain what happens if you use the slope formula to determine a numerical value for the slope of the line in part a.

c. Write down the slope formula. What must be true about the change in the input variable for the quotient to be defined?

d. What type of line results whenever the slope is undefined, as in this problem?

e. Determine the vertical and horizontal intercepts (if any).

f. What can you say about the input value of every point on a vertical line?

g. Is y a function of x? Explain.

The input of each point on a vertical line is the same constant value, d. The equation of the line is $x = d$.

EXAMPLE 2   *Write an equation for the situation described in Problem 13.*

SOLUTION

$x = 100$

SUMMARY
ACTIVITY 7.5

1. The graph of every linear function with **negative slope** is a line falling to the right.

2. A linear function having a negative slope ($m < 0$) is a **decreasing function**.

3. The **horizontal intercept** is the point at which the graph crosses the horizontal (input) axis. Its ordered-pair notation is $(a, 0)$; that is, the second coordinate is equal to zero. If the input is denoted by x, then the horizontal intercept is referred to as the x-intercept.

4. The **vertical intercept** is the point at which the graph crosses the vertical (output) axis. Its ordered-pair notation is $(0, b)$; that is, the first coordinate is equal to zero. If the output is denoted by y, then the intercept is referred to as the y-intercept.

5. The slope of a **horizontal line** is zero. Every point on a horizontal line has the same output value. The equation of a horizontal line is $y = d$, where d is a constant. For example, the graph of $y = 6$ is a horizontal line.

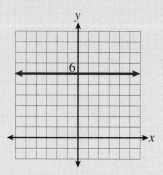

6. The slope of a **vertical line** is undefined; it has no numerical value. Every point on a vertical line has the same input value. The equation of a vertical line is $x = c$, where c is a constant. For example, the graph of $x = 5$ is a vertical line.

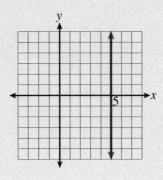

1. In a science lab, you collect the following sets of data. Which of the four data sets are linear functions? If linear, determine the slope.

a.

TIME (sec.)	0	10	20	30	40
TEMPERATURE (°C)	12	17	22	27	32

b.

TIME (sec.)	0	10	20	30	40
TEMPERATURE (°C)	41	23	5	−10	−20

c.

TIME (sec.)	3	5	8	10	15
TEMPERATURE (°C)	12	16	24	28	36

d.

TIME (sec.)	3	9	12	18	21
TEMPERATURE (°C)	25	23	22	20	19

2. a. You are a member of a health and fitness club. A special diet and exercise program has been developed for you by the club's registered dietitian and your personal trainer. You weigh 181 pounds and would like to lose 2 pounds every week. Complete the following table of values for your desired weight each week.

N, NUMBER OF WEEKS	0	1	2	3	4
W(N), DESIRED WEIGHT (lb.)					

b. Plot the data points.

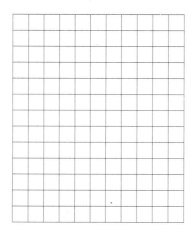

c. Explain why your desired weight is a linear function of time. What is the slope of the line containing the five data points?

d. What is the practical meaning of slope in this situation?

e. How long will it take to reach your ideal weight of 168 pounds?

3. Your aerobics instructor informs you that to receive full physical benefit from exercising, your heart rate must be maintained at a certain level for at least 12 minutes. The proper exercise heart rate for a healthy person, called the target heart rate, is determined by the person's age. The relationship between these two quantities is illustrated by the data in the following table.

A, AGE (yr.)	20	30	40	50	60
B(A), TARGET HEART RATE (beats/min.)	140	133	126	119	112

a. Does the data in the table indicate that the target heart rate is a linear function of age? Explain.

b. What is the slope of the line for this data? What are the units?

c. What are suitable replacement values (domain) for age, *A*?

d. Plot the data points on coordinate axes where both axes start with zero. Connect the points with a line.

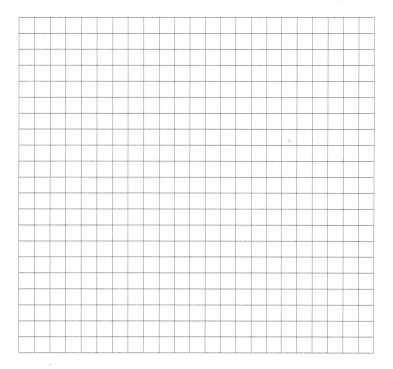

e. Extend the line to locate the horizontal and vertical intercepts. Do these intercepts have a practical meaning in the problem? Explain.

4. a. Determine the slope of each of the following lines.

i.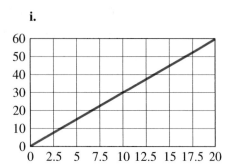

ii.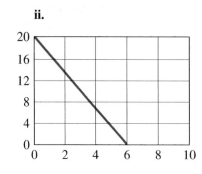

iii.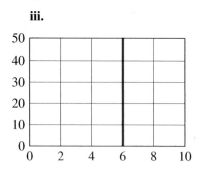

b. Determine the horizontal and vertical intercept of each of the lines in part a.

INTERCEPT	GRAPH i	GRAPH ii	GRAPH iii
Horizontal			
Vertical			

5. a. A horizontal line contains the point $(-3, 7)$. Determine and list three additional points that lie on the line.

b. Sketch a graph of the horizontal line.

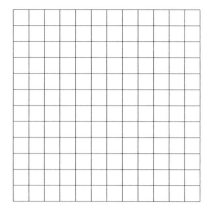

c. Identify the slope and vertical and horizontal intercepts (if they exist) of the graph.

6. Each question refers to the graph that accompanies it. The graphed line in each grid represents the total distance a car travels as a function of time (in hours).

a. How fast is the car traveling? Explain how you obtained your result.

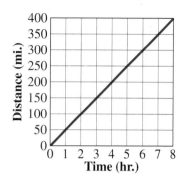

b. How can you determine visually from the following graph which car is going faster? Verify your answer by calculating the speed of each car.

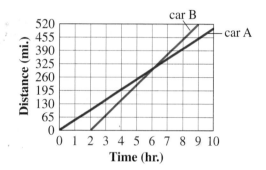

c. Describe in words the movement of the car that is represented by the following graph.

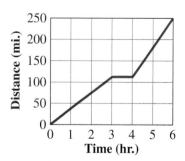

7. a. Determine the slope of each of the following lines.

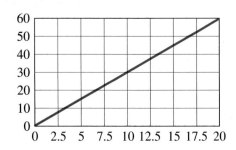 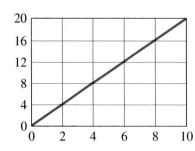 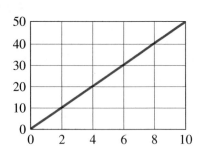

b. At first glance, the three graphs in part a may appear to represent the same line. Do they?

ACTIVITY 7.6

Charity Event

OBJECTIVES

1. Determine a symbolic rule for a linear function from contextual information.

2. Identify the practical meanings of the slope and intercepts of a linear function.

3. Determine the slope-intercept form of a linear function.

4. Identify functions as linear by numerical, graphical, and algebraic characteristics.

Professor Abrahamsen's social psychology class is organizing a campus entertainment night to benefit charities in the community. You are a member of the budget committee for this class project. The committee suggests an admission donation of $10 per person for food, nonalcoholic beverages, and entertainment. The committee members expect that each student in attendance will purchase a raffle ticket for $1. Faculty members volunteer to emcee the event and perform comedy sketches. Two student bands are hired at a cost of $200 each. Additional expenses include $1000 for food and drinks, $200 for paper products, $100 for posters and tickets, and $500 for raffle prizes. The college is donating the use of the gymnasium for the evening.

1. Determine the total fixed costs for the entertainment night.

2. a. Determine the **total revenue** (gross income *before* expenses are deducted) if 400 students attend and each buys a raffle ticket.

b. Determine the **profit** (net income *after* expenses are deducted) if 400 students attend and each buys a raffle ticket.

3. a. The total revenue (gross income) for the event depends on the number, n, of students who attend. Write an expression in terms of n that represents the total revenue if n students attend and each buys a raffle ticket.

b. Write a symbolic function rule defining the profit, $p(n)$, in terms of the number, n, of students in attendance. Remember that the total fixed costs for the entertainment night are $2200.

c. List some suitable replacement values (practical domain) for the input variable n. Is it meaningful for n to have a value of $\frac{1}{2}$ or -3?

4. a. Use the symbolic rule in Problem 3b to determine the profit if 100 students attend.

b. What is the practical meaning of the negative value for profit in part a?

5. If the gymnasium holds a maximum of 650 people, what is the maximum amount of money that can be donated to charity?

6. a. Suppose that the members of the class want to be able to donate $1000 to community charities. Write an equation to determine how many students must attend the entertainment night for there to be a profit of $1000. Solve the equation.

b. How many students must attend for there to be $2000 to donate to the local charities?

7. a. Complete the following table of values for the charity event situation.

n, NUMBER OF STUDENTS	0	50	100	200	300	400
$p(n)$, PROFIT ($)						

b. Determine the average rate of change in profit as the number of students in attendance increases from 300 students to 400 students.

c. Determine the average rate of change between consecutive data pairs in the table.

d. Is profit a linear function of the number of students attending? Explain.

8. a. Sketch a graph of the profit function.

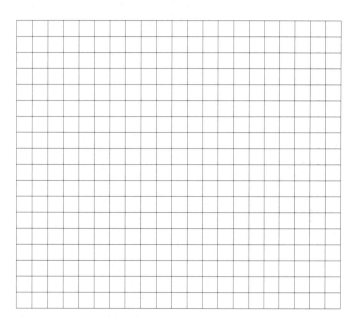

b. Why should you expect all the plotted points to lie on the same line?

9. a. Determine the slope of the line containing the data points.

b. What are the units of measurement of the slope? What is the practical meaning of the slope in this situation?

c. What is the vertical intercept of the line?

d. What is the practical meaning of the vertical intercept in this situation?

Slope-Intercept Form of an Equation of a Line

The profit function defined by $p(n) = 11n - 2200$ has a symbolic form that is representative of *all* linear functions. That is, the symbolic form of a linear function consists of the sum of two terms:

- a *variable term* (the input variable multiplied by its coefficient)
- and a *constant term* (a fixed number)

10. a. Identify the variable term in the symbolic rule $p(n) = 11n - 2200$. What is its coefficient?

    b. Identify the constant term in this symbolic rule.

    c. What characteristic of the linear function graph does the coefficient of the input variable n represent?

    d. What characteristic of the linear function graph does the constant term represent?

11. a. Consider a line defined by the equation $y = 2x + 7$. Use the equation to complete the following table.

x	−2	−1	0	1	2
y					

    b. Use the slope formula to determine the slope of the line. How does the slope compare to the coefficient of x in the equation?

    c. Determine the vertical (y-) intercept. How does it compare to the constant term in the equation of the line?

The answers to Problems 10c and d and Problem 11 generalize to all linear functions.

The coefficient of the variable term in a linear function is the *slope* of the line; the constant term (including its sign) gives the output value of the *vertical intercept* of the line.

Recall that the letter m denotes the slope of a line and $(0, b)$ is the ordered pair that represents its vertical intercept. Therefore, the symbolic rule for y, a linear function of x, is given by $y = mx + b$ and is called the **slope-intercept form** of the equation of a line.

EXAMPLE 1 *Identify the slope and vertical intercept of each of the following.*

LINEAR FUNCTION RULE	m, SLOPE	$(0, b)$, VERTICAL INTERCEPT
$y = 5x + 3$		
$y = -2x + 7$		
$y = \frac{1}{2}x - 4$		
$y = 3x + 0$ or simply $y = 3x$		
$y = 0x + 10$ or simply $y = 10$		
$y = 10 + 6x$		
$y = 85 - 7x$		

12. Identify the slope and vertical intercept of each of the following linear functions.

   a. $y = -3x + 8$

   b. $y = \frac{3}{4}x - \frac{1}{2}$

   c. $y = -5x$

   d. $y = -3$

   e. $y = 16 + 4x$

   f. $y = 110 - 3x$

   g. $p = -12 + 2.5n$

   h. $q = -45 - 9r$

**SUMMARY
ACTIVITY 7.6**

1. The average rate of change between any two input/output pairs of a linear function is always the same constant value.

2. The graph of every linear function is a line whose slope, m, is precisely the constant average rate of change of the function.

3. For every linear function, equally spaced input values produce equally spaced output values.

4. The symbolic rule for a linear function, also called the **slope-intercept form** of the line, is given by $y = mx + b$, where m is the slope and $(0, b)$ is the y- (vertical) intercept of the line.

EXERCISES
ACTIVITY 7.6

Exercises 1–5 refer to the charity event scenario in this activity. Suppose the budget committee decides to increase the admission fee to $12 per person. It is still expected that each student will purchase a raffle ticket for $1.

1. a. Write a new symbolic rule for profit in terms of the number of tickets sold.

   b. Complete the following table using the symbolic rule determined in part a.

NUMBER OF TICKETS, n	0	50	100	150	200	300	400
PROFIT, $p(n)$							

2. a. Determine the practical domain of the new profit function.

   b. Sketch a graph of the new profit function.

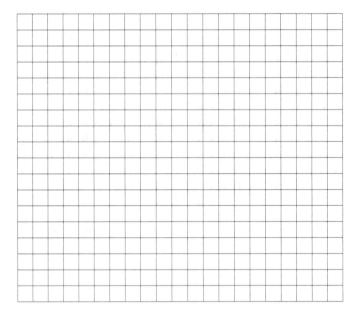

   c. What is the slope of the line containing the data points? What is the practical meaning of the slope in this situation?

    d. What is the vertical intercept of the line? What is the practical meaning of the intercept in this situation?

3. If the gymnasium could hold a maximum of 900 people instead of 650, what is the maximum amount of money that could be given to charity?

4. What attendance is needed for there to be a profit of $1000?

5. a. Is there a point where the charity event may have neither a profit nor a loss?

    b. The point where the profit is zero is called the **break-even point**. Use the idea of the break-even point to determine how many students must attend so that the class project will not incur a loss.

6. Consider the line having equation $y = -3x + 1.5$.

    a. Complete the following table.

x	−2	−1	0	1	2
y					

    b. Use the slope formula to determine the slope of the line. How does the slope compare to the coefficient of the input variable x in the equation of the line?

c. How does the vertical intercept you determined in part a compare to the constant term in the equation of the line?

7. Identify the slope and vertical intercept of each of the following.

LINEAR FUNCTION RULE	m, SLOPE	$(0, b)$, VERTICAL INTERCEPT
$y = 3x - 2$		
$y = -2x + 5$		
$y = \frac{1}{2}x + 3$		
$y = -2x$		
$y = 6$		
$y = 9 + 3.5x$		
$w = -25 + 8x$		
$v = 48 - 32t$		
$z = -15 - 6u$		

8. Housing prices in your neighborhood have been increasing steadily since you purchased your home in 2005. The relationship between the market value, V, of your home and the length of time, x, you have owned your home is modeled by the symbolic rule

$$V(x) = 2500x + 125{,}000,$$

where $V(x)$ is measured in dollars and x in years.

a. The graph of the rule is a line. What is the slope of this line? What is the practical meaning of slope in this situation?

b. Determine the vertical intercept. What is the practical meaning of this intercept in the context of this problem?

c. Determine and interpret the value $V(8)$.

9. The value of a car decreases (depreciates) immediately after it is purchased. The value of a car you recently purchased can be modeled by the symbolic rule

$$V(x) = -1350x + 18{,}500,$$

where $V(x)$ is the market value (in dollars) and x is the length of time you own your car (in years).

a. The graph of the relationship is a line. Determine the slope of this line. What is the practical meaning of slope in this situation?

b. Determine the vertical intercept. What is the practical meaning of this intercept?

c. Determine and interpret the value $V(3)$.

Software Sales

OBJECTIVES

1. Identify the slope and vertical intercept from the equation of a line written in slope-intercept form.

2. Write an equation of a line in the slope-intercept form.

3. Use the *y*-intercept and the slope to graph a linear function.

4. Determine horizontal intercepts of linear functions using an algebraic approach.

5. Use intercepts to graph a linear function.

You have been hired by a company that sells computer software products. In 2006, the company's total (annual) sales were $16 million. Its marketing department projects that sales will increase by $2 million per year for the next several years.

1. a. Let *t* represent the number of years since 2006. That is, *t* = 0 corresponds to 2006, *t* = 1 corresponds to 2007, and so on. Complete the following table.

t, NUMBER OF YEARS SINCE 2006	*s*, TOTAL SALES IN MILLIONS OF DOLLARS
0	
1	
2	
5	

b. Write a symbolic rule that would express the total sales, *s*, in terms of the number of years, *t*, since 2006.

c. Is your symbolic rule a function?

d. What is the practical domain of this total sales function?

e. Is the total sales function linear? Explain.

2. a. Determine the slope of the sales function.

b. What are the units of measurement of the slope? What is the practical meaning of the slope in this situation?

3. a. Determine the vertical (*s*-) intercept of this linear function.

b. What is the practical meaning of the vertical intercept in this situation?

The symbolic rule for the total sales function can be written using function notation as $s(t) = 2t + 16$.

4. a. Determine $s(6)$.

b. Interpret the meaning of the result in part a.

5. Use the symbolic rule $s(t) = 2t + 16$ for the total sales function to approximate the year in which total sales will reach \$32 million. What ordered pair on the graph conveys the same information?

6. Use the given symbolic rule $s(t) = 2t + 16$ to determine the total sales in the year 2011. What ordered pair conveys the same information?

7. Let x represent the input and $f(x)$ represent the output. Use function notation to write the equation of each of the following lines:

a. A line having slope $\frac{2}{3}$ and vertical intercept $(0, 7)$

b. A line having slope -3 and vertical intercept $\left(0, \frac{3}{4}\right)$

Graphing Linear Functions Using the Vertical Intercept and Slope

One way to graph a linear function by hand is to first plot the vertical intercept and then to make use of the slope.

8. Follow the steps given here for the slope-intercept method to graph the total sales function on the accompanying grid.

Step 1. Plot the vertical intercept $(0, 16)$ on the vertical axis.

Step 2. Write the slope, 2, in fractional form as $\frac{2}{1} = \frac{\text{change in total sales}}{\text{change in year}}$.

Step 3. Starting at $(0, 16)$, move 1 unit to the right and then 2 units up. Mark the point you have reached.

Step 4. The coordinates of the point you have reached are $(1, 18)$.

Step 5. Use a straightedge to draw the line through $(0, 16)$, and $(1, 18)$.

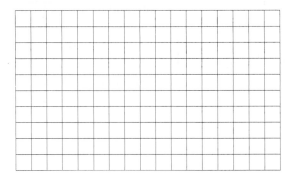

9. **a.** Start at $(0, 16)$ and explain how to use the slope to calculate the coordinates of the point $(1, 18)$ without actually moving on the graph.

b. Interpret the practical meaning of the ordered pair $(1, 18)$ in terms of the total sales situation.

10. Use the slope once again to reach a third point on the line. Interpret the practical meaning of this new ordered pair in terms of the total sales situation.

11. **a.** Use the slope to determine the change in total sales over any 6-year period.

b. Use the result of part a to determine the coordinates of the point corresponding to the year 2012.

12. Use the grid below to plot the vertical intercept as well as the points you have determined in Problems 10 and 11. Then use a straightedge to draw the line between these points.

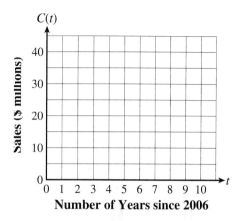

13. Identify the point on the graph whose horizontal coordinate is 4. Interpret the practical meaning of this ordered pair in terms of total sales.

Graphing Linear Functions Using Intercepts

Another way to graph a linear function is to plot its vertical and horizontal intercepts and then use a straightedge to draw the line containing these two points.

14. You have purchased a laptop computer so that you can use the software products you have acquired through your job. The initial cost of the computer is $1350. You expect that the computer will depreciate (lose value) at the rate of $450 per year.

a. Write a symbolic rule that will determine the value, $v(t)$, of the computer in terms of the number of years, t, that you own it.

b. Write the ordered pairs that represent the vertical and horizontal intercepts.
  i. To determine the vertical intercept, evaluate the expression in part a for $t = 0$ and record your result in the following table.
  ii. To determine the horizontal intercept, solve the equation in part a for $v(t) = 0$, and record your result in the table.

INTERCEPTS	t, NUMBER OF YEARS	v, VALUE OF COMPUTER
Vertical		
Horizontal		

c. On the following grid, plot the intercept points you determined in part b. Then use a straightedge to draw a straight line through the intercepts.

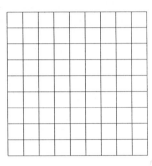

d. What is the practical meaning of the vertical intercept in this situation?

e. What is the practical interpretation of the horizontal intercept in this situation?

f. What portion of the line in part c can be used to represent the computer value situation? (*Hint:* What is the practical domain of this function?)

15. Determine the vertical and horizontal intercepts for each of the following. Then sketch a graph of the line using the intercepts. Use your graphing calculator to check your results.

a. $y = -3x + 6$

b. $f(x) = \dfrac{1}{2}x - 8$

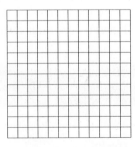

16. Identify the slope, vertical intercept, and horizontal intercept of each linear function in the following table.

LINEAR FUNCTION RULE	SLOPE	VERTICAL INTERCEPT	HORIZONTAL INTERCEPT
$y = 3x - 7$			
$f(x) = -2x + 3$			
$y = 5x + 2$			
$y = 10x$			
$y = 5$			
$g(x) = 12 + 4x$			
$v = 192 - 32t$			
$w = -25 + 4r$			
$z = -200 - 8x$			

17. Determine the intercepts and slope of the linear function having equation $3x + 4y = 12$.

SUMMARY
ACTIVITY 7.7

1. To **plot** a **linear function** using slope-intercept form:

- Plot the vertical intercept on the vertical axis.

- Write the slope in fractional form as $\dfrac{\text{change in output}}{\text{change in input}}$

- Start at the vertical intercept. Move up or down as many units as the numerator indicates, and then move to the right or left as many units as the denominator indicates. Mark the point you have reached.

- Use a straightedge to draw a line between the two points.

2. Given an equation of a line, determine its **y-intercept** by setting $x = 0$ and calculating the corresponding y-value.

continued

3. Given an equation of a line, determine its **x-intercept** by setting $y = 0$ and calculating the corresponding x-value.

4. To plot a linear function using its intercepts:

   • Determine the horizontal and vertical intercepts, and then use a straight-edge to draw the line containing the two points.

EXERCISES
ACTIVITY 7.7

In Exercises 1–6, determine the slope, y-intercept, and x-intercept of each line. Then sketch each graph, labeling and verifying the coordinates of each intercept. Use your graphing calculator to check your results.

1. $y = 3x - 4$

2. $f(x) = -5x + 2$

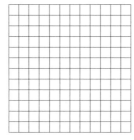 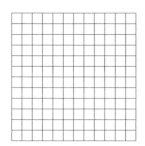

3. $y = 8$

4. $y = \dfrac{x}{2} + 5$

 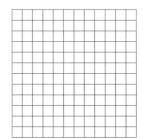

Hint: In Exercises 5 and 6, solve for *y* first.

5. $2x - y = 3$

6. $3x + 2y = 1$

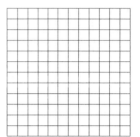

7. Graph the following linear functions in the order given. Use your graphing calculator to verify your answers. In what ways are the graphs similar? In what ways are they different?

a. $y = x - 4$

b. $f(x) = x - 2$

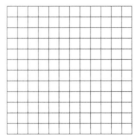

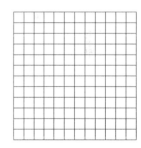

c. $g(x) = x$

d. $y = x + 2$

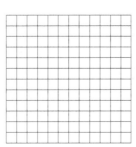

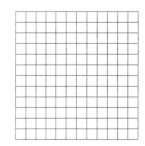

e. $y = x + 4$

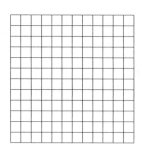

8. Graph the following linear functions in the order given. Use your graphing calculator to verify your answers. In what ways are the graphs similar? In what ways are they different?

a. $y = -4x + 2$ **b.** $h(x) = -2x + 2$

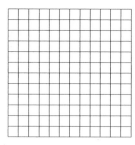
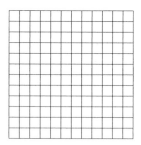

c. $y = 2$ **d.** $g(x) = 2x + 2$

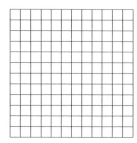
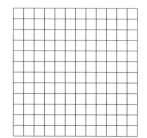

e. $y = 4x + 2$

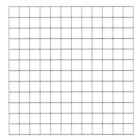

9. What is the equation of the linear function with slope 12 and y-intercept $(0, 3)$?

10. **a.** You start with $20 in your savings account and add $10 every week. At what rate does the amount in your account, excluding interest, change from week to week?

   b. Write an equation that models your savings, $s(t)$, as a function of time, t (in weeks).

11. **a.** What is the slope of the line that goes through the points $(0, 5)$ and $(2, 11)$?

   b. What is the equation (symbolic rule) of the line through these two points?

12. **a.** What is the slope of the line that goes through the points $(0, -43.5)$ and $(-1, 13.5)$?

   b. What is the equation of the line through these two points?

13. Determine the horizontal and vertical intercepts of each of the following. Use the intercepts to sketch a graph of the function.

a. $y = -3x + 12$

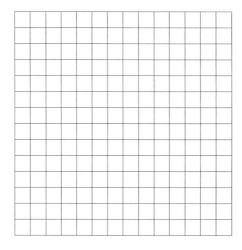

b. $y = \dfrac{1}{2}x + 6$

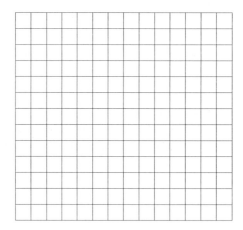

14. The average cost of a 30-second advertisement during the 1998 Super Bowl game was $1.3 million. In 2006, the average cost was $2.5 million. If x represents the number of years since 1998, the given data can be summarized as follows:

NUMBER OF YEARS SINCE 1998, x	COST OF A 30-SECOND AD, C (millions of dollars)
0	1.3
8	2.5

a. Assume that the average rate of increase in the cost of a 30-second advertisement remained constant from 1998 through 2006. Determine this rate. What characteristic of the line through $(0, 1.3)$ and $(8, 2.5)$ does this rate represent?

b. Determine the equation of the line in part a.

c. If this trend continues, what will be the cost of a 30-second ad during the 2010 Super Bowl?

15. After applying the brakes, a car traveling 60 mph continues 120 feet before coming to a complete stop. This information is summarized in the following table.

DISTANCE TRAVELED AFTER APPLYING THE BRAKES, d (ft.)	0	120
SPEED OF THE CAR, v (mph)	60	0

a. Assume that the speed, v, of the car is a linear function of the distance, d, traveled after applying the brakes. Determine the slope of the line containing the points $(0, 60)$ and $(120, 0)$. What is the practical meaning of slope in this situation?

b. Determine the equation of the line in part a.

c. Determine the speed of the car when it is 70 feet from where the brakes are applied.

1. A line is given by the equation $y = -4x + 10$.

   a. Determine its horizontal and vertical intercepts algebraically from the equation.

   b. Use your graphing calculator to confirm these intercepts.

2. **a.** Does the slope of the line having the equation $4x + 2y = 3$ have a value of 4? Why or why not?

   b. Solve the equation in part a for y so that it is in the form $y = mx + b$.

   c. What is the slope of the line?

3. Explain the difference between a line with zero slope and a line with an undefined slope.

4. Describe how you recognize that a function is linear when it is given

   a. graphically

   b. symbolically

   c. numerically in a table

5. Do vertical lines represent functions? Explain.

Exercise numbers appearing in color are answered in the Selected Answers appendix.

1. A function is linear because the rate of change of the output with respect to the input from point to point is constant. Use this idea to determine the missing input (x) and output (y) values in each table, assuming that each table represents a linear function.

a.

x	y
1	4
2	5
3	

b.

x	y
1	4
3	8
5	

c.

x	y
0	4
5	9
10	

d.

x	y
−1	3
0	8
	13
2	

e.

x	y
−3	11
0	8
3	
	2

f.

x	y
−2	−5
0	−8
	−11
4	

g. Explain how you used the idea of constant rate of change to determine the values in the tables.

2. The pitch of a roof is an example of slope in a practical setting. The roof slope is usually expressed as a ratio of rise over run. For example, in the building shown, the pitch is 6 to 24 or, in fraction form, $\frac{1}{4}$.

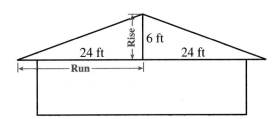

a. If a roof has a pitch of 5 to 16, how high will the roof rise over a 24-foot run?

b. If a roof's slope is 0.25, how high will the roof rise over a 16-foot run?

c. What is the slope of a roof that rises 12 feet over a run of 30 feet?

3. Determine whether any of the following tables contain input and output data that represent a linear function. In each case, give a reason for your answer.

a. You make an investment of $100 at 5% interest compounded semiannually. The following table represents the amount of money you will have at the end of each year.

TIME (yr.)	AMOUNT ($)
1	105.06
2	110.38
3	115.97
4	121.84

b. A cable-TV company charges a $45 installation fee and $28 per month for basic cable service. The table values represent the total usage cost since installation.

NUMBER OF MONTHS	6	12	18	24	36
TOTAL COST ($)	213	381	549	717	1053

c. For a fee of $20 a month, you have unlimited video rental. Values in the table represent the relationship between the number of videos you rented each month and the monthly fee.

NUMBER OF RENTALS	10	15	12	9	2
COST ($)	20	20	20	20	20

4. After stopping your car at a stop sign, you accelerate at a constant rate for a period of time. The speed of your car is a function of the time since you left the stop sign. The following table shows your speedometer reading each second for the next 7 seconds.

t, TIME (sec.)	s, SPEED (mph)
0	0
1	11
2	22
3	33
4	44
5	55
6	55
7	55

a. Graph the data by plotting the ordered pairs of the form (t, s) and then connecting the points.

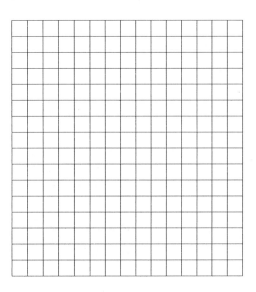

b. For what values of t is the graph increasing?

c. What is the slope of the line segment during the period of acceleration?

d. What is the practical meaning of the slope in this situation?

e. For what values of t is the speed a constant? What is the slope of the line connecting the points of constant speed?

5. a. The three lines shown in the following graphs appear to be different. Calculate the slope of each line.

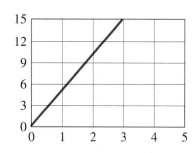 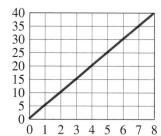 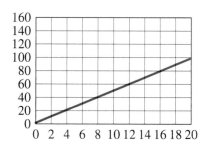

b. Do the three graphs represent the same linear function? Explain.

6. a. Determine the slope of the line through the points $(2, -5)$ and $(2, 4)$.

b. Determine the slope of the line $y = -3x - 2$.

c. Determine the slope of the line $2x - 4y = 10$.

d. Determine the slope of the line from the following graph.

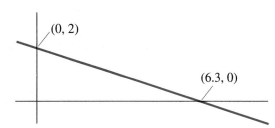

7. Determine the vertical and horizontal intercepts for the graph of each of the following.

a. $y = 2x - 6$

b. $y = -\dfrac{3}{2}x + 10$

c. $y = 10$

8. Determine the equation of each line.

a. The line passes through the points $(2, 0)$ and $(0, -5)$.

b. The slope is 7, and the line passes through the point $\left(0, \dfrac{1}{2}\right)$.

c. The slope is 0, and the line passes through the point $(2, -4)$.

9. Sketch a graph of each of the following. Use your graphing calculator to verify your graphs.

a. $y = 3x - 6$

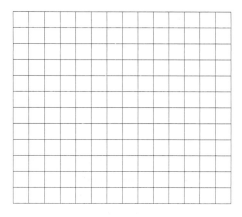

b. $f(x) = -2x + 10$

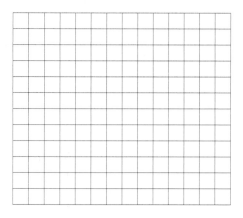

10. Write each equation in slope-intercept form to discover what the graphs have in common. Use your graphing calculator to verify your graphs.

a. $y = 3x - 4$ **b.** $y - 3x = 6$ **c.** $3x - y = 0$

11. Write each equation in slope-intercept form to discover what the graphs have in common. Use your graphing calculator to verify your graphs.

   a. $y = -2$ **b.** $y - 3x = -2$ **c.** $x = y + 2$

12. **a.** Complete the following table by listing four points that are contained on the line $x = 3$.

   b. What is the slope of the line in part a?

   c. Determine the vertical and horizontal intercepts, if any, of the graph of the line in part a.

   d. Does the graph of the line in part a represent a function? Explain.

The bracketed numbers following each concept indicate the activity in which the concept is discussed.

CONCEPT/SKILL	DESCRIPTION	EXAMPLE

Function [7.1]

A function is a rule relating an input variable and an output variable in a way that assigns a single unique output value to each input value.

x	2	4	6	8	10
y	−1	1	2	3	4

Vertical line test [7.1]

In the vertical line test, a graph represents a function of any vertical line drawn through the graph intersects the graph no more than once.

This graph is not a function.

Increasing function [7.1]

The graph of an increasing function rises to the right.

Decreasing function [7.1]

The graph of a decreasing function falls to the right.

Constant function [7.1]

The graph of a constant function is a horizontal line.

Domain of a function [7.2]

The domain of a function is the collection of all meaningful input values. That is, those input values that produce a real-valued output.

$$f(x) = \frac{3}{x + 1}$$

The domain = {real numbers, $x \neq -1$}.

CONCEPT/SKILL	DESCRIPTION	EXAMPLE
Range of a function [7.2]	The range of a function is the collection of all possible output values.	$f(x) = x^2$ The range = {real numbers ≥ 0}.
Practical domain and practical range [7.2]	The practical domain and range are determined by the conditions imposed on the situation being studied.	$C(x) = 35x + 15$ represents the cost to rent a car for x days. The practical domain = {whole numbers ≥ 1}, and the practical range = {50, 85, 120, 155, ...}.
Function notation [7.2]	The notation $f(x)$ is a way to represent the output variable. f is the name of the function and x is the input variable. "$f(x)$" does not represent multiplication.	$f(x) = 2x - 6$
Ways to represent a function [7.2]	A function can be represented numerically by a table, graphically by a curve or scatterplot, verbally by stating how the output value is obtained for a given input, and symbolically using an algebraic rule.	
Delta notation for change [7.3]	Let y_1 and y_2 represent the output values corresponding to inputs x_1 and x_2, respectively. As the variable x changes in value from x_1 to x_2, the change in input is represented by $\Delta x = x_2 - x_1$ and the change in output is represented by $\Delta y = y_2 - y_1$.	Given the input/output pairs $(4, 14)$ and $(10, 32)$, $\Delta x = 10 - 4 = 6$ and $\Delta y = 32 - 14 = 18$.
Average rate of change over an interval [7.3]	The quotient $$\frac{\Delta y}{\Delta x} = \frac{y_2 - y_1}{x_2 - x_1}$$ is called the average rate of change of y (output) with respect to x (input) over the x-interval from x_1 to x_2.	<table><tr><td>x</td><td>−3</td><td>4</td><td>7</td><td>10</td></tr><tr><td>y</td><td>0</td><td>14</td><td>27</td><td>32</td></tr></table> The average rate of change over the interval from $x = 4$ to $x = 10$ is $$\frac{\Delta y}{\Delta x} = \frac{32 - 14}{10 - 4} = \frac{18}{6} = 3.$$
Linear function [7.4]	A linear function is one whose average rate of change of output with respect to input from any one data point to any other data point is always the same (constant) value.	<table><tr><td>x</td><td>1</td><td>2</td><td>3</td><td>4</td></tr><tr><td>f(x)</td><td>10</td><td>15</td><td>20</td><td>25</td></tr></table> The average rate of change between any two of these points is 5.

CONCEPT/SKILL	DESCRIPTION	EXAMPLE
Graph of a linear function [7.4]	The graph of every linear function is a line.	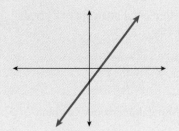
Slope of a line [7.4]	The slope of the line that contains the two points (x_1, y_1) and (x_2, y_2) is denoted by m; $m = \dfrac{\Delta y}{\Delta x} = \dfrac{y_2 - y_1}{x_2 - x_1}$.	The slope of the line containing the two points $(2, 7)$ and $(5, 11)$ is $$\frac{11 - 7}{5 - 2} = \frac{4}{3}.$$
Positive slope [7.4]	The graph of every linear function with positive slope is a line rising to the right. A linear function is increasing if its slope is positive.	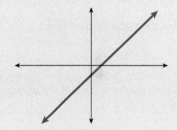
Negative slope [7.5]	The graph of every linear function with negative slope is a line falling to the right. A linear function is decreasing if its slope is negative.	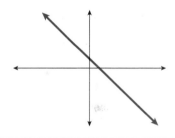
Zero slope [7.5]	The graph of every linear function with zero slope is a horizontal line. Every point on a horizontal line has the same output value.	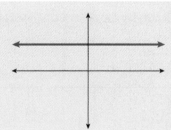
Undefined slope [7.5]	A line whose slope is not defined (because its denominator is zero) is a vertical line. A vertical line is the only line that does not represent a function. Every point on a vertical line has the same input value.	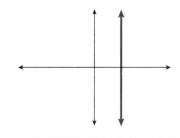

CONCEPT/SKILL	DESCRIPTION	EXAMPLE
Horizontal intercept of a graph [7.5]	The horizontal intercept is the point at which the graph crosses the horizontal axis. Its ordered-pair notation is $(a, 0)$; that is, the second coordinate is equal to zero.	A line with horizontal intercept $(-3, 0)$ crosses the (input) x-axis 3 units to the left of the origin.
Vertical intercept of a graph [7.5]	The vertical intercept is the point at which the graph crosses the vertical axis. Its ordered-pair notation is $(0, b)$; that is, the first coordinate is equal to zero.	A line with vertical intercept $(0, 5)$ crosses the (output) y-axis 5 units above the origin.
Equation of a horizontal line [7.5]	The slope, m, of a horizontal line is 0, and the output of each of its points is the same constant value, c. Its equation is $y = c$.	An equation of the horizontal line through the point $(-2, 3)$ is $y = 3$.
Equation of a vertical line [7.5]	The input of each point on a vertical line is the same constant value, d. Its equation is $x = d$.	An equation of the vertical line through the point $(-2, 3)$ is $x = -2$.
Slope-intercept form of the equation of a line [7.6]	Represent the input variable by x, the output variable by y. Denote the slope of the line by m, the y-intercept by $(0, b)$. Then the coordinate pair, (x, y), of *every* point on the line satisfies the equation $y = mx + b$.	The line with equation $y = 3x + 4$ has a slope of 3 and y-intercept $(0, 4)$. The point $(2, 10)$ is on the line because its coordinates satisfy the equation $$10 = 3(2) + 4.$$
Rewriting the equation of a line in slope-intercept form [7.7] Identifying the slope and y-intercept [7.7]	A nonvertical line whose equation is not in slope-intercept form can be rewritten in slope-intercept form by solving the equation for y. The slope can now be identified as the coefficient of the x-term. The y-intercept can be identified as the constant term.	The equation of the line $5x - 2y = 6$ can be rewritten by solving for y: $-2y = 6 - 5x$ Subtract $5x$. $\dfrac{-2y}{-2} = \dfrac{6}{-2} - \dfrac{5x}{-2}$ Divide by -2. $y = -3 + \dfrac{5}{2}x$ or $y = \dfrac{5}{2}x - 3$ The slope is $\dfrac{5}{2}$. The y-intercept is $(0, -3)$.
Using the slope and y-intercept to write an equation of the line [7.7]	Given a line whose slope is m and y-intercept is $(0, b)$, an equation of the line is $$y = mx + b.$$	An equation of the line with slope $\dfrac{2}{3}$ and y-intercept $(0, -6)$ is $$y = \dfrac{2}{3}x - 6.$$

CONCEPT/SKILL	DESCRIPTION	EXAMPLE
Determining the x-intercept of a line given its equation [7.7]	Because the x-intercept is the point whose y-coordinate is 0, set $y = 0$ in the equation and solve for x.	Given the line with equation $$y = 2x + 6,$$ set $y = 0$ to obtain equation $$0 = 2x + 6$$ $$-6 = 2x$$ $$-3 = x.$$ The x-intercept is $(-3, 0)$.

1. Determine the slope and vertical intercept of the line whose equation is $4y + 10x - 16 = 0$.

2. Determine the equation of the line through the points $(1, 0)$ and $(-2, 6)$.

3. Estimate the slope of the following line, and use the slope to determine an equation for the line.

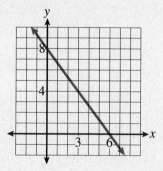

4. Match the graphs with the given equations. Assume that x is the input variable and y is the output variable. Each tick mark on the axes represents 1 unit.

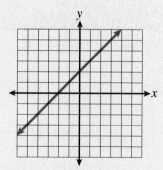 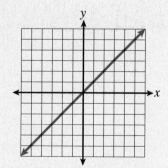 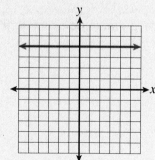

a. $y = x - 6$ **b.** $y = 4$ **c.** $y = x + 2$

d. $y = -3x - 5$ **e.** $y = x$ **f.** $y = 4 - 3x$

Answers to all Gateway exercises are included in the Selected Answers appendix.

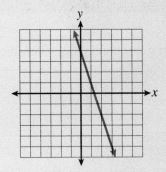 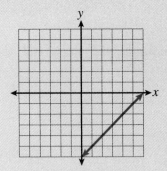 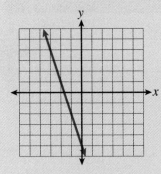

a. $y = x - 6$ **b.** $y = 4$ **c.** $y = x + 2$

d. $y = -3x - 5$ **e.** $y = x$ **f.** $y = 4 - 3x$

5. What is the equation of the line passing through the points $(0, 5)$ and $(2, 11)$? Write the final result in slope-intercept form, $y = mx + b$.

6. The equation of a line is $5x - 10y = 20$. Determine the horizontal and vertical intercepts.

7. Determine the horizontal and vertical intercepts of the line whose equation is $-3x + 4y = 12$. Use the intercepts to graph the line.

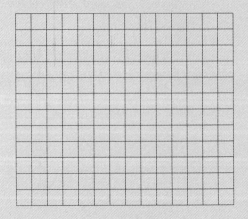

8. Determine the equation of the line that passes through the point $(0, -4)$ and has slope $\frac{5}{3}$.

CHAPTER 8

MORE PROBLEM SOLVING WITH ALGEBRA AND MATHEMATICAL MODELS

Throughout this book you have solved problems from everyday life—science, business, sports, social issues, space design, and so on—that require mathematics. This approach emphasizes the fact that searching for solutions to some kinds of problems resulted in the development of the mathematics we use today. For example, the early Egyptians developed their geometry to recalculate yearly the boundaries of the lands owned by farmers because of the seasonal flooding of the Nile River.

When applied to solve problems or to describe a situation, the mathematics used became known as the **mathematical model** for the problem or situation. In this chapter you will develop your problem-solving skills further by using mathematical models in several different formats. You will recognize these formats from the previous chapters: symbolic equations, formulas, graphs, and tables.

You are a college intern in a law office. The office manager asks you to get information about leasing a copy machine for the office. You will then use the information to estimate how much a machine will cost your office.

The sales representative from Eastern Supply Company recommends a 50-copy per minute copier for your office. The copier will cost $455 per month plus 1.5 cents a copy.

Do the following problems to figure out how much your office would pay for leasing a copier from the Eastern Supply Company.

✳ ACTIVITY 8.1

Leasing a Copier

OBJECTIVES

1. Describe a mathematical situation as a set of verbal statements.

2. Translate verbal rules into symbolic equations.

3. Solve problems involving equations of the form $y = ax + b$.

4. Solve equations of the form $y = ax + b$ for the input x.

5. Evaluate expressions $ax + b$ in the equations of the form $y = ax + b$ to obtain an output y.

1. **a.** The total monthly cost for leasing the copier depends upon the number of copies made. Identify the input variable and the output variable.

   b. Note that the monthly cost is expressed by the sum of two parts, a fixed cost of $455 and a cost of 1.5 cents per copy. The units of the two parts, dollars and cents, are different. One of the units has to be converted to the other unit. Convert 1.5 cents to dollars.

c. Write a verbal rule to determine the output (monthly cost) in terms of the input (number of copies).

d. Translate the verbal rule obtained in part c into an equation. Use *n* for the input variable and *c* for the output variable.

2. a. Use the equation obtained in Problem 1d to determine the monthly cost if 12,000 copies are made each month.

b. Calculate the monthly cost if 20,000 copies are made each month.

In Problem 1, the equation, $c = 0.015n + 455$ was developed to determine the leasing charges. In Problem 2, you determined the leasing charges by evaluating the expression $0.015n + 455$ for a known number of copies. The following example shows an algebraic approach to determine the number of copies that can be made for a known monthly cost.

EXAMPLE 1   *Suppose the monthly budget for leasing the copier from Eastern Office Supply is $800. How many copies can the law office make for that budgeted amount?*

SOLUTION

Step 1   Recognize that $800 is the output (monthly cost) value and that the unknown value is the input (number of copies) corresponding to the $800.

Step 2   Replace *c* in the equation $c = 0.015n + 455$ with 800 to obtain the equation

$$800 = 0.015n + 455.$$

Step 3   Solve the equation to determine the input value.

a.
$$\begin{array}{r} 800 = 0.015n + 455 \\ -455 \qquad\qquad -455 \\ \hline 345 = 0.015n \end{array}$$
Subtract 455 from each side of the equation to obtain 0.015n as a single term on the right side of the equation.

b.
$$\frac{345}{0.015} = \frac{\cancel{0.015}n}{\cancel{0.015}}$$
Divide each term in the equation by 0.015.

$$23000 = n$$
23,000 copies can be made.

Step 4 Check the solution:

$$c = 0.015(23000) + 455$$

$$c = 345 + 455$$

$$c = 800$$

Step 5 Interpret the solution of the equation by stating: The law office can make 23,000 copies per month on a budget of $800.

3. How many copies can the office make if the copier budget is $950?

4. The equation $120 = 3x + 90$ is solved for x as follows.

$$120 = 3x + 90$$

Step 1: $\quad \underline{-90 \qquad\quad -90}$

$$30 = 3x$$

Step 2: $\quad \dfrac{30}{3} = \dfrac{3x}{3}$

$$10 = x \quad \text{or} \quad x = 10$$

a. In step 1, what operation is used to remove 90 from each side of the equation and why?

b. In step 2, what operation is used to remove 3 from the term $3x$ and why?

5. Solve the equation $12 = 5x - 8$ for x. At each step, state the operation you used and state why you used it.

6. In each of the following, an equation is given along with a specific output value. Replace the output variable y in the given equation with the specified value and solve the resulting equation for the unknown input x. Check each answer.

a. $y = 3x - 5$ and $y = 10$ **b.** $y = 30 - 2x$ and $y = 24$

c. $y = .75x - 21$ and $y = -9$ **d.** $y = -2x + 15$ and $y = -3$

Verbal rules and equations can also be used to make lists of paired input/output values. For example, if a firm has to pay sales tax on office supplies, the firm's purchasing agent may use an equation to determine the final cost after taxes. Also, for quick reference, a table listing the most common costs before and after taxes can be made (see Problem 7).

7. Suppose your law office has to pay a 4% sales tax on office supplies it purchases. That means that, the final cost of the item is determined by multiplying the price of the item by the growth factor, $104\% = 1.04$, that is associated with the 4% sales tax.

a. Use y to represent the final cost of a purchase and x to represent the cost of the items before tax. Write an equation to calculate the final cost of a purchase.

b. Use the equation from part a to complete the following table.

COST BEFORE TAX, x (in dollars)	FINAL COST AFTER TAX, y (in dollars)
100	
	260
375	
	624

8. In each of the following problems, use the equation to complete the table.

a. $y = 4x - 11$

x	y
6	
	53

b. $y = -5x - 80$

x	y
12	
	35

**SUMMARY
ACTIVITY 8.1**

1. To determine the output y for a specified input x in an equation of the form $y = ax + b$:

   Step 1: Replace the input variable x in the expression $ax + b$ with the specified numerical value.

   Step 2: Evaluate the numerical expression to obtain the numerical value for y.

   Example: Solve $y = 2x + 1$ for y, given $x = 3$.

   $$y = 2 \cdot 3 + 1$$
   $$y = 7$$

2. To solve an equation of the form $y = ax + b$ for the unknown value of the input x, given a specified numerical value of the output y:

   Use inverse operations to isolate the unknown x. Apply the inverse operations in the following order.

   Step 1: Add the opposite of b to each side of the equation.

   Step 2: Divide each term in the resulting equation by a to isolate x and then read the value for x.

   Example: Solve $5 = 2x - 1$ for x.

   $$5 = 2x - 1$$
   $$\underline{+1 \qquad +1}$$
   $$6 = 2x$$
   $$\frac{6}{2} = \frac{2x}{2}$$
   $$x = 3$$

1. You are planning on taking some courses at your local community college on a part-time basis for the upcoming semester. For a student who carries fewer than 12 credits (the full-time minimum), the tuition is $155 for each credit hour taken. All part-time and full-time students must pay a $20 parking fee for the semester. This fixed fee is added directly to your tuition bill.

   a. Write an equation to determine the total tuition bill, t, for a student carrying fewer than 12 credit hours. Use n for the number of credit hours.

   b. Use the equation you wrote in part a to complete the following table.

Paying for Credit

NUMBER OF CREDIT HOURS, n	1	2	3	4	5	6
TOTAL TUITION, t						

   c. Determine the tuition bill if you take 9 credit hours.

   d. You have $1000 to spend on tuition. How many credit hours can you carry for the semester?

2. Use an algebraic approach to solve each of the following equations for x. Check your answers by hand or with a calculator.

   a. $10 = 2x + 12$ b. $-27 = -5x - 7$

   c. $3x - 26 = -14$ d. $24 - 2x = 38$

   e. $5x - 15 = 15$ f. $-4x + 8 = 8$

g. $12 + \dfrac{1}{5}x = 9$

h. $\dfrac{2}{3}x - 12 = 0$

i. $0.25x - 14.5 = 10$

j. $5 = 2.5x - 20$

3. A long-distance telephone rate plan costs \$4.95 a month plus 10 cents per minute, or part thereof, for any long-distance call made during the month.

a. Write a verbal rule to determine the total monthly cost for your long-distance calls.

b. Translate the verbal rule in part a into an equation using c to represent the total monthly cost and n to represent the total number of long-distance minutes for the month.

c. Determine the monthly cost if 250 minutes of long-distance calls are made.

d. If you can spend up to \$50 for long-distance calls in one month, what will your total number of long-distance minutes be for the month? Check your answer.

4. The social psychology class is planning a fund-raising project to benefit local charities. As a member of the fund-raiser budget committee, you suggest a \$10 per person admission donation for food, nonalcoholic beverages, and entertainment. The committee determines that the total fixed costs for the event (food, drinks, posters, and tickets) will total \$2100. The college is donating the use of the gymnasium for the evening.

a. The total money collected from admissions (revenue) depends on the number, n, of students who attend. Write an expression in terms of n that represents the total revenue if n students attend.

b. Profit is the money remaining after expenses are deducted from the revenue. Write an equation expressing the profit, p, in terms of the number, n, of students who attend.

c. If the gymnasium holds a maximum of 700 people, what is the maximum amount of money that can be donated to charity?

d. Suppose that the members of the fund-raiser budget committee want to be able to donate at least $1500 to local charities. How many students must attend in order to have a profit of $1500?

5. The value of many things we own, such as a car, computer, or appliance, depreciates (goes down) over time. When an asset's value decreases by a fixed amount each year, the depreciation is called straight-line depreciation. Suppose a car has an initial value of $12,400 and depreciates $820 per year.

a. Let v represent the value of a car after t years. Write a symbolic rule that expresses v in terms of t.

b. What is the value of the car after 4 years?

c. How long will it take for the value of the car to decrease below $2000?

6. The cost, c, in dollars, of mailing a priority overnight package weighing 1 pound or more is given by the formula $c = 2.085x + 15.08$, where x represents the weight of the package in pounds.

a. Determine the cost of mailing a package that weighs 10 pounds.

b. Determine the weight of the package if it cost $56.78 to mail.

7. Archaeologists and forensic scientists use the length of human bones to estimate the height of individuals. A person's height, h, in centimeters can be determined from the length of the femur, f (the bone from the knee to the hip socket), in centimeters using the following formulas:

   Male: $h = 69.089 + 2.238f$ Female: $h = 61.412 + 2.317f$

   a. A partial skeleton of a male is found. The femur measures 50 centimeters. How tall was the man?

   b. What is the length of the femur for a female who is 150 centimeters tall?

8. Let p represent the perimeter of an isosceles triangle that has two equal sides of length a and a third side of length b. Determine the length of the equal sides of an isosceles triangle having a perimeter of $\frac{3}{4}$ meter and third side measuring $\frac{1}{3}$ meter.

9. The recommended weight for an adult male is given by the formula $w = \dfrac{11}{2}h - 220$, where w represents the recommended weight in pounds and h represents the height of the person in inches. Determine the height of an adult whose recommended weight is 165 pounds.

10. Complete the following tables using algebraic methods.

a. $y = 2x - 10$

x	y
4	
	14

b. $y = 20 + 0.5x$

x	y
3.5	
	−10

c. $y = -3x + 15$

x	y
$\frac{2}{3}$	
	−3

d. $y = 12 - \frac{3}{4}x$

x	y
−8	
	−6

ACTIVITY 8.2

Windchill

OBJECTIVES

1. Evaluate expressions to determine the output for a formula.

2. Solve formulas for a specified variable.

Have you ever wondered why people blow on hot things to cool them down? Blowing creates the effect of wind. The faster the wind blows, the faster things lose their heat. This cooling effect is called **windchill**. For example, on two different days, the temperature may be 25°F, but depending on the wind, you may feel colder one of the days. If there is no wind, a temperature of 25°F may not feel very cold. However, if the wind is blowing hard, the same 25°F may feel like −10°F.

Being curious about the mathematical relationship between temperature and wind speed, you search the Internet and find a windchill chart at www.nws.noaa.gov/om/windchill/, developed by the National Weather Service. A portion of the chart, or table, is reproduced here.

WINDCHILL CHART

Wind Speed (mph)

Air Temperature (°F)	5	10	25	30
35	31	27	23	22
30	25	21		15
25	19		9	8
20	13	9		1
15	7	3	−4	−5
10	1	−4		−12
5	−5		−17	−19
0	−11	−16	−24	−26
−5	−16	−22	−31	−33
−10	−22	−28	−37	−39
−15	−28	−35		−46
−20	−34	−41	−51	−53

The table indicates, for example, that when the air temperature is 15°F and the wind speed is 10 mph, the windchill temperature is 3°F. This means that it will feel like 3°F when the wind is blowing at 10 mph.

1. **a.** What is the windchill temperature when the air temperature is 5°F and there is a 25 mph wind?

   b. What was the wind speed on the day the air temperature was 25°F and the windchill was 9°F?

c. Examine the columns of the windchill chart and list some of the patterns you discover. According to the patterns you observe, estimate the missing values in the chart.

2. The windchill temperature, w, produced by a 30-mph wind can be approximated by the formula

$$w = 1.36t - 25.86,$$

where t represents the air temperature in degrees Fahrenheit.

a. Complete the following table using the given formula. Round to the nearest whole number.

It's a Breeze

AIR TEMPERATURE, t	−15	5	30
EQUIVALENT WINDCHILL TEMPERATURE, w (30-mph wind)			

b. How do these windchill temperatures compare to the values given in the chart for a 30-mph wind?

3. Use the formula $w = 1.36t - 25.86$ in the following problems.

a. Determine the windchill temperature if the air temperature is 7°F when there is a 30-mph wind.

b. On a cold day in New York City, the wind is blowing at 30 mph. If the windchill temperature was reported to be −18°F, then what was the air temperature on that day?

Note that in the formula, $w = 1.36t - 25.86$, the variable w is on one side of the equation, isolated from the expression $1.36t - 25.86$. This allows for determining values of w directly. Simply substitute the desired value for t in the expression and evaluate. For example, in Problem 3a, 7 was substituted for t in $1.36t - 25.86$ to obtain a windchill of approximately −16°F.

$$w = 1.36(7) - 25.86 \approx -16°F.$$

However, in Problem 3b, to determine t for a given value of w the equation $w = 1.36t - 25.86$ had to be solved for t, after substituting -18 for w into the equation.

If you had to determine the corresponding t value for several different w values, you would have to solve an equation each time. It is more efficient to solve the original formula $w = 1.36t - 25.86$ for t.

EXAMPLE 1 *Solve the formula $w = 1.36t - 25.86$ for t. The procedure is similar to solving the equation $-18 = 1.36t - 25.86$ for t.*

$$
\begin{array}{ll}
\begin{aligned}
-18 \;\; &= 1.36t - 25.86 \\
+ 25.86 \;\; & \qquad\quad + 25.86 \\
\hline
7.86 &= 1.36t
\end{aligned} &
\begin{aligned}
w \;\; &= 1.36t - 25.86 \\
+ 25.86 \;\; & \qquad\quad + 25.86 \\
\hline
w + 25.86 &= 1.36t
\end{aligned} \quad \text{Add 25.86 to each side}
\end{array}
$$

$$
\begin{array}{ll}
\dfrac{7.86}{1.36} = \dfrac{1.36t}{1.36} &
\dfrac{w + 25.86}{1.36} = \dfrac{1.36t}{1.36} \quad \text{Divide each side by 1.36}
\end{array}
$$

$$
\begin{array}{ll}
5.8 = t &
\dfrac{w + 25.86}{1.36} = t
\end{array}
$$

The new formula is $t = \dfrac{w + 25.86}{1.36}$, which is approximately equivalent to $t = 0.735w + 19.015$.

To solve the equation $w = 1.36t - 25.86$ for t means to isolate the variable t, with coefficient 1, on one side of the equation, with all other expressions on the opposite side of the $=$ sign.

4. Rework Problem 3b using the new formula that is solved for t. How does your answer here compare to your answer in Problem 3b?

5. **a.** If the wind speed is 15 mph, the windchill can be approximated by the formula $w = 1.28t - 19.38$, where t is the air temperature in degrees Fahrenheit. Solve the formula for t.

   b. Use the new formula from part a to determine the air temperature, t, if the windchill temperature is $-10°F$.

Weather Balloon

6. A weather balloon carrying instruments that measure temperature is launched at sea level. After the balloon is launched, the data collected shows that the temperature dropped 0.15°F for each meter that the balloon rose.

    a. If the temperature at sea level is 50°F, determine the temperature at a distance of 60 meters above sea level.

    b. Write a verbal rule to determine the temperature at a given distance above sea level on a 50°F day.

    c. If t represents the temperature (°F) a distance of m meters above sea level, translate the verbal rule in part b into a formula.

    d. Use the formula from part c to complete the following table.

Weather or Not

METERS ABOVE SEA LEVEL, m	50	75	100
TEMPERATURE, t (°F)			

7. a. Solve the formula $t = 50 - 0.15m$ for m.

    b. Water freezes at 32°F. Determine the distance above sea level that water will freeze. Use the new formula from part a.

Crickets and Temperature

A familiar late-evening sound during the summer is the rhythmic chirping of a male cricket. Of particular interest is the snowy tree cricket, sometimes called the temperature cricket. It is very sensitive to temperature, speeding up or slowing down its chirping as the temperature rises or falls.

Data show that the number, n, of chirps per minute of the snowy tree cricket is related to the temperature t (°F) by the formula

$$t = \frac{1}{4}n + 40.$$

8. a. If a cricket chirps 60 times in 1 minute, what is the temperature?

b. Solve the equation $t = \frac{1}{4}n + 40$ for n.

c. If the temperature is 80°F, use the formula from part b to determine the expected number of chirps made by the cricket in 1 minute.

Additional Practice

9. Solve each of the following formulas for the indicated variable.

a. $A = \frac{1}{2}bh$ for h

b. $p = c + m$ for m

c. $P = 2l + 2w$ for l

d. $R = 165 - 0.75a$ for a

SUMMARY
ACTIVITY 8.2

To solve an equation for a specific variable means to isolate that variable, with coefficient 1, on one side of the equation.

EXERCISES
ACTIVITY 8.2

1. The speed, S, of an ant (in centimeters per second) is related to the temperature, t (in degrees Celsius), by the formula

$$s = 0.167t - 0.67.$$

a. If an ant is moving at 4 centimeters per second, what is the temperature?

b. Solve the equation $s = 0.167t - 0.67$ for t.

c. Use the new formula from part b to answer part a.

2. The National Weather Service reports the daily temperature in degrees Fahrenheit. The scientific community, as well as Canada and most of Europe, reports temperature in degrees Celsius. The Celsius, C, and Fahrenheit, F, temperature readings are related by the formula

$$F = 1.8C + 32.$$

a. Determine the Fahrenheit reading corresponding to the temperature at which water boils, 100°C.

b. Solve the formula $F = 1.8C + 32$ for C.

c. Use the formula from part b to determine the Celsius temperature when the outdoor temperature is 80°F.

3. The number of women enrolled in college has been steadily increasing. The following table gives the enrollment of women, in millions, in a given year.

Enrolling Along

YEAR	1970	1975	1980	1985	1990	1995	2000
WOMEN ENROLLED (in millions)	3.5	5.0	6.0	6.6	7.4	8.0	8.9

Let t represent the number of years since 1970. The number of women, n (in millions), enrolled in college can be approximated by the formula

$$n = 0.17t + 3.9.$$

a. Use the formula to estimate the year that the number of women enrolled in college will reach 10 million.

b. Solve the equation $n = 0.17t + 3.9$ for t.

c. Use the formula in part b to estimate the year that the number of women enrolled in college will reach 10 million.

4. The pressure, p, of sea water (in pounds per square foot) at a depth of d feet below the surface is given by the formula

$$p = 15 + \frac{15}{33}d.$$

a. On November 14, 1993, Francisco Ferreras achieved a record depth for breath-held diving. During the dive, he experienced a pressure of 201 pounds per square foot. What record depth did he reach?

b. Solve the equation $p = 15 + \frac{15}{33}d$ for d.

c. Use the new formula from part b to answer part a.

Solve each of the following formulas for the given variable.

5. $E = IR$ for I

6. $C = 2\pi r$ for r

7. $P = 2a + b$ for b

8. $P = R - C$ for R

9. $P = 2l + 2w$ for w

10. $R = 143 - 0.65a$ for a

11. $A = P + Prt$ for r

12. $y = mx + b$ for m

◆ ACTIVITY 8.3

Comparing Energy Costs

OBJECTIVES

1. Write symbolic equations from information organized in a table.

2. Produce tables and graphs to compare outputs from two different mathematical models.

3. Solve equations of the form $ax + b = cx + d$.

You hired an architect to design a house. She gave you the following information regarding the installation and operating costs for two types of heating systems: solar and electric. You will use the information to compare the costs for each heating system over a period of years. The following questions will guide you in making the comparisons.

Some Like It Hot

TYPE OF SYSTEM	OPERATING COST PER YEAR	INSTALLATION COST
Solar	$200	$19,000
Electric	$1400	$7,000

1. **a.** Use the information in the table to write an equation to represent the total cost of using solar heat in terms of the number of years it is in use. Let x represent the number of years of use and let S represent the total cost.

   b. Write an equation to represent the total cost of using electric heat in terms of the number of years it is in use. Let x represent the number of years of use and let E represent the total cost.

You can use the equations you wrote in Problem 1 to compare costs for the two systems in several ways. One way is to produce a table of costs for specific periods of use.

2. **a.** Use the equations from Problem 1 to complete the following table.

NUMBER OF YEARS IN USE, x	0	5	10	15
TOTAL COST FOR SOLAR HEAT, S ($)				
TOTAL COST FOR ELECTRIC HEAT, E ($)				

   b. Use the information in the table to compare the total costs of each system after each 5-year period.

   c. From comparing the total costs in the table, which system do you think is the better one for the house you are building?

You can also do comparisons by graphing the information from the table.

3. a. On the following grid, plot the data points for the solar heating system that you determined in Problem 2. Then connect the points by drawing a line through them.

   b. On the same grid, also plot the data points for the electric heating system and connect the points by drawing a line through them.

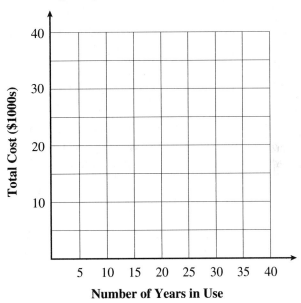

Comparing Costs of Heating Systems

   c. From the graph, when are the total costs for the heating systems the same? How much is the cost?

   d. Which heating system costs less at 15 years? at 20? Explain.

   e. From comparing the total costs on the graph, which system do you think is the better one for the house you are building?

In Problems 2 and 3 you observed that the table and the graph led to the same result: the costs are the same at 10 years of use and that the cost of the solar system was less after more than 10 years. The point at which both systems cost the same is useful in making decisions about which heating method is better in terms of cost. When used to compare costs, this point is often referred to as the **break-even point**. You can calculate the break-even point using algebra, as the following example shows.

EXAMPLE 1   *The comparison model for the two heating systems in the preceding problems includes two equations.*

$$S = 200x + 19,000$$
$$E = 1400x + 7000$$

The break-even point occurs when the outputs from the solar and electric heating systems are the same at the same time (for the same input value). This means $S = E$, or equivalently,

$$200x + 19,000 = 1400x + 7000.$$

This single equation can be solved for x to determine the number of years of use when the costs will be the same for both systems.

SOLUTION

First, add and/or subtract terms appropriately so that all terms involving the variable are on one side of the equal sign and all other terms are on the other side.

$200x + 19,000 =$	$1400x + 7000$	**Subtract 200x from both sides and combine**
$- 200x$	$= -200x$	**like terms.**
$19,000 =$	$1200x + 7000$	**Subtract 7000 from each side and combine**
$- 7,000 =$	-7000	**like terms.**
$12,000 =$	$1200x$	**Divide each term by 1200, the coefficient of x.**
	$x = 10$ yr.	

In checking the solution to the equation, you will also determine the total cost at 10 years.

$$200(10) + 19,000 = 21,000$$
$$1400(10) + 7000 = 21,000$$

The check shows that 10 is the correct solution and that the total cost after 10 years is $21,000. So the break-even point occurs at 10 years.

4. You are interested in purchasing a new car. You have narrowed the choice to a Honda Accord LX (4 cylinder) and a Passat GLS (4 cylinder). You are concerned about the depreciation of the cars' values over time and want to make some comparisons. You search the Internet and obtain the following information:

Driven Down. . .

MODEL OF CAR	MSRP (Manufacturer's Suggested Retail Price)	STRAIGHT LINE DEPRECIATION EACH YEAR
Accord LX	$22,600	$2,240
Passat GLS	$25,000	$2,640

a. Let A represent the value, in dollars, of the Accord LX after x years of ownership. Use the information in the table to write an equation to determine A in terms of x.

b. Write an equation to determine the value, P, in dollars, of the Passat GLS after x years of ownership.

c. Use the equations from parts a and b to write a single equation to determine when the value of the Accord LX will equal the value of the Passat GLS.

d. Solve the equation in part c to determine the year in which the cars will have the same value.

e. Complete the following table to compare the values of the cars over several years.

NUMBER OF YEARS YOU OWN CAR	VALUE OF ACCORD LX ($)	VALUE OF PASSAT GLS ($)
1		
4		
8		

5. Solve each of the following equations for x. Check your answers, by hand or with a calculator.

a. $2x + 9 = 5x - 12$

b. $21 - x = -3 - 5x$

c. $2x - 6 = -8$

d. $2x - 8 + 6 = 4x - 7$

SUMMARY
ACTIVITY 8.3

General Strategy for Solving Equations for an Unknown, *x*

1. Rewrite the equation to obtain a single term containing *x* on one side of the equation. Do this by adding and/or subtracting terms to move the *x* terms to one side of the equation and all the other terms to the other side. Then combine like terms that appear on the same side of the equation.

2. Solve for the unknown *x* by dividing each side of the equation by the coefficient of *x*.

3. Check the result to be sure that the value of the unknown produces a true statement.

EXERCISES
ACTIVITY 8.3

1. Finals are over and you are moving back home for the summer. You need to rent a truck to move your possessions from the college residence hall. You contact two local rental companies and get the following information for the one-day cost of renting a truck.

> Company 1: $39.95 per day plus $0.19 per mile
> Company 2: $19.95 per day plus $0.49 per mile

Let *x* represent the number of miles driven in one day.

a. Write an equation that represents the total cost in dollars of renting a truck for one day from Company 1.

b. Write an equation that represents the total cost in dollars of renting a truck for one day from Company 2.

c. Using the equations in parts a and b, write a single equation to determine the mileage for which the cost would be the same from both companies.

d. Solve the equation in part c.

e. You actually live 90 miles from the campus. Which rental company would be the better deal?

2. Two companies sell software products. In 2006, Company 1 had total sales of $17.2 million. Its marketing department projects that sales will increase by $1.5 million per year for the next several years. Company 2 had total sales of $9.6 million for software products in 2006 and predicts that its sales will increase on the average $2.3 million each year. Let x represent the number of years since 2006.

   a. Write an equation that represents the total sales, in millions of dollars, of Company 1 since 2006.

   b. Write an equation that represents the total sales, in millions of dollars, of Company 2 since 2006.

   c. Write a single equation to determine when the total sales of the two companies will be the same.

   d. Solve the equation in part c.

3. You are considering installing a security system in your new house. You get the following information from two local home security dealers for similar security systems.

   Dealer 1: $3,560 to install and $15 per month monitoring fee.

   Dealer 2: $2,850 to install and $28 per month for monitoring.

   Note that the initial cost of the security system from Dealer 1 is much higher than from Dealer 2, but the monitoring fee is lower.

   Let x represent the number of months that you have the security system.

   a. Write an equation that represents the total cost of the system with Dealer 1.

   b. Write an equation that represents the total cost of the system with Dealer 2.

   c. Write a single equation to determine when the total cost of the systems will be equal.

d. Solve the equation in part c.

e. If you plan to live in the house and use the system for 10 years, which system would be less expensive?

4. The life expectancies for men and women in the United States can be approximated by the following formulas

$$\text{Women: } E = 0.126t + 76.74$$
$$\text{Men: } \quad E = 0.169t + 69.11,$$

where E represents the length of life in years and t represents the year of birth, measured as the number of years since 1975.

a. Write a single equation that can be used to determine in what year of birth the life expectancy of men and women would be the same.

b. Solve the equation in part a.

c. What is the life expectancy for the year of birth determined in part b?

In Exercises 5–10, solve each of the given equations for x. Check your answers by hand or with a calculator.

5. $5x - 4 = 3x - 6$

6. $3x - 14 = 6x + 4$

7. $0.5x + 9 = 4.5x + 17$

8. $4x - 10 = -2x + 8$

9. $0.3x - 5.5 = 0.2x + 2.6$

10. $4 - 0.025x = 0.1 - 0.05x$

✳ACTIVITY 8.4

Volume of a Storage Tank

OBJECTIVES

1. Use the property of exponents to multiply powers having the same base.

2. Use the property of exponents to raise a power to a power.

3. Use the distributive property and properties of exponents to write an expression as an equivalent expression in expanded form.

The volume V (in cubic feet) of a partially cylindrical gasoline storage tank is represented by the formula

$$V = r^2(4.2r + 37.7),$$

where r is the radius (in feet) of the cylindrical part of the tank.

1. Determine the volume of the tank if its radius is 3 feet.

First Property of Exponents

Suppose you were asked to write the expression $r^2(4.2r + 37.7)$ as an equivalent expression without parentheses. Using the distributive property, you would multiply each term within the parentheses by r^2.

$$r^2(4.2r + 37.7)$$

The first product is $r^2(4.2r)$ and the second product is $r^2(37.7)$. In the first product you need to multiply r^2 and r. Recall that in the expression r^2, the exponent 2 indicates that the base r is used as a factor two times. In the expression $r = r^1$, the exponent 1 indicates that the base r is used as a factor once.

$$r^2 \cdot r = \underbrace{r \cdot r \cdot r}_{} = r^3$$

Base r is used as a factor 3 times.

So the volume of the tank can also be expressed as $4.2r^3 + 37.7r^2$.

2. a. Complete the following table:

INPUT r	OUTPUT FOR $r^2 \cdot r$	OUTPUT FOR r^3
2		
4		
5		

b. How does the table demonstrate that $r^2 \cdot r$ is equivalent to r^3?

3. Simplify each expression by rewriting the base with a single exponent.

a. $x \cdot x^4$ **b.** $w^2 \cdot w^5$

c. $a^2 \cdot a^3 \cdot a^4$ **d.** $x \cdot x^2 \cdot x^3$

4. What pattern do you observe in Problem 3?

The results of Problems 2, 3, and 4 lead to the first property of exponents.

First Property of Exponents

If m and n represent positive integers, then

$$b^m \cdot b^n = b^{m+n}.$$

5. Does $x^3 t^4 = xt^7$? Explain.

6. a. Multiply: $(2x^3)(3x^4)$

b. What is the coefficient of the product in part a? Explain how you obtained this coefficient.

PROCEDURE

Multiplying a Series of Factors

1. Multiply the numerical coefficients.
2. Simplify the product of the variable factors with the same base by applying the first property of exponents. That is, if m and n represent positive integers, then $b^m \cdot b^n = b^{m+n}$.

7. Multiply the following.

a. $(-3x^2)(4x^3)$ **b.** $(5a^3)(3a^5)$

c. $(a^3 b^2)(ab^3)(b)$ **d.** $(3.5x)(-0.1x^4)$

e. $(r^2)(4.2r)$

8. Use the distributive property and the first property of exponents to write each of the following expressions in expanded form.

a. $x^3(x^2 + 3x - 2)$ **b.** $-2x(x^2 - 3x + 4)$

c. $2a^3(a^3 + 2a^2 - a + 4)$ **d.** $w^2(3.5w + 2.1)$

Second Property of Exponents

Recall that the volume of a solid (three-dimensional figure) is a measure of the amount of space it encloses. Many common solids have formulas that are used to determine their volume (see Chapter 5). For example, the volume V of a cube is the product of its width, length, and height, all of which have the same length, say a.

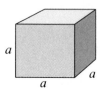

9. a. Write a formula for the volume of a cube, where a represents the length of one of its edges. (Remember that edges of a cube are the same length.)

b. Determine the volume of a cube with edge 2 centimeters.

Suppose that the length, a, of each edge of a cube is squared. The volume of the new cube can be written as $V = (a^2)^3$.

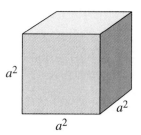

You can rewrite the expression $(a^2)^3$ more simply. First, note that the expression $(a^2)^3$ indicates that the base a^2 is used as a factor three times. Therefore,

$$(a^2)^3 = \underbrace{a^2 a^2 a^2}_{\substack{\text{Base } a^2 \text{ used} \\ \text{as a factor} \\ \text{3 times.}}} = \underbrace{a^{2+2+2}}_{\substack{\text{Property 1} \\ \text{of exponents}}} = a^6$$

The procedure just completed indicates how $(a^2)^3$ can be simplified *without* expanding. Do you see how? Problem 10 provides additional examples that you can use to confirm your observation or help you to discover the property.

10. Perform the given operation.

    a. $(t^3)^5$ **b.** $(y^2)^4$ **c.** $(x^6)^3$

The pattern demonstrated by Problem 10 leads to the second property of exponents.

Second Property of Exponents

If m and n represent positive integers, then $(b^m)^n = b^{mn}$.

11. Use the properties of exponents to simplify each of the following expressions.

a. $(3^2)^4$

b. $(y^{11})^5$

c. $2(a^5)^3$

d. $x(x^2)^3$

e. $-3(t^2)^4$

f. $(5xy^2)(3x^4y^5)$

12. Expand each of the following expressions by using the distributive property to remove the parentheses and the properties of exponents to multiply the terms.

a. $2x(x^2 + 5)$

b. $y^2(3y - 2y^3)$

c. $ab^2(3a - 2ab + 3b)$

d. $4m^5n^3(3m^2n - 5m^3n^6)$

**SUMMARY
ACTIVITY 8.4**

1. First property of exponents

If m and n represent positive integers, then

$$b^m \cdot b^n = b^{m+n}.$$

2. Second property of exponents

If m and n represent positive integers, then

$$(b^m)^n = b^{mn}.$$

3. To multiply a series of factors such as $3x^4(x^2)^3 2x^3$,

   i. Remove parentheses by applying the second property of exponents.

  ii. Multiply the numerical coefficients.

 iii. Apply the first property of exponents to variable factors that have the same base.

Therefore, $3x^4(x^2)^3 \cdot 2x^3 = 3x^4x^6 \cdot 2x^3 = 6x^{13}$.

Use the properties of exponents to simplify the expressions in Exercises 1–13.

1. $a \cdot a^3$

2. $3x \cdot x^4$

3. $y^2 \cdot y^3 \cdot y^4$

4. $3t^4 \cdot 5t^2$

5. $-3w^2 \cdot 4w^5$

6. $3.4b^5 \cdot 1.05b^3$

8. $(a^5)^3$

8. $4(x^2)^4$

9. $-(x^{10})^5$

10. $(-3x^2)(-4x^7)(2x)$

11. $(-5x^3)(0.5x^6)(2.1y^2)$

12. $(a^2bc^3)(a^3b^2)$

13. $(-2s^2t)(t^2)^3(s^4t)$

Use the distributive property and the properties of exponents to expand the algebraic expressions in Exercises 14–21.

14. $2x(x + 3)$

15. $y(3y - 1)$

16. $x^2(2x^2 + 3x - 1)$

17. $2a(a^3 + 4a - 5)$

18. $5x^3(2x - 10)$

19. $r^4(3.5r - 1.6)$

20. $3t^2(6t^4 - 2t^2 - 1.5)$

21. $1.3x^7(-2x^3 - 6x + 1)$

22. a. You are drawing up plans to enlarge a square patio. You want to triple the lengths of one pair of opposite sides and double the lengths of the other opposite sides. If x represents a side of the square patio, write an equation for the new area, A, in terms of x.

b. You discover from the plan that to allow for bushes, you must take off 3 feet from each side that was doubled. Write an expression in terms of x to represent the length of those sides.

c. Use the result from part b to write an equation without parentheses to represent the new area, A, of the patio. Remember that the lengths of the other sides of the original square patio were tripled.

23. A rectangular bin has the following dimensions:

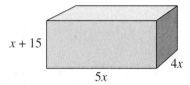

$x + 15$

$5x$

$4x$

a. Write an expression that represents the area of the base of the bin.

b. Use the result from part a to write an equation in expanded form that represents the volume, V, of the bin.

24. A cube measures b^4 units on a side. Write an equation in terms of b that represents the volume of the cube.

25. A square measures $3xy^2$ units on each side. Write an equation that represents the area, A, of the square.

26. A car travels 4 hours at an average speed of $2a - 4$ miles per hour. Let d represent the distance traveled. Write an equation that expresses d in terms of the time traveled and the average speed. Leave your final equation in expanded form.

● ACTIVITY 8.5

Math Magic

OBJECTIVES

1. Recognize an algebraic expression as a code of instructions to obtain an output.

2. Simplify algebraic expressions.

Algebraic expressions arise every time a sequence of arithmetic operations is applied to an input variable. The sequence of operations transforms a given value for the input variable into a single corresponding output value.

Perhaps you have watched magicians on TV who astonish their audiences by correctly guessing the number that a volunteer has secretly picked. In the following example of math magic, assume that the input values in the table are the numbers secretly chosen by three different volunteers.

INPUT x (number selected)	OUTPUT y (result of sequence of operations)
3	
4	
6	

Each volunteer is asked to perform the following sequence of calculations, starting with his or her secret number.

Step 1:   Add 6 to your chosen number.

Step 2:   Double the result.

Step 3:   Subtract 2.

Step 4:   Subtract your chosen number from the result in step 3.

Step 5:   This last result is the output value, which is then told to the magician.

1. a. Imagine you are a volunteer. Perform the sequence of arithmetic operations for each input value and record the end result (the output value) in the preceding table.

b. Do you see a pattern between the input values and their corresponding output values?

c. What operation does the magician need to perform in her head to correctly guess each volunteer's secret number?

If you use algebra to analyze the magician's trick in Problem 1, you will see why the output value is always 10 more than the input. The following example shows you how.

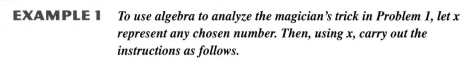

EXAMPLE 1   *To use algebra to analyze the magician's trick in Problem 1, let x represent any chosen number. Then, using x, carry out the instructions as follows.*

Step 1   add 6 to your chosen number: $x + 6$

Step 2   double the result: $2(x + 6)$
$2x + 12$

Step 3   subtract 2: $(2x + 12) - 2$
$2x + 10$

Step 4   subtract your chosen number $(2x + 10) - x$
from the result in step 3: $x + 10$

Step 4 shows that the output from this sequence of arithmetic operations is determined by $x + 10$. That is, the output is always 10 more than the secret number x. Using y to represent the output, $y = x + 10$.

To see why the magician subtracted 10 from the volunteer's output to guess the secret number correctly, solve the equation $y = x + 10$ for x to obtain the equation

$$x = y - 10.$$

This equation shows that the secret number, x, is obtained by subtracting 10 from the output that resulted from the sequence of arithmetic operations.

In Example 1, the expressions were simplified at each step. It is also possible to wait and simplify after the last step. Example 2 shows how.

EXAMPLE 2

Step 1   add 6 to x: $x + 6$

Step 2   double the result: $2(x + 6)$

Step 3   subtract 2: $2(x + 6) - 2$

Step 4   subtract your chosen number: $2(x + 6) - 2 - x$

Step 5   simplify the result: $2x + 12 - 2 - x$
$x + 10$

The equation relating the output to the input is $y = x + 10$.

2. a. Here is another trick you can try on a friend. Ask your friend to pick a number, keep it secret, and use it in the following sequence of instructions to obtain an output.

Step 1:   Add 2 to the secret number.

Step 2:   Double the result.

Step 3:   Subtract 4 to obtain the output value.

b. To analyze the trick, carry out the steps in part a using x to represent the secret number. Simplify the expressions, either as you go along or after step 3.

c. Write an equation relating the output variable y to the input variable x.

d. Solve the equation in part c to show what you have to do to guess correctly your friend's secret number.

3. a. Perform the following sequence of arithmetic operations on an input variable x to determine the corresponding output variable y. Simplify the expressions, either as you go along or after the last step.

	Going Along	**After Last Step**

Step 1:   Subtract 3 from the input, x.

Step 2:   Multiply the result by 5.

Step 3:   Add 10.

Step 4:   Divide the result by 5.

b. Write a simple equation relating the output variable y to the input variable x.

c. Solve the equation in part b for the input variable.

4. a. Determine the algebraic expression that is equivalent to the following sequence of instructions.

>   **Step 1:**   Add 7 to the input.
>
>   **Step 2:**   Multiply the result by 3.
>
>   **Step 3:**   Subtract the sum of twice the input and 12.

b. Simply the expression you obtained in step 3.

c. Write an equation for the output variable y in terms of the input variable x.

d. Write an equation that shows how to obtain the input variable from the output variable.

Many problems based on arithmetic can be solved by determining an expression that provides an algebraic model. The expression can become part of a formula or equation that can be solved. In the math magic problems, you determined an algebraic expression that modeled the trick.

In Example 2, $2x + 12 - 2 - x$ was the expression that modeled the arithmetic performed on each secret number, represented by x. When simplified to $x + 10$, it provided a formula for determining the output, represented by y. The resulting equation, $y = x + 10$, can then be solved for x to determine the secret number for any output value y.

The following problem can be solved in a similar manner.

5. In tennis, the length of a rectangular singles court is 3 feet less than 3 times its width.

a. Let w represent the width of a singles court. Write an expression using w that represents the length of the court.

b. Recall that the perimeter of a rectangle is the sum of twice the length and twice the width. Write a formula that represents the perimeter, P, of a singles court, using w to represent the width and the expression in part a to represent the length.

c. Simplify the expression in the formula you wrote in part b.

    d. If the perimeter of a singles court is actually 210 feet, what equation would you solve to find the actual width and length of the court?

    e. Solve the equation from part d to find the width and length.

SUMMARY
ACTIVITY 8.5

To simplify an algebraic expression,

    a. Remove parentheses, if necessary, by applying the distributive property.

    b. Combine like terms.

EXERCISES
ACTIVITY 8.5

1. a. Determine the algebraic expression that is equivalent to the following sequence of instructions.

    Step 1: Subtract 5 from the input.

    Step 2: Multiply the result by 4.

    Step 3: Subtract 3 times the input.

    Step 4: Add 8.

  b. Simply the expression you obtained in step 4.

  c. Write an equation for the output variable y in terms of the input variable x.

  d. Write an equation that shows how to obtain the input variable from the output variable.

2. Design your own magic trick, writing the step-by-step sequence of arithmetic operations, the corresponding algebraic expression, and the equation that can be solved to determine the original input value (secret number). Try your trick on some friends.

3. a. Select an integer and perform the following sequence of calculations.

      Step 1: Multiply by 3.

      Step 2: Add 8.

      Step 3: Subtract the original number.

      Step 4: Divide by 2.

      Step 5: Subtract 4.

b. In part a, what is the relationship between the integer you selected and the final result of the five calculations?

c. Let x represent the integer you selected. Translate each step in part a into an algebraic expression. You can simplify after each step or wait until you have written a simple polynomial using all steps.

d. If you have not done so, simplify the expression in part c. What does your result tell you about the relationship between the integer you select (represented by x) and the result of the sequence of calculations?

In Exercises 4–10, simplify the algebraic expression.

    4. $3x + 2(5x - 4)$ **5.** $3.1(a + b) + 8.7a$

    6. $6x + 2(x - y) - 5y$ **7.** $(3 - x) + (2x - 1)$

    8. $4(x + 3) + 5(x - 1)$ **9.** $3(2 - x) - 4(2x + 1)$

  10. $10(0.3x + 1) - (0.2x + 3)$

In Exercises 11–16, evaluate the expression for the given values.

    11. $3x^2 + 2x - 1$ for $x = 4$ **12.** $2(l + w)$ for $l = 3.5$ and $w = 2.8$

13. Prt for $P = 2100$, $r = 8\%$, $t = 3$ **14.** $0.3d^2 + 4d$ for $d = 2.1$

15. $4x^3 + 15$ for $x = 10$ **16.** $3(f - 20)$ for $f = -5$

17. Opposite sides of a square are each increased by 5 units and the other opposite sides are each decreased by 3 units. If x represents a side of the original square, write an equation that represents the perimeter P of the newly formed rectangle.

18. You want to boast to a friend about the stock that you own without telling him how much money you originally invested in the stock. You watch the stock market once a month for 4 months and record the following.

MONTH	1	2	3	4
STOCK VALUE	Increased $50	Doubled	Decreased $100	Tripled

a. Letting x represent the value of your original investment, write an algebraic expression to represent the value of your stock after the first month.

b. Use the result from part a to determine the value at the end of the second month, simplifying when possible. Continue until you determine the value of your stock at the end of the fourth month.

c. Do you have good news to tell your friend? Explain to him what has happened to the value of your stock over 4 months.

d. Instead of simplifying after each step, write a single algebraic expression that represents the value of the stock at the end of 4 months.

e. Simplify the expression in part d. How does the simplified algebraic expression compare with the result in part b?

A model of an object is usually an alternative version of the actual object, produced in another medium. You are familiar with model airplanes and model cars. Architects and engineers build models of buildings and bridges. Computer models are used to simulate complicated phenomena like the weather and global economies. To be useful, a model must accurately describe an object or situation, in order to better understand the actual object.

In this course, you have been using **mathematical models.** A mathematical model uses equations, formulas, tables, or graphs to describe the important features of an object or situation. Such models can then be used to solve problems, make predictions, and draw conclusions about the given situation.

The process of developing a mathematical model is called **mathematical modeling**. The development of mathematical models to help solve simple to extremely complicated problems is a very important use of mathematics.

Equations as Mathematical Models

In Activity 8.1, you developed the equation $c = 0.015n + 455$, where c represents the monthly cost in dollars of leasing a copier and n represents the number of copies. The equation represents the mathematical model used by the copier company to determine charges for leasing the machine. The equation is an efficient format for solving problems regarding the leasing of copy machines by the company.

1. As part of a community service project at your college, you are organizing a fund-raiser at the neighborhood roller rink. Money raised will benefit a summer camp for children with special needs. The admission charge is $4.50 per person, $2.00 of which is used to pay the rink's rental fee. The remainder is donated to the summer camp fund.

   a. The first step in developing a mathematical model is to identify the problem and develop a well-defined question about what you want to know. State a question that you want answered in this situation.

   b. The next step is to identify the variables involved. What two variables are involved in this problem?

   c. Which variable can best be designated as the input variable? As the output variable?

   d. Next, look for relationships and connections between the variables involved in the situation. State in words the relationship between the input and output variables.

e. Now, translate the features and relationships you have identified into an equation. Use appropriate letters to represent the variables, stating what each represents.

f. If 91 tickets are sold, use the equation model developed in part e to determine the amount donated to the summer camp fund.

g. If the maximum capacity of the rink is 200 people, what is the maximum amount that can be donated?

Formulas as Mathematical Models

In previous chapters, you used formulas that model situations in geometry, business, and science. In almost every field of study, you are likely to encounter formulas that relate two or more variables represented by letters. Problems 2 and 3 feature formulas used in the health field.

2. In order for exercise to be beneficial, medical researchers have determined that the desirable heart rate, R, in beats per minute, can be approximated by the formulas

$$R = 143 - 0.65a \text{ for women}$$
$$R = 165 - 0.75a \text{ for men,}$$

where a represents the person's age in years.

a. If the desirable heart rate for a woman is 130 beats per minute, how old is she?

b. If the desirable heart rate for a man is 135 beats per minute, how old is he?

3. The basal energy rate is the daily amount of energy (measured in calories) needed by the body at rest to maintain the basic life functions. The basal energy rate differs for individuals, depending on their gender, age, height, and weight. The formula for the basal energy rate for males is

$$B = 655.096 + 9.563W + 1.85H - 4.676A,$$

where: B is the basal energy rate (in calories)

W is the weight (in kilograms)

H is the height (in centimeters)

A is the age (in years)

a. A male patient is 70 years old, weighs 55 kilograms, and is 172 centimeters tall. He is prescribed a total daily calorie intake of 1000 calories. Determine if the patient is being properly fed.

b. A male is 178 centimeters tall and weighs 84 kilograms. If his basal energy rate is 1500 calories, how old is the male?

Tables as Mathematical Models

You have encountered tables of ordered pairs of values throughout this course. Those tables can be viewed as a type of mathematical model that represents relationships between variables. For example, the windchill table studied in Activity 8.2 allows one to predict the windchill when temperature and wind speed are known.

4. The following table gives the windchill temperature (how cold your skin feels) for various air temperatures when there is a 20 mph wind.

Blowin' in the Wind

AIR TEMPERATURE °F	40	30	20	10	0	−10	−20
WINDCHILL TEMPERATURE (20-mph wind)	30	17	4	−9	−22	−35	−48

a. What relationship do you observe between the windchill temperature and the air temperature?

b. Estimate the windchill temperature for an air temperature of $-30°F$.

c. If the wind speed is 30 mph, how would you expect the windchill temperatures in the table to change?

The following Windchill Chart, published by the National Weather Service, displays windchill temperature for many different wind speeds and air temperatures.

WINDCHILL CHART

Air Temperature (°F)

	40	35	30	25	20	15	10	5	0	−5	−10	−15	−20	−25	−30	−35	−40	−45
5	36	31	25	19	13	7	1	−5	−11	−16	−22	−28	−34	−40	−46	−52	−57	−63
10	34	27	21	15	9	3	−4	−10	−16	−22	−28	−35	−41	−47	−53	−59	−66	−72
15	32	25	19	13	6	0	−7	−13	−19	−26	−32	−39	−45	−51	−58	−64	−71	−77
20	30	24	17	11	4	−2	−9	−15	−22	−29	−35	−42	−48	−55	−61	−68	−74	−81
25	29	23	16	9	3	−4	−11	−17	−24	−31	−37	−44	−51	−58	−64	−71	−78	−84
30	28	22	15	8	1	−5	−12	−19	−26	−33	−39	−46	−53	−60	−67	−73	−80	−87
35	28	21	14	7	0	−7	−14	−21	−27	−34	−41	−48	−55	−62	−69	−76	−82	−89
40	27	20	13	6	−1	−8	−15	−22	−29	−36	−43	−50	−57	−64	−71	−78	−84	−91
45	26	29	12	5	−2	−9	−16	−23	−30	−37	−44	−51	−58	−65	−72	−79	−86	−93
50	26	19	12	4	−3	−10	−17	−24	−31	−38	−45	−52	−60	−67	−74	−81	−88	−95
55	25	18	11	4	−3	−11	−18	−25	−32	−39	−46	−54	−61	−68	−75	−82	−89	−97
60	25	17	10	3	−4	−11	−19	−26	−33	−40	−48	−55	−62	−69	−76	−84	−91	−98

Wind (mph)

Frostbite Times   ▢ 30 minutes   ▮ 10 minutes   ▨ 5 minutes

5. a. In the Windchill Chart, locate the row that lists windchill temperatures for a 30 mph wind and use it to complete the following table.

AIR TEMPERATURE °F	40	30	20	10	0	−10	−20
WINDCHILL TEMPERATURE (30-mph wind)							

b. If the wind speed is 40 mph, what is the windchill temperature if the air temperature is $-20°F$?

c. Approximately how long could you be exposed to a 20-mph wind when the air temperature is $0°F$? (That would be the frostbite time in the chart.)

Graphs as Mathematical Models

Graphs are very effective mathematical models that can be used to visualize patterns and trends between two variables.

6. Medicare is a government program that helps senior citizens pay for medical expenses. As the U.S. population ages, the expense and quality of health service becomes an increasing concern. The following graph presents Medicare expenditures from 1967 through 2004. Use the graph to answer the following questions.

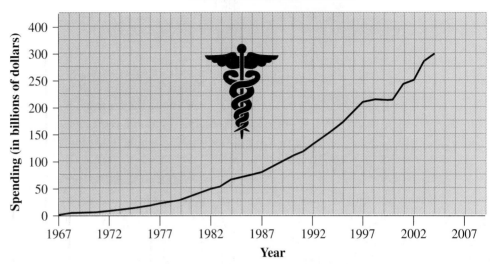

Source: Centers for Medicare and Medicaid Services

a. Use the graph to estimate the Medicare expenditures for the years listed in the following table.

YEAR	MEDICARE EXPENDITURE (billions of dollars)
1972	
1977	
1982	
1987	
1992	
1997	
2001	
2004	

b. Estimate the year in which expenditures reached $25 billion.

c. Estimate the year in which expenditures reached $100 billion.

d. Approximately how much did Medicare expenditures increase between 1987 and 1997?

e. During which 10-year period did Medicare expenditures change the least?

f. During what period was there essentially no change in Medicare expenditures?

7. Living on Earth's surface, you experience a relatively narrow range of temperatures. But if you could visit below Earth's surface or high up above the surface, even above the atmosphere, you would experience a wider range of temperatures. The graph represents a model that predicts the temperature for a given altitude. Assume the altitude is 0 at Earth's surface.

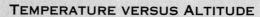

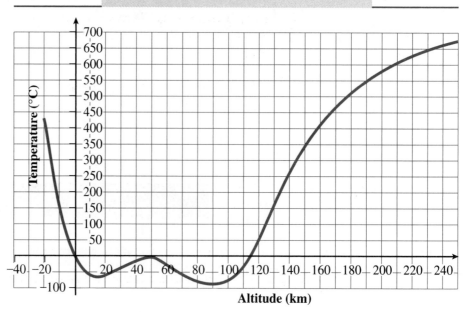

a. What is the temperature of Earth 10 kilometers below the surface?

b. The ozone layer is approximately 50 kilometers above Earth's surface. What is the approximate temperature in the ozone layer?

c. Is it warmer or cooler above and below the ozone layer?

d. Describe how the temperature changes as one moves up through the atmosphere.

e. How deep under Earth's surface does one need to go to reach a temperature of 400°C?

f. How high above Earth's surface does one need to go to reach a temperature of 400°C?

SUMMARY ACTIVITY 8.6	

1. A **mathematical model** uses equations, formulas, tables, or graphs to describe the important features of an object or situation. Such models can then be used to solve problems, make predictions, and draw conclusions about the given situation.

2. Mathematical modeling is the process of developing a mathematical model for a given situation.

EXERCISES ACTIVITY 8.6	

1. The value of almost everything you own, such as a car, computer, or appliance, depreciates (goes down) over time. When the value decreases by a fixed amount each year, the depreciation is called straight-line depreciation.

Suppose your car has an initial value of $16,750 and depreciates $1030 per year.

a. State a question that you might want answered in this situation.

b. What two variables are involved in this problem?

c. Which variable do you think should be designated as the input variable?

d. Complete the following table.

YEARS CAR IS OWNED	1	2	3	4	5
VALUE OF CAR (in dollars)					

e. State in words the relationship between the value of the car and the number of years the car is owned.

f. Use appropriate letters to represent the variables involved and translate the written statement in part e to an equation.

g. If you plan to keep the car for 7 years, determine the value of the car at the end of this period. Explain the process you used.

2. In 1966, the U.S. Surgeon General's warnings began appearing on cigarette packages. A model that predicts the percentage of the adult U.S. population that was still smoking in the years since 1966 can be represented by the formula $p = -0.62t + 42.47$, where t is the number of years after 1965 and p is the percentage of the adult population that smoked.

a. Determine the percentage of the population that smoked in 1981 ($t = 16$).

b. Using the formula, in what year would the percentage of smokers be 15% ($p = 15$)?

3. In 1965, 51.9% of all males (18 or older) smoked. The percentage, p, of males who smoke in t years after 1965 is modeled by the formula $p = -0.89t + 51.1$.

a. Determine the percentage of males smoking in the year 2000.

b. In what year would the percentage of male smokers 18 or older be 20%?

4. The average annual out-of-pocket expenses for health care for an individual can be modeled by the formula

$$c = 37.7a - 170,$$

where c is the average amount of money spent, in dollars, and a is the person's age.

a. Determine the average annual out-of-pocket health care expenses for a 30-year-old.

b. Using the formula, how old is an individual with out-of-pocket health care expenses of $2000?

5. The following formula is used by the National Football League (NFL) to calculate quarterback ratings.

$$R = \frac{6.25A + 250C + 12.5Y + 1000T - 1250I}{3A}$$

where:
R = quarterback rating
A = passes attempted
C = passes completed
Y = passing yardage
T = touchdown passes
I = number of interceptions

In the 2005–2006 regular season, quarterbacks Tom Brady, of the New England Patriots, and Brett Favre, of the Green Bay Packers, had the following player statistics.

Take a Pass

PLAYER	PASSES ATTEMPTED	PASSES COMPLETED	PASSING YARDAGE	NUMBER OF TOUCHDOWN PASSES	NUMBER OF INTERCEPTIONS
Tom Brady	530	334	4110	26	14
Brett Favre	607	372	3881	20	29

a. Determine the quarterback rating for Tom Brady for the 2005–2006 NFL football season.

b. Determine the quarterback rating for Brett Favre.

c. Visit www.nfl.com and select stats to obtain the rating of your favorite quarterback.

6. a. You want to invest so as to receive the best return on your money. You have two options.

Option 1:   Invest at 6% simple annual interest for 10 years.

Option 2:   Invest at 5% interest compounded annually.

The following table models the growth of $2000 over the 10-year period for the two options.

Interesting Choices

NUMBER OF YEARS	1	2	3	4	5	6	7	8	9	10
6% SIMPLE ANNUAL INTEREST	2120	2240	2360	2480	2600	2720	2840	2960	3080	3200
5% COMPOUNDED ANNUALLY	2100	2205	2315.30	2431	2552.60	2680.20	2814.20	2954.90	3102.70	3258.80

Describe any trends or patterns that you observe in the data.

b. The value of your investment in Option 1 can be determined by the following formula.

$$A = P + \text{Pr}t$$

where: A = value of the investment

P = principal or amount invested

r = annual percentage rate (expressed as a decimal)

t = number of years invested

Use the formula to determine the value of your $2000 investment in Option 1 after 20 years. What is the total amount of interest earned?

c. The value of your investment in Option 2 can be determined by

$$A = P(1 + r)^t$$

where: A = value of the investment

P = principal

r = annual percentage rate (expressed as a decimal)

t = number of years invested

Use the formula to determine the value of your $2000 investment in Option 2 after 20 years.

d. Which option would you choose if you were planning to invest the principal for 20 years? Explain.

7. The following table gives the number of people infected by the flu over a given number of months.

The Spread of the Flu

NUMBER OF MONTHS	0	1	2	3	4	5
NUMBER OF PEOPLE INFECTED	1	5	13	33	78	180

a. Describe any trends or patterns that you observe in the table.

b. Graph the ordered pairs in the table on the following grid. Connect successive points with line segments.

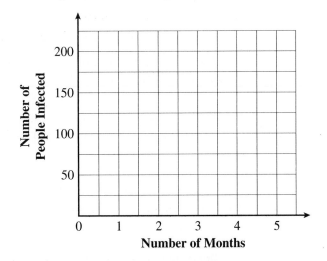

c. Describe any trends or patterns that you observe on the graph. Compare with those you made based on the table.

What Have I Learned?

You are able to get three summer jobs to help pay for college expenses. You work 20 hours per week in your job as a cashier and earn $6.50 per hour. The second and third jobs are both at a local hospital. You earn $8.50 per hour as a payroll clerk and $6.00 per hour as an aide. You always work 3 hours more per week as an aide than you do as a payroll clerk. Your weekly salary is determined by the number of hours that you work at each job.

Use what you learned in this chapter to answer the following questions about your summer job.

1. Explain how you would calculate the total amount earned each week.

2. Let x represent the number of hours that you work as a payroll clerk. Represent the number of hours that you work as an aide in terms of x.

3. Write an equation in terms of x that you can use to calculate the total amount E that you earn in a week from all three jobs.

4. Simplify the equation you obtained in Problem 3.

5. If you work 12 hours as a payroll clerk, how much will you earn that week?

6. a. Use the equation from Problem 4 to determine how many hours you must work as a payroll clerk in order to have a total salary of $500 in 1 week from all three jobs.

b. Assuming you will work six days each week, approximately how many hours must you work each day to earn $500 a week?

The part-time jobs at the hospital have been eliminated and you need to find another job. You read about a full-time summer position in sales at the Furniture Barn. You would earn $260 per week plus 20% commission on sales over $1000. You decide to quit the cashier's job and take the sales position at the Furniture Barn.

7. Explain how you would calculate the total amount earned each week.

8. Let F represent the total amount earned each week and let x represent the amount of sales for the week. Write an equation in terms of x to determine F.

9. Use the equation you wrote in Problem 8 to determine how much your sales must be to have a gross salary of $500 for the week.

How Can I Practice?

In Exercises 1–14, solve each equation for x. Check your results by hand or with a calculator.

1. $4x - 7 = 9$

2. $9 - 2x = 23$

3. $\dfrac{3}{4}x + 2 = 5$

4. $15 = 5 - 2.5x$

5. $2x - 5 = 4x + 7$

6. $3(2x + 1) = 9$

7. $2(x + 1) = 5x - 3$

8. $14 - 6x = -2x + 3$

9. $2.1x + 15 = 3.5 - 1.9x$

10. $4(2x + 1) = 2(7x + 7)$

11. $3(x - 2) + 10 = 5x$

12. $0.25(x - 2) = 0.2(x + 10)$

13. $\dfrac{1}{2}x - 6 = 3x + 4$

14. $\dfrac{1}{3}(x - 1) = 3(2x - 2)$

Answers to all How Can I Practice? exercises are included in the Selected Answers appendix.

In Exercises 15–18, use the distributive property to write each of the following products in expanded form.

15. $-5(4x - 3)$

16. $3x(2a + 4b + c)$

17. $4.5(3x - 0.2)$

18. $-4(5x - 4y + 10)$

In Exercises 19–23, solve the equation for the specified letter.

19. $P = 2a + b$ for a

20. $P = rt$ for t

21. $f = v + at$ for t

22. $3x - 4y = 8$ for x

23. $A = P(1 + rt)$ for r

24. A worker's weekly earnings are given by the formula $E = S + \frac{3}{2}rn$, where E represents the weekly earnings, S the weekly salary, r the hourly rate, and n the number of hours worked overtime. Solve the formula for r.

25. Since 1960, the median age of men at their first marriage has steadily increased. If a represents the median age of men at their first marriage, then a can be approximated by the formula

$$a = 0.11t + 22.5,$$

where t represents the number of years since 1960.

a. What is the median age of men who are married for the first time in 2005?

b. According to the formula, in what year will the median age of men be 30 at first marriage?

c. Solve the formula $a = 0.11t + 22.5$ for t.

d. Answer part b using the new formula in part c.

26. The cost of printing a brochure to advertise your lawn-care business is a flat fee of $10 plus $0.03 per copy. Let c represent the total cost of printing and x represent the number of copies.

a. Write an equation that will relate c and x.

b. Use the equation from part a to complete the following table. Begin with 1000 copies, increase by increments of 1000, and end with 5000 copies.

Duplicated Effort

NUMBER OF COPIES, x	TOTAL COST, c
1000	

c. What is the total cost of printing 8000 copies?

d. You have $300 to spend on printing. How many copies can you have printed for that amount?

In Exercises 27–34, use the properties of exponents to simplify the product.

27. $-x^3 \cdot x^5 \cdot x^2$

28. $(-2x^3)(5x^4)$

29. $(2.75x^3)(-0.2x^4)$

30. $(5s^2t^3)(-3st^2)$

31. $x^3(x^2 + 2x - 1)$

32. $(y^3)^5$

33. $(t^4)^2$

34. $3(x^2)^3(x^4)(2x)$

In Exercises 35–38, use the distributive property to perform the multiplication and combine like terms if possible.

35. $2x + 3x(x - 4) + 5x^2$

36. $3.5(2x + 4) - (2.7x + 10.6)$

37. $2x^3(4x^2 - 3x + 2)$

38. $5x(2 - 4x) - 3(x^2 - 4x - 1) + 5x^2$

39. A rectangular box has dimensions given by the following expressions.

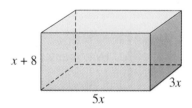

$x + 8$

$3x$

$5x$

    a. Write an equation that represents the area A of the box's base.

    b. Write an equation that represents the volume V of the box.

In Exercises 40–43, evaluate the expression for the given value(s).

40. $3t^2$ for $t = 4$

41. $2x^2 - 3y$ for $x = 3$ and $y = 2.5$

42. $P(1 + rt)$, where $P = 5$, $r = 7$, and $t = 2$

43. $180 - t - r$, where $t = 15$, and $r = -25$

In Exercises 44–47, solve the equation for x. Check your answers by hand or with a calculator.

44. $21 + 3(x - 4) = 24$ 　　　　　　**45.** $2(4x - 3) = 3(2x + 6)$

46. $2 - 5(x + 5) = 3(x - 2) - 1$ 　　**47.** $0.16x + 0.24(10 - x) = 1.8$

48. You contact the local print shop to produce a commemorative booklet for your college theater group's twenty-fifth anniversary. The print shop has quoted you a price of $750 to typeset the booklet and 25 cents for each copy produced.

　a. Write an equation that gives the total cost C in terms of the number, x, of booklets produced.

　b. Determine the total cost of producing 500 booklets.

　c. How many booklets can be produced for $1000?

　d. Suppose the booklets are sold for 75 cents each. Write an equation for the total revenue R from the sale of x booklets.

　e. How many booklets must be sold to break even? That is, for what value of x is the total cost of production, C, equal to the total amount of revenue, R?

f. Recall that the profit is revenue minus the cost $(R - C)$. How many booklets must be sold to make a $500 profit?

49. You live 7.5 miles from work, where you have free parking. Some days, you must drive to work so that you can call on clients. On other days, you can take the bus. It costs you 20 cents per mile to drive the car and $1.50 round-trip to take the bus. Assume that there are 22 working days in a month and that x represents the number of days you take the bus to work.

a. Write an expression in terms of x for the cost of taking the bus each month.

b. Write an expression in terms of x that represents the number of days that you drive.

c. Write an expression in terms of x for the cost of driving each month.

d. Write an equation in terms of x that determines the total cost of transportation, C.

e. How many days can you drive if you budget $42 a month for transportation?

f. How much should you budget for the month if you would like to take the bus only half of the time?

The bracketed numbers following each concept indicate the activity in which the concept is discussed.

CONCEPT / SKILL	DESCRIPTION	EXAMPLE
Solve $ax + b = c$ for x [8.1]	• Undo the addition of b by adding the opposite of b to each side of the equation. • Undo the multiplication of the variable by the nonzero coefficient a by dividing each side by a.	Solve for x: $2x - 5 = 11$ $2x - 5 = 11$ $\underline{+5\quad +5}$ $2x = 16$ $\dfrac{2x}{2} = \dfrac{16}{2}; \quad x = 8$
Evaluate expressions [8.2], [8.6]	To evaluate expressions for a given numerical value, substitute the value for the variable and perform the arithmetic using the order of operations.	Evaluate $2x + 10$ for $x = -2$. Substitute -2 for x: $2(-2) + 10$ $= -4 + 10$ $= 6$
Solve a formula for a given variable [8.2]	To solve the formula $y = at + b$ for t means to isolate the variable t, with coefficient 1, on one side of the equation, with all other terms on the opposite side.	Solve $y = at + b$ for t. $y = at + b$ $\underline{-b\qquad -b}$ $y - b = at$ $\dfrac{y - b}{a} = \dfrac{at}{a}$ $\dfrac{y - b}{a} = t$
Distributive property [8.3], [8.4]	$a(b + c) = ab + ac$ Extension of distributive property: $a(b + c + d + \dots) =$ $ab + ac + ad + \dots$	$3(2x^2 + 4x - 1)$ $= 6x^2 + 12x - 3$
General strategy for solving an equation for an unknown x [8.3]	1. Remove parentheses, if necessary. 2. Combine like terms on the same side of the equation. 3. Isolate the variable term. 4. Divide out the nonzero coefficient of the variable. 5. Check.	$2(x + 4) + 3x = 2x - 1$ $2x + 8 + 3x = 2x - 1$ $5x + 8 = 2x - 1$ $\underline{-2x - 8 \quad -2x - 8}$ $3x = -9$ $\dfrac{3x}{3} = \dfrac{-9}{3}$ $x = -3$ *Check:* $2(-3 + 4) + 3(-3) = 2(-3) - 1$ $2 - 9 = -6 - 1$ $-7 = -7$

CONCEPT / SKILL	DESCRIPTION	EXAMPLE
First Property of Exponents [8.4]	If m and n represent positive integers, then $$b^m \cdot b^n = b^{m+n}.$$	$$\left(x^3\right)\left(x^4\right) = x^{3+4} = x^7$$
Multiply two or more factors [8.4]	1. Multiply the numerical coefficients. 2. Apply first property of exponents where powers have the same base.	$$(3x^2y^4)(-2x^5y)$$ $$= 3(-2)x^2x^5y^4y$$ $$= -6x^7y^5$$
Second Property of Exponents [8.4]	If m and n represent positive integers, then $$(b^m)^n = b^{mn}.$$	$$(x^4)^3 = x^{4 \cdot 3} = x^{12}$$
Simplify an algebraic expression [8.5]	To simplify: 1. Apply distributive property to remove parentheses, if necessary. 2. Combine like terms.	$$2x(5x^2 + 4x - 6) + 7x^3 - 4x$$ $$= 10x^3 + 8x^2 - 12x + 7x^3 - 4x$$ $$= 17x^3 + 8x^2 - 16x$$
Mathematical Model [8.6]	Description of mathematical features of an object or situation that uses equations, formulas, tables, and/or graphs.	See Activity 8.6
Mathematical Modeling [8.6]	The process of developing a mathematical model for a given situation.	See Activity 8.6

In Exercises 1–8, solve the equation for x. Check your answers by hand or with a calculator.

1. $-18 = 2x + 8$

2. $25 + 0.15x = 70.90$

3. $1.6x - 49 = -10$

4. $3x + 10 = 6x - 11$

5. $4(x + 5) - x = 80$

6. $38 = 57 - (x + 32)$

7. $5x + 3(2x - 8) = 2(x + 6)$

8. $2.5x + 10 = 5.8(x - 2)$

In Exercises 9–14, perform the indicated operations and write your answer in simplest form.

9. $x^4 \cdot x^5$

10. $3(x^4)^5$

11. $(-2xy^2)(3x^3y)$

12. $(x^3y^4)(x^2)^4$

13. $-3x^2(x^3 - 2x^2 + 1)$

14. $10x^2 + 3x(3 - 2x)$

15. Solve each of the following for the given variable.

   a. $I = Prt$ for P

   b. $P = 2a + 2b$ for a

   c. $E = S + 1.5rn$ for r

   d. $V(P + a) = k$ for P

Answers to all Gateway exercises are included in the Selected Answers appendix.

16. Evaluate the expression for the given value(s).

a. $2x^2 - 3x + 5$ for $x = -3$ **b.** $2a + b$ for $a = 17.3$ and $b = 11.8$

c. $a - (b + c)$ for $a = 10$, $b = -6$, and $c = -8$

17. When applying for a job at a clothing store, you are offered two options for your salary. The following table shows these options.

OPTION 1	$100 per wk	Plus 30% of all sales
OPTION 2	$150 per wk	Plus 15% of all sales

a. Write an equation to represent the total salary S for option 1 if the total sales are x dollars per week.

b. Write an equation to represent the total salary S for option 2 if the total sales are x dollars per week.

c. Write an equation that you could use to determine how much you would have to sell weekly to have the same weekly salary under both plans.

d. Solve the equation in part c. Interpret your result.

e. What is the salary for the amount of sales found in part d?

18. A triathlon includes swimming, long-distance running, and cycling.

a. Let x represent the number of miles the competitors swim. If the long-distance run is 10 miles longer than the distance swum, write an expression that represents the distance the competitor runs in the event.

b. The distance the athletes cycle is 55 miles longer than they run. Use the result in part a to write an equation in terms of x that represents the cycling distance, C, of the race.

c. Write a formula that represents the total distance, d, of all three phases of the triathlon in terms of x, the number of miles that the competitors swim.

d. If the total distance of the triathlon is 120 miles, use the formula in part c to write and solve an equation to determine the swimming distance.

e. What is the length of the running and cycling portions of the race?

19. On an average winter day, a certain office of the Automobile Association of America (AAA) receives 125 calls from persons who need help starting their cars. The number varies, however, depending on the temperature. Here are some data giving the number of calls as a function of the temperature (in degrees Celsius).

AAA on the Way!

TEMPERATURE (°C)	NUMBER OF AUTO CLUB SERVICE CALLS
−12	250
−6	190
0	140
4	125
9	100

a. Sketch a graph of the data from the table.

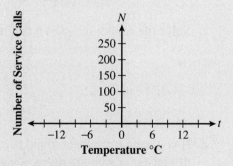

The data can be approximated by the equation

$$C = -7.11t + 153.9$$

where C is the total number of calls and t is the temperature (°C).

b. Determine how many service calls AAA can expect if the temperature drops to $-20°C$.

c. Use the given equation to predict the temperature for which AAA should expect 50 calls.

d. Solve the equation $C = -7.11t + 153.9$ for t.

e. Answer part c using the new formula from part d and compare with the answer in part c.

20. ABC Rent-a-Car offers cars at $50 a day and 20 cents a mile. Its competition rents cars for $60 a day and 15 cents a mile.

a. For each company, write an equation that determines C, the cost of renting a car for a day in terms of the distance, x, traveled.

b. Write a single equation to determine the number of miles driven in which the cost of renting is the same for each company.

c. Solve the equation in part b and interpret the result.

d. If you were planning a round trip from Washington, D.C. to New York City, a distance of about 465 miles, which company would be cheaper to rent from? Explain.

21. You have an opportunity to be the manager of a day camp for the summer. You know that your fixed costs for operating the camp are $600 per week, even if there are no campers. Each camper costs the management $10 per week. The camp charges each camper $40 per week.

Let x represent the number of campers.

a. Write an equation in terms of x that represents the total cost, C, of running the camp per week.

b. Write an equation in terms of x that represents the total income (revenue), R, from the campers per week.

c. Write an equation in terms of x that represents the total profit, P, from the campers per week.

d. How many campers must attend the camp to break even with revenue and costs?

e. The camp would like to make a profit of $600. How many campers need to enroll to make that profit?

f. How much money would the camp lose if only 10 campers attend?

LEARNING MATH OPENS DOORS: TWELVE KEYS TO SUCCESS

1. Are you in the right math course for your skill level?

Students are sometimes placed in the wrong math course for a variety of reasons. Your answers to the following questions will help you and your instructor determine if you are in the correct math course for your skill level. This information will also help your instructor understand your background more quickly, thus providing you with a better learning experience.

a. Did you register for this math course because you took a placement exam and, as a result of your exam score, you selected or were placed in this course?

b. If you were not placed in this class because of a placement exam, please list reasons you are taking this course.

c. Name _____

d. Phone and/or e-mail address _____

e. List the mathematics courses you have taken at the *college level*.

Course Title   Grade

1. _____   _____

2. _____   _____

f. List the mathematics courses you have taken at the *high school level*.

Course Title   Grade

1. _____   _____

2. _____   _____

3. _____   _____

g. Have you taken this course before?   Yes _____   No _____

h. When did you take your last mathematics course? _____

i. Are you a full-time or part-time student? _____

j. Do you have a job? _____ If yes, how many hours per week do you work? _____

k. Do you take care of children or relatives at home? _____

You should now share your information with your instructor to make sure you are in the correct class. It is a waste of a semester of time and money if the course is too easy for you or too difficult for you. Take control of and responsibility for your learning!

2. What is your attitude about mathematics?

a. Write one word that describes how you feel about learning mathematics.

_____

b. Was the word that you wrote a positive word, a negative word, or a neutral word? _____

If your word was a positive word, you are on your way to success in this course. If your word was negative, then before progressing any further, you may want to determine why you have negative feelings toward mathematics.

c. Write about a positive or negative experience that you have had related to mathematics.

_____

_____

_____

_____

If you have not had success in the past, try something different. Here are a few suggestions:

d. Make a list of all the materials (pencils, notebook, calculator) that you might need for the course. Make sure you have all the materials required for the course.

_____

_____

e. Find a new location to study mathematics. List two or three good places you can study.

1. _____   2. _____   3. _____

f. Study with a classmate. Help each other organize the material. Ask each other questions about assignments. Write down names, phone numbers/e-mail addresses of two or three other students in your class to study with.

1. _____

2. _____

3. _____

g. How did you study mathematics in the past? Write a few sentences about what you did outside of class to learn mathematics.

_____

_____

_____

h. What will you change from your past to help you become more successful? Write down your strategy for success.

_____

_____

_____

3. Do you attend all classes on time and are you organized?

Class work is vital to your success. Make it a priority to attend every class. Arrive in sufficient time and be ready to start when class begins. Start this exercise by recording the months and dates for the entire semester in each box. Then write in each box when and where your class meets corresponding to your schedule. Keep track of exam and quiz dates, deadlines, study sessions, homework, and anything else that can help you succeed in the course.

Schedule routine medical and other appointments so you don't miss class. Allow time for traffic jams, finding a parking space, bus delays, and other emergencies that may occur. Arriving late interferes with your learning and the learning of your fellow students. Make sure assignments are completed and handed in on time. Attending class and being on time and organized is in your control.

✔ Place a check in each day that you are in class. Circle the check to indicate that you were on time. Place an *a* in each day you miss class.

Sunday	Monday	Tuesday	Wednesday	Thursday	Friday	Saturday

4. When is that assignment due?

In mathematics, assignments are usually given each class time. Assignments are meant to reinforce what you learned in class. If you have trouble completing your assignment, take charge and get help immediately. The following table will help you organize your assignments and the dates they are due. Keeping a record of your assignments in one location will help you know at a glance what and when your assignment is due.

Date Assigned	Assignment	Specific Instructions	Dates	
			Due	Completed

Date Assigned	Assignment	Specific Instructions	Dates	
			Due	Completed

5. Do you keep track of your progress?

Keeping track of your own progress is a great way to monitor the steps you are taking toward success in this course. Different instructors may use different methods to determine your grade.

a. Explain how your instructor will determine your final grade for this course.

_____

_____

_____

_____

b. Use the following table to keep track of your grades in this course. (You may want to change the headings to reflect your instructor's grading system; an Excel spreadsheet may also be helpful for this exercise.)

Date	Type of Assessment	Topic(s) and/ or Chapters	Number of Points Correct	Total Number of Points	Comments

c. Determine your final average using your instructor's grading system.

6. How well do you know your textbook?

Knowing the structure of your textbook helps you use the book more effectively to reach your learning goals. Use the following guidelines to learn the structure and goals of the textbook.

a. According to your syllabus, which chapters will you be studying this semester?

b. Find and underline the titles of the chapters in the table of contents.

c. What are the key points the authors make to you in the "To the Student" section?

d. Each chapter is divided into smaller parts called clusters. Name clusters in Chapter 3.

e. Each cluster is made up of smaller sections called activities. What is the title of the activity in Chapter 2, Cluster 1, Activity 1?

f. Look at the end of each activity. There you will find the Exercises section. Doing these exercises should help you better understand the concepts and skills in the activity. Why are some of the numbers of the exercises in color?

g. Look at the end of Cluster 1 in Chapter 3. You will see a section entitled "What Have I Learned?" This section will help you review the key concepts in the cluster. What are the concepts taught in this cluster?

h. Look at the end of Cluster 1 in Chapter 3. What is the section called right after "What Have I Learned?" This section will help you practice all of the skills in the cluster. What are the skills taught in this cluster?

i. Locate and briefly review the Glossary. Select a mathematical term from the Glossary and write the term and its definition here.

7. Where does your time go?

Managing your time is often difficult. A good rule to follow when studying is to allow 2 hours of study time for each hour of class time. It is best not to have marathon study sessions, but, rather, to break up your study time into small intervals. Studying a little every day rather than "cramming" once a week helps to put the information into your long-term memory. Ask yourself this question: Is going to school a top priority? If you answered yes, then your study time must be a priority if you are going to be successful.

a. In the past, approximately how many hours per week did you study mathematics? Reflect on whether it was enough time to be successful.

b. The commitments in your life can be categorized. Estimate the number of hours that you spend each week on each category. (There are 168 hours in a week.)

Class Hours (Class) _____   Chore Hours (C) _____

Study Hours (ST) _____   Sleep Hours (Sl) _____

Work Hours (W) _____   Personal Hours (P) _____

Commute Hours (T) _____   Leisure Hours (L) _____

Other (O) _____

c. Use the information from part b to fill in the grid with a workable schedule using the appropriate letter to represent each category.

Time	Mon.	Tues.	Wed.	Thurs.	Fri.	Sat.	Sun.
12 midnight							
1:00 A.M.							
2:00							
3:00							
4:00							
5:00							
6:00							
7:00							
8:00							
9:00							
10:00							
11:00							
12:00 noon							
1:00 P.M.							
2:00							
3:00							
4:00							
5:00							
6:00							
7:00							
8:00							
9:00							
10:00							
11:00							

d. Is your schedule realistic? Does it represent a typical week in *your* life? If not, make adjustments to it now.

e. Circle the hours in your schedule that you will devote to studying.

f. Shade or highlight the hours that you will use for studying mathematics.

g. Do you have some times scheduled each day to study mathematics? How much time is devoted to mathematics each day?

h. Studying math soon after class time will help you review what you learned in class. Did you place any hours to study math close to your actual class time?

i. Scheduling time before class can help you prepare for the class. Did you schedule any study time just before class time?

j. Review your schedule once more and make any changes.

k. Periodically review your schedule to see if it is working and whether you are following it. How are you doing?

8. Where will you use mathematics?

Students often ask math instructors, "Where will I ever use this?" Here is an opportunity to show where you have used mathematics, including what you have learned from this course.

a. Describe one way in which you use math in your everyday life.

_____

b. Find an article in a newspaper that contains a graph or some quantitative information.

c. Describe ways in which you use math in your job.

_____

_____

d. Describe a problem in a course you are taking or took (not a mathematics course) that involved a math concept or skill. Include a description of the math concept or skill that is involved.

_____

_____

After you have been in this course for a few weeks, answer parts e, f, and g.

e. Write a problem from one of your courses (not a mathematics course) or from your work experience where you used concepts or skills that you have learned in *this* mathematics class.

_____

_____

f. Show how you solved the problem.

_____

_____

g. Write the math skill(s) or concept(s) that you learned in this math course that helped you solve this problem.

_____

_____

9. Do you need extra help?

Receiving extra help when you need it may mean the difference between success and failure in your math course. If you are struggling, don't wait, seek help immediately. When you go for extra help, identify specific areas in which you need help. Don't just say "I'm lost."

a. Your instructor usually will note office hours right on or near the office door or they may be listed in the syllabus. Take a few extra minutes and locate the office. List your instructor's office hours below. Write the office room number next to the hours. Circle the office hours that work with your schedule.

b. Does your college have a center where you can go for tutoring or extra help? If there is one, what is the room number? Take a minute and locate the center. When is the center open? Determine what hours would be good for you if you should need help.

c. Students in your class may also help. Write the phone numbers or e-mail addresses of two or three students in your class whom you could call for help. These students may form a study group with you. When would it be a good time for all of you to meet? Set up the first meeting.

d. You can also help yourself by helping others learn the information. By working a problem with someone else, it will help you to reinforce the concepts and skills. Set aside some time to help someone else. What hours are you available? Tell someone else you are available to help. Write the person's name here.

Extra help is also there for you during class time. Remember to ask questions in class when you do not understand. Don't be afraid to raise your hand. There are probably other students who have the same question. If you work in groups, your group can also help. Use the following chart to record the times you have needed help.

Date	Topic you needed help with	Where did you find help?	Who helped you?	Were your questions answered?	Do you still have questions?

10. Have you tried creating study cards to prepare for exams?

a. Find out from your instructor what topics will be on your exam. Ask also about the format of the exam. Will it be multiple choice, true/false, problem solving, or some of each?

b. Organize your quizzes, projects, homework, and book notes from the sections to be tested.

c. Read these quizzes, projects, homework, and book notes carefully and pick out those concepts and skills that seem to be the most important. Write this information on your study card. Try to summarize in your own words and include an example of each important concept.

d. Make sure you include:

Vocabulary Words, with definitions:

Key Concepts, explained *in your own words:*

Skills, illustrated with an example or two:

e. Reviewing this study card with your instructor may be a good exam preparation activity.

11. How can you develop effective test-taking strategies?

a. A little worry before a test is good for you. Your study card will help you feel confident about what you know. Wear comfortable clothing and shoes to your exam and make yourself relax in your chair. A few deep breaths can help! Don't take stimulants such as caffeine; they only increase your anxiety!

b. As soon as you receive your test, write down on your test paper any formulas, concepts, or other information that you might forget during the exam. This is information that you would recall from your study card.

c. You may want to skim the test first to see what kind of test it is and which parts are worth the most points. This will also help you to allocate your time.

d. Read all directions and questions carefully.

e. You may want to do some easy questions first to boost your confidence.

f. Try to reason through tough problems. You may want to use a diagram or graph. Look for clues in the question. Try to estimate the answer before doing the problem. If you begin to spend too much time on one problem, you may want to mark it to come back to later.

g. Write about your test-taking strategies.

	What test-taking strategies will you use?	*What test-taking strategies did you use?*
Test 1		
Test 2		
Test 3		
Test 4		

12. How can you learn from your exams?

a. Errors on exams can be divided into several categories. Review your exam, identify your mistakes and determine the category for each of your errors.

Type of Error	Meaning of Error	Question Number	Points Deducted
A. Concept	You don't understand the properties or principles required to answer the question.		
B. Application	You know the concept, but cannot apply it to the question.		
C. Skill	You know the concept and can apply it, but your skill process is incorrect.		
D. Test-taking	These errors apply to the specific way you take tests. **1.** Did you change correct answers to incorrect answers? **2.** Did you miscopy an answer from scrap paper? **3.** Did you leave an answer blank? **4.** Did you miss more questions at the beginning or in the middle or at the end of your test? **5.** Did you misread the directions?		
E. Careless	Mistakes you made that you could have corrected had you reviewed your answers to the test.		
	TOTAL:		

b. You should now correct your exam and keep it for future reference.

    i. What questions do you still have after making your corrections?

    ii. Where will you go for help to get answers to these questions?

    iii. Write some strategies that you will use the next time you take a test that will help you reduce your errors.

FRACTIONS

Proper and Improper Fractions

A fraction in the form $\frac{a}{b}$ is called **proper** if a and b are counting numbers and a is less than b $(a < b)$. If a is greater than or equal to b $(a \geq b)$, then $\frac{a}{b}$ is called **improper**.

Note: a can be zero but b cannot, since you may not divide by zero.

Example 1: $\frac{2}{3}$ is proper since $2 < 3$.   **Example 2:** $\frac{7}{5}$ is improper since $7 > 5$.

Example 3: $\frac{0}{4} = 0$

Example 4: $\frac{8}{0}$ has no numerical value and, therefore, is said to be **undefined.**

Reducing a Fraction

A fraction, $\frac{a}{b}$, is in **lowest terms** if a and b have no common divisor other than 1.

Example 1: $\frac{3}{4}$ is in lowest terms. The only common divisor is 1.

Example 2: $\frac{9}{15}$ is not in lowest terms. 3 is a common divisor of 9 and 15.

To **reduce a fraction** $\frac{a}{b}$ **to lowest terms,** divide both a and b by a common divisor until the numerator and denominator no longer have any common divisors.

Example 1: Reduce $\frac{4}{8}$ to lowest terms.

Solution: $\dfrac{4}{8} = \dfrac{4 \div 4}{8 \div 4} = \dfrac{1}{2}$

Example 2: Reduce $\dfrac{54}{42}$ to lowest terms.

Solution: $\dfrac{54}{42} = \dfrac{54 \div 2}{42 \div 2} = \dfrac{27}{21} = \dfrac{27 \div 3}{21 \div 3} = \dfrac{9}{7}$

Mixed Numbers

> A **mixed number** is the sum of a whole number plus a proper fraction.

Example 1: $3\frac{2}{5} = 3 + \frac{2}{5}$

Changing an Improper Fraction, $\frac{a}{b}$, to a Mixed Number

1. Divide the numerator, a, by the denominator, b.
2. The quotient becomes the whole-number part of the mixed number.
3. The remainder becomes the numerator, and b remains the denominator, of the fractional part of the mixed number.

Example 1: Change $\frac{7}{5}$ to a mixed number.

Solution: $7 \div 5 = 1$ with a remainder of 2.

$$\text{So } \frac{7}{5} = 1 + \frac{2}{5} = 1\frac{2}{5}.$$

Example 2: Change $\frac{22}{6}$ to a mixed number.

Solution: First reduce $\frac{22}{6}$ to lowest terms.

$$\frac{22}{6} = \frac{22 \div 2}{6 \div 2} = \frac{11}{3}$$

$11 \div 3 = 3$ with a remainder of 2.

$$\text{So } \frac{11}{3} = 3 + \frac{2}{3} = 3\frac{2}{3}.$$

Changing a Mixed Number to an Improper Fraction

1. To obtain the numerator of the improper fraction, multiply the denominator by the whole number and add the original numerator to this product.
2. Place this sum over the original denominator.

Example 1: Change $4\frac{5}{6}$ to an improper fraction.

Solution: $6 \cdot 4 + 5 = 29$

$$\text{So } 4\frac{5}{6} = \frac{29}{6}.$$

Exercises

1. Reduce these fractions, if possible.

   a. $\frac{12}{16}$ **b.** $\frac{33}{11}$ **c.** $\frac{21}{49}$ **d.** $\frac{13}{31}$

2. Change each improper fraction to a mixed number. Reduce, if possible.

   a. $\frac{20}{16}$ **b.** $\frac{34}{8}$ **c.** $\frac{48}{12}$ **d.** $\frac{33}{5}$

3. Change each mixed number to an improper fraction. Reduce, if possible.

a. $7\frac{2}{5}$ b. $8\frac{6}{10}$ c. $9\frac{6}{7}$ d. $11\frac{3}{4}$

Finding a Common Denominator of Two Fractions

A **common denominator** is a number that is divisible by each of the original denominators.

The **least common denominator** is the smallest possible common denominator.

A common denominator can be obtained by multiplying the original denominators. Note that this product may not necessarily be the *least* common denominator.

Example 1: Determine a common denominator for $\frac{5}{6}$ and $\frac{7}{9}$.

Solution: $6 \cdot 9 = 54$, so 54 is a common denominator.
             However, 18 is the least common denominator.

Equivalent Fractions

Equivalent fractions are fractions with the same numerical value.

To obtain an equivalent fraction, multiply or divide both numerator and denominator by the same nonzero number.

Note: Adding or subtracting the same number to the original numerator and denominator does *not* yield an equivalent fraction.

Example 1: Determine a fraction that is equivalent to $\frac{3}{5}$ and has denominator 20.

Solution: $\dfrac{3}{5} = \dfrac{3 \cdot 4}{5 \cdot 4} = \dfrac{12}{20}$ **Note:** $\dfrac{3+15}{5+15} = \dfrac{18}{20} = \dfrac{9}{10} \neq \dfrac{3}{5}$

Comparing Fractions: Determining Which Is Larger. Is $\frac{a}{b} < \frac{c}{d}$ or is $\frac{a}{b} > \frac{c}{d}$?

1. Obtain a common denominator by multiplying b and d.

2. Write $\frac{a}{b}$ and $\frac{c}{d}$ as equivalent fractions, each with denominator $b \cdot d$.

3. Compare numerators. The fraction with the larger (or smaller) numerator is the larger (or smaller) fraction.

Example 1: Determine whether $\frac{3}{5}$ is less than or greater than $\frac{7}{12}$.

Solution: A common denominator is $5 \cdot 12 = 60$.

$$\frac{3}{5} = \frac{3 \cdot 12}{5 \cdot 12} = \frac{36}{60}, \quad \frac{7}{12} = \frac{7 \cdot 5}{12 \cdot 5} = \frac{35}{60}$$

Since $36 > 35$, $\frac{3}{5} > \frac{7}{12}$.

Exercises

Compare the two fractions and indicate which one is larger.

1. $\frac{4}{7}$ and $\frac{5}{8}$ **2.** $\frac{11}{13}$ and $\frac{22}{39}$ **3.** $\frac{5}{12}$ and $\frac{7}{16}$ **4.** $\frac{3}{5}$ and $\frac{14}{20}$

Addition and Subtraction of Fractions with the Same Denominators

To add (or subtract) $\frac{a}{c}$ and $\frac{b}{c}$:

1. Add (or subtract) the numerators, a and b.

2. Place the sum (or difference) over the common denominator, c.

3. Reduce to lowest terms.

Example 1: Add $\frac{5}{16} + \frac{7}{16}$.

Solution: $\dfrac{5}{16} + \dfrac{7}{16} = \dfrac{5 + 7}{16} = \dfrac{12}{16}$ $\dfrac{12}{16} = \dfrac{12 \div 4}{16 \div 4} = \dfrac{3}{4}$

Example 2: Subtract $\frac{19}{24} - \frac{7}{24}$.

Solution: $\dfrac{19}{24} - \dfrac{7}{24} = \dfrac{19 - 7}{24} = \dfrac{12}{24}$ $\dfrac{12}{24} = \dfrac{12 \div 12}{24 \div 12} = \dfrac{1}{2}$

Addition and Subtraction of Fractions with Different Denominators

To add (or subtract) $\frac{a}{b}$ and $\frac{c}{d}$, where $b \neq d$:

1. Obtain a common denominator by multiplying b and d.

2. Write $\frac{a}{b}$ and $\frac{c}{d}$ as equivalent fractions with denominator $b \cdot d$.

3. Add (or subtract) the numerators of the equivalent fractions and place the sum (or difference) over the common denominator, $b \cdot d$.

4. Reduce to lowest terms.

Example 1: Add $\frac{3}{5} + \frac{2}{7}$.

Solution: A common denominator is $5 \cdot 7 = 35$.

$$\frac{3}{5} = \frac{3 \cdot 7}{5 \cdot 7} = \frac{21}{35}, \qquad \frac{2}{7} = \frac{2 \cdot 5}{7 \cdot 5} = \frac{10}{35},$$

$$\frac{3}{5} + \frac{2}{7} = \frac{21}{35} + \frac{10}{35} = \frac{31}{35}$$

$\frac{31}{35}$ is already in lowest terms.

Example 2: Subtract $\frac{5}{12} - \frac{2}{9}$.

Solution: Using a common denominator, $12 \cdot 9 = 108$:

$$\frac{5}{12} = \frac{5 \cdot 9}{12 \cdot 9} = \frac{45}{108}$$

$$\frac{2}{9} = \frac{2 \cdot 12}{9 \cdot 12} = \frac{24}{108}$$

$$\frac{5}{12} - \frac{2}{9} = \frac{45}{108} - \frac{24}{108} = \frac{21}{108}$$

$$\frac{21}{108} = \frac{21 \div 3}{108 \div 3} = \frac{7}{36}$$

Using the least common denominator, 36:

$$\frac{5}{12} = \frac{5 \cdot 3}{12 \cdot 3} = \frac{15}{36}$$

$$\frac{2}{9} = \frac{2 \cdot 4}{9 \cdot 4} = \frac{8}{36}$$

$$\frac{5}{12} - \frac{2}{9} = \frac{15}{36} - \frac{8}{36} = \frac{7}{36}$$

Addition and Subtraction of Mixed Numbers

To add (or subtract) mixed numbers:

1. Add (or subtract) the whole-number parts.

2. Add (or subtract) the fractional parts. In subtraction, this may require borrowing.

3. Add the resulting whole-number and fractional parts to form the mixed number sum (or difference).

Example 1: Add $3\frac{2}{3} + 5\frac{3}{4}$.

Solution: Whole-number sum: $3 + 5 = 8$

Fractional sum: $\frac{2}{3} + \frac{3}{4} = \frac{2 \cdot 4}{3 \cdot 4} + \frac{3 \cdot 3}{4 \cdot 3} = \frac{8}{12} + \frac{9}{12} = \frac{17}{12} = 1\frac{5}{12}$

Final result: $8 + 1\frac{5}{12} = 8 + 1 + \frac{5}{12} = 9\frac{5}{12}$

Example 2: Subtract $4\frac{1}{3} - 1\frac{7}{8}$.

Solution: Because $\frac{1}{3}$ is smaller than $\frac{7}{8}$, you must borrow as follows:

$$4\frac{1}{3} = 3 + 1 + \frac{1}{3} = 3 + 1\frac{1}{3} = 3\frac{4}{3}$$

The original subtraction now becomes $3\frac{4}{3} - 1\frac{7}{8}$.

Subtracting the whole-number parts: $3 - 1 = 2$.

Subtracting the fractional parts:

$$\frac{4}{3} - \frac{7}{8} = \frac{4 \cdot 8}{3 \cdot 8} - \frac{7 \cdot 3}{8 \cdot 3} = \frac{32}{24} - \frac{21}{24} = \frac{11}{24}$$

Final result is $2 + \frac{11}{24} = 2\frac{11}{24}$.

Alternatively, to add (or subtract) mixed numbers:

1. Convert each mixed number to an improper fraction.

2. Add (or subtract) the fractions.

3. Rewrite the result as a mixed number.

Example 3: Subtract $4\frac{1}{3} - 1\frac{7}{8}$.

Solution: $4\frac{1}{3} = \frac{13}{3}$ and $1\frac{7}{8} = \frac{15}{8}$

$$\frac{13}{3} - \frac{15}{8} = \frac{13 \cdot 8}{3 \cdot 8} - \frac{15 \cdot 3}{8 \cdot 3} = \frac{104}{24} - \frac{45}{24} = \frac{59}{24} = 2\frac{11}{24}$$

Exercises

Add or subtract as indicated.

1. $1\frac{3}{4} + 3\frac{1}{8}$ **2.** $8\frac{2}{3} - 7\frac{1}{4}$ **3.** $6\frac{5}{6} + 3\frac{11}{18}$ **4.** $2\frac{1}{3} - \frac{4}{5}$

5. $4\frac{3}{5} + 2\frac{3}{8}$ **6.** $12\frac{1}{3} + 8\frac{7}{10}$ **7.** $14\frac{3}{4} - 5\frac{7}{8}$ **8.** $6\frac{5}{8} + 9\frac{7}{12}$

Multiplying Fractions

To multiply fractions, $\frac{a}{b} \cdot \frac{c}{d}$:

1. Multiply the numerators, $a \cdot c$, to form the numerator of the product fraction.
2. Multiply the denominators, $b \cdot d$, to form the denominator of the product fraction.
3. Write the product fraction by placing $a \cdot c$ over $b \cdot d$.
4. Reduce to lowest terms.

Example 1: Multiply $\frac{3}{4} \cdot \frac{8}{15}$.

Solution: $\frac{3}{4} \cdot \frac{8}{15} = \frac{3 \cdot 8}{4 \cdot 15} = \frac{24}{60}, \quad \frac{24}{60} = \frac{24 \div 12}{60 \div 12} = \frac{2}{5}$

Note: It is often simpler and more efficient to cancel any common factors of the numerators and denominators *before* multiplying.

Dividing by a Fraction

Dividing *by* a fraction, $\frac{c}{d}$, is equivalent to multiplying by its reciprocal, $\frac{d}{c}$.

To divide fraction $\frac{a}{b}$ by $\frac{c}{d}$, written $\frac{a}{b} \div \frac{c}{d}$:

1. Rewrite the division as an equivalent multiplication, $\frac{a}{b} \cdot \frac{d}{c}$.
2. Proceed by multiplying as described above.

Example 1: Divide $\frac{2}{3}$ by $\frac{1}{2}$.

Solution: $\frac{2}{3} \div \frac{1}{2} = \frac{2}{3} \cdot \frac{2}{1} = \frac{2 \cdot 2}{3 \cdot 1} = \frac{4}{3}$

Note: $\frac{4}{3}$ is already in lowest terms.

Exercises

Multiply or divide as indicated.

1. $\frac{11}{14} \cdot \frac{4}{5}$ **2.** $\frac{3}{7} \div \frac{3}{5}$ **3.** $\frac{8}{15} \cdot \frac{3}{4}$ **4.** $6 \div \frac{2}{5}$

Multiplying or Dividing Mixed Numbers

To multiply (or divide) mixed numbers:

1. Change the mixed numbers to improper fractions.

2. Multiply (or divide) the fractions as described earlier.

3. If the result is an improper fraction, change to a mixed number.

Example 1: Divide $8\frac{2}{5}$ by 3.

Solution: $8\frac{2}{5} = \frac{42}{5}, \quad 3 = \frac{3}{1}$

$$\frac{42}{5} \div \frac{3}{1} = \frac{42}{5} \cdot \frac{1}{3} = \frac{42}{15}$$

$$\frac{42}{15} = \frac{42 \div 3}{15 \div 3} = \frac{14}{5}$$

$$\frac{14}{5} = 2\frac{4}{5}$$

Exercises

Multiply or divide as indicated.

1. $3\frac{1}{2} \cdot 4\frac{3}{4}$ **2.** $10\frac{3}{5} \div 4\frac{2}{3}$ **3.** $5\frac{4}{5} \cdot 6$ **4.** $4\frac{3}{10} \div \frac{2}{5}$

Fractions and Percents

To convert a fraction or mixed number to a percent:

1. If present, convert the mixed number to an improper fraction.

2. Multiply the fraction by 100 and attach the % symbol.

3. If the result is an improper fraction, change it to a mixed number.

Example 1: Write $\frac{1}{12}$ as a percent.

Solution: $\frac{1}{12} \cdot 100\% = \frac{100}{12}\% = 8\frac{1}{3}\%$

Example 2: Write $2\frac{1}{4}$ as a percent.

Solution: $2\frac{1}{4} = \frac{9}{4} \cdot 100\% = 225\%$

Exercises

Convert each fraction to a percent.

1. $\dfrac{3}{4}$ **2.** $2\dfrac{3}{5}$ **3.** $\dfrac{2}{3}$ **4.** $\dfrac{5}{9}$

To convert a percent to a fraction:

1. Remove the % symbol and multiply the number by $\dfrac{1}{100}$.

Example 1: Write $8\dfrac{1}{3}\%$ as a fraction.

Solution: $8\dfrac{1}{3}\% = 8\dfrac{1}{3} \cdot \dfrac{1}{100} = \dfrac{25}{3} \cdot \dfrac{1}{100} = \dfrac{1}{12}$

Exercises

Convert each percent to a fraction.

1. 75%   **2.** 60%   **3.** $66\dfrac{2}{3}\%$ **4.** $55\dfrac{5}{9}\%$

DECIMALS

Reading and Writing Decimal Numbers

Decimal numbers are written numerically according to a place value system. The following table lists the place values of digits to the *left* of the decimal point.

hundred million	ten million	million,	hundred thousand	ten thousand	thousand,	hundred	ten	one	*decimal point*

The following table lists the place values of digits to the *right* of the decimal point.

decimal point	tenths	hundredths	thousandths	ten-thousandths	hundred-thousandths	millionths

To read or write a decimal number in words:

1. Use the first place value table to read the digits to the left of the decimal point, in groups of three from the decimal point.

2. Insert the word *and*.

3. Read the digits to the right of the decimal point as though they were not preceded by a decimal point, and then attach the place value of its rightmost digit:

Example 1: Read and write the number 37,568.0218 in words.

			3	7	5	6	8	.
hundred million	ten million	million,	hundred thousand	ten thousand	thousand,	hundred	ten	one	*decimal point*

and

.	0	2	1	8		
decimal point	tenths	hundredths	thousandths	ten-thousandths	hundred-thousandths	millionths

Therefore, 37,568.0218 is read "thirty-seven thousand, five hundred sixty-eight" "and" "two hundred eighteen" "ten-thousandths."

Example 2: Write the number "seven hundred eighty-two million, ninety-three thousand, five hundred ninety-four and two thousand four hundred three millionths" numerically in standard form.

7	8	2,	0	9	3,	5	9	4	.
hundred million	ten million	million,	hundred thousand	ten thousand	thousand,	hundred	ten	one	decimal point

"and"

.	0	0	2	4	0	3
decimal point	tenths	hundredths	thousandths	ten-thousandths	hundred-thousandths	millionths

That is, 782,093,594.002403

Exercises

1. Write the number 9467.00624 in words.

2. Write the number 35,454,666.007 in words.

3. Write the number numerically in standard form: four million, sixty-four and seventy-two ten-thousandths.

4. Write the number numerically in standard form: seven and forty-three thousand fifty-two millionths.

Rounding a Number to a Specified Place Value

1. Locate the digit with the specified place value (target digit).
2. If the digit directly to its right is less than 5, keep the target digit. If it is 5 or greater, increase the target digit by 1.
3. If the target digit is to the right of the decimal point, delete all digits to its right.
4. If the target digit is to the left of the decimal point, replace any digits between the target digit and the decimal point with zeros as placeholders. Delete the decimal point and all digits that follow it.

Example 1: Round 35,178.2649 to the nearest hundredth.

The digit in the "hundredths" place is 6. The digit to its right is 4. Therefore, keep the 6 and delete the digits to its right. The rounded value is 35,178.26.

Example 2: Round 35,178.2649 to the nearest tenth.

The digit in the "tenths" place is 2. The digit to its right is 6. Therefore, increase the 2 to 3 and delete the digits to its right. The rounded value is 35,178.3.

Example 3: Round 35,178.2649 to the nearest ten thousand.

The digit in the "ten thousand" place is 3. The digit to its right is 5. Therefore, increase the 3 to 4 and insert four zeros to its right as placeholders. The rounded value is 40,000, where the decimal point is not written.

Exercises

1. Round 7456.975 to the nearest hundredth.

2. Round 55,568.2 to the nearest hundred.

3. Round 34.6378 to the nearest tenth.

Converting a Fraction to a Decimal

To convert a fraction to a decimal, divide the numerator by the denominator.

Example 1: Convert $\frac{4}{5}$ to a decimal.

Solution: On a calculator:

Key in $\boxed{4}$ $\boxed{\div}$ $\boxed{5}$ $\boxed{=}$
to obtain 0.8.

Using long division:
$$5\overline{)4.0}$$ quotient 0.8
$$\underline{4.0}$$
$$0$$

Example 2: Convert $\frac{1}{3}$ to a decimal.

Solution: On a calculator:

Key in $\boxed{1}$ $\boxed{\div}$ $\boxed{3}$ $\boxed{=}$
to obtain 0.3333333.

Using long division:
$$3\overline{)1.000}$$ quotient 0.333
$$\underline{-9}$$
$$10$$
$$\underline{-9}$$
$$10$$
$$\underline{-9}$$
$$1$$

Since a calculator's display is limited to a specified number of digits, it will cut off the decimal's trailing right digits.

Since this long division process will continue indefinitely, the quotient is a repeating decimal, 0.33333 . . . and is instead denoted by $0.\overline{3}$. The bar is placed above the repeating digit or above a repeating sequence of digits.

Exercises

Convert the given fractions into decimals. Use a repeating bar, if necessary.

1. $\frac{3}{5}$ **2.** $\frac{2}{3}$ **3.** $\frac{7}{8}$ **4.** $\frac{1}{7}$ **5.** $\frac{4}{9}$

Converting a Terminating Decimal to a Fraction

1. Read the decimal.

2. The place value of the rightmost nonzero digit becomes the denominator of the fraction.

3. The original numeral, with the decimal point removed, becomes the numerator. Drop all leading zeros.

Example 1: Convert 0.025 to a fraction.

Solution: The rightmost digit, 5, is in the "thousandths" place.

So, as a fraction, $0.025 = \frac{25}{1000}$, which reduces to $\frac{1}{40}$.

Example 2: Convert 0.0034 to a fraction.

Solution: The rightmost digit, 4, is in the ten-thousandths place.

So, as a fraction, $0.0034 = \frac{34}{10,000}$, which reduces to $\frac{17}{5000}$.

Exercises

Convert the given decimals to fractions.

   1. 0.4   **2.** 0.125   **3.** 0.64   **4.** 0.05

Converting a Decimal to a Percent

Multiply the decimal by 100 (that is, move the decimal point two places to the right, inserting placeholding zeros when necessary) and attach the % symbol.

Example 1: 0.78 written as a percent is 78%.

Example 2: 3 written as a percent is 300%.

Example 3: 0.045 written as a percent is 4.5%.

Exercises

Write the following decimals as equivalent percents.

   1. 0.35   **2.** 0.076   **3.** 0.0089   **4.** 6.0

Converting a Percent to a Decimal

Divide the percent by 100 (that is, move the decimal point two places to the left, inserting placeholding zeros when necessary) and drop the % symbol.

Example 1: 5% written as a decimal is 0.05.

Example 2: 625% written as a decimal is 6.25.

Example 3: 0.0005% written as a decimal is 0.000005.

Exercises

Write the following percents as decimals.

   1. 45%   **2.** 0.0987%   **3.** 3.45%   **4.** 2000%

Comparing Decimals

  1. Write the decimals one below the next, lining up their respective decimal points.

  2. Read the decimals from left to right, comparing corresponding place values. The decimal with the first and largest nonzero digit is the largest number.

Example 1: Order from largest to smallest: 0.097, 0.48, 0.0356.

Solution: Align by decimal point: 0.097

                                          0.48

                                        0.0356

Since 4 (in the second decimal) is the first nonzero digit, 0.48 is the largest number. Next, since 9 is larger than 3, 0.097 is next largest; and finally, 0.0356 is the smallest number.

Example 2: Order from largest to smallest: 0.043, 0.0043, 0.43, 0.00043.

Solution: Align by decimal point: 0.043

                                        0.0043

                                        0.43

                                        0.00043

Since 4 (in the third decimal), is the first nonzero digit, then 0.43 is the largest number. Similarly, next is 0.043; followed by 0.0043; and finally, 0.00043 is the smallest number.

Exercises

Place each group of decimals in order, from largest to smallest.

  1. 0.058   0.0099   0.105   0.02999

  2. 0.75   1.23   1.2323   0.9   0.999

  3. 13.56   13.568   13.5068   13.56666

Adding and Subtracting Decimals

1. Write the decimals one below the next, lining up their respective decimal points. If the decimals have differing numbers of digits to the right of the decimal point, place trailing zeros to the right in the shorter decimals.

2. Place the decimal point in the answer, lined up with the decimal points in the problem.

3. Add or subtract the numbers as usual.

Example 1: Add: $23.5 + 37.098 + 432.17$.

Solution:
$$
\begin{array}{r}
23.500 \\
37.098 \\
+\ 432.170 \\
\hline
492.768
\end{array}
$$

Example 2: Subtract 72.082 from 103.07.

Solution:
$$
\begin{array}{r}
103.070 \\
-\ \ 72.082 \\
\hline
30.988
\end{array}
$$

Exercises

1. Calculate: $543.785 + 43.12 + 3200.0043$.

2. Calculate: $679.05 - 54.9973$.

Multiplying Decimals

1. Multiply the numbers as usual, ignoring the decimal points.

2. Sum the number of decimal places in each number to determine the number of decimal places in the product.

Example 1: Multiply 32.89 by 0.021.

Solution:
$$
\begin{array}{r}
32.89 \\
\times\ 0.021 \\
\hline
3289 \\
6578 \\
\hline
0.69069
\end{array}
$$

32.89 → 2 decimal places
× 0.021 → 3 decimal places
0.69069 → 5 decimal places

Example 2: Multiply 64.05 by 7.3.

Solution:
$$
\begin{array}{r}
64.05 \\
\times\ \ \ 7.3 \\
\hline
19215 \\
44835 \\
\hline
467.565
\end{array}
$$

64.05 → 2 decimal places
× 7.3 → 1 decimal places
467.565 → 3 decimal places

Exercises

Multiply the following decimals.

1. 12.53×8.2 **2.** 115.3×0.003 **3.** 14.62×0.75

Dividing Decimals

1. Write the division in long division format.

2. Move the decimal point the same number of places to the right in both divisor and dividend so that the divisor becomes a whole number. Insert zeros if necessary.

3. Place the decimal point in the quotient directly above the decimal point in the dividend and divide as usual.

Example 1: Divide   92.4   by   0.25.
                          (*dividend*)   (*divisor*)

Solution: $0.25\overline{)92.4}$ becomes $25\overline{)9240}$:

$$
\begin{array}{r}
369.6 \\
25\overline{)9240.0} \\
-75 \\
\hline
174 \\
-150 \\
\hline
240 \\
-225 \\
\hline
150 \\
-150 \\
\hline
0
\end{array}
$$

So, $92.4 \div 0.25 = 369.6$.

Example 2: $0.00052 \div 0.004$
              (*dividend*)   (*divisor*)

Solution: $0.004\overline{)0.00052}$ becomes $4\overline{)0.52}$:

$$
\begin{array}{r}
0.13 \\
4\overline{)0.52} \\
-4 \\
\hline
12 \\
-12 \\
\hline
0
\end{array}
$$

So, $0.00052 \div 0.004 = 0.13$.

Exercises

1. Divide 12.05 by 2.5.   **2.** Divide 18.9973 by 78.

3. Divide 14.05 by 0.0002.   **4.** Calculate $150 \div 0.03$.

5. Calculate $0.00442 \div 0.017$.   **6.** Calculate $69.115 \div 0.0023$.

APPENDIX D
ALGEBRAIC EXTENSIONS

Properties of Exponents

The basic properties of exponents are summarized as follows:

> If a and b are both positive real numbers and n and m are any real numbers, then
>
> **1.** $a^n a^m = a^{n+m}$ **2.** $\dfrac{a^n}{a^m} = a^{n-m}$ **3.** $\left(a^n\right)^m = a^{nm}$
>
> **4.** $a^{-n} = \dfrac{1}{a^n}$ **5.** $(ab)^n = a^n b^n$ **6.** $a^0 = 1$

Note: The properties of exponents are covered in detail in Activity 4.2.

Property 1: $a^n a^m = a^{n+m}$ If you are multiplying two powers of the same base, add the exponents.

Example 1: $x^4 \cdot x^7 = x^{4+7} = x^{11}$

Note: The exponents were added and the base did not change.

Property 2: $\dfrac{a^n}{a^m} = a^{n-m}$ If you are dividing two powers of the same base, subtract the exponents.

Example 2: $\dfrac{6^6}{6^4} = 6^{6-4} = 6^2 = 36$

Note: The exponents were subtracted and the base did not change.

Property 3: $\left(a^n\right)^m = a^{nm}$ If a power is raised to a power, multiply the exponents.

Example 3: $\left(y^3\right)^4 = y^{12}$

Note: The exponents were multiplied. The base did not change.

Property 4: $a^{-n} = \dfrac{1}{a^n}$ Sometimes presented as a definition, Property 4 states that any base raised to a negative power is equivalent to the reciprocal of the base raised to the positive power. Note that the negative exponent does not have any effect on the sign of the base. This property could also be viewed as a result of the second property of exponents as follows:

Consider $\dfrac{x^3}{x^5}$. Using Property 2, $x^{3-5} = x^{-2}$. If you view this expression algebraically, you have three factors of x in the numerator and five in the denominator. If you divide out the three common factors, you are left with $\dfrac{1}{x^2}$. Therefore, if Property 2 is true, then $x^{-2} = \dfrac{1}{x^2}$.

Example 4: Write each of the following without negative exponents.

$$\textbf{a. } 3^{-2} \qquad\qquad\qquad \textbf{b. } \dfrac{2}{x^{-3}}$$

Solution: a. $3^{-2} = \dfrac{1}{3^2} = \dfrac{1}{9}$ b. $\dfrac{2}{x^{-3}} = \dfrac{2}{\dfrac{1}{x^3}} = 2 \div \dfrac{1}{x^3} = 2 \cdot x^3 = 2x^3$

Property 5: $(ab)^n = a^n b^n$ If a product is raised to a power, each factor is raised to that power.

Example 5: $(2x^2y^3)^3 = 2^3 \cdot (x^2)^3 \cdot (y^3)^3 = 8x^6y^9$

Note: Because the base contained three factors each of those was raised to the third power. The common mistake in an expansion such as this is not to raise the coefficient to the power.

Property 6: $a^0 = 1, a \neq 0$. Often presented as a definition, Property 6 states that any nonzero base raised to the zero power is 1. This property or definition is a result of Property 2 of exponents as follows:

Consider $\dfrac{x^5}{x^5}$. Using Property 2, $x^{5-5} = x^0$. However, you know that any fraction in which the numerator and the denominator are equal is equivalent to 1. Therefore, $x^0 = 1$.

Example 6: $\left(\dfrac{2x^3}{3yz^5}\right)^0 = 1$

Given a nonzero base, if the exponent is zero, the value is 1.

A **factor** can be moved from a numerator to a denominator or from a denominator to a numerator by changing the *sign of the exponent.*

Example 7: Simplify and express your result with positive exponents only.

$$\frac{x^3y^{-4}}{2x^{-3}y^{-2}z}$$

Solution: Move the x^{-3} and the y^{-2} factors from the denominator to the numerator making sure to change the sign of the exponents. This results in:

$$\frac{x^3y^{-4}x^3y^2}{2z}$$

Simplify the numerator using Property 1 and then use Property 4:

$$\frac{x^{3+3}y^{-4+2}}{2z} = \frac{x^6y^{-2}}{2z} = \frac{x^6}{2y^2z}$$

Exercises

Simplify and express your results with positive exponents only. Assume that all variables represent only nonzero values.

1. 5^{-3}

2. $\dfrac{1}{x^{-5}}$

3. $\dfrac{3x}{y^{-2}}$

4. $\dfrac{10x^2y^5}{2x^{-3}}$

5. $\dfrac{5^{-1}z}{x^{-1}z^{-2}}$

6. $5x^0$

7. $(a+b)^0$

8. $-3(x^0 - 4y^0)$

9. $x^6 \cdot x^{-3}$

10. $\dfrac{4^{-2}}{4^{-3}}$

11. $(4x^2y^3) \cdot (3x^{-3}y^{-2})$

12. $\dfrac{24x^{-2}y^3}{6x^3y^{-1}}$

13. $\dfrac{(14x^{-2}y^{-3}) \cdot (5x^3y^{-2})}{6x^2y^{-3}z^{-3}}$

14. $\left(\dfrac{2x^{-2}y^{-3}}{z^2}\right) \cdot \left(\dfrac{x^5y^3}{z^{-3}}\right)$

15. $\dfrac{(16x^4y^{-3}z^{-2})(3x^{-3}y^4)}{15x^{-3}y^{-3}z^2}$

Addition Method for Solving a System of Two Linear Equations

The basic strategy for the addition method is to reduce a system of two linear equations to a single linear equation by eliminating a variable.

For example, consider the x-coefficients of the linear system

$$2x + 3y = 1$$
$$4x - y = 9.$$

The coefficients are 2 and 4. The LCM of 2 and 4 is 4. Use the multiplication principle to multiply each side of the first equation by -2. The resulting system is

$$-2(2x + 3y = 1) \quad \text{or equivalently} \quad -4x - 6y = -2$$
$$4x - y = 9 \qquad\qquad\qquad\qquad\qquad 4x - y = 9 \quad.$$

Multiplying by -2 produces x-coefficients that are additive inverses or opposites. Now add the two equations together to eliminate the variable x.

$$-7y = 7$$

Solving for y, $y = -1$ is the y-value of our solution. To find the value of x, substitute -1 for y and solve for x in any equation that involves x and y. For an alternative to determining the value of x, consider the original system and the coefficients of y, 3 and -1 in the original system. The LCM is 3. Since the signs are already opposites, multiply the second equation by 3.

$$2x + 3y = 1 \qquad\qquad\qquad\qquad 2x + 3y = 1$$
$$3(4x - y = 9) \quad \text{or equivalently} \quad 12x - 3y = 27$$

Adding the two equations will eliminate the y-variable.

$$14x = 28$$

Solving for x, $x = 2$. Therefore, the solution is $(2, -1)$. This should be checked to make certain that it satisfies both equations.

Depending on the coefficients of the system, you may need to change both equations when using the addition method. For example, the coefficients of x in the linear system

$$5x - 2y = 11$$
$$3x + 5y = -12$$

are 5 and 3. The LCM is 15. Multiply the first equation by 3 and the second by -5 as follows:

$$3(5x - 2y = 11) \qquad\qquad\qquad 15x - 6y = 33$$
$$-5(3x + 5y = -12) \quad \text{or equivalently} \quad -15x - 25y = 60$$

Add the two equations to eliminate the x terms from the system.

$$-31y = 93$$

Solving for y, $y = -3$. Substituting this value for y in the first equation of the original system yields

$$5x - 2(-3) = 11$$
$$5x + 6 = 11$$
$$5x = 5$$
$$x = 1$$

Therefore, $(1, -3)$ is the solution of the system.

Exercises

Solve the following systems using the addition method. If the system has no solution or both equations represent the same line, state this as your answer.

1. $x - y = 3$
 $x + y = -7$

2. $x + 4y = 10$
 $x + 2y = 4$

3. $-5x - y = 4$
$-5x + 2y = 7$

4. $4x + y = 7$
$2x + 3y = 6$

5. $3x - y = 1$
$6x - 2y = 5$

6. $4x - 2y = 0$
$3x + 3y = 5$

7. $x - y = 9$
$-4x - 4y = -36$

8. $-2x + y = 6$
$4x + y = 1$

9. $\frac{3}{2}x + \frac{2}{5}y = \frac{9}{10}$
$\frac{1}{2}x + \frac{6}{5}y = \frac{3}{10}$

10. $0.3x - 0.8y = 1.6$
$0.1x + 0.4y = 1.2$

Factoring Trinomials with Leading Coefficient ≠ 1

With patience, it is possible to factor many trinomials by trial and error, using the FOIL method in reverse.

Factoring Trinomials by Trial and Error
1. Factor out the greatest common factor.
2. Try combinations of factors for the first and last terms in the two binomials.
3. Check the outer and inner products to match the middle term of the original trinomial.
4. If the check fails, then repeat steps 2 and 3.

Example 1: Factor $6x^2 - 7x - 3$.

Solution:

Step 1.   There is no common factor, so go to step 2.

Step 2.   You could factor the first term as $6x(x)$ or as $2x(3x)$. The last term has factors of 3 and 1, disregarding signs. Suppose you try $(2x + 1)(3x - 3)$.

Step 3.   The outer product is $-6x$. The inner product is $3x$. The sum is $-3x$. The check fails.

Step 4.   Suppose you try $(2x - 3)(3x + 1)$. The outer product is $2x$. The inner product is $-9x$. The sum is $-7x$. It checks. Therefore, $6x^2 - 7x - 3 = (2x - 3)(3x + 1)$.

Exercises

Factor each of the following completely.

1. $x^2 + 7x + 12$

2. $6x^2 - 13x + 6$

3. $3x^2 + 7x - 6$

4. $6x^2 + 21x + 18$

5. $9x^2 - 6x + 1$

6. $2x^2 + 6x - 20$

7. $15x^2 + 2x - 1$

8. $4x^3 + 10x^2 + 4x$

Solving Equations by Factoring

Many quadratic and higher-order polynomial equations can be solved by factoring using the zero-product rule.

Solving an Equation by Factoring
1. Use the addition principle to move all terms to one side, so that the other side of the equation is zero.
2. Simplify and factor the nonzero side.
3. Use the zero-product rule to set each factor equal to zero and then solve the resulting equations.
4. Check your solutions in the original equation.

Example 1: Solve the equation $3x^2 - 2 = -x$.

Solution: Adding x to both sides, you obtain $3x^2 + x - 2 = 0$. Since there are no like terms, factor the trinomial.

$$(3x - 2)(x + 1) = 0$$

Using the zero-product rule,

$$
\begin{array}{ccc}
3x - 2 = 0 & \text{or} & x + 1 = 0 \\
3x = 2 & \text{or} & x = -1 \\
x = \frac{2}{3} & &
\end{array}
$$

The two solutions are $x = \frac{2}{3}$ and $x = -1$. The check is left for the reader to do.

Example 2: Solve the equation $3x^3 - 8x^2 = 3x$.

Solution: Subtracting $3x$ from both sides, you obtain $3x^3 - 8x^2 - 3x = 0$. Since there are no like terms, factor the trinomial.

$$x(3x^2 - 8x - 3) = 0$$
$$x(3x + 1)(x - 3) = 0$$

Using the zero-product rule,

$$x = 0 \quad \text{or} \quad 3x + 1 = 0 \quad \text{or} \quad x - 3 = 0$$
$$3x = -1 \quad \text{or} \quad x = 3$$
$$x = -\tfrac{1}{3}$$

The three solutions are $x = 0$, $x = -\frac{1}{3}$, and $x = 3$. The check is left for the reader to do.

Exercises

Solve each of the following equations by factoring, if possible.

1. $x^2 - x - 63 = 0$

2. $3x^2 - 9x - 30 = 0$

3. $-7x + 6x^2 = 10$

4. $3y^2 = 2 - y$

5. $-28x^2 + 15x - 2 = 0$

6. $4x^2 - 25 = 0$

7. $(x + 4)^2 - 16 = 0$

8. $(x + 1)^2 - 3x = 7$

9. $2(x + 2)(x - 2) = (x - 2)(x + 3) - 2$

10. $18x^3 = 15x^2 + 12x$

GETTING STARTED WITH THE TI-83/TI-84 PLUS FAMILY OF CALCULATORS

ON-OFF

To turn on the calculator, press the (ON) key. To turn off the calculator, press (2nd) and then (ON) .

Most keys on the calculator have multiple purposes. The number or symbolic function/command written directly on the key is accessed by simply pressing the key. The symbolic function/commands written above each key are accessed with the aid of the (2nd) and (ALPHA) keys. The command above and to the left is color coded to match the (2nd) key. That command is accessed by first pressing the (2nd) key and then pressing the key itself. Similarly, the command above and to the right is color coded to match the (ALPHA) key and is accessed by first pressing the (ALPHA) key and then pressing the key itself.

Contrast

To adjust the contrast on your screen, press and release the (2nd) key and hold (▲) to darken and (▼) to lighten.

Mode

The (MODE) key controls many calculator settings. The activated settings are highlighted. For most of your work in this course, the settings in the left-hand column should be highlighted.

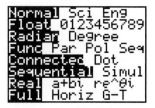

To change a setting, move the cursor to the desired setting and press (ENTER) .

The Home Screen

The home screen is used for calculations.

You may return to the home screen at any time by using the QUIT command. This command is accessed by pressing (2nd) (MODE) . All calculations in the home screen are subject to the order of operations convention.

Enter all expressions as you would write them. Always observe the order of operations. Once you have typed the expression, press (ENTER) to obtain the simplified result. Before you press (ENTER) , you may edit your expression by using the arrow keys, the delete command (DEL) , and the insert command (2nd) (DEL) .

Three keys of special note are the reciprocal key (X⁻¹) , the caret (^) key, and the negative key (−) .

Typing a number and then pressing the reciprocal command key (X⁻¹) will give the reciprocal of the number. The reciprocal of a nonzero number, n, is $\frac{1}{n}$. As noted in the screen below, when performing an operation on a fraction, the fraction MUST be enclosed in parentheses before accessing this command.

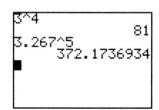

The caret key (^) is used to raise numbers to powers

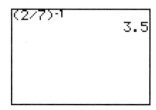

The negative key (−) on the bottom of the keyboard is different from the subtraction key (−) . They cannot be used interchangeably. The negative key is used to change the sign of a single number or symbol; it will not perform a subtraction operation. If you mistakenly use the negative key in attempting to subtract, you will likely obtain an ERROR message.

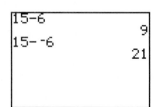

A table of some frequently used keys and their functions follows.

KEY	FUNCTION DESCRIPTION
ON	Turns calculator on or off.
CLEAR	Clears the line you are currently typing. If cursor is on a blank line when CLEAR is pressed, it clears the entire home screen.
ENTER	Executes a command.
(−)	Calculates the additive inverse.
MODE	Displays current operating settings.
DEL	Deletes the character at the cursor.
^	Symbol used for exponentiation.
ANS	Storage location of the result of the most recent calculation.
ENTRY	Retrieves the previously executed expression so that you may edit it.

ANS and ENTRY

The last two commands in the table can be real time savers. The result of your last calculation is always stored in a memory location known as ANS. It is accessed by pressing (2nd) (−) or it can be automatically accessed by pressing any operation button.

Suppose you want to evaluate $12.5\sqrt{1 + 0.5 \cdot (0.55)^2}$. It could be evaluated in one expression and checked with a series of calculations using ANS.

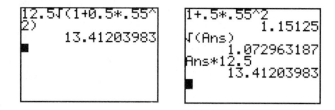

After you have keyed in an expression and pressed (ENTER), you cannot move the cursor back up to edit or recalculate this expression. This is where the ENTRY ((2nd) (ENTER)) command is used. The ENTRY command retrieves the previous expression and places the cursor at the end of the expression. You can use the left and right arrow keys to move the cursor to any location in the expression that you wish to modify.

Suppose you want to evaluate the compound interest expression $P\left(1 + \frac{r}{n}\right)^{nt}$, where P is the principal, r is the interest rate, n is the number of compounding periods annually, and t is the number of years, when $P = \$1000$, $r = 6.5\%$, $n = 1$, and $t = 2, 5$, and 15 years.

Using the ENTRY command, this expression would be entered once and edited twice.

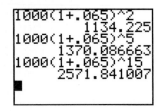

Note that there are many last expressions stored in the ENTRY memory location. You can repeat the ENTRY command as many times as you want to retrieve a previously entered expression.

Functions and Graphing with the TI-83/TI-84 Plus Family of Calculators

"Y =" Menu

Functions of the form $y = f(x)$ can be entered into the TI-83/TI-84 Plus using the "Y = " menu. To access the "Y = " menu, press the (Y=) key. Type the expression $f(x)$ after Y_1 using the (X,T,θ,n) key for the variable x and press (ENTER).

For example, enter the function $f(x) = 3x^5 - 4x + 1$.

Note the = sign after Y_1 is highlighted. This indicates that the function Y_1 is active and will be graphed when the graphing command is executed and will be included in your table when the table command is executed. The highlighting may be turned on or off by using the arrow keys to move the cursor to the = symbol and then pressing (ENTER). Notice in the screen below that Y_1 has been deactivated and will not be graphed nor appear in a table.

Once the function is entered in the "Y = " menu, function values may be evaluated in the home screen.

For example, given $f(x) = 3x^5 - 4x + 1$, evaluate $f(4)$. In the home screen, press $\boxed{\text{VARS}}$.

Move the cursor to Y-VARS and press $\boxed{\text{ENTER}}$.

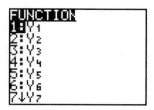

Press $\boxed{\text{ENTER}}$ again to select Y_1. Y_1 now appears in the home screen.

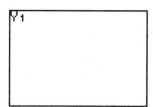

To evaluate $f(4)$, press $\boxed{(}$ $\boxed{4}$ $\boxed{)}$ after Y_1 and press $\boxed{\text{ENTER}}$.

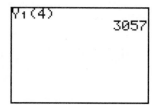

Tables of Values

If you are interested in viewing several function values for the same function, you may want to construct a table.

Before constructing the table, make sure the function appears in the "Y =" menu with its "=" highlighted. You may also want to deactivate or clear any functions that you do not need to see in your table. Next, you will need to check the settings in the Table Setup menu. To do this, use the TBLSET command (2nd WINDOW).

As shown in the screen above, the default setting for the table highlights the Auto options for both the independent (x) and dependent (y) variables. Choosing this option will display ordered pairs of the function with equally spaced x-values. TblStart is the first x-value to be displayed, and here is assigned the value -2. ΔTbl represents the equal spacing between consecutive x-values, and here is assigned the value 0.5. The TABLE command (2nd GRAPH) brings up the table displayed in the screen below.

Use the ▲ and ▼ keys to view additional ordered pairs of the function.

If the input values of interest are not evenly spaced, you may want to choose the Ask mode for the independent variable from the Table Setup menu.

The resulting table is blank, but you can fill it by choosing any values you like for x and pressing ENTER after each.

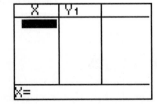

Note that the number of digits shown in the output is limited by the table width, but if you want more digits, move the cursor to the desired output and more digits appear at the bottom of the screen.

Graphing a Function

Once a function is entered in the "Y = " menu and activated, it can be displayed and analyzed. For this discussion we will use the function $f(x) = -x^2 + 10x + 12$. Enter this as Y_1 making sure to use the negation key $\boxed{(-)}$ and not the subtraction key $\boxed{-}$.

The Viewing Window

The viewing window is the portion of the rectangular coordinate system that is displayed when you graph a function.

Xmin defines the left edge of the window.

Xmax defines the right edge of the window.

Xscl defines the distance between horizontal tick marks.

Ymin defines the bottom edge of the window.

Ymax defines the top edge of the window.

Yscl defines the distance between vertical tick marks.

In the standard viewing window, $\text{Xmin} = -10$, $\text{Xmax} = 10$, $\text{Xscl} = 1$, $\text{Ymin} = -10$, $\text{Ymax} = 10$, and $\text{Yscl} = 1$.

To select the standard viewing window, press $\boxed{\text{ZOOM}}$ $\boxed{6}$.

You will view the following:

Is this an accurate and/or complete picture of your function, or is the window giving you a misleading impression? You may want to use your table function to view the output values that correspond to the input values from -10 to 10.

X	Y₁		X	Y₁		X	Y₁
-10	-188		-3	-27		4	36
-9	-159		-2	-12		5	37
-8	-132		-1	1		6	36
-7	-107		0	12		7	33
-6	-84		1	21		8	28
-5	-63		2	28		9	21
-4	-44		3	33		10	12

| X=-10 | | | X=3 | | | X=10 | | |

The table indicates that the minimum output value on the interval from $x = -10$ to $x = 10$ is -188, occurring at $x = -10$, and the maximum output value is 37 occurring at $x = 5$. Press (WINDOW) and reset the settings to the following:

$$Xmin = -10, Xmax = 10, Xscl = 1,$$
$$Ymin = -190, Ymax = 40, Yscl = 10$$

Press (GRAPH) to view the graph with these new settings.

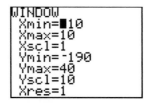 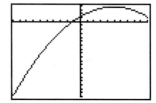

The new graph gives us a much more complete picture of the behavior of the function on the interval $[-10, 10]$.

The coordinates of specific points on the curve can be viewed by activating the trace feature. While in the graph window, press (TRACE). The function equation will be displayed at the top of the screen, a flashing cursor will appear on the curve at the middle of the screen, and the coordinates of the cursor location will be displayed at the bottom of the screen.

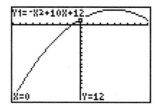

The left arrow key, (◄), will move the cursor toward smaller input values. The right arrow key, (►), will move the cursor toward larger input values. If the cursor reaches the edge of the window and you continue to move the cursor, the window will adjust automatically.

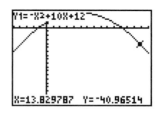

Zoom Menu

The Zoom menu offers several options for changing the window very quickly.

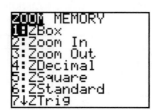

The features of each of the commands are summarized in the following table.

ZOOM COMMAND	DESCRIPTION
1: ZBox	Draws a box to define the viewing window.
2: Zoom In	Magnifies the graph near the cursor.
3: Zoom Out	Increases the viewing window around the cursor.
4: ZDecimal	Sets a window so that Xscl and Yscl are 0.1.
5: ZSquare	Sets equal size pixels on the x- and y-axes.
6: ZStandard	Sets the window to standard settings.
7: ZTrig	Sets built-in trig window variables.
8: ZInteger	Sets integer values on the x- and y-axes.
9: ZoomStat	Sets window based on the current values in the stat lists.
0: ZoomFit	Replots graph to include the max and min output values for the current Xmin and Xmax.

Solving Equations Graphically Using the TI-83/TI-84 Plus Family of Calculators

The Intersection Method

This method is based on the fact that solutions to the equation $f(x) = g(x)$ are input values of x that produce the same output for the functions f and g. Graphically, these are the x-coordinates of the intersection points of $y = f(x)$ and $y = g(x)$.

The following procedure illustrates how to use the intersection method to solve $x^3 + 3 = 3x$ graphically.

Step 1   Enter the left-hand side of the equation as Y_1 in the "Y = " editor and the right-hand side as Y_2. Select the standard viewing window.

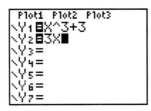

Step 2   Examine the graphs to determine the number of intersection points.

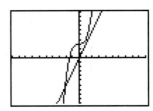

You may need to examine several windows to be certain of the number of intersection points.

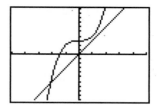

Step 3 Access the Calculate menu by pushing (2nd) (TRACE), then choose option 5: intersect.

 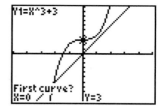

The cursor will appear on the first curve in the center of the window.

Step 4 Move the cursor close to the desired intersection point and press (ENTER).

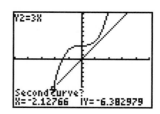

The cursor will now jump vertically to the other curve.

Step 5 Repeat step 4 for the second curve.

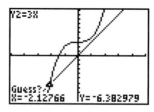

Step 6 To use the cursor's current location as your guess, press (ENTER) in response to the question on the screen that asks Guess? If you want to move to a better guess value, do so before you press (ENTER).

The coordinates of the intersection point appear below the word Intersection.

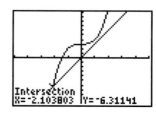

The *x*-coordinate is a solution to the equation.

If there are other intersection points, repeat the process as necessary.

Using the TI-83/TI-84 Plus Family of Calculators to Determine the Linear Regression Equation for a Set of Paired Data Values

Example 1:

INPUT	OUTPUT
2	2
3	5
4	3
5	7
6	9

Enter the data into the calculator as follows:

1. Press (STAT) and choose EDIT.

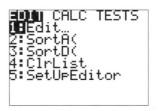

2. The calculator has six built-in lists, L1, L2, . . . , L6. If there is data in L1, clear the list as follows:

   a. Use the arrows to place the cursor on L1 at the top of the list. Press (CLEAR) followed by (ENTER) , followed by the down arrow.

   b. Follow the same procedure to clear L2 if necessary.

   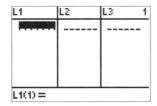

   c. Enter the input values into L1 and the corresponding output values into L2.

To see a scatterplot of the data proceed as follows.

1. STAT PLOT is the 2nd function of the ⌈Y=⌉ key. You must press ⌈2nd⌉ before pressing ⌈Y=⌉ to access the STAT PLOT menu.

2. Select Plot 1 and make sure that Plots 2 and 3 are Off. The screen shown below will appear. Select On and then choose the scatterplot option (first icon) on the Type line. Confirm that your x and y values are stored, respectively, in L_1 and L_2. The symbols L_1 and L_2 are 2nd functions of the ⌈1⌉ and ⌈2⌉ keys, respectively. Finally, select the small square as the mark that will be used to plot each point.

3. Press ⌈Y=⌉ and clear or deselect any functions currently stored.

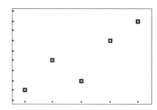

4. To display the scatterplot, have the calculator determine an appropriate window by pressing ⌈ZOOM⌉ and then ⌈9⌉ (ZoomStat).

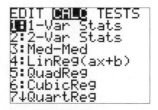

The following instructions will calculate the linear regression equation and store it in Y_1.

1. Press ⌈STAT⌉ and right arrow to highlight CALC.

2. Choose 4: LinReg (ax + b). LinReg (ax + b) will be pasted to the home screen. To tell the calculator where the data is, press ⌨(2nd) and ⌨(1) (for L1), then ⌨(,), then ⌨(2nd) and ⌨(2) (for L2) because the Xlist and Ylist are stored in L_1 and L_2, respectively. The display should look like this:

3. Press ⌨(,) and then press ⌨(VARS).

4. Right arrow to highlight Y-VARS.

5. Choose 1, FUNCTION.

6. Choose 1 for Y_1 (or 2 for Y_2, etc. if you prefer to store the regression equation in another location).

7. Press ⌨(ENTER).

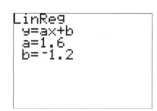

The linear regression equation for this data is $y = 1.6x - 1.2$.

8. To display the regression line on the scatterplot screen, press ⸤GRAPH⸥ .

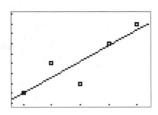

9. Press the ⸤Y=⸥ key to view the equation.

SELECTED ANSWERS

Chapter 1

Activity 1.1 Exercises: 1. $34,285. **3.** 1,306,313,812.
4. $67,000; $67,100. **8. a.** odd; 22,225 ends with an odd
digit. **9. c.** 51 is composite since 51 has factors other
than 1 and 51, namely 3 and 17. **11. a.** $31,000; $29,000

Activity 1.2 Exercises: 1. a.

$$
\begin{array}{r} 11 \\ 80 \\ +200 \\ \hline 291 \end{array}
\quad \textbf{b.}\;
\begin{array}{r} 16 \\ 50 \\ +700 \\ \hline 766 \end{array}
\quad \textbf{c.}\;
\begin{array}{r} 10 \\ 200 \\ +300 \\ \hline 510 \end{array}
$$

4. b. $49 + 71 = 120$. **5. a.** $200 + 100 + 200 = 500$.
7. a. 32; **d.** 752; **f.** 312. **10. b.** $113 + 770 + 564 = 1447$. **11. a.** $370 - 360 = 10$; **b.** $400 - 400 = 0$;
c. $370 - 360 = 10$. **12. f.** $28 - 13$; **g.** $85 + 8$

Activity 1.3 Exercises: 1. b. 4232; **h.** 206535.
3. a. $12(30 + 6) = 12 \cdot 30 + 12 \cdot 6 = 360 + 72 = 432$.
6. a. 1656; **b.** 1656; **c.** yes; **d.** The commutative property is demonstrated. **9. a.** $20 \cdot 20 = 400$ hot dog rolls;

b.
$$
\begin{array}{r} 24 \\ \times 16 \\ \hline 144 \\ 24 \\ \hline 384 \end{array}
$$
The actual number of rolls is 384.

c. The estimate is slightly higher.

Activity 1.4 Exercises: 1. a. quotient 8, remainder 0;
f. quotient 25, remainder 12; **h.** undefined.
3. b. Each student will get $1500 \div 4 = 375$ index cards.
4. a. 3; **b.** no; **c.** no. **6. a.** $4000 \div 50 = 80$;

b.
$$
\begin{array}{r} 74 \\ 52\overline{)3850} \\ 364 \\ \hline 210 \\ 208 \\ \hline 2 \end{array}
$$
c. My estimate is higher.

Activity 1.5 Exercises: 1. 10,000,000,000,000,000.
3. 53, 59. **5. d.** $22 \cdot 1 = 11 \cdot 2 = 22$.
6. a. $30 \cdot 1 = 15 \cdot 2 = 10 \cdot 3 = 6 \cdot 5 = 2 \cdot 3 \cdot 5 = 30$;
$105 \cdot 1 = 35 \cdot 3 = 21 \cdot 5 = 15 \cdot 7 = 3 \cdot 5 \cdot 7 = 105$.
8. d. $3 \cdot 2^5$. **10. d.** 32; **e.** 144. **11. a.** 5^{11}.
12. e. 15. **13. d.** yes, 16 ft. by 16 ft.

Activity 1.6 Exercises: 1. b. 145; **d.** 55. **2. d.** 60.
4. a. $884 - 34 = 850$. **5. c.** $12 + 45 - 4 = 53$.
7. e. $100/10 = 10$; **f.** $8 \cdot 20 - 4 = 160 - 4 = 156$.
8. b. $80 - 27 = 53$. **9. e.** $56 - 18 + 5 = 43$;
j. $5^2 = 25$.

What Have I Learned? 4. a. addition and multiplication:
$3 + 5 = 8 = 5 + 3; 3 \cdot 5 = 15 = 5 \cdot 3$; **b.** subtraction
and division: $5 - 1 = 4$ and $1 - 5 \neq 4; 8 \div 2 = 4$ and
$2 \div 8 \neq 4$. **5. a.** yes, $90 + 17 = 107$ and
$69 + 38 = 107$; **c.** no, $48 - 17 = 31$ and $69 - 4 = 65$.

How Can I Practice?
3. $132,000,000,000 \div 690,000,000 \approx 191$ times.
5. a. 92,956,000. **6. c.** 4660. **8. c.** $98 - 15 = 83$;
i. $95 - 25 = 70$. **9. a.** 225. **13.** 31, 37, 41, 43, 47.
15. b. $3 \cdot 3 \cdot 7 = 3^2 \cdot 7$. **18. d.** 9^6. **19. b.** approximately 5; **c.** 15. **20. d.** $(36 - 18)/6 = 18/6 = 3$;
e. $45 - 5 \cdot 8 + 5 = 45 - 40 + 5 = 10$;
h. $49 + 49 = 98$.

Gateway Review 1. one hundred forty-three dollars.
2. twenty-two million, five hundred twenty-eight thousand,
seven hundred thirty-seven. **3.** 108,091; 108,901;
108,910; 109,801; 180,901. **4.** 0 is thousands and 9 is
tens. **5. a.** odd; ends with odd digit; **b.** even; ends with
even digit; **c.** odd; ends with odd digit. **6. a.** composite,
since $145 = 5 \cdot 29$; **b.** prime, since $61 = 1 \cdot 61$, the only
factors; **c.** prime, the first one; **d.** composite, since
$121 = 11 \cdot 11$. **7. a.** 1,253,000; **b.** 900.
8. a. 8951; **b.** 896; **c.** 177; **d.** 662; **e.** 475.
9. $113 = 72 + 41$. **10. a.** associative property;
b. commutative property; **c.** The two expressions are equal
because adding 0 does not change the value of the sum.
11. They are not equal; subtraction is not commutative.
12. a. $510 + 90 + 120 + 350 = 1070$ (estimate); **b.** 1066;
c. Estimate was a little higher than actual since 1070 is
larger than 1066. **13. a.** $30 + 22$; **b.** $67 - 15$;
c. $125 - 44$; **d.** $250 - 175$; **e.** $25 \cdot 36$; **f.** $55 \div 11$;
g. 13^2; **h.** 2^5; **i.** $\sqrt{49}$; **j.** $27(50 + 17)$.
14. a. $61 + 61 + 61 + 61 + 61 = 305$; **b.** It is the same:
305. **c.** $5(61) = 5(60 + 1) = 300 + 5 = 305$.

15. a. $4(29) = 4(30 - 1) = 120 - 4 = 116$; **b.** It is faster to mentally multiply $4 \cdot 30 - 4 \cdot 1$ to obtain 116. **c.** $6 \cdot 98 = 6(100 - 2) = 600 - 12 = 588$.
16. a. associative property; **b.** commutative property; **c.** Because multiplying any number by 1 does not change the value of the number. **17. a.** $72 - 12 = 60$; $60 - 12 = 48; 48 - 12 = 36; 36 - 12 = 24; 24 - 12 = 12$; $12 - 12 = 0$ So, the quotient is 6 since there were six subtractions of 12 with a remainder of 0. **b.** $86 - 16 = 70$; $70 - 16 = 54; 54 - 16 = 38; 38 - 16 = 22; 22 - 16 = 6$ So, the quotient is 5 since there were five subtractions of 16 with a remainder of 6. **18.** $12 \div 6 = 2$ but $6 \div 12$ is not a whole number. So, since the answers are different, division is not commutative. **19. a.** 182,352; **b.** Quotient is 15 and remainder is 6. **c.** 861; **d.** 861; **e.** 1; **f.** 0; **g.** undefined; **h.** Quotient is 273 and remainder is 20.
20. a. $300 \cdot 80 = 24{,}000$ (estimate); **b.** 24,675; **c.** Estimate is lower. **21. a.** $2000 \div 40 = 50$ (estimate); **b.** Quotient is 44 and remainder is 2. **c.** Estimate is higher. **22.** No, I made a mistake since $3 \cdot 20 = 60$. The correct answer is 21. **23.** $1 \div 0$ is undefined, whereas $0 \div 1 = 0$. So, the answers are different. **24. a.** The answer is that whole number; for example, $15 \div 1 = 15$. **b.** The result is 1. It applies to any number except 0, since you cannot divide by 0. **25. a.** 1, 2, 5, 7, 10, 14, 25, 35, 50, 70, 175, 350; **b.** 1, 3, 9, 27, 81; **c.** 1, 2, 3, 4, 6, 9, 12, 18, 36.
26. a. $2 \cdot 5^2 \cdot 7$; **b.** 3^4; **c.** $2^2 \cdot 3^2$. **27. a.** 1; **b.** 49; **c.** 32; **d.** 1. **28. a.** 9^2; **b.** 3^4; **c.** 25^2; **d.** 5^4.
29. a. 3^{10}; **b.** 5^{45}; **c.** 21^{19}. **30. a.** a perfect square since $5^2 = 25$; **b.** not a perfect square since $125 = 5 \cdot 5 \cdot 5$; **c.** a perfect square since $11^2 = 121$; **d.** a perfect square since $10^2 = 100$; **e.** not a perfect square, since $200 = 2 \cdot 10 \cdot 10$. **31. a.** 4; **b.** 6; **c.** 17.
32. a. not; **b.** yes: $20^2 = 400$; **c.** not; **d.** yes: $100^2 = 10{,}000$; **e.** not.
33. a. $48 - 3(4) + 9 = 48 - 12 + 9 = 45$; **b.** $16 + 4 \cdot 4 = 16 + 16 = 32$; **c.** $243/(35 - 8) = 243/27 = 9$; **d.** $(160 - 5)/10 = 110/10 = 11$; **e.** $7 \cdot 8 - 9 \cdot 2 + 5 = 56 - 18 + 5 = 43$; **f.** $8 \cdot 9 = 72$; **g.** $36 + 64 = 100$; **h.** $(9 - 8)^2 = 1^2 = 1$.
34. They do not, since $6 + 10 \div 2 = 6 + 5 = 11$ and $(6 + 10) \div 2 = 16 \div 2 = 8$.

Chapter 2

Activity 2.1 Exercises:
1. $x + 425 = 981$
$\quad\quad -425 \quad -425$
$\quad\quad\quad\quad x = 556$
3. $x - 541 = 198$
$\quad\quad -541 \quad +541$
$\quad\quad\quad\quad x = 739$
5. $x \div 9 = 63$
$\quad\quad x = 63 \cdot 9$
$\quad\quad x = 567$
7. $13 + x = 51$
$\quad -13 \quad\quad -13$
$\quad\quad\quad x = 38$

9. $\quad 642 = 6x$
$\quad 642 \div 6 = 6x \div 6$
$\quad\quad 107 = x$
11. x = number of days driving; rental cost per day = \$75; total budget = \$600. The cost of the rental per day times the number of days driving is equal to the total cost of the rental. $75x = 600$, $x = 8$ days; Check: $75(8) = 600$; $600 = 600$. **13.** x = amount to save each month; $t = 5$ months; total cost of books and fees = \$1200. The amount that I will save each month times the number of months that I will save is equal to the total cost of books. $5x = 1200$, $x = \$240$, Check: $5(240) = 1200$; $1200 = 1200$.
15. better set: \$35; cheaper set: \$20; total receipts: \$525. x represents the number of better sets sold; $2x$ represents the number of cheaper sets sold. The number of sets sold times the cost per set equals the total receipts for that set. $35x + 20(2x) = 525$, $35x + 40x = 525$, $75x = 525$, $x = 7$; Check: $35(7) + 20(2)(7) = 525$;
$\quad\quad\quad\quad\quad 245 + 280 = 525$;
$\quad\quad\quad\quad\quad\quad\quad 525 = 525$.
17. $P = 2l + 2w$ $\quad\quad\quad 540 = 10w + 2w$
$\quad P = 2(5w) + 2w \quad 540 = 12w$
$\quad P = 540 \quad\quad\quad\quad 45 = w$
The dimensions of the field are $45 \cdot 5(45)$ or 45 ft $\cdot$ 225 feet.
Check: $540 = 2(5)(45) + 2(45)$
$\quad\quad\quad 540 = 450 + 90$
$\quad\quad\quad 540 = 540$

Activity 2.2 Exercises: 2. a. -120 points, **b.** -145 ft., **c.** \$50, **d.** -15 yd., **e.** $-\$75$; **3. b.** <, **d.** >, **e.** <; **4. c.** 32, **d.** 7; **5. a.** 6 is the opposite of -6; **6. b.** -100 feet is further below sea level.

Activity 2.3 Exercises: 1. -2; **4.** -5; **5.** $-21 + 18$ **8.** $-54 + 72$
$\quad\quad = -3$; $\quad\quad\quad = -126$;
11. $-4 + (-5) + (-3)$ **15.** $-4 + 5 + (-6)$
$\quad\quad = -12$; $\quad\quad\quad\quad = -5$;
17. $-7 - 5 = -12$. The nighttime temperature is $-12°$F. **19.** $6 + 5 = 11$. The noon temperature was $11°$F. **21.** $-600 - 500 = -1100$. My new elevation is -1100 feet; **24.** Total $= 20 + 35 + 10 - 20 - 40 + 5 - 10 + 30 = 100 - 70 = 30$. The profit is 30 million dollars.

Activity 2.4 Exercises: 3. a. $139 - I = -7$, **b.** $139 - I + I = -7 + I$
$\quad\quad\quad 139 + 7 = I$
$\quad\quad\quad\quad 146 = I$
I weighed 146 pounds at the beginning of the month.
5. a. $S = P - D$, **b.** $35 = P - 8$
$\quad\quad\quad\quad\quad\quad 35 + 8 = P$
$\quad\quad\quad\quad\quad\quad \$43 = P$, the regular price;
7. b. $S + D = P$
$\quad\quad D = P - S$;

8. b. $x - 9 = 16$ **d.** $10 - x = 6$
$$\begin{aligned} x = 25, \qquad & 10 - x + x = 6 + x \\ & 10 = 6 + x \\ & 10 - 6 = x \\ & 4 = x; \end{aligned}$$

Activity 2.5 Exercises: 1. b. $T = M + 2$,
c. $T = M + 2$
$T = 36 + 2$
$T = 38$ The total cost is \$38.
3. a. $x - y = 5$.

What Have I Learned? 4. b. negative, **e.** negative;

How Can I Practice? 1. a. -3;   **2. a.** 13, **b.** 15;
3. a. 51, **c.** -17, **e.** -84, **h.** -90, **i.** 9;
4. c. 14, **d.** -12, **g.** -53, **i.** -7;
5. b. -181, **d.** 39, **f.** -14;
6. a. $-18 + 7 = -11$, **d.** $-17 + 5 = -12$;
7. c. $23 - (-62) = 23 + 62 = 85$;
8. a. $x + 21 - 21 = -63 - 21$ $x = -84$
   Check: $-84 + 21 = -63$,
e. $x - 17 + 17 = 19 + 17$ **f.** $x - 35 + 35 = 42 + 35$
         $x = 36$ $x = 77$
   Check: $36 - 17 = 19$,   Check: $77 - 35 = 42$;
9. c. $x - 8 = 6$
         $x = 14$ The number is 14.
d. $x - 3 = 12$
         $x = 15$ The number is 15.
14. $7 - (-6) = 7 + 6 = 13$. The change in temperature was 13°F.
17. $1000 - 1200 + 800 = -200 + 800 = 600$. Her score became \$600.

Activity 2.6 Exercises: 1. $\dfrac{2}{3} = \dfrac{2 \cdot 4}{3 \cdot 4} = \dfrac{8}{12}$ $? = 8$;

4. $\dfrac{8}{28} = \dfrac{8 \div 4}{28 \div 4} = \dfrac{2}{7}$;   **6.** $\dfrac{3}{7} = \dfrac{15}{35}$ and $\dfrac{2}{5} = \dfrac{14}{35}$ so $\dfrac{3}{7} > \dfrac{2}{5}$;
7. $1\frac{2}{3}$;   **10.** $5\dfrac{3}{4} = \dfrac{5 \cdot 4 + 6}{4} = \dfrac{23}{4}$;   **12.** $\dfrac{2}{12} = \dfrac{1}{6}$ and
$\dfrac{3}{18} = \dfrac{1}{6}$ so you painted the same amount.

14. $\dfrac{5}{100} = \dfrac{1}{20}$ of the applications are accepted.

Activity 2.7 Exercises: 1. $\dfrac{6}{8} = \dfrac{3}{4}$;   **2.** $\dfrac{3}{5}$;   **8.** $\dfrac{16}{12} = \dfrac{4}{3} = 1\frac{1}{3}$;
9. $7\frac{3}{5}$;   **12.** $7 + \frac{7}{5} - 5 - \frac{4}{5} = 2\frac{3}{5}$;
13. $-7 - \frac{4}{9} + 5 + \frac{2}{9} = -2 - \frac{2}{9} = -2\frac{2}{9}$;
17. $-20 - \frac{14}{13} = -20\frac{14}{13} = -21\frac{1}{13}$;
20. $12\frac{1}{8} + 10\frac{3}{8} + 12\frac{1}{8} + 10\frac{3}{8} = 44\frac{8}{8} = 45$ ft.

I will need 45 feet of wallpaper border.

Activity 2.8 Exercises: 1. $\dfrac{1}{6} + \dfrac{3}{6} = \dfrac{4}{6} = \dfrac{2}{3}$;

3. $-\dfrac{4}{10} + \dfrac{9}{10} = \dfrac{5}{10} = \dfrac{1}{2}$;

6. $12\frac{15}{20} + 6\frac{8}{20} = 18\frac{23}{20} = 18 + 1\frac{3}{20} = 19\frac{3}{20}$;
9. $14\frac{9}{12} - 6\frac{5}{12} = 8\frac{4}{12} = 8\frac{1}{3}$;   **10.** $10\frac{7}{7} - 6\frac{3}{7} = 4\frac{4}{7}$;
14. $-7\frac{15}{24} + 2\frac{4}{24} = -7 + 2 - \frac{15}{24} + \frac{4}{24} = -5\frac{11}{24}$;
16. $2\frac{2}{7} + 3\frac{3}{8} = 2\frac{16}{56} + 3\frac{21}{56} = 5\frac{37}{56}$;
17. $-5\frac{18}{45} + \left(-6\frac{20}{45}\right) = -11\frac{38}{45}$;
19. $2\frac{2}{3} + 1 + \frac{1}{2} + \frac{5}{8} = 2 + 1 + \frac{16}{24} + \frac{12}{24} + \frac{15}{24}$
$$= 3 + \frac{43}{24}$$
$$= 4\frac{19}{24} \text{ cups;}$$

21. a. $x + \dfrac{1}{5} + \dfrac{1}{3} + \dfrac{1}{4} = 1$,

b. $x + \dfrac{1}{5} + \dfrac{1}{3} + \dfrac{1}{4} = 1$

$x + \dfrac{1 \cdot 12}{5 \cdot 12} + \dfrac{1 \cdot 20}{3 \cdot 20} + \dfrac{1 \cdot 15}{4 \cdot 15} = 1$

$x + \dfrac{12 + 20 + 15}{60} = 1$

$x = 1 - \dfrac{47}{60} = \dfrac{60}{60} - \dfrac{47}{60} = \dfrac{13}{60}$

So, $\dfrac{13}{60}$ of your final grade is determined by class participation.

23. $1\frac{1}{2} + 1\frac{1}{2} + \frac{3}{4} + \frac{3}{4} + \frac{3}{4} + \frac{3}{4} + \frac{3}{4} = 3 + \frac{15}{4} = 6\frac{3}{4}$ in.
Yes, it will fit.

25. $\dfrac{3}{10} + \dfrac{2}{10} = c$ **28.** $b = \dfrac{2}{3} - \dfrac{1}{2}$
$\qquad \dfrac{5}{10} = c$ $\qquad b = \dfrac{4}{6} - \dfrac{3}{6}$
$\qquad \dfrac{1}{2} = c$; $\qquad b = \dfrac{1}{6}$;

30. $x = -7\frac{1}{3} - 5\frac{1}{4}$
$\qquad x = -7\frac{4}{12} - 5\frac{3}{12}$
$\qquad x = -12\frac{7}{12}$;

What Have I Learned? 3. a. The statement is true by definition of improper fractions. **c.** The statement is false because the negative sign of the mixed number applies to both the integer part and the fractional part.

How Can I Practice? 1. a. $\dfrac{3 \cdot 3}{11 \cdot 3} = \dfrac{9}{33}$, **d.** $\dfrac{7 \cdot 3}{12 \cdot 3} = \dfrac{21}{36}$;
2. a. $\dfrac{3 \cdot 9 + 7}{9} = \dfrac{34}{9}$, **d.** $\dfrac{10 \cdot 13 + 8}{13} = \dfrac{138}{13}$,
e. $\dfrac{1 \cdot 31 + 27}{31} = \dfrac{58}{31}$;   **3. b.** $2\frac{2}{13}$, **c.** $7\frac{5}{12}$;
4. c. $\dfrac{36 \div 3}{39 \div 3} = \dfrac{12}{13}$, **e.** $\dfrac{54 \div 2}{82 \div 2} = \dfrac{27}{41}$;

6. a. JFK $\frac{1}{16}$; LaGuardia $\frac{1}{8} = \frac{2}{16}$; Newark $\frac{1}{2} = \frac{8}{16}$. Newark Airport had the best visibility;

7. c. $1\frac{5}{12} + 3\frac{9}{12} = 4\frac{14}{12}$ **d.** $8\frac{54}{63} + 4\frac{35}{63} = 12\frac{89}{63}$

$= 4 + 1\frac{2}{12} = 5\frac{2}{12} = 5\frac{1}{6},$ $= 12 + 1\frac{26}{63} = 13\frac{26}{63},$

g. $-8\frac{16}{24} + (-25\frac{7}{24})$ **j.** $-9\frac{15}{70} + (-11\frac{12}{70})$

$= -8 - 25 - \frac{16}{24} - \frac{7}{24}$ $= -9 - 11 - \frac{15}{70} - \frac{12}{70}$

$= -33 - \frac{23}{24} = -33\frac{23}{24},$ $= -20 - \frac{27}{70} = -20\frac{27}{70};$

8. b. $11\frac{17}{54}$, **d.** $11\frac{32}{72} - 7\frac{15}{72} = 4\frac{17}{72}$, **g.** $13\frac{3}{8}$,

k. $13\frac{2}{15} - 8\frac{12}{15} = 12\frac{17}{15} - 8\frac{12}{15} = 4\frac{5}{15} = 4\frac{1}{3}$,

m. $29\frac{21}{36} - 21\frac{30}{36}$ **o.** $17\frac{27}{42} - 9\frac{16}{42}$

$= 29 - 21 + \frac{21}{36} - \frac{30}{36}$ $= 17 - 9 + \frac{27}{42} - \frac{16}{42}$

$= 8 - \frac{9}{36} = 7 + \frac{36}{36} - \frac{9}{36}$ $= 8 + \frac{11}{42} = 8\frac{11}{42}$,

$= 7\frac{27}{36} = 7\frac{3}{4}$,

q. $-6\frac{4}{5} + 7\frac{11}{15}$

$= -6 + 7 - \frac{12}{15} + \frac{11}{15}$

$= 1 - \frac{1}{15}$

$= \frac{15}{15} - \frac{1}{15} = \frac{14}{15};$

11. c. $x = 17\frac{4}{7} + 13\frac{5}{6}$ **d.** $x = 19\frac{2}{3} - 8\frac{4}{9}$

$x = 17\frac{24}{42} + 13\frac{35}{42}$ $x = 19\frac{6}{9} - 8\frac{4}{9}$

$x = 30\frac{59}{42}$ $x = 11\frac{2}{9};$

$x = 31\frac{17}{42},$

Activity 2.9   Exercises: 3. a. $\$0.889597 \approx \$0.89$,
b. $\$0.889597 \approx \$0.9$;   **5. a.** fifty-two thousandths,
d. 0.0064, **f.** 2041.0673;   **7. a.** false, since $2 > 0$ in the
hundred-thousandths place;

Activity 2.10   Exercises: 1. 360 cm.;   **4.** 4.705 m.;
7. 4255 cg.;   **10.** 0.742 ℓ;   **12.** 124 milligrams is
smaller, since 0.15 gram = 150 milligrams.

Activity 2.11   Exercises: 1. b. 17.319, **e.** -0.0516,
f. -3.212;   **3.** $\$2.99 + \$2.99 + \$2.69 + \$4.49 +$
$\$3.29 + \$2.09 + \$2.49 = \$21.03$. $\$20$ is not enough for
everything on the list. Any item could be eliminated;

5. b.

Australia	108.847
China	110.028
France	110.159
Romania	114.283
Russia	113.235
Spain	111.572
Ukraine	112.309
USA	113.584

Gold: Romania; Silver: USA;
Bronze: Russia

Activity 2.12   Exercises: 2. a. 31.79, **e.** 1.227, **g.** -20.404,
i. 15.216, **k.** -0.00428, **l.** -0.2019;

5. Let y represent the amount of detergent you have used.
$1.75 - y = 0.5$
$1.75 - y + y = 0.5 + y$
$1.75 = 0.5 + y$
$1.75 - 0.5 = 0.5 - 0.5 + y$
$1.25 = y$
1.25 pints of detergent were already used.
7. $x = 91.4 - 11$
$x = 80.4$
The difference between the two kinds is 80.4 meters.
9. b. $0.01003 - x + x = 0.0091 + x$
$0.01003 - 0.0091 = 0.0091 - 0.0091 + x$
$0.00093 = x,$
d. $1.626 - 1.626 + b = 14.503 - 1.626$
$b = 12.877,$
f. $0.0114 + z = 0.0151$
$0.0114 - 0.0114 + z = 0.0151 - 0.0114$
$z = 0.0037;$

How Can I Practice? 1.   c. Thirteen thousand, fifty-three and
three thousand eight hundred ninety-one ten thousandths;
2. b. 611,712.00068, **e.** 9,000,000,005.28;
3. b. $0.0983 < 0.0987 < 0.384 < 0.392 < 0.561$;
4. c. 182.1000, **d.** 60.0;   **5. b.** 968.366,
d. 245.212, **f.** -138.709, **i.** 378.2877;
6. c. 245.1309, **f.** -80.488, **g.** 55.708,
h. -30.763;   **7. b.** $-6.13 + (-5.017) = -11.147$,
d. $-4.802 - (-19.99) = -4.812$;
8. b. $x - 13.14 + 13.14 = 69.17 + 13.14$
$x = 82.31,$
d. $35.17 - 35.17 + x = 12.19 - 35.17$
$x = -22.98;$
19. $\$25.37 + \$39.41 + \$52.04 = \$116.82$. I spent $\$116.82$;
20. $2105.96 - (311.93 + 64.72 + 161.11) = 1568.20$. My
take-home pay is $\$1568.20$.

Gateway Review 1. 160 words per minute is a rate.
800 words on each page and 50 pages of text means
800 times 50 pages is the total number of words that will
be read (40,000).
I am asked to find the time.
The formula rate $\cdot$ time = amount will apply.
$r \cdot t = A$
$160t = 40,000$ Divide both sides of the equation by 160.
$t = 250$ min.
Check: $160(250) = 40,000$ It will take 250 min. to read
50 pages.
2. a. 15, **b.** 23, **c.** 0, **d.** 42, **e.** 67;
3. a. -9, **b.** -6, **c.** 16, **d.** -14, **e.** 12, **f.** -8,
g. -53, **h.** -6;   **4. a.** $3 - (-3) = 6$,
b. $-5 + -2 = -7$, **c.** $-(-3) - (-7) = 10$,
d. $-2 + (-5) = -7$;   **5. a.** $x = -2$, **b.** $x = -19$,
c. $x = -15$, **d.** $x = 43$, **e.** $x = -38$;
6. a. $x + 18 = -7$ **b.** $x + 11 = 29$
$x = -25,$ $x = 18,$
c. $15 + x = -28$ **d.** $x - 20 = 39$
$x = -43,$ $x = 59,$

e. $8 - x = 12$ **f.** $x - 17 = 42$
  $-4 = x$, $x = 59$,
g. $x - 13 = -34$
    $x = -21$;

7. a. $12\frac{3}{5}$, **b.** 9, **c.** $5\frac{2}{15}$, **d.** $5\frac{12}{13}$;

8. a. $\frac{23}{5}$, **b.** $\frac{19}{7}$, **c.** $\frac{57}{11}$, **d.** $\frac{83}{8}$;

9. a. $>$, **b.** $>$, **c.** $<$, **d.** $>$, **e.** $>$, **f.** $<$;

10. a. $\frac{11}{7}$ or $1\frac{4}{7}$, **b.** $-\frac{6}{15} = -\frac{2}{5}$, **c.** $\frac{7}{11}$, **d.** $\frac{83}{56}$ or $1\frac{27}{56}$,

e. $\frac{58}{39}$ or $1\frac{19}{39}$, **f.** $-\frac{49}{36}$ or $-1\frac{13}{36}$, **g.** $\frac{1}{15}$, **h.** $-\frac{2}{33}$; **11. a.** 25,

b. $19\frac{2}{3}$, **c.** $13\frac{4}{5}$, **d.** $24\frac{17}{24}$, **e.** $19\frac{17}{18}$, **f.** $16\frac{3}{4}$, **g.** $11\frac{3}{8}$, **h.** $5\frac{1}{2}$,

i. $11\frac{2}{13}$, **j.** $1\frac{3}{4}$, **k.** $5\frac{35}{36}$, **l.** $2\frac{1}{6}$, **m.** $5\frac{9}{10}$, **n.** $7\frac{1}{28}$, **o.** $4\frac{1}{3}$,

p. $3\frac{3}{7}$, **q.** $4\frac{1}{2}$, **r.** $-14\frac{7}{18}$, **s.** $-1\frac{19}{24}$, **t.** $15\frac{7}{45}$, **u.** $-13\frac{5}{36}$,

v. $-12\frac{5}{18}$, **w.** $-7\frac{4}{5}$; **12. a.** $x = 9\frac{19}{24}$, **b.** $x = -7\frac{22}{63}$,

c. $x = -2\frac{7}{12}$, **d.** $x = -33\frac{1}{2}$, **e.** $x = -24\frac{1}{14}$, **f.** $x = 8\frac{31}{36}$;

13. a. eight hundred forty-nine million, eighty-three thousand, six hundred fifty-nine and seven hundred twenty-five ten-thousandths, **b.** thirty-two billion, four million, three hundred eighty-nine thousand, four hundred twelve and twenty-three thousand, four hundred eighteen hundred-thousandths, **c.** two hundred thirty-five million, eight hundred sixty-four and five hundred eighty-seven thousand two hundred thirty-four millionths, **d.** seven hundred eighty-four million, six hundred thirty-two thousand, five hundred forty-one and eight hundred nineteen hundred thousandths;

14. a. $65,073,412.0682$, **b.** $89,000,549,613.048$,

c. $7,612,011.05601$; **15. a.** $\frac{85}{10,000} = \frac{17}{2000}$,

b. $\frac{3834}{1000} = \frac{1917}{500}$, **c.** $\frac{425}{100} = \frac{17}{4}$, **d.** $\frac{150,125}{10,000} = \frac{1201}{80}$,

e. $\frac{712}{100} = \frac{178}{25}$; **16. a.** $692,895.10$, **b.** $692,895.098$,

c. $692,895.1$, **d.** $692,895$, **e.** $692,900$, **f.** $690,000$;

17. a. $4.00078 < 4.0078 < 4.07008 < 4.0708 < 4.078 <$ 4.78, **b.** $3.00085 < 3.00805 < 3.0085 < 3.0805 <$ $3.085 < 3.85$, **c.** $8.00046 < 8.00406 < 8.0046 <$ $8.0406 < 8.046 < 8.46$; **18. a.** -17.62, **b.** -29.07,

c. -32.12, **d.** -23.37, **e.** -40.97;

19. a. $12.68 + 7.05 = 19.73$, **b.** $98.99 - 14.85 = 84.14$,

c. $-17.32 + (-4.099) = -21.419$,

d. $3.98 - 0.125 = 3.855$; **20. a.** $x = 25.55$,

b. $x = -46.05$, **c.** $x = 48.5$, **d.** $x = -18.97$,

e. $x = 7.47$; **21. a.** $-9 + 3 = -6$. The noon temperature was $-6°$F. **b.** $3 - 5 = -2$. The evening temperature was $-2°$F. **c.** $-3 - (-8) = 5$. The change was $5°$F, **d.** $-14 - (-9) = -5°$F. The change was $-5°$F

22. $12\frac{5}{12} + 8\frac{1}{4} + 12\frac{5}{12} + 8\frac{1}{4} = 41\frac{1}{3}$ You would use $41\frac{1}{3}$

feet of border. **23.** $\frac{1}{3} + 1\frac{3}{5} = \frac{5}{15} + 1\frac{9}{15} = 1\frac{14}{15}$ You ran

$1\frac{14}{15}$ miles each way. **24.** $6\frac{1}{3} + 2\frac{1}{8} + 2\frac{1}{8} = 10\frac{7}{12}$ feet

taken up by the couch and end tables; $14 - 10\frac{7}{12} = 3\frac{5}{12}$ feet remaining. The bookcase will fit.
25. $179.99 + 14.85 = 194.84$. The price of the TV was $\$194.84$. **26.** $20 - 18.35 = 1.65$. You would receive $\$1.65$ in change. **27.** $67.95 - 10.19 = 57.76$. The sale price of the dress is $\$57.76$.
28. $1504.75 - 157.32 - 115.11 - 45.12 = 1187.20$. The cook's take-home pay is $\$1187.20$. **29.** $62.05 - 25.12 - 13.59 + 40 - 117.5 - 85.38 + 359.13 = 219.59$ You will have $\$219.59$ in your bank account.

30.

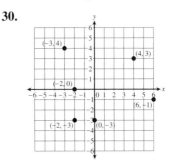

31. 0.795 g; **32.** 2750 m; **33.** 0.025ℓ; **34.** 1050 g;
35. 2350 m $= 2,350,000$ mm; **36.** 85 mℓ; **37.** $455 +$ $806 + 423 + 795 = 2479$ m $= 2.479$ km; **38.** 1250 g $- 285$ g $= 965$ g or 0.965 kg; **39.** $95 + 150 + 180 + x = 1920$ $x = 1920 - 425 = 1495$ There are 1495 mℓ left, or 1.495ℓ.

Chapter 3

Activity 3.1 Exercises: 1. a. -42 **c.** -1600 **e.** 0 **g.** 240
i. 5 **l.** 0. **2. b.** 192 **d.** -55 **e.** -36 **f.** 36.
4. Approximate depth of the water supply $= 5(-25) = -125$ ft. The daily drilling rate is -25 ft per day.
8. $22(5) + 7(-2) + 6(0) = 96$.
11. $4(-230) + 2(350) = -\$220$, a debit.

Activity 3.2 Exercises:

1. $72 + 6(-1) + 10(0) + 2(+1) = 68$. Tiger's score was 68. **3. b.** $3 + 8 = 11$

d. $4 \cdot 9 - 50 =$ 　　　　 **j.**　 $(6 - 20) \div (-2)$
　　$36 - 50 = -14$ 　　　　　　$= -14 \div (-2)$
　　　　　　　　　　　　　　　　$= 7$

l.　 $-5 + 9 \div (-3)$ 　　 **o.**　 $9 \cdot 25 \div (-1)$
　　$= -5 + -3$ 　　　　　　　$= 225 \div (-1)$
　　$= -8$ 　　　　　　　　　　$= -225$

4. a.　 $5 \cdot (-3) + 5 \cdot 4$ 　**c.**　 $4 \cdot (-6) - 4 \cdot 2$
　　$= -15 + 20$ 　　　　　　　$= -24 - 8$
　　$= 5$ 　　　　　　　　　　　$= -32$

5. a. The value is $3 \cdot (-5)^2 + 4(-3) = 3 \cdot 25 + -12$
　　　　　　　　　　　　　　　　　　$= 75 - 12 = 63$.

c. The value is　 $-5(3)(14 \cdot 3 \cdot -2 - 3(-2)^2)$
　　　　　　　　　$= -15(-84 - 12)$
　　　　　　　　　$= -15 \cdot -96 = 1440$

d. The value is $\dfrac{3(-2)(-8) - 4(4)}{4(-2)(4)} = \dfrac{32}{-32} = -1.$

7. b. $(-30)x = -150; x = 5.$ **d.** $2x = -28; x = -14.$
8. b. $s = -9$ **e.** $x = 3$ **10.** $19d = -57; d = -3,$ and the average drop in temperature is $3°F.$

How Can I Practice? 1. c. 160 **f.** 9 **h.** -6 **k.** $-30.$
2. d. $40 + -2 \cdot 2 = 36$ **f.** $-9 - 36 = -45$
g. $18 - 6 + 6 = 18$ **i.** $49 - 14 + 5 = 40.$
3. b. The answer is $(-6)^2 - (-6)(4) = 36 + 24 = 60.$
c. The answer is $2(-2 + 3) - 5(-4) = 2 \cdot 1 + 20 = 22.$
7. a. $3x = -15$ **d.** $90 = (-3)(-6)x$

$$x = \dfrac{-15}{3} = -5 \qquad 90 = 18x$$

$$x = \dfrac{90}{18} = 5$$

Activity 3.3 Exercises: 2. a. $\dfrac{6}{35}$ **d.** $-3\dfrac{3}{4}$ **e.** $\dfrac{-4}{9}$

h. $\dfrac{16}{21}.$ **3. a.** $\dfrac{10}{5} = 2$ **d.** $\dfrac{-12 \cdot 15}{26 \cdot 8} = -\dfrac{45}{52}$

e. $\dfrac{-3 \cdot 9}{10 \cdot -5} = \dfrac{27}{50}$ **f.** $\dfrac{23}{19 \cdot -46} = -\dfrac{1}{38}.$ **4. a.** $\dfrac{9}{10}$

b. He can expect $2500 \cdot \dfrac{9}{10} = 2250$ plants to grow.

7. $\$24{,}350 \cdot \dfrac{1}{10} = \$2435$ for tuition.

10. b. $\dfrac{2}{3}x = -4;$ solving, $\dfrac{3}{2} \cdot \dfrac{2}{3}x = -4 \cdot \dfrac{3}{2},$

so $x = -4 \cdot \dfrac{3}{2} = -6.$ **c.** $\dfrac{x}{7} = 9;$ solving, $\dfrac{x}{7} \cdot 7 = 9 \cdot 7,$

so $x = 63.$

11. b. $\dfrac{-10}{1} \cdot \dfrac{-x}{10} = \dfrac{4}{15} \cdot \dfrac{-10}{1};$

$x = \dfrac{4}{15} \cdot \dfrac{-10}{1} = \dfrac{-8}{3}$ or $-2\dfrac{2}{3}.$

d. $\dfrac{-24}{5} \cdot \dfrac{-5}{24}y = \dfrac{15}{32} \cdot \dfrac{-24}{5};$

$y = \dfrac{15}{32} \cdot \dfrac{-24}{5} = \dfrac{-9}{4}$ or $-2\dfrac{1}{4}.$ **f.** $\dfrac{27}{13} \cdot \dfrac{13}{27}x = \dfrac{20}{45} \cdot \dfrac{27}{13};$

$x = \dfrac{20}{45} \cdot \dfrac{27}{13} = \dfrac{12}{13}.$

Activity 3.4 Exercises: 1. a. $\dfrac{33}{5} = 6\dfrac{3}{5}$ **b.** $-\dfrac{48}{5} = -9\dfrac{3}{5}$

d. 129. **2. b.** $\dfrac{-15}{8} \cdot \dfrac{4}{3} = -\dfrac{5}{2} = -2\dfrac{1}{2}$

d. $\dfrac{38}{3} \cdot \dfrac{6}{19} = 4.$ **3. c.** $\dfrac{16}{49}$ **d.** $\dfrac{32}{243}$

h. $\sqrt{25} = 5.$

4. b. $\dfrac{2}{3}\left(\dfrac{2}{3} - 2\right) + 3 \cdot \dfrac{2}{3}\left(\dfrac{2}{3} + 4\right) =$

$\dfrac{2}{3} \cdot \dfrac{-4}{3} + 2 \cdot \dfrac{14}{3} = \dfrac{76}{9} = 8\dfrac{4}{9}$

d. $6\left(\dfrac{21}{16}\right)\left(\dfrac{1}{8}\right) - \left(\dfrac{1}{8}\right)^2 = \dfrac{63}{64} - \dfrac{1}{64} = \dfrac{62}{64} = \dfrac{31}{32}.$

5. $A = \left(\dfrac{23}{4}\right)^2 = \dfrac{529}{16} = 33\dfrac{1}{16}$ sq. ft.

7. b. $\dfrac{49}{8}w = -\dfrac{49}{2} \Rightarrow w = -\dfrac{49}{2} \cdot \dfrac{8}{49} = -4$

c. $-\dfrac{9}{5}t = -\dfrac{99}{10} \Rightarrow t = -\dfrac{99}{10} \cdot \dfrac{-5}{9} = \dfrac{11}{2} = 5\dfrac{1}{2}.$

9. a. $d = 16\left(\dfrac{1}{2}\right)^2 = 4$ ft.

How Can I Practice? 1. b. $\dfrac{30}{143}$ **d.** $\dfrac{12}{35}$ **e.** $\dfrac{6}{5}$ or $1\dfrac{1}{5}$

h. $\dfrac{14}{-16} = -\dfrac{7}{8}.$ **2. a.** $\dfrac{-3}{7} \cdot \dfrac{7}{9} = \dfrac{-1}{3}$ **d.** $\dfrac{24}{45} \cdot \dfrac{18}{15} = \dfrac{16}{25}$

f. $\dfrac{-35}{10} \cdot \dfrac{1}{-3} = \dfrac{7}{6}$ or $1\dfrac{1}{6}.$ **3. b.** $\dfrac{-17}{6} \cdot \dfrac{7}{3} = \dfrac{-119}{18}$

$= -6\dfrac{11}{18};$

d. $\dfrac{36}{5} \cdot \dfrac{5}{12} = 3$ **f.** $\dfrac{-33}{4} \cdot \dfrac{-2}{3} = \dfrac{11}{2} = 5\dfrac{1}{2}.$ **4. b.** $\dfrac{9}{11}$

c. $-\dfrac{27}{125}.$ **5. b.** $\left(\dfrac{1}{4}\right)^2 - \left(\dfrac{1}{4}\right)\left(\dfrac{-4}{3}\right) = \dfrac{1}{16} + \dfrac{1}{3} = \dfrac{19}{48}.$

6. b. $x = \dfrac{-42}{5}$ or $-8\dfrac{2}{5}$ **e.** $x = -\dfrac{1}{20}$

f. $x = \dfrac{-9}{16} \cdot \dfrac{-4}{3} = \dfrac{3}{4}.$ **9.** You will need

$\dfrac{1}{3} \cdot \dfrac{129}{2} = \dfrac{129}{6} = 21\dfrac{3}{6} = 21\dfrac{1}{2}$ ounces of split peas.

13. a. $V = 15 \cdot 30 \cdot \dfrac{11}{2} = 2475$ cu. ft.

b. Weight is $2475 \cdot \dfrac{312}{5} = 154{,}440$ lb.

Activity 3.5 Exercises: 2. a. 102.746 **c.** -10.965
f. 70,250 **g.** 5000. **4.** $\dfrac{68700}{1000} \cdot 7.48 = \$513.88$ in taxes.
6. a. \$120 million $\div$ 60 shows = 2 million per show
b. \$121.2 million $\div$ 60 shows = 2.02 million per show.

Activity 3.6 Exercises: 1. $= 38.16 + 4.66 = 42.82.$
3. $10.31 + 8.05 \cdot 0.4 - 0.0064$
$= 10.31 + 3.22 - 0.0064$
$= 13.5236$

6. $(3.14)(0.25)^2 = 3.14(0.0625) = 0.19625$ sq. in.

10. a. $\dfrac{x}{5.3} = -6.7;$ solving for $x,$

$x = (5.3)(-6.7) = -35.51.$ **c.** $42.75 = x \cdot (-7.5);$

solving for $x,$ $x = \dfrac{42.75}{-7.5} = -5.7.$ **e.** $(-9.4)x = 47;$

solving for $x,$ $x = \dfrac{47}{-9.4} = -5.$ **11. a.** $x = \dfrac{15.3}{3} = 5.1$

c. $a = \dfrac{-44.2}{-5.2} = 8.5$ **f.** $x = \dfrac{-8}{4.2} \approx -1.90.$

How Can I Practice?   Exercises: 1. -160.   **4.** 500.
6. 1.1345.   **9.** $7 \cdot 0.5 = 3.5$.

12. $\frac{1}{2}(0.7)(3.45 + 5.009) = \frac{1}{2}(0.7)(8.45) = 2.9575$.

14. $9.9 \div 0.33 - 2.7 \cdot 4 = 30 - 10.8 = 19.2$.

16. $x \cdot (-9.76) = 678.32$; solving, $x = \dfrac{678.32}{-9.76} = -69.5$.

17. $\dfrac{x}{-9.5} = 78.3$; solving, $x = (78.3)(-9.5) = -743.85$.

19. $x = \dfrac{58.65}{-2.3} = -25.5$.

22. a. $204/540 = 0.378$; in 1921, Babe Ruth's batting average was .378. **b.** $156/476 = 0.328$; Barry Bonds's batting average was .328 in 2001. **c.** Babe Ruth's average is higher by .050. **24.** 5.01, 12.00, 6.99, 14.68, 6.66, 16, 45.34, 2.83.

Gateway Review Exercises: 1. a. -152

b. $\dfrac{2 \cdot 2}{3 \cdot 3} \cdot \dfrac{-5 \cdot 3}{7 \cdot 2} = \dfrac{-10}{21}$ **c.** 7 **d.** 15,400

e. $\dfrac{14}{5} \cdot \dfrac{10}{21} = \dfrac{7 \cdot 2 \cdot 5 \cdot 2}{5 \cdot 7 \cdot 3} = \dfrac{4}{3} = 1\dfrac{1}{3}$ **f.** 0.003912.

2. a. $\dfrac{64}{169}$ **b.** -16 **c.** $\dfrac{11}{12}$. **3.** $(-1)^{13} = -1$.

4. $(-5)^2 = (-5)(-5) = 25$; $-5^2 = -(5)(5) = -25$.

5. a. $(-0.432) + (-0.9) = -1.332$

b. $\dfrac{10 - 24 - 9}{6 - 4} = \dfrac{-23}{2}$.

6. a. $2\left(\dfrac{-3}{2}\right) - 6\left(\dfrac{-3}{2} - 3\right) = -3 + 9 + 18 = 24$

b. $(-3 \cdot -2 \cdot -6) - (-2)^2 = -36 - 4 = -40$

c. $\pi(2.4)^2 \cdot (0.9) = 5.184\pi \approx 16.27776$ using $\pi \approx 3.14$.

7. a. $x = \dfrac{-72}{-12} = 6$ **b.** $x = 14 \cdot -6 = -84$

c. $x = \dfrac{-4}{9 \cdot -18} = \dfrac{2 \cdot 2}{9 \cdot 9 \cdot 2} = \dfrac{2}{81}$ **d.** $n = \dfrac{73.84}{8} = 9.23$

e. $s = \dfrac{-5 \cdot 33}{9 \cdot 20} = \dfrac{-5 \cdot 3 \cdot 11}{3 \cdot 3 \cdot 5 \cdot 4}$ **f.** $x = \dfrac{12.9}{0.0387} \approx 333.33$

$= \dfrac{-11}{12}$.

8. a. $\dfrac{x}{-15} = -7$; $x = (-7)(-15) = 105$.

b. $\left(\dfrac{-11}{12}\right)x = 2\dfrac{1}{16}$;

$x = \dfrac{33}{16} \cdot \dfrac{12}{-11} = \dfrac{3 \cdot 11 \cdot 4 \cdot 3}{4 \cdot 4 \cdot -11} = -\dfrac{9}{4} = -2\dfrac{1}{4}$

c. $1.08 = x(0.2)$; $x = \dfrac{1.08}{0.2} = 5.4$.

9. Using dimensional analysis,

$\dfrac{19}{2}$ gal. $\cdot \dfrac{16 \text{ cups} \cdot 1 \text{ serving}}{1 \text{ gal.} \cdot \dfrac{3}{4} \text{ cup}}$

$= \dfrac{19 \cdot 16 \cdot 1 \cdot 4}{2 \cdot 1 \cdot 3}$ servings $= \dfrac{608}{3} \approx 202$;

202 servings, plus a little left over.

10. $\dfrac{638,800 - 680,845}{1990 - 1930} = \dfrac{-42,045}{60} = -700.75$; so the average population decrease per year was approximately 701 persons per year.

11. $\dfrac{47,224 \text{ sq.mi.}}{18,196,601 \text{ persons}} \approx 0.00259521 \approx 0.003$ sq. mi. per person. **12.** $\dfrac{7}{10} \cdot 2.9$ million $= 2.03$ million people had farm-related occupations in 1820.

13. $\$13.79 + 270 \cdot \$0.0059714 + 270 \cdot \$0.0049600 = \$16.74$. **14.** Estimating, $\dfrac{7000}{10} = 700$ mph. If $d = 7318$ miles and $t = 11\dfrac{3}{4}$ hours, then the formula $d = r \cdot t$ yields $7318 = r \cdot 11\dfrac{3}{4}$. So, solving for r,

$r = \dfrac{7318}{\dfrac{47}{4}} = \dfrac{7318 \cdot 4}{47} \approx 623$ mph, close to the estimate.

15. a. revenue $= \$15.85b + \$9.95h$ **b.** revenue $= (15.85)(26) + (9.95)(13) = \$541.45$.

16. a. $\$81.00, \$121.50, \$162.00, \$202.50$ **b.** I multiplied the number of hours by $\$6.75$ per hour. **c.** $150 = 6.75x$; solving, $x = \dfrac{150}{6.75} \approx 22.22$ hours. I would need to work 23 hours. **17. a.** $x + 2$ **b.** $x + 2 + 2x$

c. $x + 2 + 2x + x - 4 + \dfrac{x}{4} = 4\dfrac{1}{4}x - 2$

d. $d = (52)\left(4\dfrac{1}{4}x - 2\right)$

e. $d = (52)\left(\dfrac{17}{4} \cdot 7 - 2\right) = (52)\left(\dfrac{119 - 8}{4}\right) = 1443$ mi.

Chapter 4

Activity 4.1   Exercises: 2. a. See answers to part b for the matching.

b. $\dfrac{12}{27} = \dfrac{20}{45} \approx 0.444 = 44.4\%, \dfrac{28}{36} = \dfrac{21}{27} \approx 0.778 =$

$77.8\%, \dfrac{45}{75} = \dfrac{42}{70} = 0.6 = 60\%, \dfrac{64}{80} = \dfrac{60}{75} = 0.80 = 80\%,$

$\dfrac{35}{56} = \dfrac{25}{40} = 0.625 = 62.5\%$; **4. a.** 0.296; **5. a.** $\dfrac{1720}{3200}$,

b. $\dfrac{43}{80}$, **c.** ≈ 0.538, **d.** $\approx 53.8\%$;

7.

	NUMBER OF GAMES	RATIO OF WINS TO GAMES PLAYED
Regular season:	$99 + 63 = 162$	$\dfrac{99}{162} \approx 0.611 = 61.1\%$
Playoff season:	$11 + 1 = 12$	$\dfrac{11}{12} \approx 0.917 = 91.7\%$

The White Sox played better in the playoffs relatively speaking.

9. Brand A: $\dfrac{2940}{13,350} \approx 0.22 = 22\%$

Brand B: $\dfrac{730}{1860} \approx 0.392 = 39.2\%$

Brand A dishwasher has a better repair record.

Activity 4.2   Exercises: 1. a. 8, **b.** 27, **c.** 15, **e.** 18;
l. 60,000; **3.** $25.8 \div 64\% = 25.8 \div 0.64 = 40.3125$
million. Therefore, about 40.3 million people worldwide are
infected with AIDS.   **5.** 8% of 22,500 = $0.08 \cdot 22,500 =$
1800 dollars is the state sales tax.   **7.** $\dfrac{22,000}{0.45} \approx 48,889$;
Approximately 49,000 registered voters;   **10.** Total number
of calls = $\dfrac{50}{0.05} = 1000$; I need to make about 1000 phone
calls;   **12.** Bookstore pays 20% of 90 = $0.2 \cdot 90 = 18$
dollars. Bookstore nets $65 - 18 = 47$ dollars;

Activity 4.3   Exercises: 1. 100 yd. $\cdot$ 3 ft./yd. = 300 ft.

3. 80 parts $\cdot \dfrac{3 \text{ min.}}{16 \text{ parts}} = 15$ min. It will take 15 minutes.

5. $\dfrac{\$11.50}{1 \text{ hr.}} \cdot \dfrac{40 \text{ hr.}}{1 \text{ wk.}} \cdot \dfrac{52 \text{ wk.}}{1 \text{ yr.}}$ (5 yr.) = \$119,600 sum of

the total gross salaries for the next 5 years.

7. 29,035 ft. $\cdot \dfrac{1 \text{ mi.}}{5280 \text{ ft.}} \approx 5.5$ mi.

29,035 ft. $\cdot \dfrac{1 \text{ mi.}}{5280 \text{ ft.}} \cdot \dfrac{1.609 \text{ km}}{1 \text{ mi.}} \approx 8.85$ km

29,035 ft. $\cdot \dfrac{1 \text{ mi.}}{5280 \text{ ft.}} \cdot \dfrac{1.609 \text{ km}}{1 \text{ mi.}} \cdot \dfrac{1000 \text{ m}}{1 \text{ km}} \approx 8848$ m;

9. 4.5 ℓ $\cdot \dfrac{1.06 \text{ qt.}}{1 \ell} = 4.77$ qt.

4.77 qt. $\cdot \dfrac{2 \text{ pt.}}{1 \text{ qt.}} = 9.54$ pt.;

13. 24 carat $\cdot \dfrac{1 \text{ g}}{5 \text{ carat}} = 4.8$ g

4.8 g $\cdot \dfrac{0.035 \text{ oz.}}{1 \text{ g}} = 0.168$ oz.

Activity 4.4   Exercises: 2. a. $9x = 2 \cdot 108$; $x = \dfrac{2 \cdot 108}{9} = 24$;

4. $\dfrac{\$6.99}{8 \text{ qt.}} = \dfrac{x}{12 \text{ qt.}}$; $x = \dfrac{12 \cdot 6.99}{8}$; $x = \$10.49$.   Twelve
quarts of skim milk prepared this way costs \$10.49;

7. $\dfrac{x}{1859} = \dfrac{9}{10}$; $x = \dfrac{9 \cdot 1859}{10}$; $x \approx 1673$.   1673
consumers in the sample reported problems with
transactions online.

What Have I Learned?   Exercises: 1. I answered more
questions correct on the practice exam (32) than on the
actual exam (16). I scored $\dfrac{32}{40} = \dfrac{4}{5} = 0.8 = 80\%$ on the

practice exam. I scored $\dfrac{16}{20} = \dfrac{4}{5} = 0.8 = 80\%$ on the actual
exam. No, the relative scores were the same. So, I did the
same on the actual exams as I did on the practice exam;
3. Let $x =$ the number of Florida residents over 65 years
old: $x = \dfrac{183}{1000} \cdot 15,982,378 \approx 2,924,775$. Approximately
2,924,775 Florida residents were 65 years or older in 2000.

How Can I Practice?   Exercises: 1. a. 0.25, **e.** 2.50, **f.** 0.003;

6. $\dfrac{\$22.50}{1 \text{ hr.}} \cdot \dfrac{40 \text{ hr.}}{1 \text{ wk.}} \cdot \dfrac{52 \text{ wk.}}{1 \text{ yr.}} \cdot 2$ yr. = \$93,600; I would
earn \$93,600 in 2 years.

Gateway Review   Exercises: 1. a. $\dfrac{4 \cdot 5 \cdot 7}{4} = 35$,

b. $\dfrac{4}{5} \cdot \dfrac{1}{2} = \dfrac{2}{5}$, **c.** $0.27 \cdot 44 = 11.88$, **d.** 6500,
e. $\approx 38,083.33$, **f.** ≈ 6.22;
2. a. $4 \cdot 45 = 9x$,   **b.** $4x = 4 \cdot 5$,   **c.** $3 = 2x$,
$\dfrac{4 \cdot 5 \cdot 9}{9} = x$ $x = 5$ $\dfrac{3}{2} = x$
$20 = x$

d. $2.3 \cdot 4 = 1.7x$, **e.** $\dfrac{1}{2} \cdot 6 = 7x$, **f.** $x = 12$;
$\dfrac{2.3 \cdot 4}{1.7} = x$ $\dfrac{3}{7} = x$
$5.41 \approx x$

3. Females: 70% of 1400 = $0.7 \cdot 1400 = 980$
Males: 30% of 1000 = $0.3 \cdot 1000 = 300$
Total = $980 + 300 = 1280$; Percent of student body
$= \dfrac{1280}{1400 + 1000} = \dfrac{1280}{2400} \approx 0.533 = 53.3\%$;   **4.** Total

mailing list = $600 \div \dfrac{2}{3} = 600 \cdot \dfrac{3}{2} = 900$ envelopes;

5. 10 m $\cdot \dfrac{1 \text{ ft.}}{0.3048 \text{ m}} \approx 32.81$ ft.;

6. 1. O'Neal: $229 \div 408 \approx 0.561 = 56.1\%$,
2. Garnet: $87 \div 167 \approx 0.521 = 52.1\%$, 3. Bryant:
$170 \div 342 \approx 0.497 = 49.7\%$;
7. $\dfrac{56 \text{ mi.}}{1 \text{ gal.}} \cdot 10.6$ gal. = 593.6 mi. I can travel almost
594 miles.   **8.** $\dfrac{6 \text{ mi.}}{1 \text{ hr.}} \cdot \dfrac{5280 \text{ ft.}}{1 \text{ mi.}} \cdot \dfrac{1 \text{ hr.}}{60 \text{ min.}} \cdot \dfrac{1 \text{ min.}}{60 \text{ sec.}} = 8.8$ ft.
per sec. I run at 8.8 feet per second.   **9. a.** $x = 2$,
b. $x = 90$, **c.** $x = 12$;   **10.** $\dfrac{\$5.28}{8 \text{ lb.}} = \dfrac{x}{100 \text{ lb.}}$
$x = \dfrac{\$5.28 \cdot 100 \text{ lb}}{8 \text{ lb}} = \$66.00$.

Chapter 5

Activity 5.1   Exercises: 1. a. $P = 2 \cdot 25 + 2 \cdot 15 = 80$ ft.
b. $P = 15 + 25 + 10 + 25 + 10 + 10 + 25 = 120$ ft.
c. $P = 25 + 45 + 25 + 10 + 10 + 25 + 10 + 10 = 160$ ft.
3. a. $P = 1038 + 965 + 1042 = 3045$ mi.

b. $3045 \text{ mi.} \cdot \dfrac{1 \text{ hr.}}{600 \text{ mi.}} = 5.075 \text{ hr.}$

6. Since $P = 2l + 2w$, then $75 = 2(10) + 2w$.
Solving this equation,

$75 = 20 + 2w$

$55 = 2w$

$\dfrac{55}{2} = w$ So, $w = \dfrac{55}{2} = 27.5$ meters.

Activity 5.2   Exercises: 2. If the radius measures 1 cm, then $C = 2 \cdot \pi \cdot 1 \approx 6.28$ cm. If the radius measures 3 cm, then $C = 2 \cdot \pi \cdot 3 = 6 \cdot \pi \approx 18.85$ cm. If the radius measures 6 cm, then $C = 2 \cdot \pi \cdot 6 = 12 \cdot \pi \approx 37.30$ cm. If the radius measures 10 cm, then $C = 2 \cdot \pi \cdot 10 = 20 \cdot \pi \approx 62.83$ cm.

4. a. $C = \pi \cdot 3 \approx 9.4$ cm **d.** $\dfrac{1}{4}C = \dfrac{1}{4} \cdot 2 \cdot \pi \cdot 2 = \pi$ ≈ 3.1 in.   **5.** Since $C = 2\pi r$, then $63 = 2\pi r$. Solving for r, $r = \dfrac{63}{2\pi} \approx 10.03$ inches.

Activity 5.3   Exercises:

2. $P = 4 + 3 + 4 + \dfrac{1}{2} \cdot \pi \cdot 3 = 11 + 1.5 \cdot \pi \approx$ 15.71 ft.

4. a. $P = 6 + 3.8 + 6.2 + 5.2 = 21.2$ cm

c. $P = 2 + 10 + \dfrac{1}{2} + 3 + 3 + \dfrac{1}{2} + 10 = 29$ m.

Activity 5.4   Exercises:

1. a. $A = 20 \cdot 30 + \dfrac{1}{2} \cdot 10 \cdot 12 = 600 + 60 = 660$ sq. ft.

b. $A = 30 + 30 + 6 = 66$ feet of 10-foot widths; run the carpet horizontally to cover the main part of the room. Then cut the remaining 6-foot length diagonally to fit the triangular part.

4. $A = 94 \cdot 50 = 4700$ sq. ft.

Activity 5.5   Exercises: 1. The larger pizza has area $\pi \cdot \left(\dfrac{14}{2}\right)^2 \approx 153.94$ square inches; the smaller pizza has area $\pi \cdot \left(\dfrac{10}{2}\right)^2 \approx 78.54$ square inches. So you can fit approximately two smaller pizzas into the larger one.

2. a. The diameters for a quarter, nickel, penny, and dime are: 2.4 cm, 2.1 cm, 1.9 cm, and 1.8 cm.

b. The area of a quarter is $\pi \cdot 1.2^2 \approx 4.52$ sq. cm.
The area of a nickel is $\pi \cdot 1.05^2 \approx 3.46$ sq. cm.
The area of a penny is $\pi \cdot .95^2 \approx 2.84$ sq. cm.
The area of a dime is $\pi \cdot .9^2 \approx 2.54$ sq. cm.

3. b. $A = \pi \cdot 3^2 \approx 28.27$ sq. mi.

d. $A = \dfrac{1}{4} \cdot \pi \cdot \left(\dfrac{2}{3}\right)^2 \approx 0.35$ sq. in.

Activity 5.6   Exercises: 1. Area $= 15 \cdot 25 = 375$ sq. ft.

5. $A \approx 8\left(\dfrac{1}{2} \cdot 15 \cdot 18.1\right) = 1086$ sq. in.

Activity 5.7   Exercises: 2. Solving $x + 47 = 90$, the other acute angle must be $x = 90° - 47° = 43°$.   **4.** They all must add up to 180° and all be different sizes, since the triangle is equilateral or isosceles.   **6.** The sum of the four angles must be the same as the sum of six angles in two triangles, which will be $180° + 180° = 360°$.

Activity 5.8   Exercises:

2. If they did meet at right angles, then the Pythagorean theorem would be true, and $18^2 = 12^2 + 14^2$. But $18^2 = 324$ and $12^2 + 14^2 = 144 + 196 = 340$. And $324 \neq 340$. So, the walls do not meet at right angles.

3. a. $12^2 = a^2 + 9^2$, so $a^2 = 12^2 - 9^2 = 144 - 81 = 63$.
Therefore, $a = \sqrt{63} \approx 7.94$ feet.

b. $c^2 = 10^2 + 9^2 = 181$, so $c = \sqrt{181} \approx 13.45$ feet.

5. a. $c^2 = 6^2 + 11^2 = 157$, so $c = \sqrt{157} \approx 12.53$ centimeters.   **7. a.** Yes, since $13^2 = 5^2 + 12^2$ because $169 = 169$. **b.** No, since $15^2 \neq 5^2 + 10^2$ because $225 \neq 125$.   **8.** $c = \sqrt{3^2 + 7^2} = \sqrt{58} \approx 7.62$ miles for the boat trip.   **10.** No, since $15^2 \neq 7^2 + 10^2$ (that is, $225 \neq 49 + 100$).

Activity 5.9   Exercises: 2. Setting up the proportion, $\dfrac{d}{7} = \dfrac{14}{11}$. Solving, $11d = 14 \cdot 7$, so $d = \dfrac{98}{11} \approx 8.91$ feet.

4. a. Let x represent the length of the smallest side and y represent the length of the medium side.

$\dfrac{x}{3} = \dfrac{15}{6}$ $\dfrac{y}{5} = \dfrac{15}{6}$

$6x = 45$ $6y = 75$

$x = \dfrac{45}{6}$ in. $y = \dfrac{75}{6}$ in.

So the dimensions are $7\dfrac{1}{2}$ inches by $12\dfrac{1}{2}$ inches by 15 inches.

What Have I Learned?   Exercises: 5. No, consider the following example:

2 cm [ ] Has perimeter 20 cm and area 16 square cm.
8 cm

1 cm [ ] Has perimeter 20 cm and area 9 square cm.
9 cm

So two rectangles can have the same perimeter and different areas.

How Can I Practice?   Exercises:

1. a. Perimeter $= \dfrac{1}{2} \cdot \pi \cdot 2 + 2 \cdot 4 + 2 \approx 13.14$ ft.

Area $= \dfrac{1}{2} \cdot \pi \cdot 1^2 + 4 \cdot 2 = \dfrac{\pi}{2} + 8 \approx 9.57$ sq. ft.

2. a. Area $= \dfrac{1}{2} \cdot 6 \cdot 4 = 12$ sq. m

6. a. Triangle C is a right triangle because it is the only one that satisfies $a^2 + b^2 = c^2$: $13^2 = 169 = 12^2 + 5^2$.

b.

(Answers may vary.) Setting up the proportion, $\frac{c}{5} = \frac{1}{4}$. So $c = 1.25$. So the sides of triangle D are 1 foot, 1 foot, and 1.25 feet.

c. No, since the new triangle will have sides measured by 5 feet, 7 feet, and 9 feet. However, $\frac{5}{3} \neq \frac{7}{5}$ since $1.67 \neq 1.4$.

Gateway Review

1. a. 10 sq. ft. **b.** 17 in. **c.** $B = \frac{1}{2} \cdot 8 \cdot 2 = 8$ sq. in.

2. $23 = \pi \cdot r^2$. Solving, $r^2 \approx 7.32$. Therefore, $r \approx \sqrt{7.32} \approx 2.71$ inches.

3.

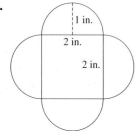

b. $P = 4 \cdot \frac{1}{2} \cdot 2 \cdot \pi \cdot 1 = 4\pi \approx 12.57$ in.

$A = 2 \cdot 2 + 4 \cdot \frac{1}{2} \cdot \pi \cdot 1^2 \approx 10.28$ sq. in.

c. $A_{\text{table}} = 12 \cdot 12 = 144$ sq. in. So, there is still space for $144 - 10.28 = 133.72$ square inches.

4. a. $A = 2 \cdot \frac{1}{2} \cdot 4 \cdot 3 + 2 \cdot \frac{1}{2} \cdot 4 \cdot 6 = 36$ sq. ft.

So, you need to buy at least 36 square feet of material.

b. You need to determine the hypotenuses of the four right triangles:

$c_1 = \sqrt{3^2 + 4^2} = 5$ ft.

$c_2 = \sqrt{6^2 + 4^2} = \sqrt{52} \approx 7.21$ ft.

So, $P \approx 2 \cdot 5 + 2 \cdot 7.21 = 24.42$ ft.
Buy at least 24.42 feet of ribbon.

5. a. $P = 22 + 17 + 19 + 7 + 15 + 3 + 22 + 7 + 17 + 19 + 7 + 15 + 22 + 18 = 210$ ft.

b. $A = 43 \cdot 40 + 18 \cdot 22 = 2116$ sq. ft.

c. The area for bedroom A is $15 \cdot 19 = 285$ square feet. The area for bedroom B is $15 \cdot 19 = 285$ square feet. The area for bedroom C is $17 \cdot 22 = 374$ square feet. So, bedroom C is the largest.

d. (Answers will vary.) The area of the living room is $18 \cdot 22 = 396$ square feet. Doubling this area would require 792 square feet. So, perhaps the easiest way to do this is to increase the length of the living room to 36 feet and keep the width the same, 22 feet. This produces an area of 792 square feet.

6. $c = \sqrt{300^2 + 200^2} = \sqrt{130,000} \approx 360.56$ feet, the measurement of the hypotenuse of the right triangle.

7. a. $V = 20 \cdot 15 \cdot 15 + \frac{1}{2} \cdot \frac{4}{3} \cdot \pi \cdot 7.5^3 \approx 5383.57$ cu. ft.

b. $V = \frac{1}{3} \cdot \pi \cdot \left(\frac{3}{2}\right)^2 \cdot 5 \approx 11.78$ cu. m

c. $V = \pi \cdot \left(\frac{5}{2}\right)^2 \cdot 8 \approx 157.08$ cubic in.

Chapter 6

Activity 6.1 Exercises: 1. d. 1989, **f.** from 1967 to 1977, **h.** from 2000 to 2004

Activity 6.2 Exercises: 1. d; **3.** g; **7.** a; **12.** h; **16.** f

Activity 6.3 Exercises: 1. b. Yes, $n = 0$ is reasonable. You might not purchase any notebooks at the college bookstore. **2. a.** 20, 40, 50. The output is 2 times the input. **3. b.** $-13, -10, -7, -4, -1, 2, 5, 8$; **4. a.** No. Owning a negative number of DVDs doesn't make sense. **b.** Yes. It means student doesn't own any DVDs. **c.** $0, 1, 2, \ldots, 1000$. **6. a.** \$159.50, **b.** Gross pay is calculated by multiplying the number of hours worked by \$7.25, the pay per hour.

Activity 6.4 Exercises: 2. $5(x - 6)$; **5.** $-2x - 20$; **7. a.** 7, **c.** -1, **e.** $\frac{2}{3}$; **8. b.** x and $\frac{1}{2}$, **d.** 2 and $(x + 3)$; **9. c.** x^2, $2x$, and 5;

11. b.

COLUMN 2	COLUMN 3
-2	-0.5
-1	-1
1	1
2	0.5

12. a. -19.5, **b.** -12, **c.** 12.5, **d.** 60

What Have I Learned? 3. a. Since input and output values are nonnegative, only the first quadrant and positive axes are necessary.

How Can I Practice? 1. c. No, negative numbers would represent distance above the surface. **2. a.** The point representing $(1995, -\$1500)$ is in quadrant III. **d.** The point representing the fact that there was no profit or loss in 2004 is located on the horizontal axis, between quadrant I and quadrant IV. **3. c.** The D.O. content changes the most between 11°C and 16°C, when it drops 1.6 ppm. **4. b.** From the graph, it appears to be approximately \$1500. **c.** The investment would double by approximately age 16; **5. a.** 4, **b.** 5, **c.** -1, **d.** -3, **e.** 4 and x^2 (or 4, x, x); **6. b.** $\frac{1}{2}x + 6$; **8. b.** 9

Activity 6.7 Exercises: 1. a. $C = 2.459x$, **c.** 12.30, 24.59, 36.89, 49.18; **3.** between 6 and 7 sec; **4. b.** -17.5;

5. $x = 3$

x	y
1	5
2	6
3	7

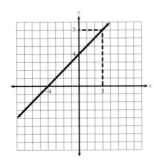

Activity 6.8 Exercises: 1. d. $1050, **e. i.** 5 credit hours;
2. b. 8 in., **c.** 6 in.; **4. d.** $590; **5. c.** $15 million;
6. a. $y = 52.5$, **b.** $x \approx 41.14$; **8. a.** $y = -198.9$,
b. $x = 23$; **10. a.** $y = 1.8$, **b.** $x = 8.2$

Activity 6.9 Exercises: 1. $y = x - 10$; **3.** $y = 9 + \frac{x}{6}$;
5. $y = -4x - 15$; **7. c.** This demonstrates the
commutative property of multiplication. **8. c.** No.
Subtraction is *not* commutative. Reversing the order in
subtraction changes the sign of the result.
10. a. i. To obtain the
output, square
the input.

x	y_1
−2	4
−1	1
0	0
2	4
3	9

12.

x	$y_5 = 1 + x^2$	$y_6 = (1 + x)^2$
−1	2	0
0	1	1
2	5	9
5	26	36

y_5: Start with $x \rightarrow$ square $\rightarrow$ add 1 $\rightarrow$ to obtain y; y_6:
Start with $x \rightarrow$ add 1 $\rightarrow$ square $\rightarrow$ to obtain y. No. They
generate different outputs.

14.

x	$y_9 = 3x^2 + 1$	$y_{10} = (3 \cdot x)^2 + 1$
−1	4	10
0	1	1
2	13	37
5	76	226

y_9: Start with $x \rightarrow$ square $\rightarrow$ multiply by 3 $\rightarrow$ add 1 $\rightarrow$ to
obtain y;
y_{10}: Start with $x \rightarrow$ multiply by 3 $\rightarrow$ square $\rightarrow$ add 1 $\rightarrow$ to
obtain y. No. They generate different outputs.

Activity 6.10 Exercises: 2. The mystery input is 15.

Activity 6.11 Exercises: 1. a. Multiply the minutes by 0.04,
and then add 2.00 to determine the total monthly cost.
b. $C = 0.04n + 2.00$, **c.** $C = 12.00, **d.** 1200 minutes;

3. b. $p = 10n - 2100$, **d.** 360 students; **4. c.** about
13 years; **6. a.** approximately 181 cm; **8.** 70 in.;
10. a. $x = -1$, **b.** $x = 4$, **d.** $x = -7$, **f.** $x = 0$,
h. $x = 18$, **j.** $x = 10$; **11. b.** $y = 21.75, x = -60$,
e. $y = 2.8, x = 100$;

x	y
3.5	21.75
−60	−10

x	y
24	2.8
100	18

Activity 6.12 Exercises: 1. a. 32.8%, **b.** 2013;
3. a. $2964, **b.** age 67;
5. a. $B = 655.096 + 9.563(55) + 1.85(172) - 4.676(70)$
≈ 1171.9 calories. He is not properly fed.
b. $61.52 \approx A$. He is about 62 years old.

Activity 6.13 Exercises: 1. a. 92.3, **b.** 70.9;
3. b. 70 miles, **c.** $3.39 \approx t$, approximately 3.4 hours;
5. a. 212°F, **b.** $\frac{F - 32}{1.8} = C$; **7. a.** 409.2 ft,
b. $\frac{33(p - 15)}{15} = d$; **9.** $\frac{C}{2\pi} = r$; **11.** $\frac{P - 2l}{2} = w$;
13. $\frac{A - P}{Pt} = r$; **15.** $m + vt^2 = g$

What Have I Learned? 1. In both cases, you need to isolate x
by performing the inverse operations indicated by $4x - 5$
in reverse order; that is, add 5, and then divide by 4.
6. a. $V \approx 79.5$ cu in.: $V \approx 57.7$ cu in. The second package
holds 11.4 cu in. less than the original one.

How Can I Practice? 1. b. $10 - x$, **d.** $-4x - 8$,
f. $\frac{1}{2}x^2 - 2$; **3. a.** $t = 2.5r + 10$; **4. a.** $x = -3$,
c. $x = 15.5$, **f.** $x = 4$, **h.** $x = 11.6$; **5. d.** $650,
e. 6125 copies. **6. a.** Multiply the number of hours of
labor by $68, and add $148 for parts to obtain the total cost
of the repair., **d.** $420, **e.** No, 3.5 hr work plus parts will
cost $386., **f.** 4 hours, **g.** $x = \frac{y - 148}{68}$; Solving for x allows
you to answer questions such as part f more quickly. It
would be especially useful if you wanted to determine the
number of mechanic hours for several different amounts of
money. **8 a.** $\frac{d}{t} = r$, **c.** $\frac{A - P}{Pt} = r$, **e.** $\frac{7}{4}(w - 3) = h$

Activity 6.14 Exercises: 2. $24x - 30$; **4.** $10 - 5x$;
6. $-3p + 17$; **8.** $-12x^2 + 9x - 21$; **10.** $\frac{5}{8}x + \frac{5}{9}$;
12. $15x^2 - 12x$; **16.** $A = P + Prt$;
17. c. $lw + 5l$; **19. a.** $y - 5$,
b. $12(y - 5) = 12y - 60$

Activity 6.15 Exercises: 1. $3(x + 5)$; **3.** $xy(3 - 7 + 1)$;
5. $4(1 - 3x)$; **7.** $st(4rt - 3rt + 10)$;
11. $5a + 8ab - 3b$; **13.** $104r - 13s^2 - 18s^3$;
15. $2x^3 + 7y^2 + 4x^2$; **17.** $3x^2y - xy^2$;
19. $2x - 2x^2 - 5$; **23.** $24 - x$; **25.** $5x - 75$;
27. $9 + x$; **29.** $7x - 15$; **31.** $5x - 5$;
33. $-x^2 - 9x$; **35. c.** $398 - 26x$

Activity 6.16 Exercises: 1. c. Yes, the news is good. The
value of my stock increased sixfold.
2. a. $3[\frac{-2n + 4}{2} - 5] + 6$, **b.** $-3n - 3$;
4. b. $8x - 5y + 13$, **e.** $13x - 43$

Activity 6.17   Exercises: 1. a. $C = 0.49x + 25.95$,
c. $0.49x + 25.95 = 0.69x + 19.95$, **e.** Company 2 is
lower if you drive less than 30 miles.
3. d. $y = 16.50x + 90$, **e.** \$288, **g.** \$255, **i.** $x = \frac{y - 90}{16.5}$;
This form of the equation would be useful when I am
setting a salary goal and need to determine the number of
hours I must work.   **4. c.** $0.85(12 - x)$, **f.** 7 roses and
5 carnations;   **6.** $x = -1$;   **8.** $x = -2$;   **10.** $x = 81$;
12. $t = 3$;   **14.** $x = -11$;   **16.** $x = 2500$;   **18.** $0 = 0$.
The solution is all real numbers.   **22. a.** $x = \frac{y - b}{m}$,
c. $h = \frac{A - 2\pi r^2}{2\pi r}$, **e.** $y = \frac{3x - 5}{2}$, **g.** $P = \frac{A}{1 + rt}$

What Have I Learned? 2. a. By order of operations, $-x^2$
indicates to square x first, then negate. For example,
$-3^2 = -(3)(3) = -9$. **b.** The negative sign can be
interpreted as -1 and by the distributive property reverses
the signs of the terms in parentheses.   **6. b.** $2x$. The given
code of instruction leads to doubling the starting value.
Therefore, I would divide the resulting value by 2 to obtain
the starting value.

How Can I Practice?

1.

x	13 + 2 (5x − 3)	(10x + 10)	10x + 7
1	17	20	17
5	57	60	57
10	107	110	107

Expression a and expression c are equivalent.
2. b. $3x^2 + 15x$, **d.** $-2.4x - 2.64$,
f. $-6x^2 - 4xy + 8x$;   **3. b.** $2x(3y - 4z)$, **e.** $2x(x - 3)$;
4. b. $x^2y^2 + 2xy^2$;   **5. b.** i. add 5 to x; ii. square result;
iii. subtract 15;
6. a. $6 - x$, **c.** $3x^2 + 3x$, **e.** $-4x - 10$;
7. $V = 25(2x - 3)$;   **9. c.** $D = 198x - 45$ miles;
10. c. $600 = 280 + 0.20(x - 1000)$, **d.** $x = 2600$.
I must sell \$2600 worth of furniture in order to have
a gross salary of \$600.   **11. a.** $S = 200 + 0.30x$,
b. $S = 350 + 0.15x$, **d.** $x = \frac{150}{0.15} = \$1000$. I would
have to sell about \$1000 worth of furniture per week
to earn the same weekly salary from either option.
12. c. $x + (x + 10) + (x + 65) = 3x + 75$

Gateway Review

1.

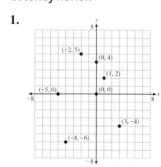

2. a. $x + 5$, **b.** $18 - x$,
c. $2x$, **d.** $\frac{4}{x}$, **e.** $3x + 17$,
f. $12(8 + x)$,
g. $11(14 - x)$, **h.** $\frac{x}{7} - 49$;
3. a. $x = 9$, **b.** $y = -24$,
c. $x = 2.5$, **d.** $x = -12$,
e. $y = -2$, **f.** $x = 16$,
g. $x = 144$, **h.** $y = \frac{5}{6}$,
i. $x = 72$;

4. a. $A = \dfrac{63 + 68 + 72 + x}{4} = \dfrac{203 + x}{4}$,

b. He must score 61.   **5. a.** $x = 5$, **b.** $y = 42$,
c. $x = 6$, **d.** $x = -7.75$, **e.** $y = -66$, **f.** $x = 139.5$,
g. $x = -96$, **h.** $y = 27$;   **6. a.** The input variable is the
number of miles driven.   **b.** The output variable is the cost
of rental for a day.   **c.** $y = 25 + 0.15x$;
d.

INPUT, x	100	200	300	400	500
OUTPUT, y	40	55	70	85	100

e.

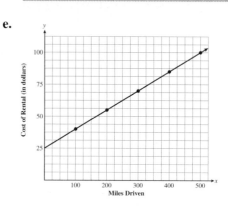

f. The cost to travel round trip from Buffalo to Syracuse is
just under \$75.   **g.** \$70.90,   **h.** I can drive approximately 425
miles.   **i.** approximately 433 miles,   **j.** (Answers will vary.)
7. My total annual home sales must be \$714,286 in order
to gross \$30,000.   **8. a.** $I = 2000(0.05)(1) = \$100$,
b. $I = 3000(0.06)(2) = \$360$;
9. a. $P = 2(2.8 + 3.4) = 12.4$,
b. $P = 2\left(7\frac{1}{3} + 8\frac{1}{4}\right) = 31\frac{1}{6}$;

10.

x	(4x − 3)²	4x² − 3	(4x)² − 3
−1	49	1	13
0	9	−3	−3
3	81	33	141

None are equivalent.   **11. a.** $3x + 3$,
b. $-12x^2 + 12x - 18$, **c.** $4x^2 - 7x$, **d.** $-8 - 2x$,
e. $12x - 25$, **f.** $17x - 8x^2$;   **12. a.** $4(x - 3)$,
b. $x(18x + 60 - y)$, **c.** $-4(3x + 5)$;
13. a. $6x^2 - 6x + 3$, **b.** $x^2 - 3x + 7$;
14. a. $10x - 35y$, **b.** $2a + b - 3$,
c. $-10x + 20w - 10z$, **d.** $2c - 1$;   **15. a.** $x = 20$,
b. $x = 3$, **c.** $x = -13$, **d.** $x = 0$, **e.** $x = 4$, **f.** $x = 7$,
g. $x = -3$, **h.** $0 = 27$. Since 0 does not equal 27, there is
no solution.   **i.** $18x + 16 = 18x + 16$. All real numbers
are solutions.   **16. a.** \$280, **b.** \$196, **c.** $0.70x$,
d. $0.7(0.7x) = 0.49x$, **e.** \$196. The price is the same.
f. The original price is \$300.   **17. a.** $500 - n$, **b.** $2.50n$,
c. $4.00(500 - n)$, **d.** $2.50n + 4.00(500 - n) = 1550$,
e. $n = 300$ student tickets and 200 adult tickets were sold.
18. a. $C = 1200 + 25x$, **b.** $R = 60x$,
c. $P = 35x - 1200$, **d.** 35 campers, **e.** 52 campers,

f. $500, **g.**

(34.29, 2057.14)

The answer is the same.

19. a. $P = \frac{I}{rt}$, **b.** $t = \frac{f - v}{a}$, **c.** $y = \frac{2x - 7}{3}$;
20. a. $C = 750 + 0.25x$, **b.** $875, **c.** A thousand book-
lets can be produced for $1000. **d.** $R = 0.75x$, **e.** To
break even, 1500 booklets must be sold. **f.** To make a $500
profit, 2500 booklets must be sold. **21. a.** $22 - x$,
b. $2.50x$, **c.** $(22 - x)(0.30)(15) = 4.50(22 - x)$,
d. $2.50x + 4.50(22 - x) = 2.50x + 99 - 4.50x$
$$= 99 - 2x,$$
e. 7.5. I can drive seven days. **f.** $77

Chapter 7

Activity 7.1   Exercises: 1. Graph 1, Generator A; Graph 2,
Generator B; Graph 3, Generator D; Graph 4, Generator C;
Graph 5, Generator E; Graph 6, Generator F;
3. a. Input: selling price; output: number of units sold,
b. As the selling price increases, the number of units sold
increases slightly at first, reaches a maximum, and then
declines until none are sold.   **6. a.** The graph in part a
represents a function. It passes the vertical line test.
b. The graph in part b does not represent a function. It fails
the vertical line test.

Activity 7.2   Exercises: 1. a. $C(n) = 2n + 78$,
d. (Answers will vary.) The number of students who can
sign up for the trip is restricted by the capacity of the bus. If
the bus holds 45 students, then the practical domain is the
set of integers from 0 to 45. **f.** If 24 students go on the trip,
the total cost of the trip will be $126.   **2. c.** This data set
represents a function because each input value is assigned a
single output value.   **4. a.** $\{-3, -2, -1, 0, 1, 2, 3, 4\}$,
d. The maximum value of f is 6, and it occurs when x is 4.
g. $f(3) = 5$;   **5. a. i.** -4, **ii.** $(2, -4)$;
7. $g(-3) = -4$;   **9.** $p(5) = 69$,   **11.** $x = 3$;
13. $w = 30$;

Activity 7.3   Exercises: 2. c. The graph is horizontal during
the 1930s and 1950s.   **e.** When the median age of first-
marriage increases, the graph rises. When the median age of
first marriage decreases, the graph falls. When the median
age of first marriage remains unchanged, the graph is horizontal. When the change in first-marriage median age is the
greatest, the graph is steepest.   **3. a.** For the years from
1900 to 1950, the average rate of change was -0.062 yr. of
age/yr.   **d.** For the years from 1900 to 1940, the average rate
of change was -0.04 yr. of age/yr.   **4. a.** -0.16 degree
per hour, **c.** The temperature drops at an average rate of
1.5 degrees per hour from 6 P.M. to 10 P.M.

What Have I Learned? 1. No; the definition of a function
requires that each input value, including $x = 0$, produce
exactly one output value.   **4.** The statement $H(5) = 100$
means that for the function $H(x)$, an input value of $x = 5$
corresponds to an output value of 100.   **8.** $f(1)$ represents

the output value when the input is 1. Because $f(1) = -3$,
the point $(1, -3)$ is on the graph of f.   **9.** After 10 minutes,
the ice cube weighs 4 grams.   **11.** If the rate of change of
a function is negative, then the initial output value on any
interval must be larger than the final value. We can
conclude that the function is decreasing.

How Can I Practice? 1. b. Yes, for each number of credit
hours (input), there is exactly one tuition cost (output).
e. The most credit hours I can take for $700 is 5.
4. a. $F(x) = \$2.50 + \$2.20x$;   **6.** $g(-4) = 6$;
8. $h(-3) = 16$;   **9.** $s(6) = 3$;   **14. c.** You leave home,
drive for 2 hours at a constant rate, and then stop for 1 hour.
Finally, you continue at a slower (but constant) speed than
before.   **16. c.** -5 lb./wk., **e.** The average rate of change
indicates how quickly I am losing weight.
17. a. 9.2 gal./yr., **c.** -4.93 gal./yr., **e.** -1.98 gal./yr.

Activity 7.4   Exercises: 1. c. For all the data points to be on a
line, the rate of change between any two data points must be
the same, no matter which points are used in the calculation.
3. b. The average rate of change is not constant, so the data
is not linear.   **5. a.** 50 feet higher, **b.** 5.2% grade;
6. b. at least 240 inches long;

Activity 7.5   Exercises: 1. a. linear $\left(\text{constant rate of}\right.$
change $= \frac{1}{2}\left.\right)$, **c.** not linear (average rate of change not
constant);   **2. d.** Every week I hope to lose 2 pounds.
3. b. The slope of the line for this data is $-\frac{7}{10}$ beats per
minute per year of age.   **4. a. ii.** $m = \frac{-10}{3}$;
6. a. 50 mph, **b.** The line representing the distance
traveled by car B is steeper, so car B is going faster. Car A a
rate of 50 mph; car B a rate of 74 mph;   **7. b.** No, their
slopes are all different. The number of units represented by
each tick mark is different on each graph, producing
different slopes.

Activity 7.6   Exercises: 1. a. $p(n) = 13n - 2200$ dollars;
2. c. The slope is 13. The profit increases by $13 for each
additional student attending.   **d.** The vertical intercept is
$(0, -2200)$. The class project has a loss of $2200 if no
students attend.   **5. b.** 170 students are needed to break
even.   **8. a.** The slope of the line is 2500, indicating that
the value of my home increased at a constant rate of
$2500 per year since 2005.   **b.** The vertical intercept is
$(0, 125,000)$. In 2005, the value of my house was $125,000.
c. $V(8) = 2500(8) + 125,000 = 145,000$ and
$2005 + 8 = 2013$. The market value of my house in 2013
will be $145,000.

Activity 7.7   Exercises:

1. slope is 3;
   y-intercept is $(0, -4)$;
   x-intercept is $\left(\frac{4}{3}, 0\right)$.

3. slope is 0;
  y-intercept is (0, 8);
  There is no *x*-intercept.

5. slope is 2;
  y-intercept is (0, −3);
  x-intercept is $\left(\frac{3}{2}, 0\right)$ or
  (1.5, 0).

7. e.

The graphs all have the same slopes but different vertical intercepts. They are parallel.

9. $y = 12x + 3$;   **11. b.** The *y*-intercept is (0, 5). The equation is $y = 3x + 5$.

13. a.

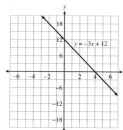

The horizontal intercept is (4, 0); the vertical intercept is (0, 12).

15. a. The slope is −0.5, indicating that the speed of the car is decreasing at a constant rate of 0.5 mph for each foot that it travels. **b.** $v = -0.5d + 60$, **c.** 25 mph;

What Have I Learned? 4. a. The graph is a straight line. **b.** It can be written in the form $y = mx + b$. **c.** The rate of change is constant.

How Can I Practice? 1. b. *y*: 12, $m = 2$, **e.** *x*: 6, *y*: 5, $m = -1$, **f.** *x*: 2, *y*: −14, $m = -1.5$;   **2. a.** 7.5 ft; **3. b.** Yes, the data represents a linear function because the rate of change is constant, $28 per month. **4. d.** For each second that passes during the first 5 seconds, speed increases 11 mph.   **5. b.** Yes; the three graphs represent the same linear function. They all have the same slope, 5, and the same vertical intercept, (0, 0).   **6. a.** The slope is undefined. **c.** The slope is 0.5.   **7. b.** The vertical intercept is (0, 10); the horizontal intercept is $\left(\frac{20}{3}, 0\right)$.
8. a. $y = 2.5x - 5$, **b.** $y = 7x + \frac{1}{2}$, **c.** $y = -4$;
11. a. $y = 0x - 2$, **b.** $y = 3x - 2$, **c.** $y = x - 2$.
The lines all have the same vertical intercept (0, −2).

b. $y = 3x - 2$ **c.** $y = x - 2$

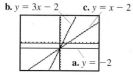

a. $y = -2$

12. a. (Answers will vary.)

x	3	3	3	3
y	−4	0	2	5

c. The horizontal intercept is (3, 0). There is no vertical intercept.

Gateway Review 1. The slope is −2.5, the vertical intercept is (0, 4);   **2.** The equation is $y = -2x + 2$.
3. Vertical intercept is (0, 8). An equation for the line is $y = \frac{-4}{3}x + 8$.   **4.** row 1: c, e, b; row 2: f, a, d;
5. Vertical intercept is (0, 5). Equation is $y = 3x + 5$;
6. The vertical intercept is (0, −2); the horizontal intercept is (4, 0).

7.

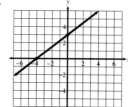

The vertical intercept is (0, 3); the horizontal intercept is (−4, 0).

8. $y = \frac{5}{3}x - 4$;   **9. a.** (2 , 2),
b.   **c.**

Chapter 8

Activity 8.1   Exercises:
2. a. $-2 = 2x$ **c.** $3x = 12$ **e.** $5x = 30$
      $x = -1$, $x = 4$, $x = 6$,
g. $\frac{1}{5}x = -3$ **i.** $0.25x = 24.5$
      $x = -15$, $x = 98$;
3. a. Multiply the number of minutes by 0.10 and then add 4.95 to get the answer. **b.** $c = 0.10n + 4.95$,
c. $c = 0.10 \cdot 250 + 4.95 = \$29.95$,
d. $50 = 0.10n + 4.95$
      $45.05 = 0.10n$
          $n = 450.5$ I will have 450 minutes for calls.
4. a. $10n$, **b.** $p = 10n - 2100$,
c. $p = 10 \cdot 700 - 2100 = \$4900$,
d. $1500 = 10n - 2100$
      $3600 = 10n$
          $n = 360$;
6. a. $c = 2.085 \cdot 10 + 15.08 = \$35.93$,
b. $56.78 = 2.085x + 15.08$
      $41.70 = 2.085x$
          $x = 20$ lb.;

8. $\dfrac{3}{4} = 2a + \dfrac{1}{3}$

$3 = 8a + \dfrac{4}{3}$

$9 = 24a + 4$

$\dfrac{5}{24} = a$. Check: $\dfrac{5}{24} + \dfrac{5}{24} + \dfrac{1}{3} = \dfrac{18}{24} = \dfrac{3}{4}$ The equal

sides measure $\dfrac{5}{24}$ meter.

10. a.

X	Y
4	−2
12	14

$y = 2 \cdot 4 - 10$
$y = 8 - 10$
$y = -2$
$14 = 2x - 10$
$24 = 2x$
$x = 12,$

c.

X	Y
$\frac{2}{3}$	13
6	−3

$y = -3 \cdot \dfrac{2}{3} + 15$

$y = 13$

$-3 = -3x + 15$
$-18 = -3x$
$x = 6;$

Activity 8.2   Exercises:

1. a. $4 = 0.167t - 0.67$
$4.67 = 0.167t$
$t \approx 27.96$
$\approx 28°C,$

b. $\dfrac{s + 0.67}{0.167} = t$,   **c.** $t = \dfrac{4 + 0.67}{0.167} = \dfrac{4.67}{0.167} \approx 28°C;$

3. a. $10 = 0.17t + 3.9$
$6.1 = 0.17t$
$t = 35.88 \approx 36$ yr.
$1970 + 36 = 2006$ (the year),

b. $\dfrac{n - 3.9}{0.17} = t$,   **c.** $t = \dfrac{10 - 3.9}{0.17} = \dfrac{6.1}{0.17} \approx 36$ yr.;

$1970 + 36 = 2006$ (the year);   **5.** $\dfrac{E}{R} = I;$ **7.** $P - 2a = b;$

9. $\dfrac{P - 2l}{2} = w;$ **11.** $\dfrac{A - P}{Pt} = r$

Activity 8.3   Exercises:

1. a. cost $= 0.19x + 39.95$,   **b.** cost $= 0.49x + 19.95$,
c. $0.19x + 39.95 = 0.49x + 19.95$,
d. $0.19x + 39.95 = 0.49x + 19.95$

$\underline{-0.19x \qquad\qquad -0.19x}$
$39.95 = 0.30x + 19.95$
$\underline{- 19.95 \qquad\quad - 19.95}$
$20.00 = 0.30x$

$x = \dfrac{20}{.30} = 66.66 \approx 67$ mi.,

e. Company 1 is better if you drive more than 67 miles.
3. a. cost $= 3560 + 15x$,   **b.** cost $= 2850 + 28x$,
c. $3560 + 15x = 2850 + 28x,$

d. $3560 + 15x = 2850 + 28x$
$\underline{\quad -15x \qquad\qquad -15x}$
$3560 \qquad = 2850 + 13x$
$\underline{-2850 \qquad\quad -2850}$
$710 = 13x$

$\dfrac{710}{13} = \dfrac{13x}{13}$ $x \approx 55$ months,

e. 10 years is equivalent to 120 months. Dealer 1 is better
for over 55 months of use.

6. $3x - 14 = 6x + 4$ **8.** $4x - 10 = -2x + 8$
$\underline{-3x \qquad\quad -3x}$ $\underline{+2x \qquad\qquad +2x}$
$14 = 3x + 4$ $6x - 10 = 8$
$\underline{\quad -4 \qquad -4}$ $\underline{\quad +10 \quad +10}$
$-18 = 3x$ $6x \qquad = 18$
$x = -6;$ $x = 3;$

10. $4 - 0.05x = 0.1 - 0.05x$
$\underline{\quad +0.05x \qquad\quad +0.05x}$
$4 + 0.025x = 0.1$
$\underline{-4 \qquad\qquad -4}$
$0.025x = -3.9$
$x = -156;$

Activity 8.4   Exercises: 1. a^4;   **3.** y^9;   **5.** $-12w^7$;   **7.** a^{15};
9. $-x^{50}$;   **11.** $-5.25x^9y^2$;   **13.** $-2s^6t^8$;   **15.** $3y^2 - y$;
17. $2a^4 + 8a^2 - 10a$;   **19.** $3.5r^5 - 1.6r^4$;
21. $-2.6x^{10} - 7.8x^8 + 1.3x^7$;   **23. a.** $5x(4x) = 20x^2$,
b. $V = 20x^2(x + 15) = 20x^3 + 300x^2$;
25. $A = (3xy^2)^2 = 9x^2y^4$;

Activity 8.5   Exercises:

4. $3x + 10x - 8$ **5.** $3.1a + 3.1b + 8.7a$
$13x - 8;$ $11.8a + 3.1b;$
7. $3 - x + 2x - 1$ **9.** $6 - 3x - 8x - 4$
$x + 2;$ $-11x + 2;$
11. $3(4)^2 + 2(4) - 1$ **13.** $2100(0.08)(3) = 504;$
$48 + 8 - 1$
$55;$
15. $4(10)^3 + 15$ **17.** $2(x + 5) + 2(x - 3)$
$4000 + 15 = 4015;$ $2x + 10 + 2x - 6$
$4x + 4;$

Activity 8.6   Exercises:

2. a. $p = -0.620(16) + 42.47 = 32.55\%,$
b. $15 = -0.62t + 42.47$
$-27.47 = -0.62t$
$t \approx 44$ yr.
$1965 + 44 = 2009;$
4. a. $C = 37.7(30) - 170 = \$961,$
b. $2000 = 37.7a - 170$
$2170 = 37.7a$
$a \approx 58$ years old;

How Can I Practice?

1. $\begin{aligned}4x &= 16\\ x &= 4;\end{aligned}$ **2.** $\begin{aligned}-2x &= 14\\ x &= -7;\end{aligned}$ **3.** $\begin{aligned}\frac{3}{4}x &= 3\\ x &= 4;\end{aligned}$ **4.** $\begin{aligned}10 &= -2.5x\\ x &= -4;\end{aligned}$

5. $\begin{aligned}-12 &= 2x\\ x &= -6;\end{aligned}$ **6.** $\begin{aligned}6x + 3 &= 9\\ 6x &= 6\\ x &= 1;\end{aligned}$ **7.** $\begin{aligned}2x + 2 &= 5x - 3\\ 5 &= 3x\\ x &= \frac{5}{3} = 1\frac{2}{3};\end{aligned}$

8. $\begin{aligned}14 - 3 &= 4x\\ 11 &= 4x\\ x &= \frac{11}{4} = 2\frac{3}{4};\end{aligned}$ **9.** $\begin{aligned}4x &= -11.5\\ x &= \frac{-11.5}{4} = -2.875;\end{aligned}$

10. $\begin{aligned}8x + 4 &= 14x + 14\\ -10 &= 6x\\ x &= \frac{-10}{6} = -1\frac{2}{3};\end{aligned}$ **11.** $\begin{aligned}3x - 6 + 10 &= 5x\\ 3x + 4 &= 5x\\ 4 &= 2x\\ x &= 2;\end{aligned}$

12. $\begin{aligned}0.25x - 0.5 &= 0.2x + 2\\ 0.05x &= 2.5\\ x &= 50;\end{aligned}$ **13.** $\begin{aligned}-10 &= 2.5x\\ -4 &= x\end{aligned}$

14. $\begin{aligned}\frac{1}{3}x - \frac{1}{3} &= 6x - 6\\ 5\frac{2}{3} &= 5\frac{2}{3}\\ 1 &= x;\end{aligned}$ **15.** $-20x + 15;$

16. $6ax + 12bx + 3cx;$ **17.** $13.5x - 0.9;$

18. $-20x + 16y - 40;$ **19.** $\frac{P - b}{2} = a$ **20.** $\frac{P}{r} = t;$

21. $\frac{f - v}{a} = t;$ **22.** $x = \frac{4y + 8}{3};$

23. $\begin{aligned}A &= P + Prt\\ A - P &= Prt\\ \frac{A - P}{Pt} &= r;\end{aligned}$ **24.** $\begin{aligned}E - S &= \frac{3}{2}rn\\ \frac{2(E - S)}{3n} &= r;\end{aligned}$

25. a. $\begin{aligned}t &= 2005 - 1960 = 45\\ a &= 0.11(45) + 22.5 = 27.45 \text{ years},\end{aligned}$

b. $\begin{aligned}30 &= 0.11t + 22.5\\ 7.5 &= 0.11t\\ t &= \frac{7.5}{0.11} \approx 68\\ 1960 + 68 &= 2028,\end{aligned}$ **c.** $t = \frac{a - 22.5}{0.11},$

d. $t = \frac{30 - 22.5}{0.11} \approx 68;\ 1960 + 68 = 2028,$

26. a. $c = 10 + 0.03x,$

b.

NUMBER OF COPIES, x	TOTAL COST, c
1000	40
2000	70
3000	100
4000	130
5000	160

c. $c = 10 + 8000(0.03) = 250$ dollars,

d. $300 = 10 + 0.03x;\ 290 = 0.03x;\ x = \frac{290}{0.03} = 9666.\overline{6}.$
I can have almost 9700 copies printed for $300.

27. $-x^{10};$ **28.** $-10x^{7};$ **29.** $-0.55x^{7};$ **30.** $-15s^{3}t^{5};$
31. $x^{5} + 2x^{4} - x^{3};$ **32.** $y^{15};$ **33.** $t^{8};$
34. $6x^{6}x^{4}x = 6x^{11};$
35. $\begin{aligned}&2x + 3x^{2} - 12x + 5x^{2}\\ &8x^{2} - 10x;\end{aligned}$ **36.** $\begin{aligned}&7x + 14 - 2.7x - 10.6\\ &4.3x + 3.4;\end{aligned}$
37. $8x^{5} - 6x^{4} + 4x^{3};$
38. $\begin{aligned}&10x - 20x^{2} - 3x^{2} + 12x + 3 + 5x^{2}\\ &-18x^{2} + 22x + 3;\end{aligned}$
39. a. $A = (5x)(3x) = 15x^{2}$ **b.** $V = 15x^{2}(x + 8);$
40. $3(4)^{2} = 3(16) = 48;$
41. $2(3)^{2} - 3(2.5) = 18 - 7.5 = 10.5;$
42. $5(1 + 7(2)) = 5(1 + 14) = 5(15) = 75;$
43. $180 - 15 - (-25) = 180 - 15 + 25 = 190;$
44. $\begin{aligned}21 + 3x - 12 &= 24\\ 9 + 3x &= 24\\ 3x &= 15\\ x &= 5;\end{aligned}$ **45.** $\begin{aligned}8x - 6 &= 6x + 18\\ 2x &= 24\\ x &= 12;\end{aligned}$
46. $\begin{aligned}2 - 5x - 25 &= 3x - 6 - 1\\ -5x - 23 &= 3x - 7\\ -16 &= 8x\\ x &= -2;\end{aligned}$
47. $\begin{aligned}0.16x + 2.4 - 0.24x &= 1.8\\ -0.08x + 2.4 &= 1.8\\ -0.08x &= -0.6\\ x &= \frac{-0.6}{-0.08} = 7.5;\end{aligned}$
48. a. $C = 750 + 0.25x,$
b. $C = 750 + 0.25(500) = 750 + 125 = 875,$
c. $\begin{aligned}1000 &= 750 + 0.25x\\ 250 &= 0.25x\\ x &= \frac{250}{0.25} = 1000,\ \ 1000 \text{ booklets can be produced.}\end{aligned}$
d. $R = 0.75x,$
e. $\begin{aligned}R &= C\\ 0.75x &= 750 + 0.25x\\ 0.50x &= 750\\ x &= \frac{750}{0.50} = 1500,\end{aligned}$
1500 booklets must be sold to break even. The cost and revenue would both be $112.
f. $\begin{aligned}0.75x - (750 + 0.25x) &= 500\\ 0.75x - 750 - 0.25x &= 500\\ 0.50x - 750 &= 500\\ 0.50x &= 1250\\ x &= \frac{1250}{0.50} = 2500\end{aligned}$
2500 booklets must be sold to make a $500 profit.
49. a. $1.50x,$ **b.** $22 - x,$
c. $(22 - x)(0.20)(15) = 3(22 - x),$
d. $\begin{aligned}C &= 1.50x + 3(22 - x) = 1.50x + 66 - 3x\\ &= 66 - 1.50x,\end{aligned}$

e. $42 = 66 - 1.50x$
$-24 = -1.50x$
$x = \dfrac{-24}{-1.50} = 16$

Driving days $= 22 - 16 = 6$

I can drive for 6 days a month if I budget \$42 per month.

f. $x = 11$, $C = 1.50(11) + 3(11)$, $C = 49.50$. I must budget \$49.50 to be able to take the bus only half of the time.

Gateway Review

1. $-26 = 2x$; $x = -13$;   **2.** $0.15x = 45.9$;

$x = \dfrac{45.9}{0.15} = 306$;

3. $1.6x = 39$; $x = 24.375$;   **4.** $21 = 3x$; $x = 7$;
5. $4x + 20 - x = 80$
$3x + 20 = 80$
$3x = 60$; $x = 20$;

6. $38 = 57 - (x + 32)$
$38 = 57 - x - 32$
$38 = 25 - x$; $x = 25 - 38$; $x = -13$;

7. $5x + 3(2x - 8) = 2(x + 6)$
$5x + 6x - 24 = 2x + 12$
$11x - 24 = 2x + 12$
$9x = 36$; $x = 4$;

8. $2.5x + 10 = 5.8x - 11.6$
$21.6 = 3.3x$
$x = \dfrac{21.6}{3.3} = 6.\overline{54}$;

9. x^9;   **10.** $3x^{20}$;   **11.** $-6x^4y^3$;
12. $x^3y^4x^8 = x^{11}y^4$;
13. $-3x^5 + 6x^4 - 3x^2$;
14. $10x^2 + 9x - 6x^2 = 4x^2 + 9x$;

15. a. $P = \dfrac{I}{rt}$ **b.** $\dfrac{P - b}{2} = a$ **c.** $\dfrac{E - S}{1.5n} = r$

d. $P = \dfrac{k}{V} - a$;

16. a. $2(-3)^2 - 3(-3) + 5 = 2(9) + 9 + 5 = 32$,
b. $2(17.3) + 11.8 = 34.6 + 11.8 = 46.4$,
c. $10 - (-6 + (-8)) = 10 - (-14) = 24$;
17. a. $S = 100 + 0.30x$, **b.** $S = 150 + 0.15x$,
c. $100 + 0.30x = 150 + 0.15x$,
d. $100 + 0.30x = 150 + 0.15x$

$0.15x = 50$; $x = \dfrac{50}{0.15} \approx 333.33$

For \$333.33 in sales per week, the salaries for both options would be the same.

e. The salary is approximately $100 + 0.30(333.33) \approx$ \$200;   **18. a.** $x + 10$, **b.** $C = x + 10 + 55 = x + 65$,
c. $x + x + 10 + x + 65 = 3x + 75$,
d. $120 = 3x + 75$
$45 = 3x$
$x = 15$ mi.,
e. Running: $15 + 10 = 25$ mi.
Cycling: $25 + 55 = 80$ mi.;

19. a.

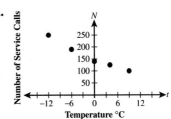

b. $C = -7.11(-20) + 153.9 = 296.1 \approx 296$ calls,
c. $50 = -7.11t + 153.9$
$7.11t = 153.9 - 50$
$t = \dfrac{103.9}{7.11} \approx 14.6$, about 15°C,

d. $\dfrac{C - 153.9}{-7.11} = t$, **e.** $t = \dfrac{50 - 153.9}{-7.11} \approx 14.6$;

20. a. ABC: $C = 50 + 0.20x$
Competition: $C = 60 + 0.15x$,
b. $50 + 0.20x = 60 + 0.15x$,
c. $50 + 0.20x = 60 + 0.15x$,
$0.05x = 10$; $x = 200$ mi.,
d. It would be cheaper to rent from the competition.
21. a. $C = 600 + 10x$, **b.** $R = 40x$,
c. $P = 40x - (600 + 10x) = 30x - 600$,
d. $30x - 600 = 0$; $30x = 600$; $x = 20$ campers,
e. $30x - 600 = 600$; $30x = 1200$; $x = 40$ campers,
f. $30(10) - 600 = 300 - 600 = -300$. The camp would lose \$300.

GLOSSARY

A **absolute value of a number** The size or magnitude of a number. It is represented by the distance of the number from zero on a number line. The absolute value is always nonnegative.

acute angle An angle that is smaller than a right angle (measures less than $90°$).

addends The numbers that are combined in addition. For example, in $1 + 2 + 7 = 10$, the numbers 1, 2, and 7 are the addends.

addition The arithmetic operation that determines the total of two or more numbers.

algebraic expression A mathematical set of instructions (containing constant numbers, variables, and the operations among them) that indicates the sequence in which to perform the computations.

angle The figure formed by two rays meeting at a same point. The size of the angle is the amount of turn needed to move one ray to coincide with the other ray.

area A measure of the size of a region that is entirely enclosed by the boundary of a plane figure, usually expressed in square units.

associative property of multiplication For all numbers a, b, and c, $(ab)c = a(bc)$. For example, $(2 \cdot 3) \cdot 4 = 6 \cdot 4 = 24$ and $2 \cdot (3 \cdot 4) = 2 \cdot 12 = 24$.

B **break-even point** The point at which two mathematical models for determining cost or value will result in the same quantity.

C **circumference of a circle** The distance around a circle. If a circle has radius r, diameter d, and circumference C, then $C = 2\pi r$ and $C = \pi d$.

coefficient A number (constant) that multiplies a variable.

common factor A factor contained in each term of an algebraic expression.

commutative property of multiplication For all numbers a and b, $ab = ba$, which means that changing the order of the factors does not change the result.

completely factored form An algebraic expression written in factored form where none of its factors can themselves be factored any further.

D **decimal number** A number with a whole part, to the left of the decimal point, and a fractional part, to the right of the decimal point.

denominator The number written below the line of a fraction; the denominator represents the number of equal parts into which a whole unit is divided.

difference The result of subtracting the subtrahend from the minuend. For example, in $10 = 45 - 35$, the number 10 is the difference, 45 is the minuend, and 35 is the subtrahend.

digit Any whole number from 0 to 9.

dividend In a division problem, the number that is divided into parts. For example, in $27 \div 9 = 3$, the number 27 is the dividend, 9 is the divisor, and 3 is the quotient.

distributive property The property of multiplication over addition (or subtraction) that states that $a \cdot (b + c) = a \cdot b + a \cdot c$.

divisor In a division problem, the number that divides the dividend. For example, in $27 \div 9 = 3$, the number 27 is the dividend, 9 is the divisor, and 3 is the quotient.

domain The set (collection) of all possible input values for a function.

E **equation** A statement that two algebraic expressions are equal.

equivalent fractions Fractions that represent the same ratio. For example, $\frac{4}{6}$ and $\frac{10}{15}$ both represent the ratio $\frac{2}{3}$. Divide both the numerator and denominator of $\frac{4}{6}$ by 2 to obtain $\frac{2}{3}$. Similarly, divide both the numerator and denominator of $\frac{10}{15}$ by 5 to obtain $\frac{2}{3}$.

even number A whole number that is divisible by 2, leaving no remainder.

exponent If a number N is raised to a power P, meaning

$$N^P = \overbrace{N \cdot N \cdot \ldots \cdot N}$$

$$(P \text{ factors})$$

the power P is also called an *exponent*.

exponential form A number written in the form b^x, where b is called the base and x is the power or exponent. For example, 2^5.

F **factor** A number a that divides another number b and leaves no remainder is called a factor of b. For example, 4 is a factor of 12 since $\frac{12}{4} = 3$.

factorization The process of writing a number as a product of factors.

factored form An algebraic expression written as the product of its factors.

formula An algebraic statement describing the relationship among a group of variables.

function A rule (given in tabular, graphical, or symbolic form) that relates (assigns) to any permissible input value exactly one output value.

G **greatest common factor** The largest factor that exactly divides each term in an expression.

H **horizontal axis** The horizontal number line of a rectangular coordinate system. When graphing a relationship between two variables, the input (independent) variable values are referenced on this axis.

horizontal intercept A point where a line or curve crosses the horizontal axis.

I **improper fraction** A fraction whose numerator is greater than or equal to its denominator.

input Replacement values for a variable in an algebraic expression, table, or function. The value that is listed first in a relationship involving two variables.

integers The collection of all of the positive counting numbers $\{1, 2, 3, 4, \ldots\}$, zero $\{0\}$, and the negatives of the counting numbers $\{-1, -2, -3, -4, \ldots\}$.

inverse operation An operation that "undoes" another operation. For example, subtraction is the inverse of addition, so if 4 is added to 7 to obtain 11, then 4 would be subtracted from 11 to get back to 7. Multiplication and division are inverses of each other. The inverse of squaring is taking the square root. Negation is its own inverse, as is taking a reciprocal.

L **least common denominator (LCD)** The smallest number that is a multiple of each denominator in two or more fractions.

like terms Terms that contain identical variable factors (including exponents) and may differ only in their numerical coefficients.

linear function A function that has the form $f(x) = mx + b$ and whose graph is a straight line.

linear regression equation The equation of the line that best represents a set of plotted data points.

lowest terms Phrase describing a fraction whose numerator and denominator have no factors in common.

M **mathematical model** Description of the important features of an object or situation that uses equations, formulas, tables, or graphs to solve problems, make predictions, and draw conclusions about the given object or situation.

median The middle value in an ordered list containing an odd number of values. In a list containing an even number of values, the median is the arithmetic average of the two middle values.

minuend In subtraction, the number being subtracted from. For example, in $10 = 45 - 35$, the number 45 is the minuend, 35 is the subtrahend, and 10 is the difference.

mixed number The sum of an integer and a fraction, written in the form $a\dfrac{b}{c}$, where a is the integer, and $\dfrac{b}{c}$ is the fraction.

N **negative numbers** Numbers that are less than zero.

numeral A symbol or sequence of symbols called digits that represent a number.

numerator The number written above the line in a fraction; the numerator specifies the number of equal parts of a whole that is under consideration. For example, $\frac{3}{4}$ means there are three parts under consideration and each part is a quarter of the whole.

numerical coefficient A number that multiplies a variable or coefficient.

O

obtuse angle An angle that is larger than a right angle (measures more than 90°).

odd number Any whole number that is not even, that is, if the number is divided by 2, the remainder is 1.

order of operations An agreement for evaluating an expression with multiple operations. Reading left to right, do operations within parentheses first; then exponents, followed by multiplications or divisions as they occur, left to right; and lastly, additions or subtractions, left to right.

ordered pair Two numbers or symbols, separated by a comma and enclosed in a set of parentheses. An ordered pair can have several interpretations, depending on its context. Common interpretations are as the coordinates of a point in the plane and as an input/output pair of a function.

origin The point at which the horizontal and vertical axes of a rectangular coordinate system intersect.

output Values produced by evaluating an algebraic expression, table, or function. The value that is listed second in a relationship involving two variables.

P

parallel lines Lines in a plane that never intersect.

parallelogram A four-sided plane figure whose opposite sides are parallel.

perpendicular lines Two intersecting lines that form four angles of equal measure (four right angles).

plane A plane is a flat surface where a straight line joining any two points on the plane will also lie entirely in the plane.

practical domain The domain determined by the situation being studied.

practical range The range determined by the situation being studied.

prime factorization A way of writing an integer as a product of its prime factors and their powers. For example, the prime factorization of 18 is $2 \cdot 3^2$. For each integer there is only one prime factorization, except for the order of the factors.

prime number A whole number greater than 1 whose only whole-number factors are itself and 1. For example, 2 and 5 are prime numbers.

product The resulting number when two or more numbers are multiplied.

proportion An equation stating that two ratios are equal.

proportional reasoning The thought process by which a known ratio is applied to one piece of information to determine a related, but yet unknown, second piece of information.

Pythagorean theorem The relationship between sides of a right triangle: the sum of the squares of the lengths of the two perpendicular sides (legs) is equal to the square of the length of the side opposite the right angle (hypotenuse). 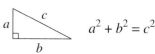 $a^2 + b^2 = c^2$

Q   **quadrants** The four regions of the plane separated by the vertical and horizontal axes in a rectangular coordinate system. The quadrants are numbered from I to IV. Quadrant I is located in the upper right with the numbering continuing counter-clockwise. Therefore, quadrant IV is located in the lower right.

quotient The result of dividing one number by another.

R   **range** The set (collection) of all possible output values for a function.

rate of change A quotient that compares the change in output values (numerator) to the corresponding change in input values (denominator). In context, a rate of change can be recognized by the word *per*, as in "miles per hour" or "people per year."

ratio A quotient that represents the relative measure of similar quantities. Ratios can be expressed in several forms—verbal, fraction, decimal, or percent. For example, 4 out of 5 or 80% of all dentists recommend toothpaste X.

rational number A number that can be written in the form $\frac{a}{b}$, where a and b are integers and b is not zero.

ray Part of a line that has one end point but extends indefinitely in the other direction. Sometimes a ray is called a *half-line*.

reciprocal Two numbers are reciprocals of each other if their product is 1. Obtain the reciprocal of a fraction by switching the numerator and denominator. For example, the reciprocal of $\frac{3}{4}$ is $\frac{4}{3}$.

rectangle A four-sided plane figure with four right angles.

remainder In division of integers, the whole number that remains after the divisor has been subtracted from the dividend as many times as possible.

right angle One of four equal-size angles that is formed by two perpendicular lines, measuring 90°.

rounding The process of approximating a number to a specified place value.

S   **scaling** The process of assigning a fixed distance between adjacent tick marks on a coordinate axis.

slope-intercept form The form $y = mx + b$ of a linear function in which m denotes the slope and b denotes the y-intercept.

square A closed four-sided plane figure with sides of equal length and with four right angles.

square root The square root of a nonnegative number N is a number M whose square is N. The symbol for square root is $\sqrt{}$. For example, $\sqrt{9} = 3$ because $3^2 = 9$.

subtraction The operation that determines the difference between two numbers.

subtrahend In subtraction, the number that is subtracted. For example, in $10 = 45 - 35$, the number 45 is the minuend, 35 is the subtrahend, and 10 is the difference.

sum In addition, the total of the addends. For example, in $1 + 2 + 7 = 10$, the number 10 is the sum.

symbolic rule A shorthand code that indicates a sequence of operations to be performed on the input variable, x, to produce the corresponding output variable, y.

T **terms** Parts of an algebraic expression separated by the addition, $+$, and subtraction, $-$, symbols.

triangle A closed three-sided plane figure.

V **variable** A quantity that takes on specific numerical values and will often have a unit of measure (e.g., dollars, years, miles) associated with it.

verbal rule A statement that describes in words the relationship between input and output variables.

vertical axis The vertical number line of a rectangular coordinate system. When graphing a relationship between two variables, the output (dependent) variable values are referenced on this axis.

vertical intercept The point where a line or curve crosses the vertical axis.

vertical line test A visual method of determining if a given graph is the graph of a function. A graph represents a function if and only if any vertical line that is drawn intersects the graph in at most one point.

W **whole numbers** The collection of numbers that includes the counting numbers, 1, 2, 3, . . ., and the number 0.

Z **zero power** Any nonzero number raised to the 0 power is 1. For example, $10^0 = 1$.

INDEX

A

Absolute value on number line, 90–92
Actual measure, 290–92
Acute angles, 361
Acute triangles, 363
Addends, 11
  missing, 15
Addition
  associative property of, 13, 101
  commutative property of, 12, 101
  distributive property of multiplica-
    tion over, 23, 496–99
  from left to right rule for, 52
  in order of operations, 51
  key phrases, examples. and
    arithmetic expressions, 17
  of decimals, 172–73, A-28
  of fractions
    with different denominators,
      A-18
    with same denominators,
      140–41, A-18
  of integers, 96–98
  of mixed numbers, 141–42, A-19
  of whole numbers, 10–18
  properties of integers, 100
Addition method for solving system
    of two linear equations,
    A-33–A-34
Algebra in calculating break-even
    point, 677–78
  simplifying, 690
Algebraic expressions, 420–23
  equivalent, 455–57
  evaluation of, 422–23, 36
  evaluating, 217–18
  simplifying, 513
Algebraic method
  of solving equations, 465–67
    of form $ax = b, a \neq 0$, 445–46
    of form $x + a = b$ using,
      446–49
Angles, 328
  acute, 361
  corresponding, 374

measuring, 361–63
obtuse, 361
right, 328, 360
straight, 360
vertex of, 328
Area
  of circle, 349–52
  of parallelogram, 345
  of rectangle, 344
  of square, 343
  of triangle, 346
Arithmetic expressions, 17
Assignment, due dates for, A-4–A-5
Associative property
  of addition, 13, 101
  of multiplication, 24
Astronomical distances, 40, 41
Attitude about mathematics, A-2–A-3
Average rate of change, 580–81
  graphical interpretation of, 581–82
Axis
  horizontal, 395, 401
  vertical, 395, 401

B

Base 60 number system, 360
Base
  of exponential expressions,
    40, 54, 209
  of parallelogram, 349
Base-10 number system, 2
  reading numbers in, 2
Bermuda Triangle, 334
Brahmagupta, 88
Break-even point, 627, 677–78

C

Calculator, 50–55
Calculators. *See also* TI-83/TI-84 Plus
    family of calculators
Cartesian coordinate system, 401, 402
Celsius scale, 265

Circle
  area of, 349–52
  circumference of, 335–36
  diameter of, 335
  radius of, 335
Circumference of circle, 335–36
Classes, attending on time, A-3
Coefficient, 421
Common denominator, 135, A-17
Common factor, 502
  factoring sum of terms containing,
    503
Commutative property
  of addition, 12, 100
  of multiplication, 24
Comparison
  of decimals, 160–62
  of fractions, 134–36
  of integers, 90
  of whole numbers, 3
Completely factored form, 503
Composite numbers, 5
Contradiction, 523
Coordinate
  horizontal, 403
  vertical, 403
Coordinate systems
  rectangular, 112–14
Corresponding angles, 374
Corresponding sides of similar
    triangles, 374
Counting numbers, 2, 79, 88
Cross multiplication, solving
    proportions by, 315–16
Cube of number, 45
Cumulative grade point average, 255

D

Data set, median value in, 5
Decimal fraction, rounding,
    to specified, 164
Decimals, 160
  adding, 172–73
  addition of, A-28